Avian Anatomy
Integument

Part I

Alfred M. Lucas, Ph.D.,

Zoologist and Research Professor in Poultry Science

Peter R. Stettenheim, Ph.D.,

Zoologist and Assistant Research Professor in Poultry Science

Agriculture Handbook 362

———————⋈◆⋈———————

Avian Anatomy Project
Poultry Research Branch
Animal Science Research Division
Agricultural Research Service
United States Department of Agriculture

In Cooperation With
Department of Poultry Science
Michigan Agricultural Experiment Station
College of Agriculture and Natural Resources
Michigan State University

Washington, D.C.   Issued September 1972

Requests for illustrations should be addressed to:

USDA Avian Anatomy Project
Poultry Science, Anthony Hall
Michigan State University
East Lansing, Mich. 48823

Preface

An accurate, detailed reference work on the anatomy of domestic fowl and laboratory birds has long been needed. Descriptive anatomy has always been recognized as an indispensable foundation for subsequent studies on function, both normal and abnormal.

A project on basic anatomical studies began in 1944 at the Regional Poultry Research Laboratory in East Lansing, Mich. At that time, the need was keenly felt for more information on normal anatomy so that pathologists working on leukosis in poultry could more accurately analyze their findings. This need led to the publication, "Atlas of Avian Hematology." When this study was completed, there still existed need for studies on avian anatomy, both gross and microscopic. Under the administration and with the encouragement of Berley Winton, former director of the Laboratory, studies were begun in this field.

For convenience of study, we have divided the text into the following organ systems: integumentary, skeletal, muscular, vascular, nervous, respiratory, digestive, excretory, male and female reproductive, and endocrine. This volume is devoted to the integument. Studies of the integument were based on domestic fowl—chicken, turkey, and duck, and on two other birds that are used in laboratories—Common Coturnix and Common Pigeon. Emphasis has been put on the chicken. It is still true, as Parker said about 80 years ago (1891:213), that "The Common Fowl will always be a convenient and useful bird to the biologist, whatever part of the organization is the subject of research; and in this special field—Morphology—he who knows the Fowl well is ready-prepared to interpret the structure of all kinds of birds."

During the 19th century and early in the 20th century when anatomical foundations were being laid for the fields of human and veterinary medicine and for studies on the phylogeny of vertebrates, only a relatively small group of scientists was contributing to the anatomy of birds. Ornithologists interested in anatomy were concerned mainly with taxonomic problems, and even today there has not yet been published a complete description of any species of bird, either wild or domestic. Consequently, fulfillment of this project is not a duplication of the work of the past. It is a new research study dependent on the literature of the past for ideas, guidance, and terminology but aimed toward new objectives.

In any project of this magnitude and cost, the question is always asked, who will use this type of information? Detailed anatomical data is needed by many disciplines, largely within the fields of poultry, medical, and zoological sciences. More specifically, this information is needed in such fields as marketing, breeding, nutrition, endocrinology, physiology, pharmacology, parasitology, pathology, laboratory diagnoses of disease, research and production in pharmaceutical houses, experimental medicine, surgery, analysis of behavior, general zoology, comparative anatomy, wildlife research, ornithology, and paleontology. Of course, use of the information will vary in each of these fields. Finally, this material is being prepared with another important group in mind—teachers. It is not anticipated that these reference volumes will be used as texts in the classroom, but it is hoped that those who write books for students in zoology, veterinary medicine, wildlife, and ornithology will find helpful material in the text and illustrations.

In spite of the broad scope of the project and its magnitude, limits must be established. We shall not try to solve the problems of specialists in other fields of science. For example, in our study on the normal anatomy and histology of the sternal bursa, no attempt will be made to determine how fluids are accumulated within the cavity. It is not possible to undertake electron microscope studies of the tissues, but we certainly encourage others to do so. Nor are we attempting to solve the specialized problems of ornithologists, physiologists, or pathologists.

Descriptive anatomy, well done, does not become obsolete. Therefore, if our observations and descriptions are accurate, what we do here should be just as useful at the end of the century as it is now. By the same token we must be cognizant of most of the literature on avian anatomy, including much on the reptiles, for at least the past 150 years. This literature, most of it on wild birds, provides guidance and terminology for these studies. Because of lack of uniformity, the terminology requires an inordinate amount of study. We hope that our careful evaluation of old terminology and thoughtful consideration of new names, where they are necessary, will provide at least some advancement toward an acceptable nomenclature for avian anatomy.

Those who use this volume will note such omissions as the gross anatomy of skeletal muscles, ligaments, nerves, blood vessels, and lymphatics to the skin. These subjects cannot be dealt with adequately in a volume on the integumentary system because most of them exist as terminal units of systems arising deep in the body. We shall, however, report on these subjects at a later time.

The ideas and information presented in this book have come from our own investigations as well as from the scientific literature. We have frequently attempted to verify or clarify the findings of others by examining similar anatomical material ourselves. All this has called for the preparation of enormous numbers of tissue sections, specially treated pieces of skin, feathers, and other specimens. Many times it was necessary to develop new techniques or to adopt ones that had been developed for use on mammalian tissues. The task of preparing our specimens was performed mainly by Effie M. Denington, a member of the project staff for many years. Many of our observations were made possible by the care and effort she gave to this work. Her written account of techniques and devices that were specially developed for preparing or illustrating our specimens is the basis for chapter 10.

ALFRED M. LUCAS
PETER R. STETTENHEIM

Contents

Part I

	Page
Preface	III
Chapter 1—Topographic anatomy	1
Introduction	1
Terms used in anatomy	3
Terms of orientation	3
Terms for parts, regions, and palpable structures	5
Regions of the head	5
Chicken and turkey	6
Cranium	8
Forehead region	8
Crown region	10
Base of head	12
Face	12
Orbital region	13
Suborbital region	14
Postorbital region	14
Auricular region	14
Nasal region	15
Oral region	16
Rictal region	17
Malar region	17
Ventral surface of head	18
Interramal region	18
Hyoid region	18
Submalar region	19
Common Coturnix	19
Cranium	19
Forehead region	19
Crown region	19
Base of head	19
Face	19
Orbital region	19
Suborbital region	19
Postorbital region	19
Auricular region	20
Nasal region	20
Oral region	20
Rictal region	20
Malar region	20
Ventral surface of head	20
White Pekin Duck	20
Cranium	21
Forehead region	21
Crown region	22
Base of head	22

	Page
Chapter 1—Topographic anatomy—Continued	
Regions of the head—Continued	
White Pekin Duck—Continued	
Face	22
Orbital region	22
Suborbital region	23
Postorbital region	23
Auricular region	23
Nasal region	23
Oral region	23
Rictal region	25
Malar region	25
Ventral surface of head	25
Interramal region	25
Hyoid region	25
Submalar region	25
Other domestic anserines	25
Common Pigeon	27
Cranium	27
Forehead region	27
Crown region	27
Base of head	27
Face	28
Orbital region	28
Suborbital region	28
Postorbital region	28
Auricular region	28
Nasal region	29
Oral region	29
Rictal region	29
Malar region	29
Ventral surface of head	29
Interramal region	29
Hyoid region	29
Submalar region	29
Great Horned Owl	30
Cranium	30
Forehead region	30
Crown region	30
Base of head	31
Face	31
Orbital region	31
Suborbital region	31
Postorbital region	31
Auricular region	32

Chapter 1—Topographic anatomy—Continued

Regions of the head—Continued

Great Horned Owl—Continued

Face—Continued

Nasal region............................. 32
Oral region.............................. 32
Rictal region............................ 33
Malar region............................ 33

Ventral surface of head..................... 33

Regions of the body and appendages............. 33

Neck....................................... 36
Chicken................................. 38
Turkey.................................. 40
Common Coturnix......................... 40
White Pekin Duck........................ 40
Common Pigeon........................... 40

Trunk...................................... 43
Chicken................................. 44
Turkey.................................. 48
Common Coturnix......................... 48
White Pekin Duck........................ 48
Common Pigeon........................... 51

Tail....................................... 51
Chicken................................. 51
Turkey.................................. 52
Common Coturnix......................... 55
White Pekin Duck........................ 55
Common Pigeon........................... 55

Anterior appendage......................... 56
Chicken and other species................ 57

Posterior appendage........................ 61
Thigh and shank.......................... 61
Chicken............................... 63
Other species......................... 63

Foot....................................... 64
Chicken............................... 67
Other species......................... 68
Pads and interpad spaces............... 71

Chapter 2—Principles of pterylosis............. 73

Definitions.................................. 73
Pterylae..................................... 74
Capital tracts............................. 76
Spinal tracts............................. 77
Caudal tracts............................. 78
Ventral tracts............................ 78
Lateral body tract........................ 79
Anterior appendage tracts................. 79
Brachial tracts........................ 79
Alar tracts............................ 83
Posterior appendage tracts................ 90
Powder down patches......................... 92
Apteria..................................... 92

Chapter 3—Pterylosis and ptilosis of domestic birds................................. 97

Pterylosis of the head........................ 97
Capital tracts and apteria.................. 97
Chicken................................. 97
Frontal tract........................ 97
Coronal tract........................ 98
Occipital tract...................... 98
Auricular tract...................... 98
Postauricular tract.................. 99
Temporal tract....................... 100
Loral tract.......................... 100
Superciliary tract................... 100
Ocular tracts........................ 100
Genal tract.......................... 100
Rictal tract......................... 100
Malar tract.......................... 101

Turkey.................................. 101
Frontal tract........................ 101
Coronal tract........................ 101
Occipital tract...................... 101
Auricular tract...................... 101
Postauricular tract.................. 102
Temporal tract....................... 102
Loral tract.......................... 102
Superciliary tract................... 102
Ocular tracts........................ 102
Genal tract.......................... 102
Rictal tract......................... 102
Malar tract.......................... 102
Poult ptilosis....................... 102

Common Coturnix......................... 102
White Pekin Duck........................ 103
Common Pigeon........................... 103

Pterylosis excluding the head................. 104
Introduction............................. 104
Chicken.................................. 106
Spinal tracts and apteria............... 106
Dorsal cervical tract................ 106
Interscapular tract.................. 106
Dorsopelvic tract.................... 109
Ventral tracts and apteria.............. 109
Ventral cervical tract............... 109
Pectoral tract....................... 111
Sternal and abdominal tracts......... 111
Cloacal circlet...................... 111
Caudal tracts and apteria............... 111
Dorsal caudal tract.................. 111
Oil gland circlet.................... 113
Ventral caudal tract................. 113
Rectrices............................ 113
Upper tail coverts................... 113
Under tail coverts................... 113
Lateral body tract and apterium......... 113

Chapter 3—Pterylosis and ptilosis of domestic birds—Continued

Pterylosis excluding the head—Continued
  Chicken—Continued
    Brachial tracts (upper arm)................... 114
      Humeral tract........................... 114
      Subhumeral tract........................ 114
      Posthumeral tract....................... 114
    Alar tracts and apteria (lower arm and hand).... 115
      Upper surface of the hand.................. 115
      Upper surface of the carpal region........... 116
      Upper surface of the forearm................ 116
      Under surface of the wing—direction of rows. 117
      Under surface of the hand.................. 117
      Under surface of the carpal region........... 117
      Under surface of the forearm................ 117
    Femoral tract................................. 120
    Crural tract and apteria...................... 121
    Metatarsal and digital tracts and apteria....... 121
  Turkey... 121
    Spinal tracts and apteria..................... 121
    Ventral tracts and apteria.................... 121
    Caudal tracts and apteria..................... 123
    Lateral body tract and apterium.............. 124
    Brachial tracts and apteria................... 124
    Alar tracts and apteria....................... 124
      Upper surface of the hand.................. 124
      Upper surface of the carpal region........... 124
      Upper surface of the forearm................ 124
      Under surface of the hand.................. 127
      Under surface of the carpal region........... 127
      Under surface of the forearm................ 127
    Femoral tract................................. 127
    Crural tract and apteria...................... 127
  Common Coturnix............................... 128
    Spinal tracts and apteria..................... 128
    Ventral tracts and apteria.................... 132
    Caudal tracts and apteria..................... 132
    Lateral body tract and apterium.............. 134
    Brachial tracts and apteria................... 134
      Humeral tract........................... 134
      Subhumeral tract........................ 134
      Posthumeral tract....................... 134
    Alar tracts and apteria....................... 134
      Upper surface of the hand.................. 134
      Upper surface of the carpal region........... 135
      Upper surface of the forearm................ 136
      Under surface of the hand.................. 138
      Under surface of the carpal region........... 138
      Under surface of the forearm................ 138
    Femoral tract................................. 138
    Crural tract and apteria...................... 138
  White Pekin Duck............................... 139
    Spinal tracts and apteria..................... 140
    Ventral tracts and apteria.................... 140

Chapter 3—Pterylosis and ptilosis of domestic birds—Continued

Pterylosis excluding the head—Continued
  White Pekin Duck—Continued
    Caudal tracts and apteria..................... 143
    Lateral body tract and apterium.............. 143
    Brachial tracts and apteria................... 143
    Alar tracts and apteria....................... 145
      Upper surface of the hand.................. 145
      Upper surface of the carpal region........... 145
      Upper surface of the forearm................ 145
      Under surface of the hand.................. 145
      Under surface of the carpal region........... 145
      Under surface of the forearm................ 145
      Downs.................................... 148
    Posterior appendage tracts and apteria......... 148
  Common Pigeon................................. 148
    Spinal tracts and apteria..................... 148
    Ventral tracts and apteria.................... 150
    Lateral body tracts and apteria............... 150
    Powder down patches......................... 150
    Caudal tracts and apteria..................... 151
    Brachial tracts and apteria................... 152
    Alar tracts and apteria....................... 153
      Upper surface of the hand.................. 153
      Upper surface of the carpal region........... 153
      Upper surface of the forearm................ 153
      Under surface of the hand.................. 156
      Under surface of the carpal region........... 156
      Under surface of the forearm................ 156
    Posterior appendage tracts and apteria......... 156
  Ptilosis... 157
    Feather coat excluding head................... 157
      Chicken................................... 157
        Dorsal cervical tract (hackle).............. 157
        Interscapular tract (cape)................. 157
        Dorsopelvic tract and anterior end of the dorsal
          caudal tract........................... 158
        Posterior part of the dorsal caudal tract (tail
          feathers and coverts)................... 158
        Ventral cervical tract (front of neck plumage).. 163
        Pectoral tract (breast plumage)............. 164
        Sternal tract............................. 164
        Abdominal tract (fluff)................... 164
        Ventral caudal tract...................... 164
        Lateral body tract........................ 164
        Femoral tract (lower thigh plumage and rear
          body feathers)......................... 164
        Crural tract (hock plumage)............... 165
        Humeral tract (wing front and shoulder)..... 165
        Posthumeral tract........................ 165
        Subhumeral tract........................ 165
        Alar tracts............................... 165
          Feather coat of the folded wing........... 165
          Feather coat on the upper side of the ex-
            tended wing........................... 168

Chapter 3—Pterylosis and ptilosis of domestic birds—Continued

Ptilosis—Continued

Feather coat excluding head—Continued

Chicken—Continued

Alar tracts—Continued
Feather coat on the under side of the extended wing...... 169

General considerations........ 172
Turkey.............. 175
Dorsal cervical and interscapular tracts...... 175
Dorsopelvic tract............ 175
Caudal tracts............ 176
Ventral cervical and pectoral tract.......... 177
Sternal and abdominal tracts.............. 178
Lateral body tract.............. 178
Femoral and crural tracts................ 179
Brachial tracts............ 181
Common Coturnix.......... 182
Dorsal and ventral neck.............. 182
Dorsal and pelvic tracts............ 182
Ventral surface of the body.............. 182
Posterior appendage tracts.............. 182
Anterior appendage tracts.............. 183
White Pekin Duck........... 183
Dorsal and ventral neck.............. 184
Dorsopelvic tract............ 184
Pectorosternal and abdominal tracts........ 184
Caudal tracts............ 185
Lateral body tract and apterium.......... 185
Posterior appendage tracts.............. 185
Brachial tracts............ 185
Alar tracts............ 186
Common Pigeon............ 188
Dorsal and ventral neck.............. 188
Dorsopelvic tract............ 188
Pectorosternal tract............ 189
Abdominal tract............ 189
Caudal tracts............ 189
Alar tracts............ 189
Posterior appendage tracts............ 192
Feather weight and number............ 193
Feather counts............ 193
Chickens............ 193
Wild birds............ 193
Effect of season on feather counts.......... 194
Feather weights............ 195
Chicken............ 195

Chapter 4—Molts and plumages of domestic chickens............ 197

Introduction............ 197
Phenomenon of molting............ 197
Terminology............ 197
Methods of study............ 199

Chapter 4—Molts and plumages of domestic chickens—Continued

Gross appearance of growing feathers.............. 199
Development of plumages........................ 203
Histories of separate tracts...................... 203
Primary remiges............................. 203
Secondary remiges.......................... 205
Rectrices.................................. 206
Capital tracts.............................. 207
Spinal tracts............................... 207
Pectoral and ventral cervical tracts............ 207
Sternal and abdominal tracts................. 209
Humeral tracts............................. 209
Upper alar tracts.......................... 210
Under alar tracts.......................... 210
Femoral tracts............................. 211
Crural tracts.............................. 211
Dorsal caudal tract........................ 211
Ventral caudal tract....................... 211
Changing composition of feathering............ 211
0 days.................................... 212
8 days.................................... 212
19 days................................... 212
35 days................................... 212
55 days................................... 212
77 days................................... 212
103 days.................................. 212
131 days.................................. 212
171 days.................................. 213
Timing and order of molting.................... 213
Establishment in the embryo................. 213
Comparison of sexes........................ 213
Comparison of breeds of chickens............. 228
Primary remiges............................ 229
Secondary remiges.......................... 229
Rectrices.................................. 230
Body and limb tracts....................... 230
Comparison of molts and plumages in chickens and other gallinaceous birds............ 230
General sequence.......................... 231
First molt and second plumage.............. 231
Second molt and third plumage.............. 231
Third molt and fourth plumage.............. 232
Additional molts and plumages.............. 232
Molting of rectrices........................ 232
Discussion................................ 233

Chapter 5—Structure of feathers.............. 235

Introduction.................................. 235
Contour feathers.............................. 235
Typical body feathers........................ 235
Preview of major parts...................... 235
Calamus................................. 236
Rachis................................... 237
Vanes and the measurements of barbs......... 239
Ramus................................... 241

Chapter 5—Structure of feathers—Continued

Contour feathers—Continued
  Typical body feathers—Continued

    Plumulaceous barbules...................... 242
    Pennaceous barbules........................ 245
      Base................................... 246
      Proximal barbules...................... 247
      Distal barbules........................ 248
      Comparison and functional analysis......... 249
    Simplified barbules........................ 251
    Microstructure of vanes in relation to texture... 252
    Afterfeather............................... 252
      Type 1................................. 253
      Type 2................................. 253
      Type 3................................. 253
      Type 4................................. 253
      Type 5................................. 253
      Type 6................................. 255
      Type 7................................. 255
  Remiges and rectrices........................ 255
    Calamus................................... 256
    Rachis.................................... 256
    Vanes and measurements of barbs.............. 256
    Ramus.................................... 258
    Barbules.................................. 259
    Afterfeather............................... 261
  Ear coverts................................. 262
Semiplumes.................................. 263
Down feathers............................... 264
  Natal downs................................ 264
  Definitive downs............................ 266
  Oil gland feathers.......................... 267
  Powder down................................ 269
Bristles.................................... 270
  Distribution............................... 270
  Structure and color........................ 272
  Semibristles............................... 273
  Function.................................. 273
Filoplumes.................................. 274
  Distribution............................... 274
  Structure................................. 275
  Function.................................. 276

Chapter 6—Shape, structure, and texture of feathers of domestic birds................. 277

Introduction................................ 277
Single Comb White Leghorn Chicken.............. 278
  Dorsopelvic tract.......................... 278
    Anterior end, near midline................. 279
    Anterior end, near borders................. 279
    Middle, near midline...................... 280
    Middle, near borders...................... 280
    Posterior end, near midline................. 280
    Posterior end, near borders................. 280
  Interscapular tract......................... 280
  Dorsal cervical tract....................... 280

Chapter 6—Shape, structure, and texture of feathers of domestic birds—Continued

Single Comb White Leghorn Chicken—Continued
  Dorsal cervical tract—Continued

    Posterior end............................. 280
    Anterior end............................. 282
  Ventral cervical tract....................... 283
  Pectoral tract............................. 283
  Sternal tract.............................. 286
  Abdominal tract............................ 287
  Femoral tract............................. 287
    Anterior border, dorsal corner.............. 287
    Posterior border.......................... 287
  Crural tract............................... 289
    Upper end................................ 289
    Lower end................................ 290
  Humeral tract.............................. 290
  Alar tracts................................ 291
    Primary remiges........................... 291
      Proximal barbules..................... 292
      Distal barbules....................... 292
    Secondary remiges......................... 294
    Alular remiges............................ 295
    Upper major primary coverts................ 296
    Upper minor primary coverts, upper marginal coverts of the hand......................... 296
    Carpal remex............................. 296
    Upper major secondary coverts.............. 296
    Upper median secondary coverts............. 298
    Upper minor secondary coverts, upper marginal coverts of the prepatagium................. 299
    Upper alular coverts...................... 300
    Posthumeral tract........................ 300
    Under major primary coverts, under carpal remex covert, under major secondary coverts....... 301
    Under median secondary coverts............. 301
    Under minor primary coverts, under minor secondary coverts, under forearm tract, under prepatagial apterium...................... 301
    Under marginal coverts.................... 301
    Subhumeral tract......................... 301
  Caudal tracts.............................. 302
    Rectrices................................ 302
    Upper major tail coverts.................. 303
    Upper median tail coverts................. 303
    Dorsal caudal tract...................... 304
    Under tail coverts, ventral caudal tract......... 304
  Capital tracts............................. 304
    Occipital tract........................... 304
    Coronal tract............................ 305
    Frontal tract............................ 305
    Loral tract.............................. 305
    Superciliary tract........................ 307
    Temporal tract........................... 307
    Genal tract.............................. 307
    Malar tract.............................. 308

Chapter 6—Shape, structure, and texture of feathers of domestic birds—Continued

Single Comb White Leghorn Chicken—Continued

Capital tracts—Continued

Rictal tract................................... 308
Ocular tract (upper and lower)............... 308
Auricular tract.............................. 308
Interramal tract............................. 309
Submalar tract............................... 309
Semiplumes................................... 310
Distribution and gross appearance............ 310
Variation in downy texture................... 310
Structural basis for downy texture........... 311
Down feathers................................ 313
Distribution and gross appearance............ 313
Downy barbs.................................. 314
Oil gland feathers........................... 315
Filoplumes................................... 316
Location..................................... 316
Size... 318
Structure.................................... 318
Bronze Turkey................................ 318
Dorsopelvic tract............................ 319
Anterior portion............................. 319
Posterior portion............................ 319
Interscapular tract.......................... 320
Dorsal cervical tract........................ 320
Ventral cervical tract....................... 320
Pectoral tract............................... 320
Contour feathers............................. 320
Semiplumes................................... 320
Sternal tract................................ 321
Abdominal tract.............................. 321
Femoral tract................................ 322
Crural tract................................. 322
Humeral tract................................ 322
Primary remiges.............................. 322
Secondary remiges............................ 322
Upper major primary coverts.................. 323
Upper marginal coverts of the prepatagium.... 323
Rectrices.................................... 323
Capital tracts............................... 323
Semiplumes and downs......................... 326
Semiplumes................................... 326
Down feathers................................ 326
Oil gland feathers........................... 327
Filoplumes................................... 327

Chapter 6—Shape, structure, and texture of feathers of domestic birds—Continued

Beltsville White Turkey........................ 327
White Pekin Duck.............................. 328
Body contour feathers........................ 328
Gross appearance............................. 328
Downy barbs.................................. 328
Pennaceous barbs............................. 329
Afterfeather................................. 330
Remiges and rectrices........................ 330
Down feathers................................ 330
Body downs................................... 330
Oil gland feathers........................... 331
Filoplumes................................... 331

Common Pigeon................................ 331
Body contour feathers........................ 331
Gross appearance............................. 331
Downy barbs.................................. 332
Pennaceous barbs............................. 332
Distal barbules.............................. 333
Proximal barbules............................ 333
Afterfeather................................. 333
Remiges and rectrices........................ 333
Down feathers and semiplumes................. 334
Down feathers................................ 334
Semiplumes................................... 334
Oil gland feathers........................... 335
Powder feathers.............................. 335
General nature............................... 335
Distribution................................. 335
Structure.................................... 335
Fat quills................................... 338
Filoplumes................................... 338

Common Coturnix.............................. 338
Body contour feathers........................ 338
Gross appearance............................. 338
Downy barbs.................................. 338
Pennaceous barbs............................. 339
Afterfeather................................. 339
Remiges and rectrices........................ 340
Down feathers and semiplumes................. 340
Semiplumes................................... 340
Down feathers................................ 340
Oil gland feathers........................... 340
Filoplumes................................... 340

Part II (abridged)

Page

Chapter 7—Growth of follicles and feathers. Color of feathers and integument............. 341

Historical introduction.......................... 341
   Descriptive approach to the morphogenesis of feathers................................ 341
   Analytical approach to the morphogenesis of feathers................................ 341
   Studies of the formation of keratin............. 342
   Studies of the color of feathers................. 342
   Studies of the roles of hormones in molting and development of feathers...................... 343
   Studies of the anatomy and physiology of feather follicles................................ 344
   Implications of feather development for theories of feather evolution......................... 344
Embryonic development and structure of follicles and feathers............................ 347
   Chicken....................................... 347
   Duck.. 353
Anatomy of a fully grown follicle and its associated structures................................. 357
   Growth and general morphology................ 357
   Histology of the follicle wall................... 358
   Arrangement of blood vessels.................. 360
   Innervation.................................... 361
   Retention of a feather in its follicle............. 362
Development and structure of regenerating contour feathers............................... 363
   Occurrence of regeneration..................... 363
   Relationship of the follicle to the feather blastema.. 363
   Activation of the blastema..................... 364
   Morphogenetic potential of the blastema........ 365
   Structure of a papilla and formation of pulp...... 365
   Development of a blastema into a feather........ 367
   Keratinization of the feather................... 378
   Final steps in development of a feather........... 380
   Summary of feather differentiation.............. 384
Development of special feathers................... 384
   Introduction................................... 384
   Powder feathers............................... 386
   Filoplumes.................................... 388
Color of skin and feathers....................... 391
   Pigmentary colors............................. 392
   Structural colors.............................. 403
   Color modifiers................................ 411
   Patterns of pigmentation....................... 412
   Changes in color.............................. 417

Page

Chapter 8—Feather and apterial muscles....... 421

Gross morphology................................ 421
   General....................................... 421
   Chicken....................................... 423
   Turkey.. 438
   Common Coturnix.............................. 447
   White Pekin Duck............................. 449
   Common Pigeon................................ 457
Subgross morphology............................. 461
   General....................................... 461
   Chicken....................................... 461
   Blood vessels and nerves to the integument....... 467
Micromorphology and physiology.................. 478

Chapter 9—Microscopic structure of skin and derivatives............................ 485

Introduction..................................... 485
   Terminology................................... 485
Histology of apteria............................. 489
   Chicken....................................... 489
Histology of pterylae............................ 509
   Chicken....................................... 509
Sternal apterium and bursa....................... 514
   Chicken and turkey............................ 514
Comb.. 531
   Gross morphology.............................. 531
   Development and histology...................... 535
Wattle... 547
   Gross morphology and histology................. 547
Rictus... 552
   Gross morphology and histology................. 552
Earlobe.. 558
   Gross morphology and histology................. 558
Turkey... 564
   Frontal process................................ 564
   Caruncle...................................... 571
   Beard and papilla.............................. 571
Beak of chicken.................................. 579
   General....................................... 579
   Histology...................................... 580
Cere... 592
   Great Horned Owl............................. 592
   Common Pigeon................................ 593
Scutellation of nonfeathered feet.................. 595
   Chicken and turkey............................ 695
Scutellation of feathered feet..................... 598
   Chicken....................................... 598

Chapter 9—Microscopic structure of skin and derivatives—Continued

Scales.. 602

    Histology................................... 602

Digital claw.................................... 606

    Histology................................... 606

Metatarsal spur................................ 609

    Growth..................................... 609

Interdigital web................................ 612

    Chicken.................................... 612

Uropygial gland................................ 613

    Gross morphology........................... 613

Secretory activity of skin epidermis.............. 627

    Preliminary evidence........................ 627

    Study of selected tissues.................... 627

Sebaceous glands of external ear................. 635

Chapter 10—Techniques...................... 637

Introduction................................... 637

Anesthesia and killing.......................... 637

    Anesthesia.................................. 637

    Killing..................................... 638

Gross examination of the body.................. 638

    Determination of body regions............... 638

    Methods for plotting pterylosis.............. 638

    Molting records and growth of feathers........ 639

X-ray techniques............................... 640

Preparation of skeletons........................ 640

    Roughing out and drying.................... 640

    Management of a dermestid colony............ 641

    Fumigation and final cleaning................ 641

Study of whole feathers and feather parts.......... 641

    Exploded view of the feather tracts.......... 641

    Whole mounts.............................. 642

Chapter 10—Techniques—Continued

Preparation of tissue sections.................... 644

    Recording data............................. 644

    Selecting tissues............................ 645

    Immobilization of tissues during fixation........ 645

    Fixation and infiltration..................... 646

    Placement of serial sections with a water bath.... 646

    Processing calcified tissues.................. 647

    Embedding and sectioning feathers and other keratinized structures...................... 647

Staining tissue sections......................... 649

    General techniques.......................... 649

    Techniques for connective tissues............ 650

    Technique for fat........................... 651

    Techniques for striated muscle............... 652

    Techniques for nerves....................... 652

Preparation and staining of whole pieces of skin... 653

    Techniques for muscular and elastic tissues..... 653

    Techniques for nerves....................... 656

Demonstration of blood vessels in whole specimens.. 657

    Injection casting with latex.................. 657

    Perfusion with physiological ink.............. 658

Anatomical illustration.......................... 660

    Drawing the outline......................... 660

    Rendering techniques and materials............. 666

    Overlays................................... 667

    Labeling................................... 667

    Techniques for photographing feathers........... 668

Acknowledgments............................ 671

Literature cited............................. 673

Appendix A: Classfied list of birds mentioned in this volume............................. 697

Appendix B: Latin-English equivalents for terms used in this volume................. 703

Index.. 721

CHAPTER 1

Topographic Anatomy

INTRODUCTION

Topographic anatomy deals with the description of parts and regions of the body. The term is applied more frequently to surface anatomy than to the descriptions of internal organ morphology, yet it can apply to both.

Terms for external parts and regions of the avian body are often applied by ornithologists to birds with plumage intact. As a result, often the names chosen are more descriptive of groups of feathers than of regions of the naked body. Both poultrymen and ornithologists have chosen terms for birds with plumage intact that fitted the particular species they were studying, and they have used either a few terms or as many as needed. In the "American Standard of Perfection" (1953)[1] are presented the feathered areas of a male and a female chicken. Comparable areas have been named for the turkey (Jull, 1930; Marsden and Martin,1949); for a falcon (Evans, 1899); for several kinds of birds (Tunnicliffe, 1945); for a duck (Kortright, 1942; Delacour, 1951); for a duck and a goose (Jull, 1930); for a pigeon (Levi, 1957); and for passerines, i.e., perching birds (Mivart, 1892; Marshall, 1895; Coues, 1903; Reichenow, 1913; Chapman, 1920; Witherby, et al., 1940; Delacour and Mayr, 1946; Peterson, 1947; Roberts, 1949; Pough, 1957; Jørgensen, 1958; and many others). The subject of feathered areas for domestic fowl is discussed in detail in chapter 3.

Homologous areas of feather coats sometimes have been given different names by different groups of scientists. Poultrymen, for example, speak of "saddle," "sweep of back," and "fluff," but these terms are not in general usage by ornithologists. The terms "cape" and "hackle" are applicable chiefly to gallinaceous birds and are used by both ornithologists and poultrymen.

Sometimes the boundary of an area on a feathered bird does not correspond to the boundary of an area having the same name on a deplumed bird. A good example is the junction of breast and abdomen. In a feathered bird the breast includes the area in front of the legs forward to the neck, and the abdomen is the area extending from between the legs to the vent. In a plucked bird, however, the breast is the ventral surface of the thorax and includes the full length of the sternum, even where part of it lies between the legs and even where part of it supports some of the abdominal viscera. Nitzsch (1867: 27) faced this problem and stated: "I give the name of the breast to the whole region of the body that lies over the sternum." In order to sharpen terminology it seems desirable to describe structures and regions of the plucked body separately from plumage (ptilosis). Many terms used to identify structures or regions will be the same as those used in ptilology although, as already indicated, their boundaries may differ somewhat. Confusion will be avoided, however, if the word "region" is used to designate a specific surface area on the plucked bird, and "tract" or "pteryla" is used to designate an area on the skin where a group of feathers is implanted.

Another example of the ambiguous usage of a name is the word "shank." For ornithologists it means the lower leg or crus, but for poultrymen it means the metatarsal portion of the foot. It is used here to designate the lower leg, not the ankle region. We do not wish to burden the literature with additional anatomical terms; rather, we wish to bring together whenever possible a unified terminology for poultrymen, ornithologists, and veterinary anatomists. Much of our basic information on the anatomy of birds comes from publications by ornithologists, many of whom have studied extensively various aspects of anatomy with meticulous care.

The same kinds of questions confront us on selecting terminology for studies on gross anatomy and histology as they did for studies in the "Atlas of Avian Hematology" Lucas and Jamroz (1961). Should one choose an inappropriate term for birds merely because it is in common usage for man or some mammal? The following policy was developed during the progress of the work on blood: If a term is equally appropriate for bird and mammal the mammalian term will be utilized, but if a mammalian term is not applicable to the condition found in birds or if a particular term has become firmly established in avian literature, the avian term will be utilized in many instances even if it differs from the equivalent term used in mammalian literature. This policy is not always easy to follow because human and mammalian terminologies are so widely used and firmly established that frequently decisions must be made on an arbitrary basis. Some of the difficulties that can be encountered in avian hematology were discussed by Lucas (1959).

---

[1] References to Literature Cited (p. 673) are indicated by the name of the author (authors) or title of the publication followed by the year of publication.

1

Our policy governing the choice of terminology, in general, agrees with that prepared in Paris by the International Anatomical Nomenclature Committee and approved at the sixth International Congress of Anatomists in meetings of the Paris Nomina Anatomica (PNA). The principles that guided the committee in their decisions on nomenclature were as follows (1956: vi):

> (a) That, with a very limited number of exceptions, each structure shall be designated by one term only.
> (b) That every term in the official list shall be in Latin, each country to be at liberty to translate the official Latin terms into its own vernacular for teaching purposes.
> (c) That each term shall be, so far as possible, short and simple.
> (d) That the terms shall be primarily memory signs, but shall preferably have some informative or descriptive value.
> (e) That structures closely related topographically shall, as far as possible, have similar names—e.g., *Arteria femoralis*, *Vena femoralis*, *Nervus femoralis*, etc.
> (f) That differentiating adjectives shall be, in general, arranged as opposites—e.g., major and minor, superficialis and profundus, etc.
> (g) That eponyms shall not be used in the Official Nomenclature of Gross or Macroscopic Anatomy.

The terms used in the Nomina Anatomica were consulted frequently during the course of this work in order to utilize wherever possible the same term for birds as for man. For example, the suggestion made in the PNA that *Arteria anonyma* be changed to *Truncus brachiocephalicus* is now as applicable to birds as to mammals, and the change from *Arteria mammaria interna* to *Arteria thoracica interna* gives scientists a name they can use in avian anatomy.

The problem of exact etymology always enters into the use of scientific words. We have followed a policy laid down by the PNA, namely, that a term inaccurate only from an etymological aspect would not be changed if the term were well established and acceptable in common usage. There are, however, problems in avian terminology that are no longer problems in human anatomical terminolgy because repeated congresses have been held to eliminate synomyms and at the same time provide a terminology that is internationally acceptable. Efforts are now being made by the World Association of Veterinary Anatomists to select terminology suitable for avian species. In this volume, the English translation of Latin terms generally has been used in both text and figures. Usually the first time a term is used, the English name will be followed in parenthesis by the Latin equivalent. These names have been assembled in Appendix B where they have been organized into groups by subject. Appendix A contains a list of common and scientific names for birds mentioned in this volume.

In the early phases of our research on the avian integument, we decided upon the kinds of birds that should be studied. The domestic chicken, turkey, and duck were selected because they are economically important to the poultry industry. The Common Pigeon and Common Coturnix were also included because they are often used in research and teaching. Among the breeds and varieties of domestic fowl, we conducted most of our studies on the Single Comb White Leg-horn Chicken, dark variety of Bronze Turkey, and White Pekin Duck. Our Common Coturnices were laboratory descendants of *Coturnix coturnix japonica*. The Common Pigeons we used were collected locally from city buildings and country barns. A pigeon of the Archangel breed was used for certain studies. (See Levi, 1957 and 1965, for description of breeds of the Common Pigeon.)

We will try to treat adequately each of the five species listed, but where two or more species are closely similar, only one of them will be described fully. In some chapters where the subject matter is detailed and complex, too much space would be needed to repeat the description for all five species, but in this first chapter on topographic anatomy, each of the five species will be described rather fully. Wherever possible we will designate the breed and variety on which a particular study is being made.

It is undoubtedly apparent that we have omitted the designations of the chicken as *Gallus gallus*, of the turkey as *Meleagris gallopavo*, of the duck as *Anas platyrhynchos*, and of the pigeon as *Columba livia*. This omission is intentional because species names of the presumed ancestors of domestic descendants do not adequately identify the birds the authors studied.

The confusion that would develop if poultrymen and those who use the fowl for their researches were to identify all chicken breeds by the name "*Gallus gallus*" can be demonstrated by a few examples: *Gallus gallus* has a single comb, it also has a rose comb; *Gallus gallus* has red earlobes, white earlobes, and nearly black earlobes; an adult male *Gallus gallus* weighs about 13 pounds, and an adult male *Gallus gallus* weighs less than 2 pounds. *Gallus gallus* has a sex dimorphism in the feather coat at maturity; in the same species, the feather coat is alike in adult males and females.

Obviously identification of the material we have used, by its generic and specific names leads to contradictions when describing various specimens. Something more exact and definite is needed. This is available in the descriptions accompanying the breed and variety names given to the different kinds of domestic fowl by the "American Standard of Perfection." When applied, the contradictions disappear, and the reader and author are on common ground with the same kind of chicken, turkey, duck, or pigeon in mind as the the description of its anatomy proceeds.

The "American Standard of Perfection" (1953) lists 65 breeds and 188 varieties of chickens, including the bantams; a single breed of turkey subdivided into seven varieties; there are 12 breeds and 14 varieties of ducks, and nine breeds of geese, of which one is divided into two varieties.

A critique on the ancestry of the chicken is beyond the scope of this publication, but enough of the literature on the subject should be mentioned to indicate that there have been different opinions. Beebe (1926: 19) stated that all domestic chickens came from the Red Jungle Fowl, *Gallus gallus*. It is probably correct to add that this is the generally accepted belief today among ornithologists.

Danforth (1958) suggested that *Gallus sonneratii* may have contributed to the ancestral gene pool; among others,

Hutt (1949) discussed (p. 10) the possibility of a polyphyletic origin for chickens, which he summarized (p. 13) as follows:

> The correct zoological name of the domestic fowl must, for the present at least, depend somewhat upon the particular faith of the writer who uses it. There is no provision in the International Code of Zoological Nomenclature whereby mere domestication of a wild species justifies changing its name. Those who believe that all domestic fowls are descended from the Red Jungle Fowl should therefore stick to *Gallus gallus*. On the other hand, if several distinct wild species produce by hybridization a new animal sufficiently different from any of them to justify its being considered a separate species, a new name is in order. The use of the familiar term *Gallus domesticus* is therefore probably permissible, but only to those who believe in a polyphyletic origin of domestic fowls.

Davenport (1914:313) suggested,

> It is, indeed, pretty certain that two distinct species have contributed to the formation of our well known races:—one is the Jungle Fowl, which is still found wild, and the other is the unknown ancestor of the Aseel or Malay Fowl, probably the oldest fowl in domestication, for it has been bred for over 3,000 years. It is still possible that the ancestor of this bird or its bones may be found in the interior of New Guinea, Borneo, or the Philippines.

Davenport cited many basic differences between the Jungle Fowl and the Aseel. Grzimek (1932) suggested that some domestic chickens may have come from *Gallus varius*, the Java Jungle Fowl, and Tegetmeier (1873: 308) recorded that hybrids had been produced between this species and the domestic fowl. It was Jull's (1952: 6) opinion that modern breeds of chickens arose from all four wild species of *Gallus*.

As Hutt (1949) indicated, one suddenly passes from scientific testing to accepting by faith the assumptions made by those who preceded us. As long as the descriptions written to identify a wild species fail to be inclusive enough so that domestic breeds presumably derived from them can be identified as belonging to that species by the description given, there is no reason to accept the idea that all breeds of a group of domestic birds have genetic relationship to the presumed ancestral type. Again one comes to the conclusion that the use of taxonomic names for wild species should be avoided when identifying domestic birds. The only substitute one has at present is to use the breed and variety names of domestic chickens, turkeys, and ducks.

TERMS USED IN ANATOMY

Terms of Orientation

The planes of the body, lines of direction, and points of relative position follow the terminology for quadruped animals. Thus, the back, or top side, of a bird is dorsal (*dorsalis*), the underside is ventral (*ventralis*), and the lateral sides are right (*dexter*) and left (*sinister*). The end toward the head of a bird is anterior (*anterior*), cranial (*cranialis*), or rostral (*rostralis*); that toward the tail is posterior (*posterior*), caudal (*caudalis*), or terminal (*terminalis*).

The body has three fundamental planes—sagittal (*sagittalis*), frontal (*frontalis*), and transverse (*transversus*) (fig. 1,*A*). A sagittal plane passes through the body dorsoventrally, either through or parallel to the anteroposterior axis. The midsagittal plane, or median plane (*medius*) divides the body into right and left halves. The term "parasagittal" is used for the planes to the right and left of the median plane. The single term "sagittal" can be used for the midplane and for any plane parallel to the midplane. The frontal planes pass through the body at right angles to the sagittal planes and divide the body into dorsal and ventral parts. The transverse plane is at right angles to the other two planes and thus cuts across the body dorsoventrally.

Medial (*medialis*) and medially signify, respectively, the placement or movement of one object in relation to a more laterally placed object. This relationship or movement is always within a frontal plane as shown in figure 1, *B*, which is at right angles to the midsagittal plane. In the diagram the circles lie medial to the crosses and the crosses, lateral to the circles. Movements along the connecting lines toward the midsagittal plane are referred to as medially or mediad; and movement in the opposite direction as laterally or laterad. These terms also apply to vessels and nerves where no actual movement is involved; the terms indicate the direction in which these vessels and nerves course through the body.

Mesial (central) and mesially (centrally) are often confused in usage with medial and medially. Medial refers to position in relation to the sagittal plane (fig. 1, *B*), whereas mesial refers to position in relation to the anteroposterior axis (fig. 1, *C*). A line joining a mesial structure and its peripheral point of reference lies along a radius emanating from the anteroposterior axis (APA in fig. 1, *B, C*). Mesially (or mesiad) indicates a centripetal direction of movement along this radius. The antonyms to these are peripherally and peripheral. Only in one location are medial and mesial identical. This is shown in figure 1, *C*, by the letter M.

Numerous terms, in addition to those involving orientation of the body as a whole, can be applied for purposes of comparison. Some examples are external (*externus*) and internal (*internus*); superficial (*superficialis*) and deep (*profundus*); superior (*superior*) and inferior (*inferior*); apical (*apicalis*) and basal (*basalis*); distal (*distalis*) and proximal (*proximalis*); ascending (*ascendens*) and descending (*descendens*); afferent (*afferens*) and efferent (*efferens*); central (*centralis*) and peripheral (*periphericus*); major (*major*) and minor (*minor*); long (*longus*) and short (*brevis*); and strong (*robustus*) and weak (*infirmus*). Occasionally three levels of comparison are designated by the use of the terms "intermediate" (*intermedius*) combined with the terms "peripheral" and "central", "medial" and "lateral," "distal" and "proximal," and so on.

The ideal, of course, is the use of comparative terms for opposites, such as major and minor; or if there is an intermediate, then major, median, and minor. This is often impossible because during the course of evolution one member of a pair of structures may have been lost. In order to identify

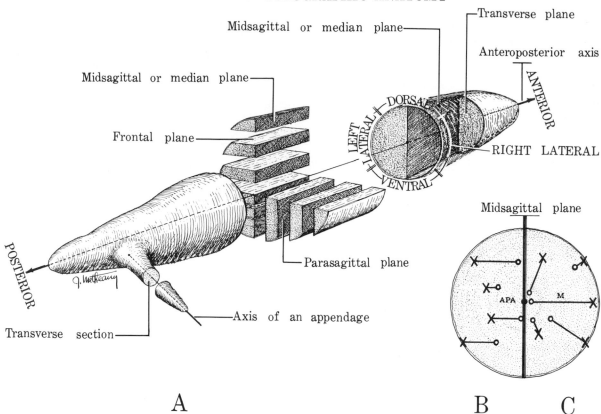

A

B   C

FIGURE 1.—Axes of the body and appendages and the planes of section in a bilaterally symmetrical animal.

A, planes and axes labeled on a manikin.

B and C, the halves of a cross section of a bilateral body that illustrate and contrast the meaning of medial and mesial. In B the circles lie medial to the crosses, and in C the circles lie mesial to the crosses.

Abbreviations: APA, anteroposterior axis; M, a line so oriented that the small circle is both mesial and medial to the cross. (See p. 3 for further explanation.)

the homologous structure with that in other species, it seems better to retain the comparative term even when its counterpart does not exist or when one of the pair of names has been changed. It is for this reason that a chicken has an *m. tibialis anterior* but no *m. tibialis posterior*, according to the terminology of Hudson et al. (1959).[2] Of course, many homologies are yet unidentified, and one is then forced to select terms based on their descriptive qualities or their placement in relation to other structures.

Because structure is the basis for function, some terms that indicate movement have been applied to anatomy. Those frequently used are: adductor (*adductor*), a muscle that draws toward the axis of the body or toward the axis of an appendage; abductor (*abductor*), a muscle that moves away from the axis of the body or the axis of an appendage; extensor (*extensor*), a muscle that extends an appendage, a part of an appendage, or one part of the body in relation to another; flexor (*flexor*), a muscle that draws parts together toward the body or toward an adjacent part; levator (*levator*) or erector (*erector*), a muscle that raises or elevates a part; depressor (*depressor*), a muscle that lowers a part; pronator

(*pronator*), a muscle that tends to rotate the wing bones forward and ventrally (when the wing is extended); and a supinator (*supinator*), a muscle that tends to rotate wing bones backward and dorsally (when the wing is extended). Examples of muscles that indicate function are: *m. flexor hallucis longus; m. extensor hallucis longus; m. abductor pollicis; m. adductor pollicis; m. pronator sublimis;* and *m. supinator brevis.* Many muscles, however, are named to indicate their connections, position, or relation to structures such as: *m. coracobrachialis, m. entepicondylo-ulnaris, m. iliotibialis, m. ischiofemoralis, m. serratus superficialis,* and *m. interosseus dorsalis.*

By their movement, appendages often shift their orientation to planes of the body, and the position on which the terms of orientation are based must, therefore, be decided arbitrarily. In birds the wings are a case in point. At rest, along the side of the body, the two surfaces of each wing are oriented laterally and medially and may be referred to as outer and inner surfaces; extended as in flight, these become dorsal and ventral. Both sets of terms are used in the literature. If reference is being made only to the wing, dorsal and ventral seem preferable, but if the anatomy of the wing is being compared with that of the forelimb of other tetrapods, it would be awkward to use any other terms except lateral and medial. The terms used on a specific occasion

---

[2] See also the table of synonyms for muscles of the limb given by Fisher (1946: 694–696) and by Ede (1964).

should be appropriate for the subject and context of the discussion. We have considered the wing extended laterally as in flight to be the anatomical position for a bird. Terms of direction have been chosen for digit II when the digit is fully abducted, as shown in figure 26 and not when adducted as shown in figure 25. Therefore, digit II has an anterior tip, a posterior base, dorsal and ventral surfaces, and proximal and distal margins. A somewhat similar example that causes confusion are the surfaces of the toes which, if placed in the same axis as the leg, become anterior (upper surface) and posterior (under surface). However, because the axes of the toes are almost always at an angle to the axis of the leg, the upper and under surfaces then become dorsal and ventral and equivalent terms are "dorsum" and "sole." Plantar (*plantaris*) surface is another equivalent of sole or ventral surface. If either sole or plantar surface is used, it should be applied also, theoretically, to the posterior surface of the metatarsus or instep, but usually anterior and posterior, are used in descriptions of this upright portion of the foot.

Terms for Parts, Regions, and Palpable Structures

The study of topographic anatomy has developed terminologies depending on the application or purpose of their use. Three groups or classes of terms will be discussed in this chapter: (1) Parts of the avian body (*partes corpori avis*); (2) regions (*regiones*), surfaces (*facies*), margins (*margines*), and lines (*lineae*) of the body; and (3) underlying palpable structures.

The parts and the regions of the body may be equivalent, but they are not synonymous. The parts of the body are the anatomical units of which the organism is composed, and they include internal as well as external structures. Regions are units of the body surface that are bounded by arbitrary lines. An example will indicate the differences in meaning among these concepts: The knee is a part of the body—a structural unit—composed of knee cap, knee joint, bones, muscles, vessels, and nerves immediately adjacent to the joint. The region of the knee is an area on the surface of the leg circumscribed by imaginary lines. Because there are really no limiting anatomical reference points, it is apparent that

one person's estimate of upper and lower boundaries for the region of the knee may differ from another's. The knee joint is the place where the bones of upper and lower legs form a moveable junction, and this is more restricted in meaning than the term "knee" referring to a part of the body.

The distinction between region and part is often neglected in writing and speaking. It is correct but awkward to say, for example, forehead region, crown region, and face region instead of forehead, crown, and face. The latter terms actually connote parts of the head rather than regions. Also it becomes a matter of choice whether one should say nasal region or region of the nose; the former has precedence in human anatomy and is the more literal translation of the Latin, *regio nasalis*.

Surfaces of the whole body or of a part of the body are the areas into which the outside of a three-dimensional object can be subdivided. Oftentimes the boundaries of surfaces are the same as those for regions and are equally arbitrary. The principal surfaces are dorsal, lateral, and ventral. Sometimes anterior and posterior surfaces are used if the body or part of the body is so shaped.

Many bones or parts of bones can be palpated through the skin. The skeletal system, together with its joints, is useful in establishing points of reference for regions, surface areas, and other landmarks. It is generally useful in the placement of incisions in the skin for operations and in locating various nerves, arteries, and veins as well as finding particular skeletal muscles.

Another class of landmarks is that of the skeletal muscles and tendons themselves. Some are so clearly defined and so well separated from adjacent muscles and tendons that they produce distinct elevations of the skin. In the same way as the bones, they serve as topographic reference points, not only for themselves but also for hidden structures that are not apparent when viewing the surface of the body. The muscles and tendons most distinctly seen are those beneath the wing, especially if the carcass is lean and the skin is thin. In small passerine birds the skin is often very thin; it is nearly transparent in the freshly plucked specimen so that it is possible to see exact boundaries for many body and leg muscles.

REGIONS OF THE HEAD

The major divisions of the body along the anteroposterior axis are the head (*caput*), neck (*collum*), trunk (*truncus*) (composed of thorax, *thorax*, and abdomen, *abdomen*), and tail (*cauda*). Appendages arising from the trunk are a pair of anterior members (*membra anteria*), the wings (*alae*), and a pair of posterior members (*membra posteria*), the limbs. The head, including the hyoid, and the external pharyngeal regions are discussed for the five species under consideration before other parts of the body are discussed.

The head, especially the beak, is greatly diversified among various groups of birds. Boundaries for regions are more variable in this part of the body than in any other part.

Some of these differences of shape are illustrated in figure 2. A few notes regarding the birds illustrated are given in the following paragraphs.

Albatrosses (fig. 2, *A*) and fulmars (fig. 2, *B*) spend their lives at sea except during breeding and as fledglings. A characteristic of these birds, order Procellariiformes, is that the nostrils open in tubes. In albatrosses, these tubes are separate, but in fulmars they are united in a partly divided tube on the crest of the beak. Another characteristic of this order is that the bones of the beak are covered by several discontinuous horny plates separated by suture lines. Coues (1903: 1021) provided seven names for the various plates and gave the location of each. A third characteristic of the order Procellariiformes is the hooked upper bill. It is an effective means of catching and holding such slippery live food as fish, and it is also useful in tearing apart the carcasses of larger animals.

The flamingos (suborder Phoenicopteri) including the American Flamingo (*Phoenicopterus ruber*, fig. 2, *C*) have a beak sharply bent downward at the middle of its length. When the bird is feeding, the head is partially inverted so that the distal half of the upper beak can rest against the bottom. Jenkin (1957) examined in detail the feeding mechanisms of the three genera within the suborder. In *Phoenicopterus* the upper bill is relatively thin and broad, which Jenkin classified as the low-keeled type. The lower jaw of each side forms a deep, wide groove in which the tongue, by sliding forward and backward, produces a pumping action. At the edges where the upper and lower beaks are in close proximity, both have lamellae that serve as filters. Food may consist of small worms and crustacea and mud from the bottom.

Flamingos in the other genera (*Phoeniconaias* and *Phoenicoparrus*) have narrow but thick dorsal beaks, triangular in shape, that fit into V-shaped grooves of the lower beaks. The rodlike tongue moves in a small tubular groove. The diet is composed of microscopic organisms. The lamellae are close together and often are frayed to increase the effectiveness of filtering. Large lamellae at the edges of the gape have a horizontal orientation and serve to exclude large bodies from entering the mouth.

The White Pekin Duck (fig. 2, *D*) feeds on formulated foods placed in troughs, but its ancestral progenitor, the Mallard, utilizes its highly specialized mouth and beak to strain from muddy waters small animals and plants, small seeds, leaves, insect larvae, worms, small molluscs, and small vertebrates. Objects as large as acorns may be ingested, and these are effectively triturated by the grit of the gizzard. Swans (fig. 2, *E*) have a similar food-gathering mechanism. Ducks, geese, and swans have a thickened epidermis that forms a nail at the end of the upper beak; ducks have a nail also on the tip of the lower beak. The nail and the hooked type of beak aid in holding small slippery objects.

Several kinds of birds have developed an elongated beak. Among these are avocets (fig. 2, *F*), curlews, woodcocks, snipes, sandpipers, ibises, herons, cranes, limpkins, hummingbirds, wood-hoopoes, jaçamars, and certain wood hewers (e.g., *Campylorhamphus trochilirostris*). Elongated beaks are used for catching insects or for probing into water, wet sand, flowers, and rotted wood. In the young avocets the beak is straight or curved downward; in the adult it curves upward. The bird moves its head from side to side while passing mud and water between its partly opened jaws. Its food includes aquatic insects, molluscs, small fish, and frogs. Sometimes lizards are included in the diet.

Puffins have a compressed, very deep beak (fig. 2, *G*), which is unlike that of auks and murres who are other members of the same family. The outer layer of the beak has a horny covering that is divided into nine plates; like the feathers, this covering is molted every fall. During the period while the plates are shed, the beak is smaller than it generally is, and it resembles the less modified beaks of other alcids. These and other seasonal changes on the head have been described by Bureau (1877, 1879).

Bills of many different shapes occur among the passerines. The strongly hooked bill of a shrike (fig. 2, *H*) makes the bird an effective predator of insects, spiders, lizards, small mammals, and other birds. The notch behind the tip makes the bill more effective for grasping prey. An even more strongly hooked beak is seen in the Gray Butcherbird (*Cracticus torquatus*), which has food habits similar to the shrike although belonging to a different family (Austin and Singer, 1961).

The House Sparrow (*Passer domesticus*) (fig. 2, *I*) has a straight, pointed, conical beak that is typical of many grain and seedeaters. The drawing of the plucked head shows some of the regions and structures of the head that are discussed at greater length in the domestic birds.

Chicken and Turkey

The head is the most anterior part of the body and includes the openings of the nose, mouth, eyes, and ears. It carries special sense organs—olfactory, ocular, auditory, and gustatory. The osseous structures consist of cranium, sclerotic rings, and supporting structures for the nose, mouth, and tongue. The head includes the brain, many muscles, nerves, blood vessels, glands, and a tongue. In some birds the skin of the head has produced such special appendages as the comb and wattles of chickens (figs. 4 and 28) and the frontal appendage and dewlap of turkeys (figs. 5 and 31).

The head of a bird has approximately the shape of a four-sided pyramid, the base of which is the posterior surface where the head joins the neck. The four triangular surfaces are dorsal, ventral, right, and left sides. All of these triangles have their apexes at the tip of the beak. Among the heads illustrated in figure 2, this feature is shown best in the plucked sparrow. The pyramid is not symmetrical because the dorsal surface is bulged outward by the enclosed brain, and the ventral surface is concave because of the curvature of the lower jaws and beak. The head of the chicken fits this typical pattern when the comb and wattles are removed; the pattern can be more readily seen in the nearly naked head of the turkey.

Accounts of the topographic anatomy of birds generally have been very brief and are based on a fully feathered specimen (i.e., Coues, 1903; Reichenow, 1906). The first attempt to define the regions of a defeathered bird was apparently that of Komarek (1958). We did not know of this work until after our own, similar investigation was finished.

Our investigation was patterned after that followed in human anatomy except that we used dashed lines to indicate boundaries in parts of the nose and ear that are located below the surface of the head. Sometimes we found that one named part of the body was superimposed upon an area assigned a region name for another part. An outstanding example of this can be seen in the Great Horned Owl (*Bubo virginianus*) where the external ear lies within the orbital region (fig. 21, p. 30).

The lines on the external surface of the head, such as shown in figures 3 to 5, 13, 18, and 21, may seem to be placed in an arbitrary way, but a great deal of study went into their

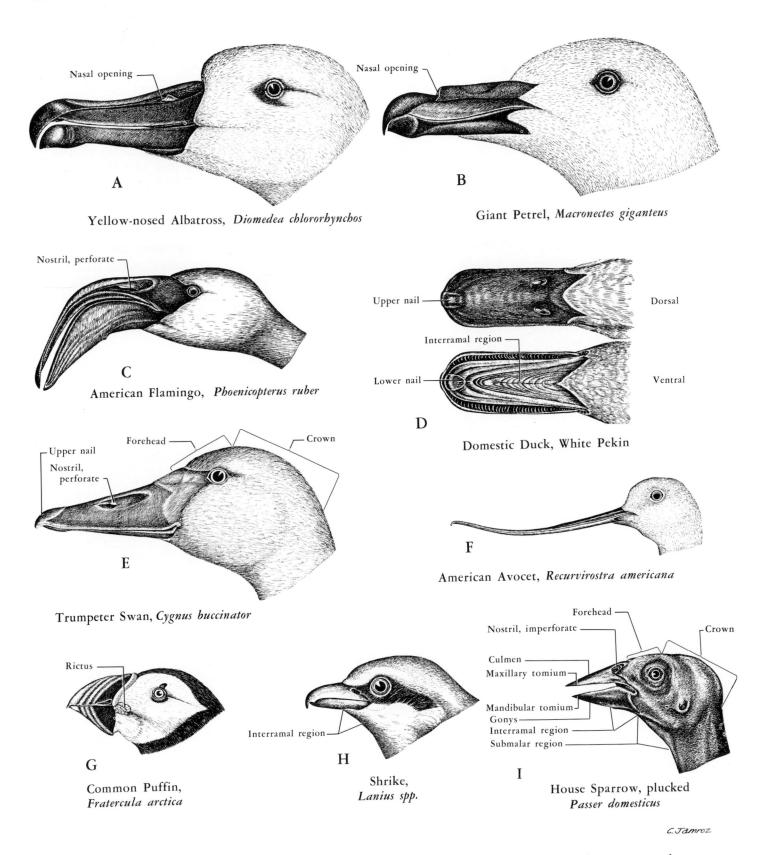

A — Yellow-nosed Albatross, *Diomedea chlororhynchos*

B — Giant Petrel, *Macronectes giganteus*

C — American Flamingo, *Phoenicopterus ruber*

D — Domestic Duck, White Pekin

E — Trumpeter Swan, *Cygnus buccinator*

F — American Avocet, *Recurvirostra americana*

G — Common Puffin, *Fratercula arctica*

H — Shrike, *Lanius spp.*

I — House Sparrow, plucked *Passer domesticus*

FIGURE 2.—Examples showing the diversity of bill shapes of various birds. Abbreviation: spp., species.

placement. Because these lines were located in relation to the underlying skeleton, we have included illustrations of the head that show the regional boundaries superimposed on the skeleton. Labeled drawings of the skull also are provided to aid in locating bones mentioned in the text. The osteology of the skull will not be discussed in this volume.

We used many radiographs of heads to establish the relationships of internal structures and external parts. This was particularly true for the parts of the ears and that portion of the nose leading to the internal choana. These passageways were sometimes filled with radiopaque material, and boundary lines were painted on the surface with radiopaque material before radiographs were made. Some of these techniques are described briefly in chapter 10. In spite of an extended study, we found it necessary to place certain boundary lines rather arbitrarily.

Because the shape of the head varies considerably among birds, regional boundaries that are fixed for one species may need to be modified for another species. To illustrate some of the extreme conditions, we included the head of the Great Horned Owl (*Bubo virginianus*) in the discussion. The principles that we followed for establishing regional boundaries should become evident from the illustrations of this species and those of the domestic birds that were our chief concern. The reader should be able to follow easily these illustrations to define boundaries on other kinds of birds.

Drawings of the heads of an adult and an immature Single Comb White Leghorn Chicken are shown at the beginning of the series on regions of the head, but no drawings of the skull and jaws are included because these bones are closely similar to those of the turkey. The external features of the head of the chicken and turkey seem superficially different, but actually the regions for the two are closely alike.

Cranium

Forehead region.—The top of the head can be divided into forehead (*frons*) and crown (*corona*) (figs. 3 to 5). The forehead has a shape approaching that of a rectangle. It is slightly wider at the caudal end than it is at the nasal end. The long dimension parallels the axis of the head. The anterior boundary is located at the junction of the frontal and nasal bones (figs. 6 and 7). The ends of these bones rest on the underlying column of the mesethmoid bone, where dorsally it expands into a flattened plate. Here are the frontonasal hinge (*ginglymus nasofrontalis*) and the apex of the frontonasal angle (*angulus nasofrontalis*). The hinge pin is a transverse line around which the nasal arch may move slightly in respect to the forehead. The position of

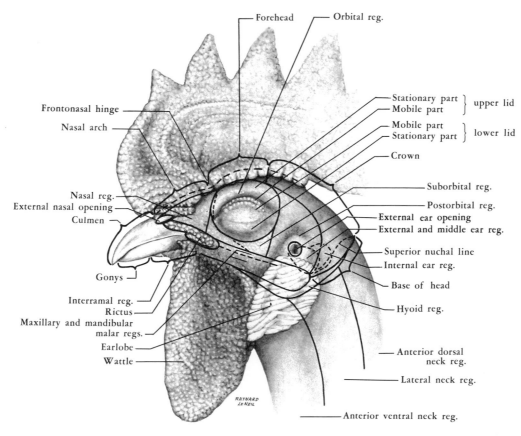

Figure 3.—Regions of the left side of the deplumed head of a male Single Comb White Leghorn Chicken. Dashed lines show the continuation of the nasal region beneath the orbital and suborbital regions, the boundary of the internal parts of the ear, superior nuchal line, and the division of malar region into maxillary and mandibular parts. The several boundaries crossing the earlobe are shown in solid lines. Abbreviation: reg(s)., region(s).

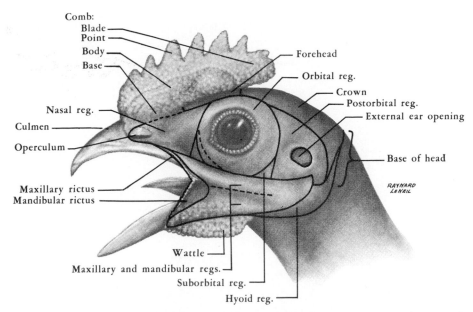

Comb:
Blade
Point
Body
Base
Forehead
Orbital reg.
Crown
Postorbital reg.
External ear opening
Nasal reg.
Culmen
Operculum
Base of head
Maxillary rictus
Mandibular rictus
RAYNARD LeNEIL
Wattle
Maxillary and mandibular regs.
Suborbital reg.
Hyoid reg.

FIGURE 4.—Regions of the left side of a deplumed head of a 28-day old chicken. The attachments for comb and wattle are shown for initial areas of growth. The relatively large orbital region almost obliterates the suborbital region. The open mouth reveals the two parts of the rictus. Abbreviation: reg(s)., region(s).

the two leaves of the hinge determine the frontonasal angle. In the Single Comb White Leghorn Chicken, the hinge line, or the beginning of the forehead, is covered by the anterior end of the comb (*crista*). The hinge line in a 74-day-old male was opposite the second point of the comb. Therefore, this point of the comb serves to locate, in a general way, the underlying hinge. But points on combs are variable and should not be relied upon exclusively. The magnitude of the frontonasal angle for a particular bird depends on the position of the beak at rest, whether elevated or depressed.[3] In the turkey it lies beneath the frontal process (*processus frontalis*), usually toward the more caudal part of the base of this organ.[4] The caudal end of the upper beak is not a reliable identifying point for the beginning of the forehead. In the turkey the beak ends short of this region, and in the puffin (fig. 2, *G*) the beak would appear to overlap the forehead to a slight extent.

In the recently hatched Single Comb White Leghorn Chicken, potential comb tissue is implanted on the head as far forward as the operculum (*operculum nasi*). The actual

elevated comb extends caudally to a point approximately above the middle of the eyelid slit (*rima palpebrarum*), but the area of skin devoid of feather surrounding the base of the comb, called the comb plate, continues to the boundary between forehead and crown. As the bird grows older, more of this caudal tissue is utilized in the formation of the comb; even by 74 days of age the comb has extended to the crown and caudally to the lid slit.

The anterior end of the brain has been chosen as the dividing line between forehead and crown, a reference point on the bird that is not apparent externally. Numerous skulls and wet specimens were examined to locate an external structure that had some constancy of position in respect to the anterior end of the brain, and the caudal half of the lid slit was found to be in fairly reliable agreement. The common boundary for forehead and crown in the chicken and turkey (figs. 3 and 5) falls within the caudal third of the lid slit.

Each lateral boundary of the forehead is in part an arbitrary line that begins at the frontonasal hinge (figs. 3 to 6), crosses the body of the prefrontal bone, and extends caudally along the orbital margin of the frontal bone to the transverse caudal boundary. A portion of the lateral boundary associated with the orbital margin of the frontal bone can be readily palpated, but the anterior portion cuts across the surfaces of bones and is somewhat less exactly placed.

The four parts of the comb in the Single Comb White Leghorn Chicken are illustrated in figures 4, 27, 28, and 322, *A*. The portion attached to the periosteal tissues of the skull constitutes the base (*basis cristae*), and it may overhang the nostril opening (*apertura externa nasi*) and extend caudally to the crown region (*regis coronalis*). The base is broad, and immediately above it is the body (*corpus cristae*) in which the comb is not so thick. From the dorsal margin of

---

[3] Elevation of the beak upward has been described for many birds; it is readily observed in the duck. However, on the recently killed specimens of turkey and chicken, the beak could not be elevated beyond the position occurring in death, but it could be considerably depressed. We are of the opinion that death did not produce an elevation of the beak but that it is usually elevated except when pulled downward by the beak musculature.

[4] The frontonasal angle is formed by the plane of the nasal arch meeting the plane of the forehead. In the chicken and turkey (figs. 3 to 6) it is apparent that this angle is almost 180°. The frontonasal angle is considerably less in the Long-eared Owl (*Asio otus*), is still less in the Great Horned Owl (*Bubo virginianus*) (figs. 22 and 24), and equally as small in the Yellow-nosed Albatross (*Diomedea chlororhynchos*) (fig. 2, *A*).

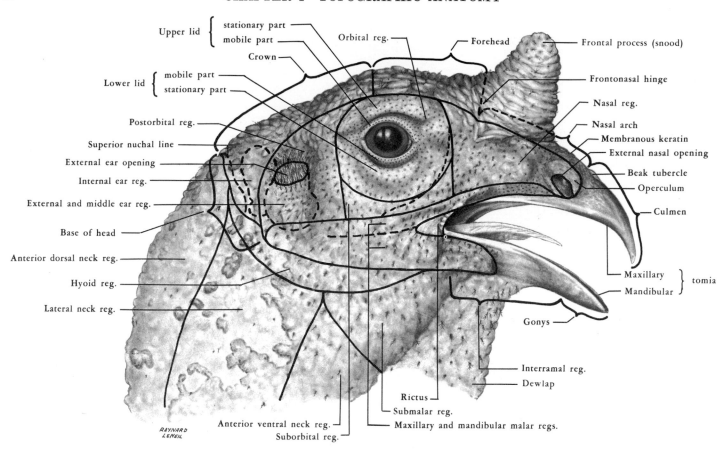

FIGURE 5.—Regions on right side of the head of the Bronze Turkey. See figure 3 for significance of dashed lines. Abbreviations: proc., process; reg(s)., region(s).

the body, a number of points (*cuspides cristae*) that are variable in size project upward, the smallest lying at the anterior and posterior ends of the row. Immediately behind the body, caudal to a line extending from the posterior end of the base to the posterior point, is a backward extended portion called the blade (*lamina cristae*). Combs of other breeds differ from this basic pattern for the single comb. They are classed as buttercup (*crista ranuncularis*), V-shaped (*crista v-formalis*), pea (*crista pisalis*), rose (*crista rosea*), strawberry (*crista fragaria*), and cushion (*crista pulvinaris*) combs. Each of these combs is described in chapter 9 (p. 531). Hybridization may produce the walnut comb and other types of combs. Some of these combs are relatively small and are limited to the forehead region; the strawberry comb scarcely covers the forehead region. The V-shaped comb of the Malay Bantam also covers only part of the forehead. In addition to the comb, there may be a feathered crest (*crista*) as in the Houdan, the Sultan, the crested Polish breeds, and other breeds. In some crested breeds the cranial bones and the underlying brain protrude into the crest (Gaskoin, 1856).

The casque of the cassowaries is a bony growth from the top of the skull, involving chiefly crown and forehead. The forehead of the male Andean Condor (*Vultur gryphus*) carries a semirigid structure that is similar to a comb but is without points. The shields of coots, gallinules, and the

American Jaçana (*Jacana spinosa*) cover most of the forehead. The large bill of the toucans extends caudally to the edge of the eye and covers the anterior part of the forehead. Many birds have developed specialized modifications of their plumage in the region of the forehead or the crown. Examples are the curled pompadourlike crest of the Great Curassow (*Crax rubra*); the radiating crest of strawlike bristles on the Crowned Crane (*Balearica pavonina*); the tall, compressed crest of the Blue Crowned Pigeon (*Goura cristata*); the long, overhanging crest of the Ornate Umbrellabird (*Cephalopterus ornatus*); the low, broad crest of the Plumed Helmet Shrike (*Prionops plumata*); and the conical crest of the Cardinal (*Cardinalis cardinalis*).

The frontal process (leader, snood, or frontal appendage of the turkey) is a fleshy, flexible, extensible, narrow cylindrical process, that protrudes outward from the skin covering the nasal arch (fig. 5). It appears to be uniform from base to tip except for gradation in diameter, and hence is not subdivided into named parts. Unlike the comb, the snood contains numerous smooth muscles and large tortuous arteries and veins, each of which carries an external layer of longitudinal muscles. It lacks, however, the fibromucoid layer that is characteristic of the comb of adult male and laying female chickens. The structures of these organs are described in detail in chapter 9 (p. 564).

Crown region.—The crown, or vertex of the head is usually

represented by the most elevated portion of the cranium. Beneath the upward bulge lie the cerebral hemispheres and some of the more posterior parts of the brain. Shufeldt (1909:175) has described this part of the head as " . . . a pair of domelike eminences posterior to the orbits and formed by the frontal lobe."

The transverse anterior boundary of the crown is also the posterior boundary of the forehead, as noted on page 9. The posterior boundary of the crown is the dorsal and lateral margins of the base of the head. The location of this boundary can be described best by referring to the osseous structures in this region (figs. 6 and 7). The vertical plane of the base of the skull, composed largely of the exoccipital and supraoccipital bones, meets the planes in the region of the crown produced by the parietal and squamosal bones almost at right angles. In the turkey this junction is relatively sharp and can be readily palpated, but it is more rounded in the chicken. The dorsal muscles of the neck are attached to the base of the skull, and in older birds part of this attachment is marked by a definite ridge, the superior nuchal line. In both chickens and turkeys, the line extends laterally and ventrally to merge into the bony structure that produces the paroccipital process. This process is the ridge formed by the caudal margin of the osseous external ear canal and is readily palpable in the live bird. The paroccipital process does not have the same form in all birds. It may be close to or far from the postarticular process of the lower jaw, and it may be long or short (compare figs. 7, 15, 17, 20, 22, and 24). In parrots it is particularly long.

The placement of the right and left lateral boundaries for the crown is arbitrary, because no skeletal or external anatomical features are there to serve as reference points. We have drawn a line for the lateral boundary along each side of the head as a continuation of the lateral boundary of the forehead. This line extends backward above the eye, arches over the ear opening, and then turns ventrally to terminate at the paroccipital process. On the point of this process, it joins the caudal boundary of the crown. The lateral boundaries of the forehead and of the crown form one line that separates the dorsal surface of the head from the lateral surfaces of the face.

Although we are concerned primarily with domestic birds, we examined a few wild birds to indicate the limits of applicability of our descriptions to birds in general. The placement of the highest point within the crown varies widely among birds. In the domestic chicken and turkey it is far forward, immediately behind the forehead. In the Ruffed Grouse (*Bonasa umbellus*) and in many passerines, for example, the Blue Jay (*Cyanocitta cristata*), it is slightly more posterior. The highest point of the head even lies outside the crown in a few birds such as the American Woodcock (*Philohela minor*), where the lateral margins of the portion of the frontal bone forming the forehead are elevated above the crown.

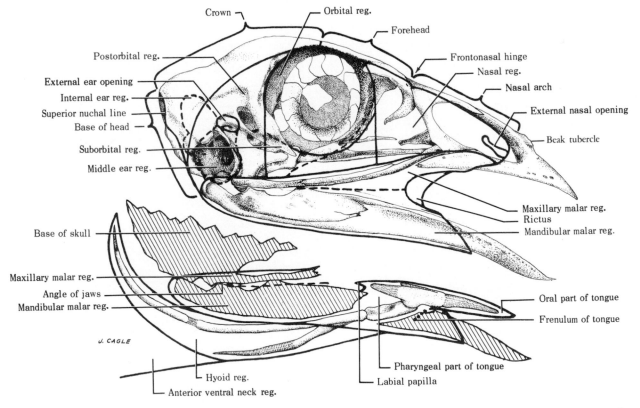

FIGURE 6.—Boundary lines for regions of the external surface of the turkey head as superimposed on its skeleton. The purpose is to indicate the function of underlying palpable structures in establishing region boundaries. See figure 3 for significance of dashed lines. Abbreviation: reg., region.

The shape of the skull is related to the flexion of brain stem and the contours of the major division of the brain. A statistical study of the relationship of the shape of skull to the shape of the brain was made by Tulner and Dullemeijer (1957). They concluded from an examination of nine representative species that the relatively large brain in the Carrion Crow (*Corvus corone*) was accommodated within the cranial cavity by a caudal extension of the telencephalon and a relative shortening of the cerebellum. They did not observe an encroachment of the telencephalon over the cerebellum. In the Mallard (*Anas platyrhynchos*), a bird that also possesses a large telencephalon, there was, in addition, a strong curvature of the myelencephalon. This may provide extra space for the cerebellum.

Cobb (1960) selected examples of birds that demonstrated this point. Edinger (1941) observed that, ". . . the brain in birds, formed an arc around the back of the orbit." He showed that the angle between the bottom of the brain and the axis of the bill was 15° for the Double-crested Cormorant (*Phalacrocorax auritus*), 34° for the Herring Gull (*Larus argentatus*), 47° for the Short-eared Owl (*Asio flammeus*), and 117° for the American Woodcock (*Philohela minor*). Extreme differences in brain-bill angle are shown by Portmann and Stingelin (1961:2, fig. 2). Brain placement influences shape and thereby influences placement of boundary lines for regions of the dorsal and caudal parts of the head.

Another important factor that affects the shape of the cranium is the size and placement of the eyes. The influence of this factor on the shape of the head may be readily observed in a profile study of skulls of such birds as domestic chicken, owls, and woodcock.

Base of head.—The base of the head is that area occupied by the occipital bones, a supracoccipital above, a pair of exoccipitals laterally and lateroventrally, and a basioccipital ventral to the foramen magnum between the wings of the exoccipitals. The base of the skull is an approximately vertical plate to which are attached numerous muscles extending along the vertebrae of the neck. Being thus covered, the base of the head can be seen only in part in the deplumed bird. The horseshoe-shaped dorsal and lateral margins can be identified by the superior nuchal lines and by the other landmarks previously discussed as identifying the caudal end of the crown. Ventrally the paroccipital processes are joined by a faintly visible groove that was produced by junction of base and floor of the skull, as shown in figure 8 by the dotted line. This groove lies too deep to be palpated in the deplumed bird.

Face

The face (*facies*) is composed of two parts—front and sides. The front carries the bill (*rostrum*) and nose (*nasus*); the sides carry the eyes (*oculi*) and lateral parts of the mouth.

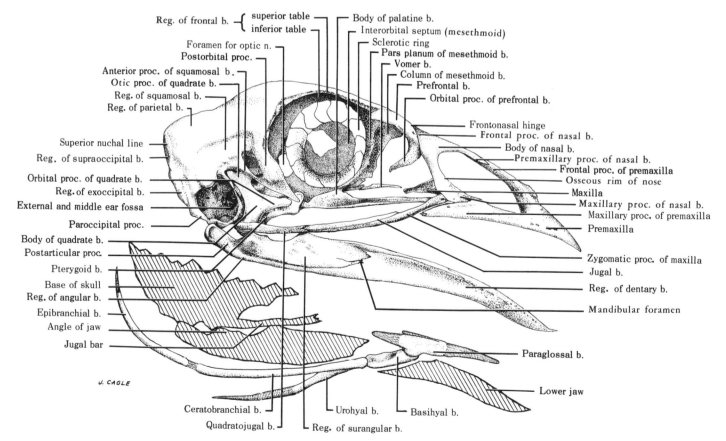

FIGURE 7.—Right lateral view of skull and jaws of a Bronze Turkey. The skeleton of the tongue and hyoid are shown in relation to the lower jaw and base of the skull. Abbreviations: b., bone; proc., process; reg., region.

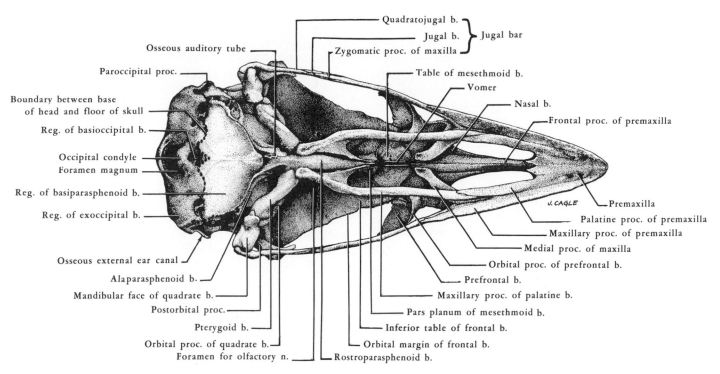

FIGURE 8.—Ventral view of skull of Bronze Turkey. Abbreviations: b., bone; n., nerve; proc., process; reg., region.

It is impractical to draw a boundary line between these two parts, chiefly because the large gape of the mouth lies not only at the front of the face but extends caudally beneath the eyes; the jaws of the mouth continue along the sides of the face to the ear region (*regio auris*). Therefore, to define the boundaries of the structures within the face is more important than to try to define boundaries for front and side.

Orbital region.—Each orbital fossa contains optic globe, muscles, glands, and fat pads. The globe (*bulbus oculi*) is large, and its periphery is nearly equivalent to the outer limits of the orbital fossa; the muscles, glands, and fat lie largely medial to the globe. The periphery of the fossa is the osseous boundary of the orbital region, but this is not palpable throughout its entire circumference; therefore, the periphery of the globe serves instead. As one might expect, the shape of the orbital region approximates a circle, but not all parts have the same curvature (figs. 3 to 5).

The dorsal portion of the fossa is formed by the inferior table of the frontal bone (fig. 7); anteriorly the margin of the fossa swings forward beneath the platelike body of the prefrontal bone where it meets the longitudinal ridge of the mesethmoid, then it follows this ridge ventrally and curves caudally along the palatine bone; more exactly, it follows the articulation between the interorbital septum (mesethmoid bone) and the body of the palatine. Caudally the fossa crosses the tip of the pterygoid bone and the tip of the orbital process of the quadrate bone, and then passes dorsally just caudal to the optic foramen until it meets again the inferior table of the frontal bone. The orbital process and the orbitosphenoid (alisphenoid) bone slightly overhang the extreme posterior limits of the orbital fossa.

The circular boundary for the orbital region is based on the periphery of the globe rather than on the extreme limits of the orbital fossa established by the skeleton. The periphery of the globe of the eye can be palpated through the skin of the face. It is indicated by the line on the surface of the face in figures 3 to 5, which shows that the dorsal part of the region shares a portion of the lateral boundary of the crown and, in particular, the forehead. The anterior margin lies considerably caudal to the orbital process of the prefrontal bone; ventrally the anterior margin swings downward in a long arc that continues as the ventral margin somewhat above the malar region. From this point a smooth curved boundary extends upward to rejoin the lateral boundary of the crown. The caudal margin of the orbital region can be located by palpating the postorbital process of the orbitosphenoid (alisphenoid) bone. This process may be joined by the anterior process of the squamosal bone (fig. 7). The lateral face of the eyeball and the margin of the pupil are supported by the sclerotic ring, consisting of overlapping plates encircling the eye. The ventral margin of the circle formed by the plates can usually be palpated, but because the plates are supported by dense connective tissues, it is difficult to feel the peripheral edge in the chicken and turkey.

Two eyelids cover the globe; when closed their free margins form the lid slit. When the eyes are open, the margins of the lids parallel the periphery of the iris and have the form approaching that of a circle; only a slight angle persists at the corners. The lids fold under the adjacent more rigid skin; when the lids are closed the lid slit is usually straight or forms a slight crescent with the concavity downward. The dorsal, ventral, and lateral limits of the lids can be determined best by placing a blunt probe beneath them and pressing against the reflected margins of the conjunctival cavity. In the chicken and turkey, these limits extend nearly to the peripheral margin of the globe. This is the basis for defining the upper and lower lids as loose folds of skin covering the globe and for the statement that the lids occupy a large portion of the space enclosed within the orbital region.

The upper lid contains two parts—a mobile part (*palpebra superior pars mobilis*)that can be folded under the inner table of the frontal bone and a stationary part (*palpebra superior pars immobilis*) adjacent to the edge of the frontal bone. The lower lid is also composed of two parts—one mobile (*palpebra inferior pars mobilis*)and one stationary (*palpebra inferior pars immobilis*); the former is recognized as the typically flexible skin that can be folded downward beneath the stationary part. The mobile part is thin and has several rows of small feathers near its free edge, but much of its surface is bare. The stationary part is similar in appearance to adjacent parts of the face and also bears reduced contour feathers. The upper mobile lid participates only slightly in the closure of the eye; most of the closure comes from the lower mobile lid. The lid slit crosses the eye above the pupil.

The glabrous free edges of both lids are crossed transversely by shallow grooves. Between these the delicate tissues form a row of soft, low tumid elevations, which become prominent in older birds. At the outer edge of this fleshy margin is a row of eyelashes or cilia, which are small bristle feathers, usually visible only with the aid of a lens.

The third eyelid or nictitating membrane (*membrana nictitans*) lies within the conjunctival cavity. When retracted it is a crescent-shaped body concentrated in the anterior corner of the eye. The superior and inferior limbs lie along the corresponding margins of the conjunctival cavity nearly to the posterior corner of the eye. When the nictitating membrane closes in the chicken, the upper part advances more than the lower part so that the leading edge crosses the eye at about a 45° angle.

Suborbital region.—The dorsal boundary of the suborbital region (*regio suborbitalis*) is the lower curve of the orbital region, and the ventral boundary is the dorsal margin of the maxillary malar region (*regio malaris maxillaris*) (figs. 3 to 5). The latter boundary is a straight line. The height of the suborbital region differs among species of birds. In the chicken and turkey, this region is intermediate between the extremes that may be observed. In the domestic duck the suborbital region is large (fig. 13); in the Great Horned Owl it is small, and the orbital region is so extensive that it touches the jugal bar (fig. 21). Sometimes in the same species the orbital region may be larger at hatching or soon after than it is in the adult. As a consequence in the 28-day-old chicken (fig. 4), the suborbital region is reduced to two small triangles separated by the orbital region, whereas in the adult (fig. 3) the suborbital region is one continuous area. The suborbital region of the adult Common Coturnix is greatly reduced and resembles in this respect that of the young chicken.

The anterior and posterior boundaries are entirely arbitrary in that they have no relationship to the underlying bones and spaces. They have been drawn parallel to each other and as tangents to the orbital region. These tangential lines project ventrally in such a way that they intersect at about right angles the superior margin of the maxillary malar region.

The osseous structures that underlie each suborbital region are the body of the palatine and part of its maxillary process (figs. 6 and 7); the anterior tip of pterygoid and quadrate bones; and the soft tissues belonging to the roof of the mouth and the lower, caudal limits of the nasal cavity (*fossa nasalis*). In figures 3 to 5 the dashed lines mark where the caudal boundary of the nasal region (*regio nasalis*) crosses the suborbital region. Figures 6 and 7 show some of the bones that underlie the suborbital region.

Postorbital region.—The postorbital region (*regio postorbitalis*) lies between the combined orbital and suborbital regions and the base of the skull. The shape of the postorbital region in different species varies from a short half-crescent to a long half-cresent. If the axis of the brain has a large angle in respect to the axis of the bill—as in the chicken, turkey, and duck—then the postorbital region has the form of a broad, short, half-crescent (figs. 3 to 5 and 13); but if the angle between the two axes is less, then the postorbital region is a narrower, more elongated half-crescent, as in the Great Horned Owl (fig. 21).

The postorbital region has three boundaries: (1) the outer curvature of the crescent, (2) the inner curvature of the crescent, and (3) the transection of the crescent or base. The first is a region boundary already described and defined, namely, the lateral boundary of the crown; the second boundary has been described also and is in part the dorsocaudal boundary for the orbital region and in part the caudal boundary of the suborbital region. The third boundary is the base, or ventral, boundary and is largely a straight line but not entirely so. Its caudal end arises at the paroccipital process, namely, from the junction point of boundaries for base of head and lateral edge of the crown. From here a line extends to the end of the postarticular (retroarticular) process of the malar region, and from this point forward it shares a common boundary with the malar region as far as the suborbital region.

Auricular region.—The external ear opening is within the postorbital region in most birds—an exception is the Great Horned Owl. The opening is flush with the surface; a sound-collecting organ, or auricle, of mammals is absent. Three parts of the ear—external auditory canal, middle ear, and internal ear—are common to both birds and mammals. All of these structures, except the external ear opening, are beneath the surface, and in figures 3 and 5 the boundaries of these structures are represented by dashed lines. The middle ear lies beneath the postorbital region; the internal ear is beneath both this region and the crown. The placement of these parts differs among various species of birds as may be noted by comparing figures 3, 5, 13, 18, and 21.

The opening of the external ear is circular in the chicken

(figs. 3 and 4); it is often a flattened oval in the turkey (fig. 5). The external ear canal extends from the dorsally placed ear opening, downward as well as inward, to the middle ear (figs. 3, 5, and 6). The boundaries of the semicircular canals as seen from a lateral view were determined from X-ray photographs of the frontally sectioned heads (fig. 9) and hemisected heads (fig. 24).

The earlobe (*lobus auricularis*) of the adult chicken (figs. 3 and 28) is a fleshy, pendent thickening of skin located almost directly ventral to the external ear opening and overlies the caudal end of the jaw. It is devoid of feathers. In the young chicken it has the shape of a half moon horizontally placed. The earlobe nearly covers the bony portion of the underlying middle meatus. It might have a protective function because it is composed of dense collagenic connective tissues; if so, then it is difficult to understand why an earlobe is found in so few species, unless perhaps the combat techniques of chickens differ from those of other birds. In fighting, the chicken often aims a metatarsal spur toward the side of of the head.

The earlobe in leghorns is white, sometimes chalky, and sometimes iridescent. The white color of earlobes is not typical for chickens in general. In 55 of the 65 varieties listed in the "American Standard of Perfection" (1953), the earlobe is bright red; in only three breeds do white earlobes occur. In some varieties of Modern Game, in the Black Sumatra, and in the Silkie, earlobes are purple, approaching black. An extreme development of the earlobes occurs in the White-faced Black Spanish Chicken. In this breed, the skin of the face, ocular, and auricular areas are united into a white, naked, fleshy, biblike fold that extends down the neck to below the tips of the wattles (fig. 10).

Nasal region.—The nose, like the eye and ear, is a more extensive organ than it appears to be externally. The external nasal openings, or external nares, are located on each side of the beak at the basal end. The opening on each side is a curved, slit-shaped space that is overhung by a cartilaginous scale or operculum (*operculum nasi*). In the chicken the operculum forms a curved shelf above the nasal opening (figs. 4 and 11), but in the turkey it lies in a flat plane parallel to the side of the beak (fig. 5). The osseous rim of the nose is far more extensive than the nares and is the oval-shaped margin formed by the processes of the premaxillary and nasal bones (fig. 7).

The statement is frequently made that the external nasal opening is located in the beak. This is true in the White Pekin Duck (fig. 13) but not in the chicken, turkey, and most other birds. The horny substance of the beak is membranous around the nasal opening. The soft tissues pass above and below the nasal opening. Caudal to the opening, the membranous tissue merges with the skin of the face. Therefore, instead of considering the nostril as a perforation of the beak, one can consider that extensions of the beak have grown backward, above, and below the skin of the face

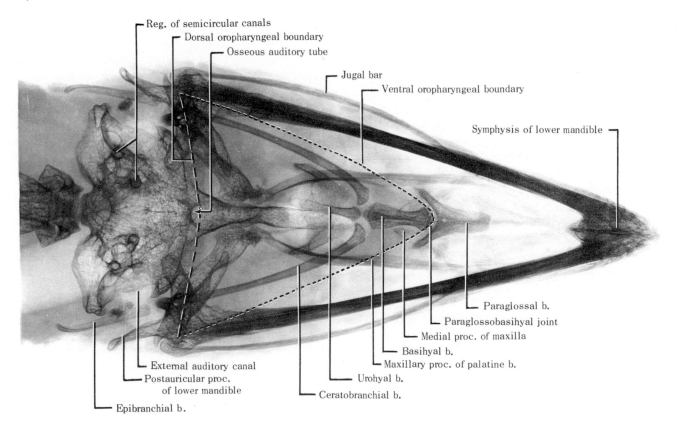

FIGURE 9.—Positive radiograph of lower half of a Bronze Turkey head, showing hyoid, jaws, and base of skull on which reference lines have been placed for the boundaries between oral and pharyngeal cavities. Dashed line is dorsal oropharyngeal boundary; dotted line, ventral oropharyngeal boundary. Abbreviations: b., bone; proc., process; Reg., Region.

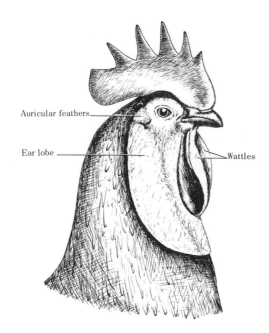

Auricular feathers

Ear lobe

Wattles

FIGURE 10.—Head of male White-faced Black Spanish Chicken, showing confluence of white skin of face, rictus, and earlobes. The extended earlobes form a bib in front of the neck and beneath the wattles. (See also Davenport, 1909, pl. 3, color.) (Redrawn by Casimir Jamroz from "American Standard of Perfection," 1938–40, p. 228.)

that carries the nostril. In some birds this backward extension of the beak has grown so far that the nostril is entirely surrounded. The relation of hard beak to the nostril and soft keratin of the operculum is shown in the Great Horned Owl (fig. 21).

Passage through the external nares leads into a large nasal cavity. The lateral wall of this cavity carries two conchae (turbinates); the medial wall, or internarial septum, carries a cartilaginous ridge projecting laterally into the respiratory meatus (fig. 362, p. 581). The full extent of the nasal cavity can be comprehended best by making a hemisection of the head slightly to one side of the midline; in this place the maximum size of the cavity can be determined. The nasal cavity is enclosed by a cartilaginous capsule that lies supported by a few skeletal trusses of the beak. Part of this capsule may ossify as in the Chinese Goose (fig. 17, ossified septum), whereas in the pigeon, the ossification is minimal (fig. 20).

The most rostral tip of the nasal cavity lies between the external nares (in the chicken and turkey) and the extreme anterior angle of the osseous nasal fossa. The dorsal edge of the nasal capsule is supported by the nasal arch (arcus nasalis), composed of the overlapping nasal processes of the premaxillae and the premaxillary processes of the nasal bones (fig. 7). The capsule continues caudally past the frontonasal hinge to the middle of the mesethmoid table. The dorsal and caudal limits of the capsule make a sharp angle behind the superior margin of the eye. The posterior margin of the nasal cartilage is curved; its location in the

chicken (figs. 3 and 4) and in the turkey (fig. 5) is shown by dashed lines. It approximately parallels the anterior and ventral boundaries of the orbital region. The orbital fossa and the nasal cavity meet at the ridge located on the lateral face of the mesethmoid column.

The cavity of the nose passes beyond the body of the palatine bone and opens into the oral cavity by way of a long slit, the internal nares (apertura interna nasi), or choana, (fig. 362). The anterior end of the choana begins at the forward tip of the vomer bone, the location of which is shown in figure 7. In the turkey this tip lies directly below the frontal process. The slit of the choana extends caudally to the fossa of the auditory tube opening (compare fig. 7 with figs. 8 and 362). The ventral edge of the septum lies at a higher level than the lateral edge of the choana, the skeletal support for the margin of the septum being the rostroparasphenoid and the vomer (figs. 7 and 8). We have indicated the lower margin of the nose (figs. 3 to 5) as being common to the dorsal margin of the jaw, and this is true for the lateral edge of the choana (fig. 362, p. 581). Between the nasal capsule and the skin are two spaces, but these have not been included within the boundaries of the nasal region, although they do overlap to a large extent. The nasal region, as is evident from the description thus far, is a triangle, and the three sides are dorsal, ventral, and posterior.

Oral region.—The oral region (regio oris) includes the mouth slit, or gape (rima oris); the malar (regio malaris) and rictal regions (regio rictalis), each of which is divided into maxillary and mandibular parts; and the upper and lower beaks. The covering of the beak or bill is a keratinized thickening of the corneum of epidermis called a rhamphotheca. Usually it is rigid and hard, but in ducks it is leathery and flexible. In most birds the upper beak has the shape of a gable roof; the sloping sides meet at the dorsal medial line, called the culmen. The shape or curvature of the culmen (fig. 2) is used as an identifying characteristic in the taxonomic descriptions of many birds. The culmen of the chicken and turkey is convex with the curvature increasing toward the tip (figs. 3 to 5).

The two rami of the lower jaws meet in the midline at their anterior ends and fuse for a variable distance according to the species of birds. In most birds this line of fusion is relatively short, as it is in the chicken and in the turkey (fig. 9). The fused tips of the lower jaws are covered with beak keratin, and the extent of fusion of the beak in the midline generally corresponds to the extent of fusion of the underlying bones. In birds with cone-shaped bills like the House Sparrow (fig. 2, I), this fusion is over half the length of the lower beak; the same is true in the puffins (fig. 2, G). The profile line of the fused portion of the lower beak is the gonys. Coues (1903:109) gave the history of the term "gonys," which means knee, and pointed out that it was erroneously substituted for the word "genys" meaning lower jaw or chin. Sometimes the term is used incorrectly to indicate the lower outline of the whole beak. The gonys of the lower bill is equivalent to the culmen of the upper bill.

The term "chin" (mentum) is usually applied by ornithologists to the plumage beneath the rami of the jaws but the connotation is that of an anatomical structure, based on its usage in man and mammals. We suggest that the term *"mentum"* be applied to the anterior portion of the lower beak where the right and left halves are united—in the area of the symphysis. The term "mental angle" is often used and is defined as the angle made by the right and left rami of the lower beak as they fuse at the gonial line. Instead of *mentum*, Coues (1903:109) applied the term *"myxa"* which he defined as ". . . that portion of the rami which correspond to the length of the gonys." The word *"myxa"* has not been extensively used in the literature, and it would seem desirable to use the term *"mentum"* instead.

The cutting edges of the upper and lower beaks are the upper and lower tomia. The upper, or maxillary, tomium (*tomium maxillare*) of the chicken and turkey is a curve with the concavity downward. The lower, or mandibular, tomium (*tomium mandibulare*) approximately parallels the curvature of the upper tomium except at the tip. When the mouth is closed, the tomial edges of the lower beak slip inside and past the tomial edges of the upper beak, resulting in a slight shearing action (fig. 362). Among different species of birds (fig. 2), the tomia may be straight, curved upward or downward, serrated, angled along their length, and they may have a variety of other forms.

The caudal extension of the beak substance merges gradually into a more membranous type of keratin. Along the culmen of older turkeys on a level with the anterior end of the nasal region is a small, bony exostosis (fig. 6). It is absent from the premaxilla of younger birds. Thus far no name has been found for this bony elevation that carries over it a layer of keratinized beak substance. We suggest that it be called the beak tubercle.

The comb of the Single Comb White Leghorn Chicken arises caudal to the beak. In the newly hatched chicken, the beak is well separated from the comb, but in old birds, especially males, the comb grows forward and overlies the caudal end of the beak. An intermediate state of development is shown in figure 4.

Before hatching, a conical body of hard keratin develops at the tip of the upper beak. This conical body is often referred to as an egg tooth. It assists the chick in breaking the shell, and after hatching is sloughed within one to a few days. The term "egg tooth" has been applied to this tubercle in birds, but the term is more appropriate for a structure having the same function in lizards and snakes. As Lange (1931:394) has pointed out, the egg tooth of lizards and snakes has nothing to do with the "Eischwiele" of the crocodiles, turtles, and birds. The term "Eischewiele" suggested by Rose (1892) has been translated by Hamilton (1952:375) as egg callosity and by Bellairs (1960:134) as egg caruncle. Appropriate terms to distinguish between the true egg teeth of lizards and snakes and the horny elevation on crocodiles, turtles, and birds would be desirable. This, possibly, may come about sometime in the future.

Rawles (1960: 210) regarded the egg tooth of embryos as a calcareous protuberance. Mayaud (1950: 11) stated that it is keratinized and does not contain calcareous deposits. Kingsbury et al. (1953) regarded the egg tooth as a keratinized structure. Clark (1961) reviewed the occurrence of the egg tooth in wild birds and observed that in some species such a "tooth" was present on the lower beak as well as on the upper beak.

Rictal region.—The caudal extension of the lower beak retains the hard keratin along the sides and lower margins, but above the tomial edges is a transition to the soft tissues of the rictus. The point of transition is approximately the same on the edge of the upper beak.

When the gape is open, a triangle of soft tissue apparently joins the upper and lower jaws. The gape ends at the edge of this tissue curtain, which is on both the right and left sides and forms the ricti. When the mouth is closed, the ricti are folded so that the tomial edges lie close together (fig. 3); the point of reflection is often called a rictal commissure. However, when the mouth is fully open, there is no commissure (figs. 4 and 11); there may be a point of abrupt transition. In the chicken the maxillary rictus is swollen and vascular like the comb and wattles, whereas the mandibular rictus is thin and relatively avascular (fig. 11). In an 11-day-old specimen the two parts of the rictus are alike, namely, thin and pale. These are essentially similar at about a month and a half, but by 74 days of age (male) a streak of red has grown down from the comb and crosses the face into the upper part of the maxillary rictus. The maxillary and mandibular parts of the rictus in the turkey are alike (fig. 5).

Malar region.—The malar region (*regio malaris*) includes the soft tissues that cover the jaws (figs. 3 to 6). In these illustrations separation is shown by a dashed line extending from the caudal end of the rictus to the angle of the jaws. A separation of the malar region into two parts has been made, namely, maxillary (*regio malaris maxillaris*) and mandibular (*regio malaris mandibularis*). The anterior end of the maxillary malar region begins below the nasal region. It is composed of soft tissues that cover the upper part of the maxillary process of the premaxilla and continues along the jugal bar to the joint of the jaw. The anterior end of the mandibular malar region begins at the transition of hard beak to the soft skin covering the lower jaw and continues to the caudal end of the jaw including the postarticular process. Examination of the facial skeleton (figs. 6 and 7) shows that the maxillary malar region is narrow because the narrow jugal bar is a thin bone and that the mandibular malar region is wide because the lower jaw is wide. When the jaws close, the upper edge of the lower jaw slides medially behind the upper jaw.

The wattles of the 11-day-old Single Comb White Leghorn Chicken are little more than slight folds of skin along the ventral margins of the jaws beginning caudal to the hard keratin of the lower bill and extending about half the distance to the angle of the jaw. Measurements on the growth of wattles (*paleae*) are given in chapter 9. At the age of about 45 days, the wattles are definitely pendulous. The anterior origin of each is from the inferior margin and also from the lateral surface of the lower jaw. Caudally each wattle extends nearly to the joint of the jaws, and when large it in-

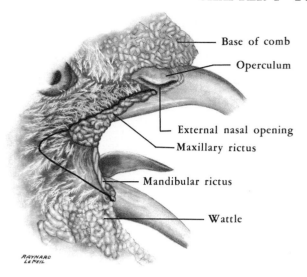

Base of comb

Operculum

External nasal opening

Maxillary rictus

Mandibular rictus

Wattle

RAYNARD
LeMEIL

FIGURE 11.—Rictus of an adult Single Comb White Leghorn Chicken from the right side. The maxillary part has the red color and rugosity of the comb, whereas the mandibular part has the thin, smooth character found in the young bird. When the jaws are forcibly separated the free edges of the rictus may form a uniformly curved line as shown here, but when partially separated, an angle will be present as shown in figure 4.

cludes some or the feathered skin. By 74 days the wattle of the male has the same caudal limit as that in the younger chick, namely about half of the mandibular malar region, but its weight pulls the feathered skin downward so that the upper part of the wattle appears to be feathered. As the tissues of a wattle grow, the wattle becomes suspended by nearly the entire length of the mandibular region as far back as the earlobe. The two surfaces are the medial and lateral laminae. The medial lamina (*lamina externa*) is carried by the submalar region and the lateral lamina (*lamina interna*), by the mandibular malar region.

Ventral surface of head

As applied to the feathered bird, the term "throat" has an indefinite meaning and is closely equivalent to what Coues (1903) called the gular region. Anatomically, the throat is equivalent to the pharynx. Even this is hard to define in birds, chiefly because the oral cavity and pharynx are not separated by a simple transverse plane. The jaws, which form the margins of the oral cavity, extend so far caudally that they enclose not only all of the oral cavity but most of the pharynx as well.

The lower surface of the pharynx has the shape of a triangle that projects forward into the oral cavity (figs. 9, 29, and 32); the upper surface is a slightly bowed line joining the angles of the jaws (fig. 9). In order to establish a boundary between mouth and pharynx, several arbitrary landmarks have been used. Calhoun (1954:3) who reviewed the literature on this subject reported that in the chicken, ". . . Grossman (1927) set aside the transverse row of papillae on

the root of the tongue as a 'convenient' mark for separating the two cavities while Heidrich (1908) designated a row of papillae in the palate for the same purpose." Arbitrary boundaries might be satisfactory if one were concerned with only a single species, but such boundaries are of little value if they are to apply to birds in general.

We suggest that a workable transverse boundary might be established for all birds if it were based on embryology of the visceral arches. The first arch forms the framework of the mouth, and the next arch (hyoid) is associated with the pharynx. With this in mind, the oropharynx boundary in the roof of the mouth could be placed between internal nares and the common opening for the auditory tubes as indicated by the dashed line in figure 9. The lateral ends of the boundary are established by the angles of the jaws. This line places the internal nares entirely within the mouth cavity and the openings of the auditory tubes in the anterior end of the pharynx.

The tongue, located on the floor of the oropharynx, has its musculature attached to various parts of the hyoid. Our concern here is with the median rod, composed of three bones—the paraglossum (endoglossum), basihyal, and urohyal[5] (figs. 7 and 9). The paraglossum extends forward almost to the tip of the tongue. Is this forward extension part of the hyoid apparatus? Bellairs and Jenkin (1960:279) stated that, "The paraglossum is now believed to be a structure evolved *de novo* in birds, and not derived from the basibranchial (Crompton, 1953; Fourie, 1955)." DeKock (1955: 173) was of the same opinion. If this conclusion is valid, then the anterior end of the basihyal becomes the boundary between mouth and pharynx. In the chicken and turkey, the paraglossobasihyal joint can be palpated easily; it coincides in position with the lingual papillae, the landmark originally suggested by Grossman (1927). The approximate boundary of the ventral wall of the pharynx is delineated in figure 9. The projection of this boundary to the interramal and submalar regions is shown in figures 29 and 32 by dashed lines.

Interramal region.—The interramal region is a triangular area that has its apex in the soft, or membranous, tissue beginning behind the gonys and its lateral boundaries along the lower margin of each mandible. The caudal end of each rictus is joined by a transverse line that forms the common boundary between interramal and submalar regions (figs. 29 and 32). In the chicken the interramal space may include the anterior edges of the medial laminae of the wattles. In the turkey (fig. 5) and in the Silkie Bantam (fig. 323, *B*, p. 534), a dewlap arises in the interramal region and continues along the ventral midline of the neck.

Hyoid region.—The hyoid region has already been dis-

---

[5] Hammond and Yntema (1964) presented synonyms from the literature for the hyoid bones, but in their own writing followed Parker and Haswell (1940). The following are some equivalents: paraglossum = basihyal; basihyal = basibranchial I; urohyal = basibranchial II; ceratobranchial and epibranchial are the same terms in both sources. Jollie (1962:78) used the following terms: endoglossal for paraglossal; copula 1 for basihyal and copula 2 for urohyal.

cussed, particularly in reference to the oral cavity, pharynx, and tongue. To each side of the caudal end of the basihyal is attached a horn (*cornu*), composed of ceratobranchial and epibranchial bones and cartilages (figs. 7 and 9). The basihyal lies medial to the mandible, and the cornua emerge below the mandible at about the level of the rictus.[6] This is well shown in the owl in figure 24, page 33. Each cornu follows the curvature of the lower margin of the jaw and extends dorsally along the junction of head and neck. In the chicken and turkey, the cartilaginous tip terminates at what has been determined as the dorsal boundary of the neck or a little beyond this boundary (figs. 3 to 5). The hyoid region is shaped like a crescent with the concavity upward and forward. The inner boundary often coincides with the junction of crown and base of head, with a small portion of the transverse boundary of the postorbital region, and with the inferior malar boundary extended forward to the point where the hyoid passes medial to the lower jaw. The outer boundary extends from the malar region along a sweeping curve caudally upward until it reaches the base of the head.

Submalar region.—The submalar region (*regio submalaris*) is a four-sided area on the ventral surface of the head. Its anterior boundary is the same as the posterior boundary of the interramal region; its posterior boundary is a transverse line that joins the caudal ends of the lower jaws. The lateral boundaries are the ventral margins of the lower jaws, and thus the submalar region shares its boundaries with the malar regions on each side. When the hyoid drops below the level of the jaw, it is included within the submalar region and is part of it. The submalar region as defined by these external landmarks is relatively simple but when defined in terms of underlying structures, it becomes complicated.[7] The underlying structures of the malar region include most of the ventral wall of the pharynx, the base of the tongue, part of the hyoid, and part of the oral cavity. It may include the larynx, which is part of the ventral neck.

The anterior end of the pharynx has already been defined as the junction between the basihyal and paraglossal bones. This approximates the common boundary between the interramal and submalar regions, but the relationship between the external boundary and the joint of the hyoid is not a fixed one, chiefly because tongue and larynx readily shift position, forward and backward. This shifting is especially true of the larynx of the chicken. In the embalmed chicken, the caudal boundary of the submalar region includes the upper larynx, but in the freshly killed specimen the larynx and the pharynx tissues supporting it may stretch backward so far that the larynx lies almost at the common boundary between anterior and posterior ventral neck regions. This elasticity of the pharynx wall is not as great in the turkey as it is in the chicken.

Common Coturnix

The Common Coturnix is a small galliform, in which most topographic features are similar to those of the chicken and turkey. The following description of the regions of the head will be limited largely to details in which this quail differs from the chicken and turkey.

Cranium

Forehead region.—In the absence of comb or snood, the boundaries of the forehead region, in the quail are relatively easy to place by following the same landmarks established for chicken and turkey, namely, frontonasal hinge for the anterior boundary, tip of the brain for the posterior boundary, and margins of the frontal bone for the lateral boundaries. In coturnix as in other galliforms, a plane across the anterior end of the brain passes through the posterior third of the lid slit. The lateral margins of the forehead lie on top of the head rather than at the angle between top and side because the frontal bones opposite the orbital regions are narrow. This structure in turn appears to be associated with the large orbit that extends dorsally as far as the upper level of the frontal bone. Each lateral margin crosses the body of the prefrontal bone, but both it and the prefrontal process are very small in the Common Coturnix.

Crown region.—The skeletal landmarks for establishing the boundaries of the crown in coturnix are the same as those described for the chicken and turkey.

Base of head.—The base of the head in coturnix is somewhat broader than it is high. Coturnix skulls from specimens 155 days of age did not show a superior nuchal line.

Face

Orbital region.—The orbital region is relatively larger in the quail than it is in the adult chicken or turkey. As already mentioned, the dorsal margin lies on the level with the top surface of the frontal bone. The lower margin lies behind the jugal bar, and thus a suborbital region does not exist in the quail. A similar situation exists in the young Single Comb White Leghorn Chicken in that the large size of the orbit eliminates, or nearly eliminates, the suborbital region.

Suborbital region.—The suborbital region of the adult coturnix is reduced to two small triangles, a situation probably brought about by eyes that are large relative to the size of the head.

Postorbital region.—In coturnix the shape and boundary landmarks for the postorbital region are the same as those in the chicken and turkey.

---

[6] If the musculature of the throat is relaxed, as it often is in the chicken, an X-ray may show the entire axis of the hyoid dropped below the inferior margin of the mandible.

[7] There must be a reasonable limit to the number of boundary lines for internal structure that can be projected and drawn on the surface of the body. The hyoid is a good example; another example would be the full extent of pneumatization from the middle ear. The hyoid of the Green Woodpecker (*Picus viridis*) curls around the crown above the right eye and penetrates the right nasal cavity (Leiber, 1907). Parker (1879 pl. 5, fig. 1) depicted the horns of the hyoid passing over the crown in the same species of woodpecker. In the Red-shafted Flicker (*Colaptes cafer*) the same may be observed (Shufeldt, 1900:588). It seems better to regard these as exceptions than to modify the general plan that has been developed for outlining regions of the head.

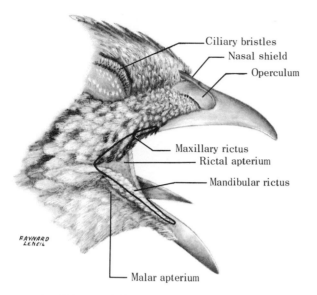

Ciliary bristles
Nasal shield
Operculum

Maxillary rictus
Rictal apterium

Mandibular rictus

Malar apterium

FIGURE 12.—Rictus of the Common Coturnix from the right side. Part of the rictus is feathered, part is bare.

Auricular region.—In coturnix the external ear opening is round and external to the squamosal process of the quadrate bone. The canal swings caudally and ventrally to the tympanum. Even in these points the differences from the chicken and turkey are minor.

Nasal region.—No essential difference was observed in the nasal region of coturnix and that of the chicken and turkey. The apex is located a slight distance farther forward in the quail than in the chicken and turkey.

Oral region.—The beak of coturnix has a shape similar to

that of the chicken and turkey, but it differs in one detail. The nasal arch carries a small **Y**-shaped piece, inverted so that the stem of the **Y** lies along the nasal arch. Into the crotch of the **Y** is inserted the caudal tip of the beak. The arms of the **Y** extend forward and downward along the angle between beak and operculum.

Rictal region.—The rictus of coturnix has a pigmented, dark-brown margin that is rolled outward (fig. 12); the maxillary and mandibular portions are alike. In the chicken and turkey when the gape is at its maximum, the angle between maxillary and mandibular parts disappears (fig. 11), but in coturnix an angle is retained because the rictus is attached farther forward on the lower jaw than it is on the upper jaw (fig. 12).

Malar region.—The postarticular process in the coturnix is relatively short; as a result, the caudal end of the malar region is rounded and lies close to the articular joint.

Ventral surface of head

The interramal, hyoid, and submalar regions of coturnix are the same as those in the chicken and turkey. The cartilaginous tip of the epibranchial cartilage may extend a little higher dorsally in the quail than in these other galliforms.

White Pekin Duck

The skeletal anatomy of the heads of ducks, geese, and swans is sufficiently alike that a description of the regions of one of these—the White Pekin Duck—adequately represents the others (figs. 13 and 14). In spite of considerable differences in the skeletal system of galliforms and anseriforms, the landmarks for placement of region boundaries remain

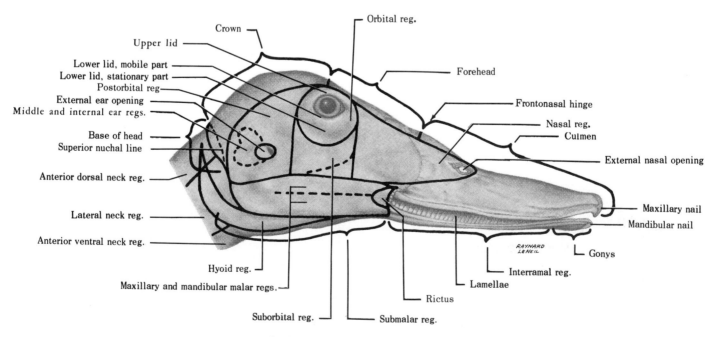

Crown
Upper lid
Orbital reg.
Lower lid, mobile part
Lower lid, stationary part
Postorbital reg.
External ear opening
Middle and internal ear regs.
Base of head
Superior nuchal line
Anterior dorsal neck reg.
Lateral neck reg.
Anterior ventral neck reg.
Hyoid reg.
Maxillary and mandibular malar regs.
Suborbital reg.
Submalar reg.
Rictus
Lamellae
Interramal reg.
Gonys
Mandibular nail
Maxillary nail
External nasal opening
Culmen
Nasal reg.
Frontonasal hinge
Forehead

FIGURE 13.—Right side of the deplumed head of a Mallard (*Anas platyrhynchos*) showing regions. The wild species is not identical with the White Pekin Duck (compare with fig. 14, *A*). See figure 3 for significance of dashed lines. Abbreviation: reg(s)., region(s).

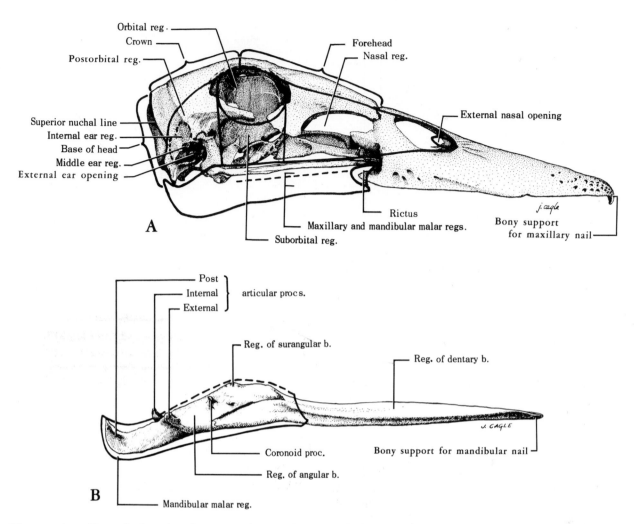

FIGURE 14.—Boundaries of regions superimposed on the skull and lower jaw of a male White Pekin Duck.

A, the relationship of the orbital region to highest point of the crown differs somewhat between Mallard (fig. 13) and White Pekin Duck. See figure 15 for names of the skull bones. See figure 3 for significance of dashed lines.

B, the dashed line over the jaw indicates the portion hidden behind the jugal bar when the mouth is closed. Abbreviations: b., bone; proc(s)., process(es); reg(s)., region(s).

about the same. The anserines have more extensive fusion of bones in the fore part of the head than do the galliforms. The term "prosopium" was applied by Mivart (1895) to the fused premaxillaries, maxillaries, and nasals of the parrot beak and is equally applicable to the White Pekin Duck. What we labeled "prefrontal bone" in figure 15 was named "lachrymal" by Humphrey and Clark (1964, fig. 4, A) in their illustration of the skull of a goose, *Anser* spp. Our acceptance of the term "prefrontal" is based on the work of Gregory (1920:129 and 234), which was accepted by Romer (1945: fig. 207) and by Jollie (1957, 1962). Jollie (1957:414) discussed the change on the basis of earlier literature.

Cranium

Forehead region.—The anterior boundary of the forehead region is the frontonasal hinge. Externally, the hinge line is not readily apparent, but in the skull of the duck it can be identified easily by a palpable flexible joint that is located laterally at each end of the hinge line. Below the hinge a small concavity of the prosopium receives the rounded anterior spur of the prefrontal bone (fig. 15). As shown clearly in the skull of a 28-day-old White Pekin Duck, the hinge line lies between the anterior (premaxillary) and posterior (frontal) processes of the nasal bone. Externally the hinge line crosses the caudally pointed extensions of the orange-colored beak, about half way between the tips and the bottom of the U-shaped depression in the midline (fig. 2, *D*, dorsal view). Usually the hinge joint can be palpated through the soft keratin of the beak.

The posterior boundary of the forehead in ducks, as in the other birds described, lies at the anterior end of the brain. Externally the plane of this boundary crosses the caudal third of the lid slit. In the White Pekin Duck, the frontal bone can be palpated readily. The level of the anterior end of the brain corresponds to the narrowest part of the frontal bone between the *bulbi oculi*. Each lateral boundary extends from the hinge line along the angle of the head produced by

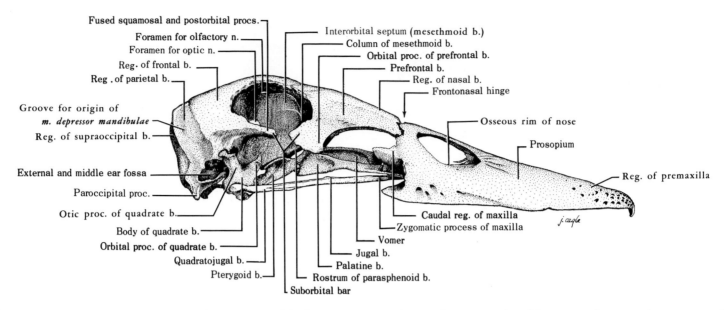

Fused squamosal and postorbital procs.
Foramen for olfactory n.
Foramen for optic n.
Reg. of frontal b.
Reg . of parietal b.
Groove for origin of
m. depressor mandibulae
Reg. of supraoccipital b.
External and middle ear fossa
Paroccipital proc.
Otic proc. of quadrate b.
Body of quadrate b.
Orbital proc. of quadrate b.
Quadratojugal b.
Pterygoid b.
Suborbital bar

Interorbital septum (mesethmoid b.)
Column of mesethmoid b.
Orbital proc. of prefrontal b.
Prefrontal b.
Reg. of nasal b.
Frontonasal hinge
Osseous rim of nose
Prosopium
Reg. of premaxilla
Caudal reg. of maxilla
Zygomatic process of maxilla
Vomer
Jugal b.
Palatine b.
Rostrum of parasphenoid b.

j. cagle

FIGURE 15.—Skull of a White Pekin Duck (male). Same base drawing as figure 14, *A*, with an overlay carrying names of bones. Abbreviations: b., bone; *m., musculus*; n., nerve; proc(s)., process(es); reg., region.

the fusion of frontal and prefrontal bones. Then it follows the curved orbital margin of frontal bone to the posterior boundary already established.

Crown region.—Compared with the galliforms studied, the White Pekin Duck has a long forehead and a short crown. The boundaries of the crown are based on the same landmarks that were applied to birds already described; differences are in proportions and details. The inferior tip of the paroccipital process extends farther ventrally than in the galliforms, and in the duck it lies at about the same level as the dorsal tip of the postarticular process. The lateral margin of the crown extends from the frontal table above the eye, diagonally downward behind the ear, to the inferior tip of the paroccipital process. In its path the margin crosses the groove associated with the *m. depressor mandibulae* (figs. 14, *A*, and 15). Caudal to this muscle is the well-developed superior nuchal line. It crosses and is identical with the boundary between parietal and occipital bones, as determined on a 28-day-old specimen. The caudal boundary of the crown joins its lateral boundary at about the level of the ear rather than at the extreme free tip of the paroccipital process as it does in galliforms.

Base of head.—The superior nuchal line in the duck establishes most of the dorsal and lateral boundaries for the base of the head (figs. 13 and 14, *A*). The ventral boundary extends from the inferior tip of the paroccipital process, across the base of the skull, and along the line between exoccipital, basioccipital, and the basiparasphenoid (basitemporal) bone. This line is irregular, and the two small styloid processes present near the boundary are part of the exoccipital bones and therefore are part of the base of the head. On the skull of the 28-day-old duckling, where many bones are not yet fused, the caudal part of the parietal bone, clearly turns downward to form the upper part of the base of the head. Most of the parietal is involved in the groove that

bears the body of the *m. depressor mandibulae*. The relationships of bones at the base of the head are shown by Howard (1929) for the Snow Goose (*Anser caerulescens* (= *Chen hyperboreus*)), and for a goose by Humphrey and Clark (1964). In the White Pekin Duck, the boundary that separates base of the head from floor of the skull is similar to that shown for the turkey (fig. 8).

Face

Orbital region.—The eye of the White Pekin Duck and of the Mallard is small compared to the size of the head, and it lies close to the dorsal surface. The globe of the eye has the dorsal part of the circle near the orbital margin of the frontal bone, the anterior and posterior parts cut across the orbital fossa, and the inferior part lies behind the process representing the fused squamosal and postorbital processes (fig. 14, *A*).[8] These processes are joined by a fascial band. The orbital fossa has an irregular shape caused partly by the large glands adjacent to the eye; the nasal gland lies along the concave margin of the frontal bone and extends to the caudal end of the nasal fossa. The large lacrimal gland fills the forward end of the nasal fossa, and the Harderian gland lies on its lateral surface.

The total peripheral extent of the conjunctival cavity beneath the upper and lower lids covers about two-thirds to three-fourths of the total anterior surface of the globe. Its ventral extent is not as great as in the galliforms described. There are mobile and stationary parts to both upper and lower lids; the stationary part of the lower lid is supported by the suborbital bar, and the mobile part folds inside the bar. The upper mobile lid is much shorter than the lower one. The caudal limbs of the nictitating membrane extend poste-

_____

[8] These two processes together are called the suborbital bar (fig. 15).

riorly along the perimeter of the pupil for about two-thirds of its circumference. The membrane appears to be reduced or absent from the posterior third of the conjunctival cavity.

Suborbital region.—This region is more extensive in the White Pekin Duck than in other birds examined. The area has four boundaries—the dorsal one is concave and is shared with the orbital region. The lateral boundaries are formed as tangents that extend ventrally from each side of the orbital region. The lateral boundaries approach the dorsal margin of the malar region perpendicularly, and the portion of the dorsal margin of the malar region between these lines forms the ventral boundary of the suborbital region (fig. 13). Beneath the surface of the suborbital region lies the orbital process of the quadrate bone, the pterygoid bone, some of the interorbital septum, and much of the jaw musculature (figs. 14, *A* and 15).

Postorbital region.—In the duck this region has the shape of the upper half of a broad crescent. The dorsocaudal boundary is the same as the lateral boundary of the crown, the anterior boundary is shared with the orbital and suborbital regions, and the ventral boundary extends from the paroccipital process to the tip of the postarticular process and has a common boundary with the posterior part of the malar region (fig. 14, *A*). In the skeleton of the skull, a space that exists between the middle ear region and the postarticular process has been arbitrarily included in the malar region.

Auricular region.—This region in the duck is located entirely within the postorbital region. The external ear opening is approximately round and is almost directly peripheral to the middle ear (compare figure 13 with figure 14, *A*). The placement low on the skull of the external ear opening is demonstrated by the fact that a ledge, produced by an osseous ridge below the middle ear, intrudes into the ventral wall of the canal, and a tendon protrudes into the caudal wall. These two indentations reduce the canal passageway to about one-third of its diameter at the surface of the head. In the chicken and turkey, the external auditory canal turns ventrally to approach the tympanic membrane, but in the White Pekin Duck the passageway is short and direct. The outlines of middle ear region and semicircular canals are shown by dashed lines within the postauricular area. These outlines are clearly defined in X-rays of the head.

Nasal region.—The nasal region is extensive and triangular in the White Pekin Duck. The apex lies at the anterior end of the nasal fossa, a short distance in front of the external nasal opening. The dorsal margin courses below the nasal arch, across the hinge line, and below the forehead as far as the caudal end of the table of the mesethmoid. Within this table is contained a sinuslike extension of the nasal cavity, dorsal to the olfactory concha. The caudal boundary follows the column of the mesethmoid and then the upper third or half of the suborbital region and, as indicated by the dashed lines in figures 13 and 14, *A*, it then diagonally crosses the suborbital space to join the malar region. Here is located the caudal end of the choana or internal nares. The ventral nasal boundary extends from the apex across the fused plate of nasal and maxillary bones, and it continues caudally as a

boundary in common with the malar region as far as the middle of the suborbital region where it joins its caudal boundary. The choana begins at the anterior end of the large, bladelike vomer bone and continues as an open slit to the posterior boundary of the nasal region.

The external nasal opening is oval and lacks an operculum; the tip of the rudimentary inferior concha is visible through the opening. The external nasal opening in the White Pekin Duck has an intermediate placement in the bill; in the Muscovy Duck (fig. 16, *A*) it is near the caudal end, and in the male Chinese Goose it is far forward (fig. 16, *B* and 17). The nasal septum opposite the nasal openings is perforate, and thus it is possible to pass a probe through from one side to the opposite side of the beak. The nostrils of galliforms, Common Pigeon, and Great Horned Owl are imperforate. Examples of perforate nostrils are shown in figure 2, *C* and *E*. Coues (1903:110) listed, in addition, the Turkey Vulture (Turkey-buzzard, *Cathartes aura*) and Sandhill Crane (*Grus canadensis*). These examples may be extended to include all New World vultures and all cranes. Van Tyne and Berger (1959: 40) included the rails.

Oral region.—In the duck the beaks are flattened, the gape is long, and the rictus is small (fig. 13). The soft keratin covering the beaks remains flexible and leathery. Rigidity is given the keratin by the underlying bones; where the rhamphotheca spans the nasal fossa the keratin is particularly flexible. The rhamphotheca not only covers completely the area of the nares but extends caudally along the ridge made by the fusion of frontal and prefrontal bones to a point on each side of the head (fig. 2, *D*, dorsal view). Between these two points the line of the beak curves downward to form a U-shaped extension of the skin of the forehead on which are implanted short feathers. The caudal margin of the beak on the side of the face is curved also, with the concavity toward the eye.

The tomial margin of the maxilla is strengthened by a thickened ridge of keratin. This margin is somewhat better developed in the Muscovy Duck (fig. 16, *A*) than in the White Pekin Duck. At the anterior end of the rhamphotheca, in the anserine birds, is a nail supported by a thickened patch of bone at the tip of premaxillaries.

The lower beak, covered also by membranous keratin, extends caudally the same distance as in the upper beak. It also has a supporting roll or bar of keratin along the tomium. A nail is present, and when the mouth is closed it holds a position almost at right angles to the upper nail and therefore would have a slight shearing action (fig. 13). The mandibular nail is absent in the goose shown in figure 16, *B*. The nail is the only portion of the beak in anseriform birds that has the character of the horny beak found in most birds. The profile of the nail represents the gonys of the lower beak and is relatively short (fig. 2, *D*, ventral view).

Along the tomia of both jaws is a series of keratinized serrations or lamellae, and facing these is a row of lamellae on each side of the tongue. Goodman and Fisher (1962:43) described the food habits of the Mallard and other ducks as follows:

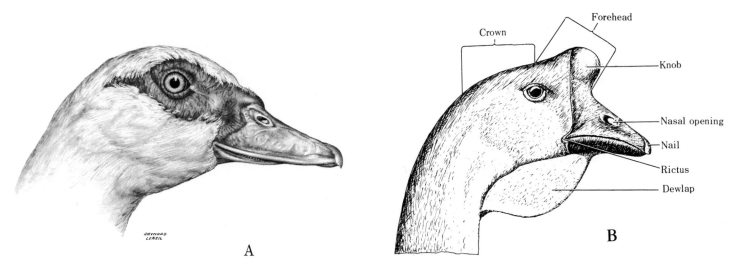

FIGURE 16.—Heads of two anseriform birds.

A, White Muscovy Duck showing the bare, red carunculate skin.
B, African Goose (male) showing characteristic knob and dewlap.

(Redrawn from "American Standard of Perfection," 1938–40, p. 456, by Casimir Jamroz.)

The blade-like lamellae . . . provide an apparatus for filtering of solid particles from a watery medium. The water and food particles enter anteriorly near or at the tip of the bill and the water only leaves through the sides of the bill; the food particles are strained out by the lamellae of the bill and the projections on the tongue.

The culmen of the White Pekin Duck is approximately a straight line with a slight elevation over the external nostril and a slight depression in front of it. Coues (1903:109) questioned whether the term "culmen" can properly be applied to the duck based on his definition of the culmen, namely, ". . . *highest middle lengthwise line of bill;* it begins where feathers end on the forehead, and extends to tip of upper mandible." It would seem as if this definition was

adequately fulfilled by the beak of the duck; the beak may not be greatly elevated, but it is not flat.

The dorsal and ventral boundaries between oral and pharyngeal portions of the mouth cavity are basically similar to those of galliforms. The paraglossobasihyal joint lies approximately at the level of the anterior end of the vomer (fig. 15); in relation to an external landmark, it lies in the interramal region a slight distance caudal to the feathered area (fig. 2, *D*, ventral view). The joint is such a large one that it can be palpated through the thin skin of the interramal region. The paraglossobasihyal joint marks the anterior tip of the dividing line between pharyngeal and oral portions of the tongue and the floor of the mouth. Inside the mouth another landmark for this joint is the large row of

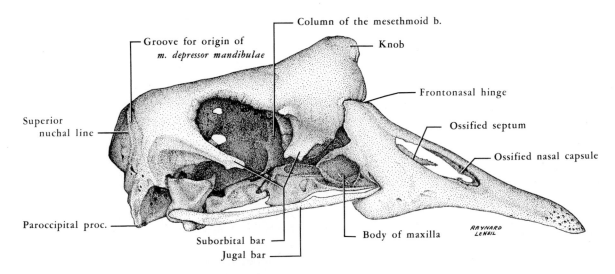

FIGURE 17.—Skull of a domestic goose—either African or Chinese. Specimen No. 19374, from the U.S. National Museum. The presumed ancestor (*Anser cygnoides*) of both of these breeds of domestic geese lacks a knob and is thereby morphologically different. Abbreviations: b., bone; *m., musculus*; proc., process.

papillae arranged transversely across the tongue. From these papillae the boundary lines extend diagonally along the grooves between the larynx and the inner lateral wall of the lower jaws to the joints of the jaws. On the dorsal surface of the oropharynx, the boundary between the oral and pharyngeal parts falls between the caudal end of the choana and the tissue barrier in front of the common opening that leads to the auditory tubes. Two laterally directed lines extend to the joints of the jaws. The dorsal pharynx region is short and is followed almost immediately by the beginning of the esophagus.

Rictal region.—The rictus of the White Pekin Duck is small (fig. 13) and does not have maxillary and mandibular parts as in galliforms and in the Great Horned Owl. The gape of the mouth would be relatively small were it not for the fact that the upper jaw can be elevated an additional amount by bending at the frontonasal hinge. Among 17 species of Anatidae examined by Goodman and Fisher (1962, table 40, p. 175) the amount of elevation varied from 7° to 22°. The angle was least in fish-eating species, most in grazers, and intermediate in those that sieved their food from water, like the Mallard.

Malar region.—The malar region includes both the upper and lower jaws. The boundaries can be defined as follows: From the palpable margin of the jugal bar, around the articulation with the quadrate enclosing the space between the ear and postarticular process and along the caudal and ventral curvature of the postarticular process, and under the edge of the jaw to the end of the beak (fig. 13). The malar region has a maxillary and a mandibular part, the separation of which is indicated by a dashed line in figures 13 and 14, *A*. The mandibular malar region is shown also in figure 14, *B*, the dashed line in this case indicates the portion of this region hidden behind the jugal bar.

Ventral surface of head

Interramal region.—The boundaries for the interramal region in the duck agree with those already given for other domestic fowl. The region lies caudal to the mandibular symphysis, between the inferior margins of the mandibles. The posterior boundary is a transverse line that joins the right and left ricti (fig. 2, *D*, ventral view and fig. 13). Most of the interramal region in the duck is a thin, membranous skin devoid of feathers; only a small, triangular portion at the caudal end is feathered. The posterior boundary of the interramal region forms the anterior boundary of the submalar region.

Hyoid region.—In the White Pekin Duck as in other birds examined, the bones of the hyoid emerge from below the level of the malar region at a point opposite the suborbital region. The position of the urohyal determines the ventral extent of the hyoid region, a spatial relationship best seen in X-rays of the bisected head. The concave dorsal and anterior boundary of the hyoid region is common with the inferior malar margin and dorsally follows the contour of the base of the head. When the skin is removed, the epibranchial

bone and cartilage are found to lie in the angle between the *m. depressor mandibulae* and the neck. The tip may curl forward to a point dorsal to the ear or the entire epibranchial portion of the hyoid horn may shift caudally to expose the lateral neck region between hyoid and base of the skull as shown in figure 13. As the hyoid passes around the caudal end of the jaws, part of it slips in behind the postarticular process.

Submalar region.—The anterior boundary of the submalar region of the duck crosses the ventral surface of the head at the level of the rictus; the posterior boundary crosses at the level of the caudal end of the lower jaws. The lateral boundaries are the lower edges of the mandibles. The separation between pharyngeal and oral regions is indicated by dashed lines in the submalar and interramal regions (fig. 38). On the ventral side of the head, the submalar region includes the hyoid region; the reason for not attempting to outline a hyoid region ventrally has already been stated in footnote 7 (p. 19).

Other Domestic Anserines

The domestic Muscovy Duck has white or colored plumage, depending on the variety. The white variety shown in figure 16, *A*, has an extensive bare area across the face, the anterior part of which extends from dorsal midline to rictus and follows the caudal boundary of the beak. The dorsal margin diagonally crosses the forehead, extends along the crown slightly above the orbital region, and continues around the eye into the postorbital region to terminate near the junction of the base of the head and the neck. The ventral boundary begins at this point, arches across the postorbital region above the external ear opening, swings downward across the face at about the junction of orbital and suborbital regions, crosses part of the nasal region, and then turns abruptly downward to the rictus.

Male and female domestic Chinese Geese, both brown and white varieties, have large frontal knobs completely covered by the rhamphotheca. The upward protrusion of the forehead is even more extensive in the male and female African Goose. In the African Goose the beak keratin covers only part of the knob (fig. 16, *B*), and both sexes have a dewlap. The dewlap is lacking in both sexes of the Chinese Goose. The names "African" and "Chinese" Geese are confusing because both breeds come from China. A breed of domestic fowl called the "Egyptian Goose" is distributed from Egypt to the Cape of Good Hope. It differs from the African breed mentioned previously in that it lacks both knob and dewlap. Both African and Chinese Geese may have been derived from a species of wild goose (*Anser cygnoides*) found in China. The wild species, however, lacks a frontal knob. Brief descriptions of the breeds and varieties of domestic geese are recorded by the American Poultry Association (1938-40 and 1953) and by Grow (1956).

The osteology of the skull reveals the structural basis for the knob (fig. 17). Fusion is extensive, as in the skulls of other adult anserines. Without the availability of young stages it is not possible to determine if the knob is formed entirely or only partly of frontal bones and if the frontal processes of the nasal bones are involved.

In figure 17 some bones of the skull are labeled in order to facilitate comparisons with figure 15. A detailed study of the skull bones for the duck and the goose illustrated here is inappropriate at this time, but a few differences might be mentioned. The external nasal openings of the duck (figs. 13 and 16, *A*) are more caudally placed on the beak than they are in the goose (fig. 16, *B*) or in the swan (fig. 2, *E*). The relative distance between hinge and eye fossa is much greater in the duck than in the goose; therefore the forehead is longer in the duck than in the goose. The orbital fossa of the duck is smaller than it is in the goose. The table of the mesethmoid contains the dorsocaudal part of the nasal cavity in the duck. In the skull of the goose there is some indication that the knob might also carry an extension from the nasal cavity. Final conclusions on this point must await a study of soft tissues.

The prefrontal bone is more extensive in the duck than it is in the goose; consequently, in the former there is a wide gap between the two parts of the suborbital bar. In the goose the maxilla is expanded, whereas in the duck it is small and pointed. Where the duck has but a small filigree of bone receiving the internal ramus of the ophthalmic nerve, the goose has a well-developed canal, and in the median plane, an extension upward to form an osseous nasal septum.

The upper tomium of the duck is straight or slightly convex, but the curve for the goose is concave. The groove for the *m. depressor mandibulae* is much greater in the duck than in the goose. In the latter, however, a crest of bone projects between the cervical muscle masses that are attached to the base of the skull; this crest of bone is absent in the duck. The crest carries with it the occipital wall of the base of the head and allows the basal end of the skull to be seen in a profile view of the head. A similar conformation occurs in the Common Pigeon. The occipital condyle of the duck carries a midsagittal groove revealing the bipartite character of the condyle; this groove is absent in the goose. The paroccipital process of the duck is wide and carries the extension of the broad groove of the *m. depressor mandibulae*, but in the goose the process is a narrow ridge. The rim of the osseous external meatus of the duck is small, and the margins fold inward, whereas that of the goose is large and flaring. None of these skeletal or topographic differences change the basic

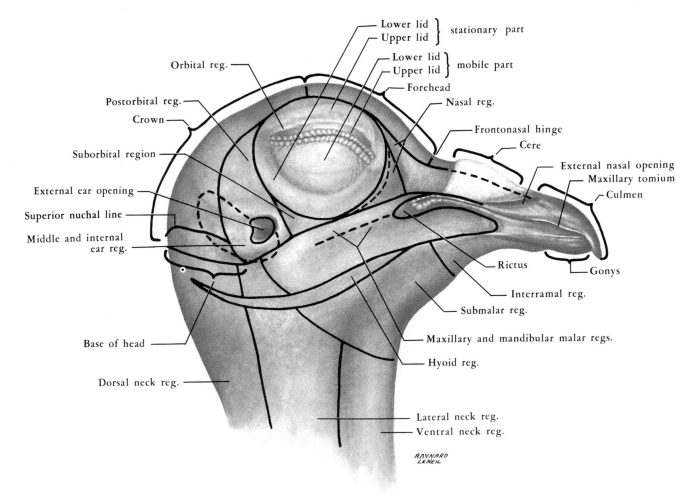

FIGURE 18.—Right side of the deplumed head of the Common Pigeon with boundary lines for regions. See figure 3 for significance of the dashed lines. Abbreviation: reg(s)., region(s).

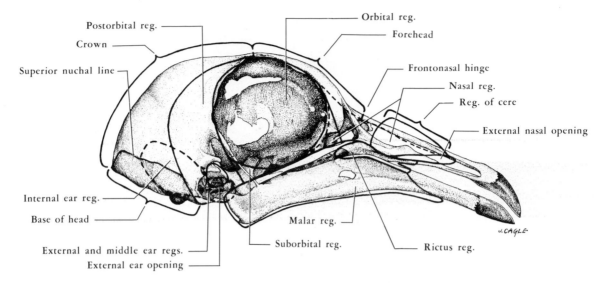

FIGURE 19.—Right side of skull and jaws of Common Pigeon with boundary lines for regions superimposed. See figure 3 for significance of the dashed lines. Abbreviation: reg(s)., region(s).

pattern for regions of ducks and geese but do modify slightly some of the proportions.

Common Pigeon

Sources of our material were varied, but most pigeons were brought to the laboratory by farmers who probably collected them from barn lofts. Some specimens were bought from breeders. All specimens are considered to be representative of pigeons used in laboratories. For the purpose of identifying regions, minor differences among specimens were of no significance.

The authors have used the names Common Pigeon, Domestic Pigeon, Laboratory Pigeon, Rock Pigeon, and Rock Dove. The American Ornithologists' Union "Check List of North American Birds" has used the common name "Rock Dove," ever since *Columba livia* was entered in its fourth edition (1931:153). The distinction between pigeon and dove is not clearly defined in the literature that has come to our attention. Newton and Gadow (1893-96) indicated that the terms have been used interchangeably. Thomson (1964:217, 632) suggested that the pigeon and dove have been separated on the basis of size and referred to *Columba livia* as the Rock Pigeon. We prefer to use the name "pigeon" because it is a name more readily and commonly associated with the bird we are talking about than the word "dove."

The pattern of regions for the Common Pigeon is the same as already described for other domestic species and will not be redescribed in detail (figs. 18 and 19). Instead emphasis will be placed on points of difference.

Cranium

Forehead region.—The frontonasal hinge in the pigeon forms the transverse boundary between forehead and nasal arch. The placement of the hinge line is somewhat more anterior in the pigeon than it is in birds described thus far

because the table of the mesethmoid is fused with the overlying bones and extends several millimeters beyond the junction of the frontal bone and the caudal ends of the nasal bones (fig. 20). As Bock (1963) pointed out for the ostrich, such fusions prevent upward movement of the jaw. In the pigeon the flexion takes place in front of the mesethmoid bone and hence involves the narrow part of the premaxillary processes of the nasal bones and the frontal processes of the premaxillary bones. The frontonasal hinge lies in the feathered area caudal to the cere (figs. 18 and 19).

Projection of the hinge laterally carries it across the maxillary processes of the nasal bones. Figure 20, a lateral view of the pigeon's skull, does not show the various parts of the nasal bone, but in dorsal view the frontal process of the nasal bone is lacking or else obliterated by fusion with the anterior edge or the pneumatic frontal bone.

The caudal and lateral boundaries of the forehead are closely similar to those already described for other birds. The caudal boundary crosses the lid slit near the middle, which is in a plane with the narrowest point of the frontal bones. These bones are palpable.

Crown region.—The brain of the pigeon is large and is tilted caudally. As a result, the base of the head is shifted almost parallel to the long axis of the head (figs. 19 and 20). This shift in axis of the brain produces a crown of relatively great span. The superior nuchal line in the Common Pigeon is a ridge that is distinct enough to be palpable. The lateral boundary of the crown arches across the side of the skull, ventrally behind the osseous part of the middle and external ear to the tip of the paroccipital process. The caudal boundary, follows the superior nuchal line and intersects the lateral boundary dorsal to the paroccipital process, approximately on a level with the external ear opening.

Base of head.—As already mentioned, the base of the pigeon head lies nearly parallel to the axis of the head; the foramen magnum is directed ventrally instead of caudally. The sur-

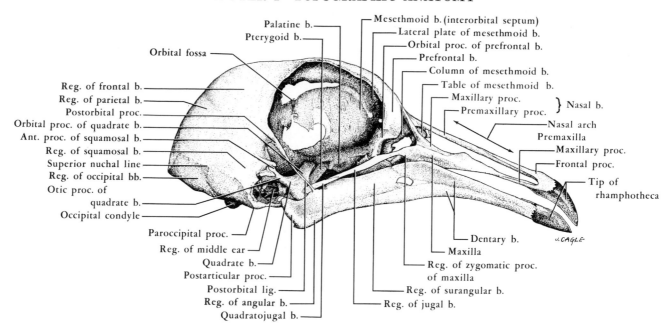

FIGURE 20.—Right side of skull and jaws of the Common Pigeon with some bones labeled. Same base drawing as in figure 19. Abbreviations: ant., anterior; b(b)., bone(s); lig., ligament; proc., process; reg., region.

face of this base is not a flat plane; hence, the caudal surface of the skull can be seen in profile view because it bulges beyond the level of the superior nuchal line (figs. 19 and 20). A more extreme example of this has already been mentioned in domestic breeds of geese with knobs (fig. 17).

Face

Orbital region.—In the pigeon the peripheral margin of the globe is extensive and anteriorly extends from the frontal bone to the prefrontal bone and then to the jugal bar; posteriorly, it extends to the postorbital process and then to the frontal bone. The anterior osseous face of the orbital fossa of the pigeon differs from that of the domestic galliforms in that the column of the mesethmoid, the prefrontal, and its process fuse into a transverse plate of thin bone. In the pigeon connection with the nasal fossa region is limited to a flattened passageway below this plate of bone, whereas in the chicken and turkey the two fossae are broadly connected. Because the orbital process of the prefrontal bone reaches the jugal bar, a triangular space is established that is bounded by the prefrontal, the maxillary process of the nasal bone, and zygomatic process of the maxilla. Pycraft (1903:11) called this space the lachrymonasal fossa.

The conjunctival cavity of the pigeon does not appear quite as extensive as that in the chicken; it reaches nearly to the peripheral edge of the sclerotic bones. The lids were defined as the skin overlying the conjunctival cavity; in the pigeon the mobile upper and lower lids lie well within the limits of the conjunctival cavity, but there is some restriction of what have generally been considered here as stationary parts. The upper mobile lid is folded under the stationary part along the line shown in figure 18. The lower mobile part

is large, thin, and devoid of feathers. The lid slit is curved with the concavity downward and crosses the globe above the level of the pupil. The lower and upper stationary lids are marked by rows of small feathers characteristic of the face. The nictitating membrane is similar to that already described in other birds.

Suborbital region.—The suborbital region in the pigeon is reduced to two small triangular areas, having been eliminated almost entirely by the large orbital region and the elevated jugal bar (figs. 18 and 19). The vertical boundaries of the suborbital region are tangents to the orbital region and meet the dorsal margin of the malar region at right angles. These lines in the pigeon are tilted forward because the jugal bar is directed upward and forms an angle with the maxillo-premaxillary portion of the beak (figs. 19 and 20).

Postorbital region.—The anterior and posterior boundaries of the postorbital region have been identified already (figs. 18 and 19). The ventral boundary, as in other birds, extends from the inferior tip of the paroccipital process to the dorsal tip of the postarticular process and shares part of its boundary with the malar region.

Auricular region.—The external ear opening in the pigeon is nearly round, but its caudal margin is pushed inward by a muscle and tendon that pass beneath the soft tissues. The short external canal extends downward to the osseous portion of the external ear and the middle ear, as indicated by dashed lines in figure 18 and the rim of bone in figure 19. Its lower margin overlaps a small portion of the malar region. The internal ear is located chiefly in the postorbital region, but the semicircular canals, shown by the dashed lines, underlie the base of the head and extend dorsocaudally to the crown region.

Nasal region.—In the pigeon, the nasal region is elongated and narrow. Although it has the triangular shape similar to that in other birds, the dorsoventral margins are close together and nearly parallel. Anterior to the orbital region, the caudal end of the nasal region expands; the most inferior portion lies beneath the orbital region and immediately opens into the choanae. The caudodorsal corner is below the mesethmoid. Whether an aperture leads from this portion of the nasal cavity to the pneumatic cells of the mesethmoid and frontal bones was not determined.

The external nasal opening is broadly dilated at the anterior tip but is compressed to a narrow slit at the caudal end. Membranous keratin lies above the nasal opening at the anterior end of an overhanging scale, or operculum. This tissue merges into the thickened white cere that saddles the nasal arch (fig. 18). The tissue of the cere is soft, and its white color is due to a flaky thickening of the *stratum corneum* that has sufficient opacity to obscure the red of the dermal blood vessels.

Coues (1903:107) observed that a cere is found in parrots, in birds of prey, and in plovers. He questioned whether the term could properly be applied to pigeons, and perhaps it should be regarded as part of the head rather than the beak. He mentioned that sometimes the cere is feathered as in the extinct Carolina Parakeet (*Conuropsis carolinensis*). Beddard (1898:5) defined the cere as ". . . simply the basal part of the beak which has remained soft." According to this definition, the term appears applicable to pigeons. Mayaud (1950:8) listed the Columbiformes as one of the orders in which a cere is present.

The fleshy inferior edge of the cere follows the edge of the operculum and is folded inward along the edge of the jaw. The caudal margin makes an abrupt transition to feathered skin of the nasal region and forehead. The cere may provide protection for the elongated nasal fossa. It is possible to readily penetrate the nasal cavity through the cere (fig. 374, p. 593); it is very easily done through the thin skin of the feathered area immediately caudal to the cere.

The paired internal nasal openings, or choanae, are elongated double slits readily visible within the roof of the oral cavity. The caudal ends of the choanae lie beneath the globe of the eye.

Oral region.—The upper beak of the pigeon is slightly epignathous and is relatively short because it ends caudally at the nasal opening and cere. The culmen therefore has a uniform curvature. At the caudal end of the upper beak, a low rugosity sometimes is present on the nasal arch, in a position similar to that of the beak tubercle of the turkey and Great Horned Owl. The maxillary tomium is straight or slightly undulating. The gonys has a slight curvature and is relatively short. The hard keratin of the lower beak continues caudally as two narrow pointed extensions, each following a margin of the lower jaw. The upper extension merges into the mandibular rictus. The mandibular tomium is essentially a straight line. In the pigeon, we separated oral and pharyngeal cavities on the basis of similar features found in other birds.

Rictal region.—The rictus in the pigeon is a simple fold that extends along the edges of the jaws. The rostral end of the maxillary rictus originates below the cere; the mandibular, at about the same level on the lower jaw. The rictus is shaped somewhat like that of the Common Coturnix; it is closely attached to the edge of the upper jaw and makes approximately a right angle where it turns downward to join the lower jaw which it approaches at a small angle. The caudal edge of the gape is fleshy and slightly thickened. Posterior to this is a small area of relatively thin skin. The caudal boundary of the rictus can be established more easily by examining the inner surface of the oral cavity than the outer surface. The bulge produced by the levator muscles of the lower jaw protruding into the buccal cavity marks the caudal end of the rictus. On the outer surface of the rictus as well as on the surface of the mandibular malar region especially in the interramal region, the skin has a white flaking that is similar to that of the cere but is not so abundant.

Malar region.—The soft tissues caudal to the beak and overlying the upper and lower jaws form the malar region in the pigeon. The angle formed by the forward and hind parts of the jaws is reflected in the angle between malar regions and beaks.

Ventral surface of head

Interramal region.—The interramal region is readily located, and in the pigeon it is bounded on the basis that was used for other birds already described. The flaked white character of the deplumed skin has already been mentioned.

Hyoid region.—Dissections, X-ray photographs, and palpation demonstrated that the two bones of the cornu of the hyoid were arranged almost in a straight line in the pigeon. In other types of birds examined thus far, the epibranchial bone and cartilage made an angle with the ceratobranchial, epibranchial bone thereby takes a position in the angle between the base of the head and the beginning of the neck. In the pigeon the ceratobranchial parallels the lower margin of the mandible and, as shown in figure 18, is tilted downward. Therefore, in passing around the lowest point of the angular bone, the epibranchial directly crosses the muscles of the neck rather than arches upward along the postarticular process and the superior nuchal line.

In species of birds already studied, the boundary line between the dorsal and lateral regions of the neck extends to the hyoid region and ends there. It has already been recognized that the hyoid region is part of the neck as it is also part of the submalar region. Therefore, when the tip of the cornu lies caudal to the head, some of the neck is visible between hyoid and head. In figure 18 this space has been crossed by a continuation of the lateral margin of the dorsal neck region.

Submalar region.—The erect neck and the head set at right angles to it have produced a broad submalar region in the pigeon. As a result, the caudal boundary of this region is longer in the pigeon than in birds illustrated earlier.

Great Horned Owl

The same detailed investigation was not attempted on this wild species—Great Horned Owl (*Bubo virginianus*)—as was performed on domestic and laboratory species, chiefly because fresh and preserved material in adequate amounts was not available. Six skulls and one hemisected, embalmed head were used. The outline of the auricular region was obtained from an X-ray of the hemisected head as well as from a study of soft tissues and skeleton.

The Great Horned Owl was included because several features of the head are considerably modified from those found in domestic and laboratory birds. The owl should serve, therefore, as a proving ground for the general applicability of the landmarks and criteria for establishing boundaries of the head. Some of these differences are: (1) In the the owl the axis of the brain almost parallels the axis of the neck and therefore is nearly at right angles to the beak; in the chicken and turkey axes of beak and brain lie nearly in the same line. (2) The large eye is directed forward at less than 45° from the median plane, thereby producing a large overlap and giving more than the average binocularity. In most other birds the lateral placement of eyes permits less binocularity than eyes in the forward position. (3) The eye globe is supported and constricted by a very large sclerotic ring. The ring in domestic birds is relatively small. (4) The nasal region is more complex than it is in domestic birds. (5) The external ear is expanded to give greater auditory acuity.

In spite of these differences from domestic birds, we found the landmarks previously described for most regions of the head to be applicable in establishing boundaries for head regions in the owl. Thus, we assume that what we describe in this chapter is generally applicable to wild birds.

Cranium

Forehead region.—The frontonasal hinge in the Great Horned Owl is readily identified by the overhanging "brow" of the forehead. This "brow" produces a smaller nasal angle than is generally found in birds. The lateral boundary of the forehead extends outward and cuts back abruptly (fig. 23) as it follows the lateral margin of the frontal bone. The anterior thickened portion has a flattened lateral surface (fig. 22) that supports the broad sclerotic ring.

The anterior end of the brain reaches the plane of the most constricted part of the frontal bone and, therefore, the caudal limit of the forehead is easily identified by palpation. On the other hand, this boundary has no relationship to the lid slit as it has in birds previously examined. In fact, the transverse plane of this boundary crosses the sclerotic ring and the lower end of the external ear opening (figs. 21 and 23). In spite of this seeming caudal extension of the forehead, it is short in the owl.

Crown region.—The dome-shaped crown of the owl protrudes upward and backward, conforming to the upper surface of the brain. This tends to bring the caudal part of the crown in the same plane as the base of the head (figs. 21

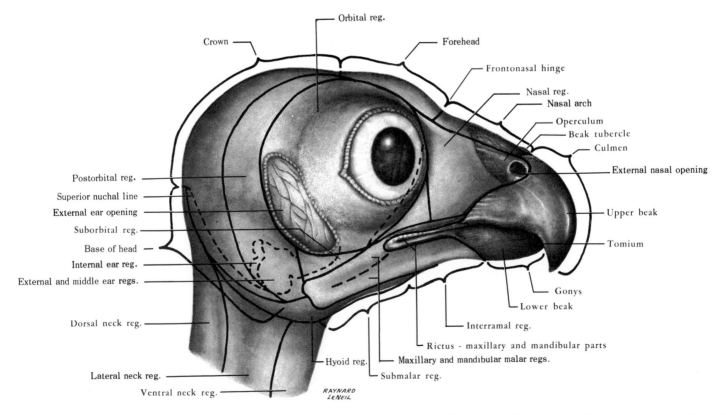

FIGURE 21.—Right side of the head of the deplumed Great Horned Owl (*Bubo virginianus*) showing regions. See figure 3 for significance of dashed lines. Abbreviation: reg(s)., region(s).

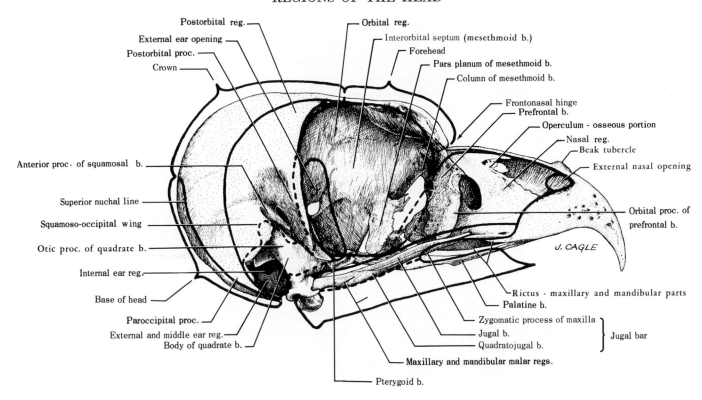

FIGURE 22.—Great Horned Owl (*Bubo virginianus*) showing regions of the surface of the head superimposed on the skull and upper jaw. Names for bones are also included in the drawing. See figure 3 for significance of dashed lines. Abbreviations: b., bone; n., nerve; proc., process; reg(s)., region(s).

and 22). The caudal margin, namely, the superior nuchal line, is barely palpable. Except for a small dip downward in the midline, it projects directly laterally and then curves ventrally to end at the inferior tip of the paroccipital process. The lateral margin of the crown is a line arbitrarily curved downward to meet the line that bounds the base of head and continues on a short distance to the tip of the paroccipital process.

Base of head.—The superior nuchal line in the owl forms the dorsal and lateral boundaries of the base of the head. The fusion of skull bones is so complete that there are no observable traces of suture lines for frontals, parietals, occipitals, or the parabasisphenoid. It is assumed that the irregular ridge that joins the inferior tips of the paroccipital processes caudal to the condyle represents a close approximation to the exact ventral boundary for the base of the head. As in other birds studied, the base of the head in the owl is masked by the muscles and bones of the neck.

Face

Orbital region.—The fact that the globe of the eye in the owl is directed forward at approximately a 45° angle to the midsagittal plane of the head foreshortens the margin of the globe when seen in lateral view. The eyes of owls are supported by broad sclerotic plates, and like the globe are foreshortened also when viewed laterally (figs. 23 and 24). The circular boundary for the orbital region has been drawn (figs. 21 and 22) so as to follow the proximal margin of the sclerotic

ring on both its outer and inner margins as well as the osseous limits of the orbital fossa.

Examination of the skull shows that the base of the globe rests against the caudal wall rather than against the medial wall of the orbital fossa. As in other birds, the anterior margin of the owl's skull is the column of the mesethmoid that offers some support to the large globe by a bony extension, the *pars planum* (fig. 22).

The owl's eyelids are large, and both may move toward each other in closing. Sometimes, however, only one lid moves—the upper lid closes to meet the lower and sometimes the lower lid lifts to meet the upper. The closed lid slit crosses the upper third of the eye. Both upper and lower lids have stationary as well as mobile portions. The nictitating membrane is folded largely along the dorsal margin of the conjunctival cavity.

Suborbital region.—A suborbital region might be considered nonexistent in the owl. One can project tangents from the anterior and posterior margins of the globe, perpendicular to the malar region and thus produce an anterior and a posterior triangular corner as was done for the pigeon. These areas, however, are so small that it may be better to omit a suborbital region altogether for this group of birds.

Postorbital region.—The postorbital region is long and narrow because of the large size of the eye and the vertical slope of the crown. The boundaries have the same landmarks that were established for other species and need not be repeated here.

Auricular region.—The ear of the owl differs from that in other birds by the large size of the external canal. Although birds have no auricle, the flap of skin that bears feathers and is supported by the broad postorbital process serves this function for the owl; the external ear opening is an elongated, flattened oval. In other species of birds, this opening has always been located within the postorbital region, but in the owl it lies in the orbital region (figs. 21 to 24). This structure is well shown in figure 24, where a small amount of radiopaque material was applied to the edge of the opening. The sclerotic plates are visible beneath the opening. Dissection through the anterior wall of the ear canal confirms the same conclusion, that the ear opening overlaps the bones of the eye and hence lies within the boundary of the orbital cavity.

The soft portion of the ear canal dips downward abruptly to the osseous portion located between the quadrate bone and the paroccipital process. The shadow of the quadrate is shown in figure 24, and because the middle ear region is caudal to this, it lies superimposed on most of the semicircular canals. These canals are shown clearly in the X-ray, and in figures 21 and 22 they are represented by dashed lines, not far beyond the osseous margin of the external and middle ear. As judged by the dashed lines enclosing the semicircular canals in figures 6, 14, *A*, and 19, the placement of these canals and their relationship to the middle ear vary widely among species of birds.

Nasal region.—The external nasal opening in the owl is relatively small, approximately round, and placed high on the beak. As indicated by the placement of boundary lines in figures 21 and 22, the extent of the nasal region is short and high, whereas in the pigeon it is long and narrow. The internal structure of the nose is too complex to discuss beyond the fact that the large maxillary bulla restricts the lower portion of the nasal cavity and that the transverse shelf between ossified septum and outer wall of the prosopium produces a blind passage that extends to the forward end of the beak.

For the anterior two-thirds of its length, the common choana in the owl is a narrow slit; the posterior third is an oval passageway. The vomer in the owl is similar to that of the pigeon and is limited to a small triangular bone that is attached to the infolded scrolls of the body of the palatine bone, but continuing from it is a septum of soft tissue wedged in between the maxillary bullae. The nasal cavity is imperforate and even the osseous fossa is imperforate except for a small oval area through the septum near the roof of the nose and another near the choanae. Caudal to the external nasal opening is a membranous keratin covering the underlying nasal fossa (fig. 21). The owl has no operculum as occurs in galliforms. The nasal capsule is largely cartilage, but part of it at the posterior end of the nasal fossa is ossified in adult specimens.

Oral region.—The owl's upper beak is short and strongly epignathous. It is covered with hard keratin (fig. 21) as far caudally as the beginning of the external nasal opening. The culmen is strongly curved; the tomium is undulating and curves downward at the tip. The keratin of the lower beak is

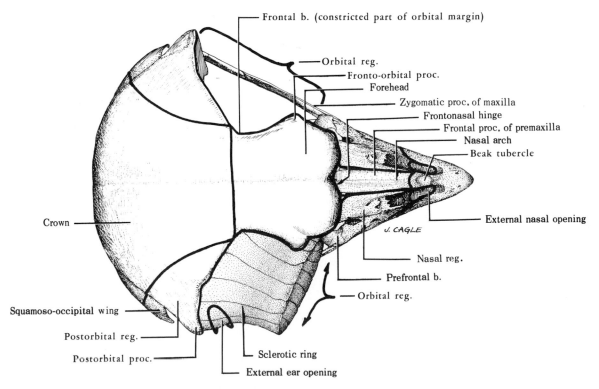

Figure 23.—Dorsal view of the skull of the Great Horned Owl (*Bubo virginianus*) with the sclerotic ring in place on the right side. Outlines of some regions and openings are superimposed on the skull. Abbreviations: b., bone; mar., margin; proc., process; reg., region.

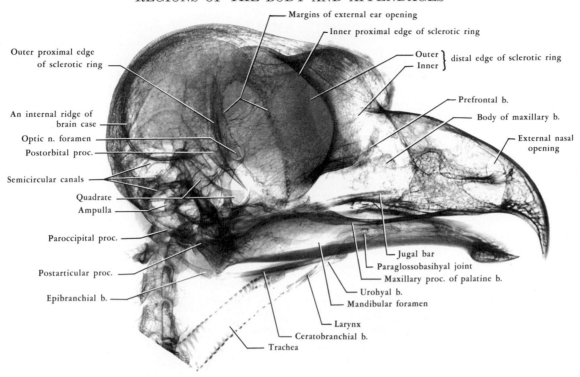

Margins of external ear opening
Inner proximal edge of sclerotic ring
Outer proximal edge of sclerotic ring
Outer } distal edge of sclerotic ring
Inner
Prefrontal b.
Body of maxillary b.
An internal ridge of brain case
External nasal opening
Optic n. foramen
Postorbital proc.
Semicircular canals
Quadrate
Ampulla
Paroccipital proc.
Postarticular proc.
Jugal bar
Paraglossobasihyal joint
Maxillary proc. of palatine b.
Urohyal b.
Mandibular foramen
Epibranchial b.
Larynx
Ceratobranchial b.
Trachea

FIGURE 24.—Positive radiograph of the right half of the hemisected head of the Great Horned Owl (*Bubo virginianus*); taken from the lateral surface. Abbreviations: b., bone; n., nerve; proc., process.

blunt and covers the symphysis. The gonys is slightly curved. The caudal boundaries of the beaks lie nearly opposite each other when the mouth is closed, and the keratins of both merge into the fleshy tissues of the rictus.

On the nasal arch opposite the anterior end of the nasal fossa, several owl specimens had beak tubercles of varying degrees of prominence. A possible cause for the tubercles is repeated trauma at the point of transition from the thinned, horny keratin to the flexible membranous keratin. The tubercle strengthens the nasal arch in this region. The membranous keratin lies above the external nasal opening as far caudally as the beginning of the feathered skin of the nasal arch, it may represent a cere. In caged owls it is fleshy and abraded from contact with the cage wall. If repeated injury to this same area occurred in the wild, it might account for the exostosis of bone seen in some specimens.

The separation of oral and pharyngeal cavities, in the owl uses the same landmarks that were described for other birds; the location of paraglossobasihyal joint is indicated in figure 24. The oral portion of the tongue is short, and the frenulum is attached near its anterior end. The paraglossobasihyal joint lies anterior to the lingual papillae. The best landmark in this species of owl is the V-shaped separation between the right and left groups of lingual papillae. The joint lies just beneath the forward-directed apex of the V.

Rictal region.—The ricti of the owl are narrow where they extend along the edges of the jaws; at the gape the rictus is slightly more fleshy. Caudal to the gape the cheek area of the rictus is small (fig. 21).

Malar region.—The malar region is long and relatively narrow and ends caudally at the joint of the jaw because the owl has no postarticular process. The extension of the dorsal line for the maxillary malar region to the beak is arbitrary because the fused bones of the prosopium show no suture lines (fig. 22). The dorsal boundary of the malar region is common to three other regions—nasal, orbital, and postorbital. The mandibular malar region corresponds to the lower jaw as far as the bill, and in figure 21 a dashed line was used to separate maxillary and mandibular malar regions.

Ventral surface of head

The interramal, hyoid, and submalar regions in the owl utilize the same landmarks that are described for domestic birds and, therefore, will not be reiterated. The dorsal tip of the epibranchial cartilage and bone ends at about the level of the superior nuchal line (fig. 21).

REGIONS OF THE BODY AND APPENDAGES

Regions for the head were described by presenting the material for each species in succession. This procedure was justified because the heads of the various birds sometimes differ significantly, and it would have been difficult to group them together under one description. There is considerably more uniformity among species with regard to the other regions of the body. The remaining body regions will be described mainly on the basis of our studies of the chicken, together with such comments as may be pertinent for the quail, turkey, duck, and pigeon.

Regions and appendages for each kind of bird are presented in three views—dorsal, lateral, and ventral. There is some overlap of regions in the three views, but this is desirable and aids in visualizing these areas in terms of a three-dimensional body. In dorsal and ventral views, the head and neck are extended forward, the wings laterally, and the legs caudally. In lateral view the wing is forcibly elevated, and thus the ventral surface of the wing is shown. Both wings, both legs, and the right and left halves of the body are illustrated. This has been done largely for three reasons: (1) Details of regions vary somewhat from bird to bird; on the two halves these variations could be illustrated; (2) comprehension of regions is somewhat easier if the whole bird rather than a bisected specimen is illustrated; and (3) it is possible to distribute labels on the two halves of the body.

Regional boundaries for the head are not repeated because they have already been described. However, regions on the ventral surface of the head—interramal, hyoid, and submalar—are repeated, because this view shows them more clearly than the lateral view. In addition, dashed lines have been drawn to separate approximate oral and pharyngeal portions of the submalar region.

Dashed lines are used in other parts of the body in two ways: (1) To mark the location of such joints as shoulder, knee, phalangeal, etc., and (2) to show separation between parallel bones and to indicate the region associated with each bone, such as the ulnar and radial regions of the forearm and the region of each phalynx of the manus.

In studying the regions of the head, a look at the skeleton of the parts was found useful. In addition, some knowledge of the remainder of the skeleton is necessary in order to associate region boundaries and palpable bones. Therefore, some major landmarks are shown in figure 25 for the Single Comb White Leghorn Chicken. Some differences occur between the skeleton of the chicken and that of the turkey, quail, duck, and pigeon.

A superficial view of the muscles on the left side of the chicken is shown in figure 26. Like the skeleton, muscles serve as palpable landmarks in some parts of the body, especially the ventral surface of the wing, where muscles and tendons are easily identifiable through the thin skin. Each of these two organ-systems will be reviewed briefly so that reference may be made to them in describing body regions.

The number of vertebrae of the axial skeleton varies among birds and also among individuals of the same species. Separation of the vertebrae within the same bird into cervical, thoracic, lumbar, sacral, and coccygeal varies also because of a lack of agreement among scientists. The neck of the Single Comb White Leghorn Chicken is considered here to include the first 16 or 17 vertebrae. Free cervical ribs, namely those attached to the vertebrae but not to the sternum, are associated with the last two of this series. The first thoracic vertebra is defined as the most anterior one with a complete rib composed of two parts—the upper vertebral member and the lower sternal member. In the chicken, the dividing line between neck and thorax, based on type of rib, crosses the band of fused neural spines. It is possible to palpate, but only with some difficulty, the space between the neural spine of C_{16} and the fused neural spines of C_{17} and T_{1-3}. The pigeon has 14 cervical vertebrae.

Four thoracic ribs are present in the chicken, turkey, coturnix, and pigeon; hence, the thorax includes but four vertebrae (fig. 25). Each sternal member of a rib articulates with a facet on the lateral margin of the sternum. The last or fourth thoracic vertebra is free and not fused with the others anterior to it. It is the only freely movable vertebra in the total length of the back, namely between the base of neck and the movable coccygeal vertebrae. Caudal to the four thoracic ribs are usually one, sometimes two "floating ribs" that may have two parts, but the sternal part is attached to the last thoracic rib rather than to the sternum. The ribs are palpable, especially at the caudal angle where vertebral and sternal members articulate. The uncinate processes also are useful landmarks. Deep palpation through the overlying pectoral musculature can identify the space between last cervical rib, its uncinate process, and the angle of the first thoracic rib.

The lumbar, sacral, and caudal vertebrae between the bones of the pelvic girdle constitute the synsacrum. The chicken generally has four lumbar, five sacral, and six caudal vertebrae. An additional, six caudals plus a pygostyle (the coccygeal vertebrae of the tail) are external to the synsacrum. Sometimes the separation between the last fused caudal vertebra and the first free vertebra of the tail can be palpated accurately, but often it is missed by one. At the end of the vertebral column is a pygostyle, a tapered bone composed of probably six terminal vertebrae fused together. The lateral processes of the movable coccygeal vertebrae as well as the caudal tip of the pygostyle is readily palpable.

The pectoral girdle is composed of three bones on each side arranged somewhat like a tripod (fig. 25). The slender, curved clavicles, or furcula, extend from the region of the shoulder joint to the midline where they join in a flattened plate, the hypocleidium. Practically all of the "wishbone" is palpable. A strong robust bone that arises also in the shoulder region and articulates in a deep groove along the anterior edge of the sternum is the coracoid. Only the dorsal end of the coracoid is palpable; the remainder is covered effectively by the thick pectoral and supracoracoid muscles. The third bone of the girdle is the scapula, a slender flattened bow-shaped blade whose anterior end is not palpable because it is beneath the shoulder joint under the heavy musculature of this area. The remainder of the blade is readily palpable; the caudal tip may sometimes elevate the skin slightly.

The pelvic girdle has numerous palpable surfaces, margins, and points. The anterior end of the ilium (fig. 25) is a shovel-shaped blade, the anterior edge of which can be palpated through overlying muscles. The median dorsal ridge lies just beneath the skin and the lateral margin of the dorsal plate. The latter is located in the postacetabular part

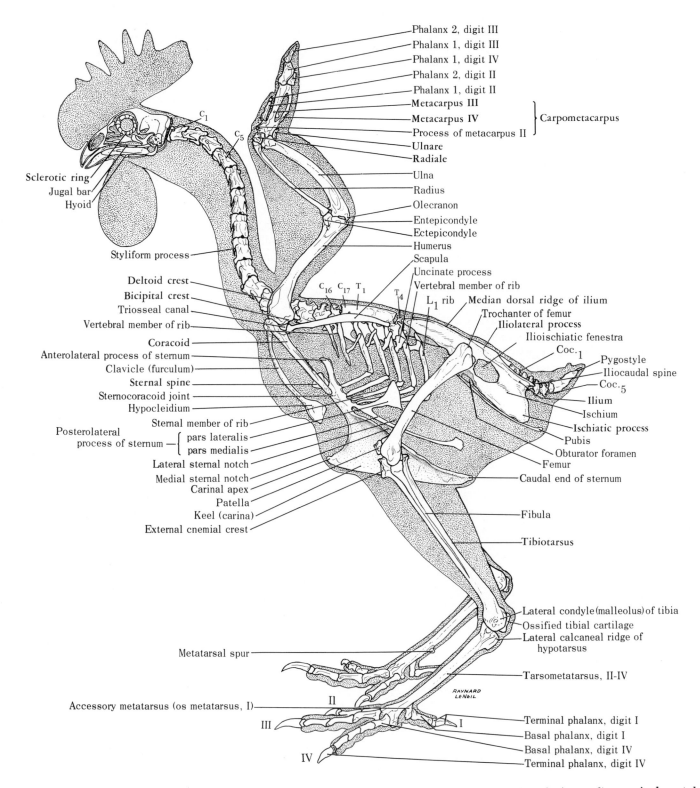

Phalanx 2, digit III
Phalanx 1, digit III
Phalanx 1, digit IV
Phalanx 2, digit II
Phalanx 1, digit II
Metacarpus III
Metacarpus IV ⎱ Carpometacarpus
Process of metacarpus II ⎰
Ulnare
Radiale
Ulna
Radius
Olecranon
Entepicondyle
Ectepicondyle
Humerus
Scapula
Uncinate process
Vertebral member of rib
Median dorsal ridge of ilium
Trochanter of femur
Iliolateral process
Ilioischiatic fenestra
Pygostyle
Iliocaudal spine
Ilium
Ischium
Ischiatic process
Pubis
Obturator foramen
Femur
Caudal end of sternum
Fibula
Tibiotarsus
Lateral condyle (malleolus) of tibia
Ossified tibial cartilage
Lateral calcaneal ridge of hypotarsus
Tarsometatarsus, II-IV
Terminal phalanx, digit I
Basal phalanx, digit I
Basal phalanx, digit IV
Terminal phalanx, digit IV

Sclerotic ring
Jugal bar
Hyoid
Styliform process
Deltoid crest
Bicipital crest
Triosseal canal
Vertebral member of rib
Coracoid
Anterolateral process of sternum
Clavicle (furculum)
Sternal spine
Sternocoracoid joint
Hypocleidium
Posterolateral process of sternum ⎰ pars lateralis
                                   ⎱ pars medialis
Sternal member of rib
Lateral sternal notch
Medial sternal notch
Carinal apex
Patella
Keel (carina)
External cnemial crest
Metatarsal spur
Accessory metatarsus (os metatarsus, I)

RAYNARD LeNEIL

FIGURE 25.—Lateral view of the skeleton of the Single Comb White Leghorn Chicken. Abbreviations: C., cervical vertebra; Coc., coccygeal vertebra; L., lumbar vertebra; T., thoracic vertebra.

of the ilium and is covered merely by the thin sheet of the iliotibialis tendon so that it also is readily palpable. At the posterior end is the iliocaudal spine.

At right angles to the dorsal plate is the lateral plate, the upper half of which is ilium and the lower half ischium;

the lower caudal angle of the latter is the ischiatic process. The margin between the iliocaudal spine and ischiatic process is readily palpable. The terminal end of the pubis is particularly prominent. The more anterior parts of this slender bone are too well covered by muscle to be palpated.

The sternum of carinate birds is a broad plate from the ventral surface of which there projects a large keel, or *carina*. In the chicken, turkey, and quail, deep incisures cut into the horizontal plate. These incisures, or notches, (fig. 25) produce an anterolateral process and a posterolateral process of the sternum. The latter is divided into lateral and medial parts. All processes are palpable. The caudally directed processes are readily visible through the skin, but the anterior one is covered by the massive breast musculature. The ventral margin of the keel is quite obvious from the carinal apex to the caudal end. The edge of the sternal spine (fig. 25) can be felt by pushing a finger into the the thoracic inlet, especially when the crop is empty. The sternal spine lies at the anterior end of the sternum and represents a vertical fusion of right and left sternal plates.

The shoulder joint is not palpable, but it can be approximated when the wing is moved manually and the location noted in muscles that move and those that do not. For this type of information X-ray photographs are more exact. The bicipital crest of the humerus is readily palpable. Distally the shaft of the humerus can be readily felt between the *mm. biceps brachii* and *triceps humeralis*.

The radius and ulna can be palpated beneath the overlying muscles, but the details are vague. This is especially true where the tendons are attached to the bones of the carpus and manus. X-ray photographs were an indispensible tool in these studies where the results of palpation seemed indefinite.

The trochanter of the femur is particularly prominent; some of the shaft may be identified by palpation on the medial surface and, of course, the condyles are readily apparent in most of their details. The patella, suspended by strong tendons, is not sharply defined, whereas the cnemial crests are very prominent. The upper end of the fibula can be located only approximately, but the condyles of the tibia among the long tendons of the foot are readily palpable and bulge outward beneath the skin.

The hypotarsus, a caudal projection of bone attached to the upper end of the tarsometatarsus, protrudes the scales of the metatarsus (instep of the foot), but the strong tendons of this region make exact palpation somewhat difficult. The toes and their phalanges are readily identifiable, but the distal end of the tarsometatarsus bone (fig. 25) is obscured by the thick metatarsal pad (fig. 28). Likewise, the location of the two ends of the accessory metatarsus (fig. 25) requires considerable manual manipulation.

With these skeletal landmarks in mind, it is possible to locate consistently the boundaries for regions of the avian body. The superficial muscles serve the same purpose, but they are somewhat less useful than bones because their plasticity allows deformation, and because the fascia around and between muscles tends to create smooth surfaces from muscle to muscle. Even after removal of the skin, distinctions between muscles are not always readily apparent.

The boundaries of the thigh follow the anterior margin of the *m. sartorius* and the posterior margin of the *m. semi-*

tendinosus. The anterior angle of the elbow region is identified with the angle between *m. biceps brachii* and *m. extensor metacarpi radialis*. Two of the three margins of the prepatagium (propatagium, see footnote 12, p. 57) are established by these same muscles. Arbitrarily the caudomedial margin cuts across the *mm. propatagialis longus et brevis* and the *pectoralis propatagialis*. The palpable trachea, esophagus, and crop as well as the triangular fossa of the thoracic inlet are useful landmarks.

Neck

The neck (*collum*) is cylindrical and joins head to thorax. Its bony support among bird species ranges from 8 to about 26 cervical vertebrae (Coues, 1903:98). The column of bones is enclosed in muscle, and below this lie the pharynx, larynx, trachea, esophagus, and crop. Just as the number of vertebrae is variable, so is the length of the neck. As pointed out by Coues, the neck length is in direct proportion to leg length. In addition, the neck must be long enough that the beak can reach the oil gland. Some small birds appear to have relatively short necks, and when covered with plumage, their heads seem to rest on the shoulders with no sharp line of demarcation to distinguish neck and trunk. The typical sigmoid shape of the neck (S-curve or reverse curve) in long-necked birds is well shown in the deplumed chicken (figs. 26 and 28), turkey (fig. 31), and duck (fig. 37). The curve is present to a lesser degree in small birds.

The vertebrae forming the curve may be divided into three parts: An anterior group—composed in the chicken of atlas, axis, and the two following vertebrae—forms the top horizontal part of the sigmoid curve; a middle group of six vertebrae forms the vertical portion; and a caudal group of seven vertebrae, of which the caudal 5 to 5½ lie between the shoulder joints, forms the lower, horizontal part. In the turkey the curve of the neck is a smooth S-shape, and it is not possible to assign the point of flexion with any particular vertebral joint. The White Pekin Duck has one flexure near the base of the head and another a short distance in front of the shoulders (fig. 37). The necks of the Common Coturnix and pigeon tend to be less curved (figs. 34 and 40), at least as the bird holds its head and neck when standing in an erect postion. In the pigeon the upper cervical flexure tends to be absent because the base of the head tends to be horizontal instead of vertical (figs. 18 and 19), and the neck without making a signifcant bend is already placed at right angles to the axis of the beak.

There are four longitudinal surfaces of the neck—dorsal (*dorsum colli*), ventral (*venter colli*), and two lateral (*latis colli*) right and left. The boundaries of these areas are somewhat arbitrary because the surfaces represent four sectors of a circle as indicated in figure 1, *A*. The dorsal neck as an organ includes the dorsal skeletal and muscular tissues that extend from the base of the head to the first thoracic vertebra. The upper third of the dorsal neck is anterior dorsal region, or nape, (*dorsum anterius colli*); the lower two-thirds is poste-

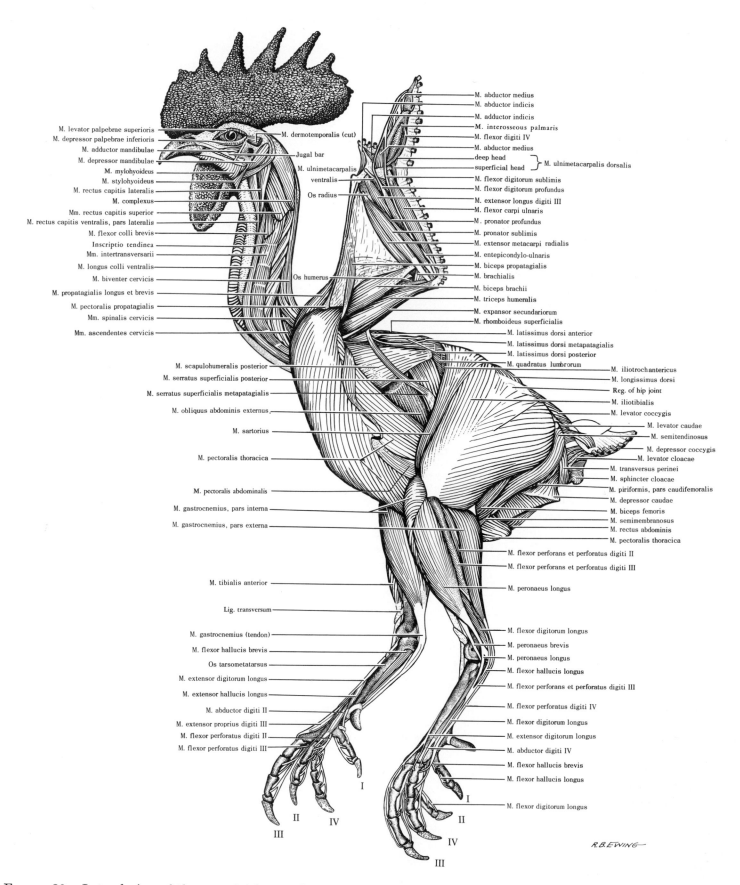

FIGURE 26.—Lateral view of the superficial musculature of the Single Comb White Leghorn Chicken. Abbreviations: *Lig.*, *Ligamentum*; *M(m)., Musculus(i)*; Reg., Region.

rior dorsal region, or scruff, (*dorsum posterius colli*). The separation for these two is somewhat arbitrary and is associated more with the curvature of the upper neck than with a particular vertebra.

The ventral neck has often been called the throat of the plumed bird but, as discussed on page 18, it is anatomically equivalent to the pharynx because of overlap between the oral region, pharyngeal region, larynx, and upper trachea. It has not been possible to divide the under surface of the head and upper ventral neck into areas having simple, readily understandable boundary lines that are strictly, anatomically correct. For this reason the term "interramal region" was applied to that area in the plumed bird often named "chin" and "submalar region" to that area which has been named "throat." Caudal to the submalar region is the short anterior ventral region (*regio anterior colli ventralis*), and this area together with the submalar region constitutes what the authors understand Coues (1903) included under the term "gular region," and the longer posterior ventral region (*regio posterior colli ventralis*) sometimes has been designated the "jugal region." This division into two parts has not been applied to the pigeon or quail because their necks do not have a well-defined sigmoid shape.

The foregoing brief review of the skeletal system revealed that the neck extends caudally beyond the shoulder and this fact introduces some difficulties in naming the parts of the trunk. On the drawings, two boundaries for the caudal end of the neck have been indicated: The arbitrary boundary between neck and trunk is shown by a solid line; the anatomical boundary between neck and trunk, by a dashed line. The area between the two is what the authors call the interscapular neck. The anterior of these two boundaries has been placed to cross the dorsal neck in line with the anterior margins of the shoulders. One thinks of this among mammals as the dividing line between neck and thorax, but in birds the pectoral girdles extend forward beyond the base of the neck by several vertebrae. Thus, the base of the neck lies considerably caudal to the anterior margin of the wing. The anatomical boundary of neck and body has a fairly constant relationship to the scapula. In skeletons of both domestic and wild birds examined,[9] a transverse line at the caudal end of the neck crosses the scapula in its middle third.

Chicken

The anterior dorsal region of the base of the neck in the chicken has an anterior boundary formed by the junction of

crown and base of head (fig. 27). The right and left lateral boundaries are approximately parallel in the area between head and shoulder (fig. 28). The basis for placing these lines was (1) that the lateral boundary should lie directly above the edge of the underlying skeletal and muscular neck, and (2) that the dorsal neck should occupy approximately one-quarter of the neck as seen in transverse section. At the level of the shoulder region, the lateral boundaries diverge and follow the cervicoalar grooves[10] as far caudally as the transverse line between anatomical neck and thorax.

In the chicken are four transverse boundaries for the dorsal neck region (*regio colli dorsalis*), all of which have been mentioned: (1) anterior boundary at the base of the head, (2) separation of anterior and posterior dorsal regions, (3) arbitrary boundary between neck and trunk, and (4) anatomical boundary between neck and thorax. The term "interscapular region" (*regio interscapularis*), was selected to designate the basal end of the posterior dorsal neck because it corresponds approximately to the area occupied by the interscapular tract. Of course, similar names should be used for similar areas, except where they cause confusion.

The lateral neck region (*regio colli lateralis*) is somewhat more difficult to define than the dorsal region; this will become evident as the description proceeds. The anterior boundary is the base of the head (fig. 28). It includes the dorsal part of the hyoid region but, as already indicated in the discussion of the regions of the head, it seems desirable to set the hyoid region apart even though it does overlap part of the submalar and part of the lateral neck regions.

The dorsal boundary of the lateral neck region in the chicken is shared with the lateral boundary of the dorsal neck region and has already been defined. However, it should be noted that the lateral boundary passes above the cervical patagium (*patagium cervicale*) as far as the shoulder region. The caudal boundary of the lateral neck shares a common boundary with the anterior margin of the shoulder (*omus*). This boundary crosses the cervical patagium ventrally along the curvature of the shoulder to intersect the ventral margin of the lateral neck region. Three facts should be noted: (1) That the lateral neck region includes the cervical patagium; (2) that the posterior boundary of the lateral neck region is not located as far caudally as the posterior boundary of the dorsal neck region; and (3) that there is no transverse boundary separating anterior and posterior parts.

The ventral margin of the lateral neck region is described under the topic of the ventral neck, which begins at the submalar region (figs. 28 and 29) and extends to the infracaudal end of the thoracic inlet (*transitus thoracatus*). The ventral

---

[9] The skeletons examined were those of: Great Blue Heron (*Ardea herodias*), Horned Grebe (*Podiceps auritus*), Whistling Swan (*Cygnus columbianus*), Canada Goose (*Branta canadensis*), Ring-necked Pheasant (*Phasianus colchicus*), Single Comb White Leghorn Chicken, Chukar (*Alectoris chukar*), American Woodcock (*Philohela minor*), Bonaparte's Gull (*Larus philadelphia*), Common Pigeon (*Columba livia*), Budgerigar (*Melopsittacus undulatus*), Blue Jay (*Cyanocitta cristata*), Cedar Waxwing (*Bombycilla cedrorum*), and Rose-breasted Grosbeak (*Pheucticus ludovicianus*).

[10] As far as the authors are aware, the term "cervicoalar groove" (*fossa cervicoalaria*) is introduced here for the first time. It is the groove that is produced by the junction of the wing musculature and trunk where the wing is extended. Caudally, the groove flattens out to merge with the contour of the dorsal body surface. It may be poorly shown in specimens with a large amount of adipose tissue in the cervical patagium (*patagium cervicale*).

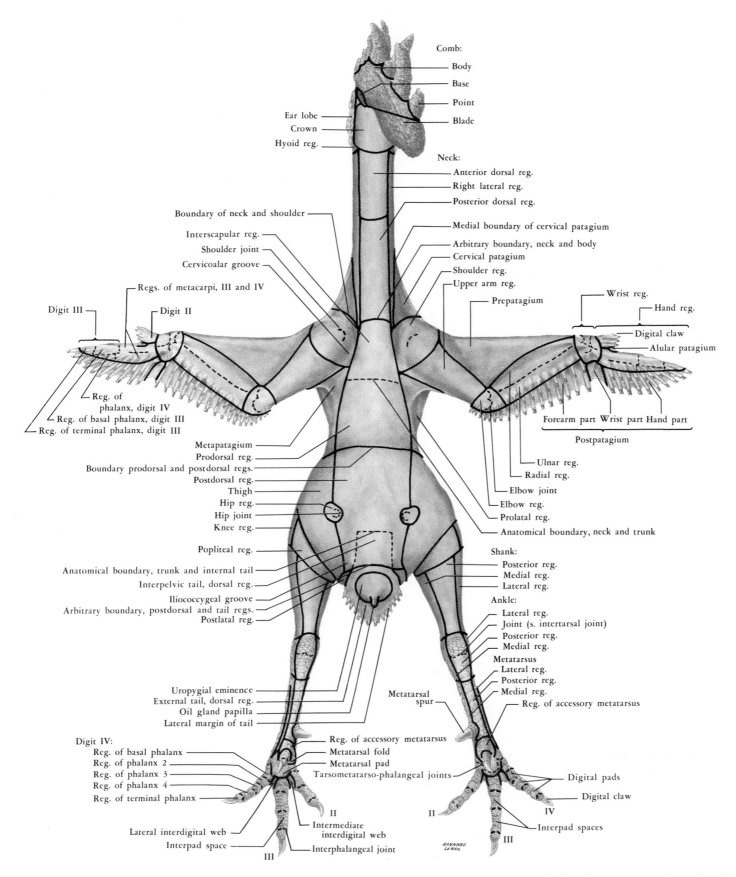

FIGURE 27.—Dorsal view of a male Single Comb White Leghorn Chicken showing regions. Abbreviations: reg(s)., region(s); s., synonym.

neck region (*regio colli ventralis*) is divided into two parts: A short anterior ventral region and a longer posterior ventral region. The transverse line separating them is located at the inside curve of the first bend of the neck (fig. 28). The caudal end of the ventral neck region is not a transverse line, but is a V-shaped boundary that generally follows the muscles overlying the clavicle. The apex of the V is located at the inner edge of the hypocleidium (fig. 29). The lateral boundaries of the ventral neck region are parallel for most of their length but flare outward at the caudal end to participate in the common junction of lateral and ventral necks, shoulder region, and proventer.

Turkey

The regions of the neck in the turkey will be discussed only on points wherein they differ from those of the chicken. The carunculate skin extends down the neck somewhat less than half way to the shoulder (figs. 30 and 31). Caudally, the caruncles are of increasing size, and they are largest at the junction between the bare area of the neck and the beginning of the plumage. However, the seeming bare head and neck bear widely distributed small bristle and contour feathers arranged in rows (fig. 217, p. 324).

In the turkey the dorsal neck region broadens in its caudal half or two-fifths, and its lateral boundaries continue into the cervicoalar grooves. The arbitrary and anatomical boundary between neck and trunk is the same as in the chicken, and the last cervical vertebra is fused with the dorsal spines of the thoracic vertebrae. The lateral neck region is similar to that of the chicken but, because the cervical patagium may contain so much fat, this web of skin may be a thick pad between lateral neck and shoulder as shown in figure 32.

The ventral neck region is divided into anterior and posterior parts as in the chicken. In the posterior part a beard—a tuft of stiff keratinous filaments—projects downward from the midventral area. The filaments are implanted in an elevated oval of skin laterally compressed and free from feathers. We followed the "American Standard of Perfection" (1938–40), Marsden and Martin (1949), and Schorger (1957) in use of the term "beard" (*barba*). Bulliard (1926) referred to it as a brush.

The dewlap—wattle or throat wattle (*palear*)—is usually small in the wild *Meleagris gallopavo* but is well developed in the domestic Bronze Turkey. It begins in the interramal region, extends along the midline of the submalar region, and continues on the anterior ventral neck to near the caudal end of the carunculate area.

Common Coturnix

This species of laboratory bird has a shorter neck relatively than the chicken or turkey (figs. 33 to 35). The neck does not arch backward as in the chicken before turning downward, and this gives to the neck but a single flexure (fig. 34). Even when the neck is strongly retracted over the body, the upper flexure has its greatest prominence at the base of the head rather than several vertebrae beyond. For these reasons, boundary lines between the anterior and posterior dorsal and the ventral neck regions have been omitted in this species. This same procedure was followed in the pigeon.

The cervical patagium (fig. 33) has some fat but not enough to give it a rounded character as in the domestic turkey. The regions and their boundaries are similar in other respects to those of the two galliforms already described.

White Pekin Duck

The flattened pontoon form of the duck modifies the shape of some regions. There is a definite double flexure of the long neck (fig. 37); thus it has anterior and posterior parts of the dorsal and ventral regions (figs. 36 to 38). The neck is slender, hence the dorsal, ventral, and lateral regions are narrow and have parallel boundaries. At the caudal end these boundaries diverge slightly.

Because of its large content of fat, the cervical patagium occupies the full width of the lateral cervical region at the base of the neck. This situation is similar to that in the turkey. The fat continues on to the dorsal surface of the shoulder, and this decreases the depth of the cervicoalar groove.

A transverse line across the dorsal surface of the neck at the level of the extreme forward end of the shoulder marks the arbitrary boundary of neck and trunk. The anatomical boundary is established by the junction of last cervical and first thoracic vertebrae. These are not fused in the duck as in the chicken and turkey, but innumerable ossified tendons lie along the sides of the neural spines and bridge the spaces, giving them rigidity. These spicules of bone make it difficult to palpate the spaces between spines, therefore the best reference point is the middle of the scapula. It is interesting to note that in commercial processing of ducklings, the neck is severed just in front of the last cervical rib—in other words, about one vertebra anterior to the anatomical boundary of neck and trunk. The interscapular region, which is the basal end of the dorsal neck, is approximately four and one-half vertebrae in length. Because of the semicircular shape of the fused clavicles in the duck the caudal boundary of the posterior ventral neck is rounded (fig. 38) instead of forming an angle as in the chicken.

Common Pigeon

In the pigeon, as in the Common Coturnix, the base of the head lies beneath the skull and nearly at right angles to its axis. The vertical portion of the neck approaches the head

---

FIGURE 28.—Left lateral view of a male Single Comb White Leghorn Chicken showing regions. Abbreviations: reg(s)., region(s); s., synonym.

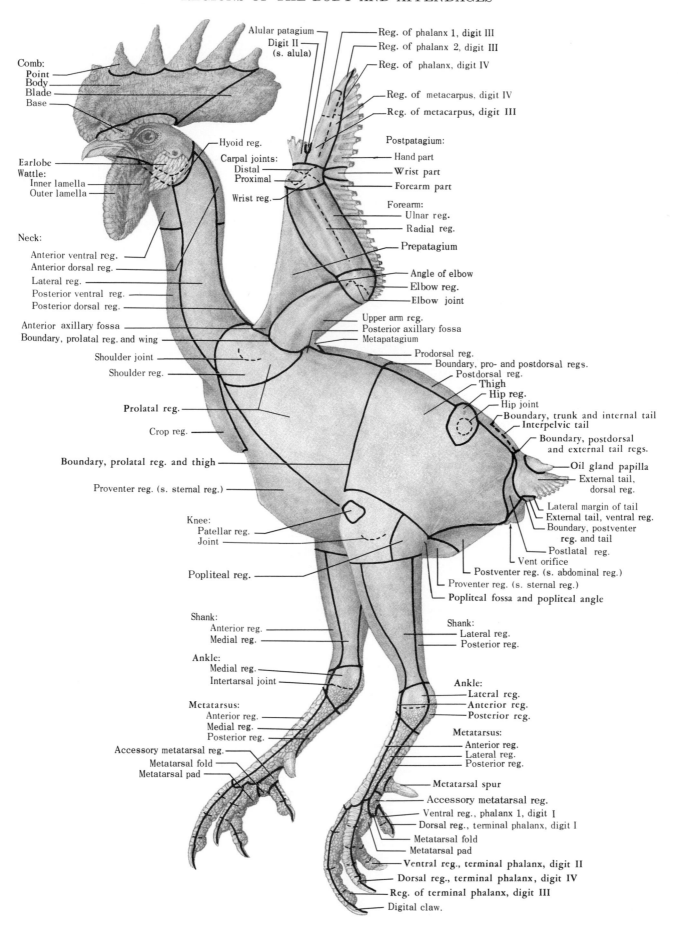

Comb:
Point
Body
Blade
Base

Alular patagium
Digit II (s. alula)

Reg. of phalanx 1, digit III
Reg. of phalanx 2, digit III
Reg. of phalanx, digit IV

Reg. of metacarpus, digit IV
Reg. of metacarpus, digit III

Hyoid reg.

Postpatagium:

Earlobe
Wattle:
Inner lamella
Outer lamella

Carpal joints:
Distal
Proximal
Wrist reg.

Hand part
Wrist part
Forearm part

Forearm:
Ulnar reg.
Radial reg.

Neck:
Anterior ventral reg.
Anterior dorsal reg.
Lateral reg.
Posterior ventral reg.
Posterior dorsal reg.
Anterior axillary fossa
Boundary, prolatal reg. and wing
Shoulder joint
Shoulder reg.

Prepatagium

Angle of elbow
Elbow reg.
Elbow joint

Upper arm reg.
Posterior axillary fossa
Metapatagium

Prodorsal reg.
Boundary, pro- and postdorsal regs.
Postdorsal reg.
Thigh
Hip reg.
Hip joint
Boundary, trunk and internal tail
Interpelvic tail
Boundary, postdorsal and external tail regs.

Prolatal reg.

Crop reg.

Boundary, prolatal reg. and thigh

Proventer reg. (s. sternal reg.)

Oil gland papilla
External tail, dorsal reg.

Lateral margin of tail
External tail, ventral reg.
Boundary, postventer reg. and tail

Knee:
Patellar reg.
Joint

Postlatal reg.
Vent orifice
Postventer reg. (s. abdominal reg.)
Proventer reg. (s. sternal reg.)
Popliteal fossa and popliteal angle

Popliteal reg.

Shank:
Anterior reg.
Medial reg.

Shank:
Lateral reg.
Posterior reg.

Ankle:
Medial reg.
Intertarsal joint

Ankle:
Lateral reg.
Anterior reg.
Posterior reg.

Metatarsus:
Anterior reg.
Medial reg.
Posterior reg.

Metatarsus:
Anterior reg.
Lateral reg.
Posterior reg.

Accessory metatarsal reg.
Metatarsal fold
Metatarsal pad

Metatarsal spur
Accessory metatarsal reg.
Ventral reg., phalanx 1, digit I
Dorsal reg., terminal phalanx, digit I
Metatarsal fold
Metatarsal pad
Ventral reg., terminal phalanx, digit II
Dorsal reg., terminal phalanx, digit IV
Reg. of terminal phalanx, digit III
Digital claw.

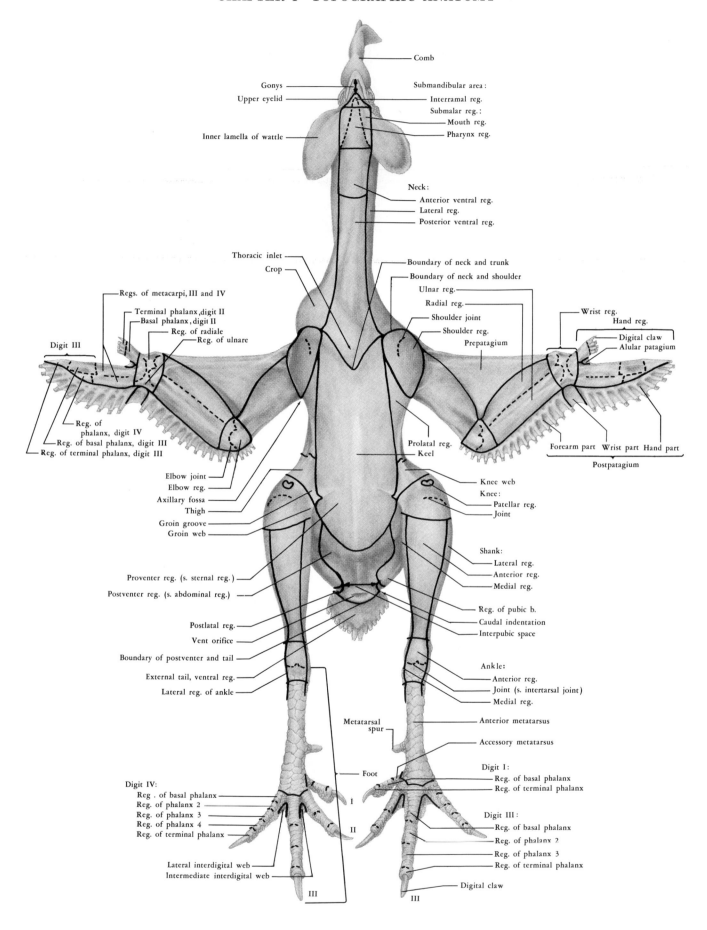

Comb

Gonys

Upper eyelid

Inner lamella of wattle

Submandibular area :
Interramal reg.
Submalar reg. :
Mouth reg.
Pharynx reg.

Neck :
Anterior ventral reg.
Lateral reg.
Posterior ventral reg.

Thoracic inlet
Crop

Boundary of neck and trunk
Boundary of neck and shoulder
Ulnar reg.
Radial reg.
Shoulder joint
Shoulder reg.
Prepatagium

Regs. of metacarpi, III and IV
Terminal phalanx, digit II
Basal phalanx, digit II
Reg. of radiale
Reg. of ulnare

Digit III

Wrist reg.
Hand reg.
Digital claw
Alular patagium

Reg. of
phalanx, digit IV
Reg. of basal phalanx, digit III
Reg. of terminal phalanx, digit III

Forearm part Wrist part Hand part
Postpatagium

Prolatal reg.
Keel

Elbow joint
Elbow reg.
Axillary fossa
Thigh
Groin groove
Groin web

Knee web
Knee :
Patellar reg.
Joint

Shank :
Lateral reg.
Anterior reg.
Medial reg.

Proventer reg. (s. sternal reg.)
Postventer reg. (s. abdominal reg.)

Reg. of pubic b.
Caudal indentation
Interpubic space

Postlatal reg.
Vent orifice
Boundary of postventer and tail
External tail, ventral reg.
Lateral reg. of ankle

Ankle :
Anterior reg.
Joint (s. intertarsal joint)
Medial reg.

Metatarsal
spur

Anterior metatarsus
Accessory metatarsus

Foot

Digit I :
Reg. of basal phalanx
Reg. of terminal phalanx

Digit IV :
Reg . of basal phalanx
Reg. of phalanx 2
Reg. of phalanx 3
Reg. of phalanx 4
Reg. of terminal phalanx

Digit III :
Reg. of basal phalanx
Reg. of phalanx 2
Reg. of phalanx 3
Reg. of terminal phalanx

Lateral interdigital web
Intermediate interdigital web

Digital claw

I

II

III

III

from below and does not make an S-shaped curve, although the rounded surface of the crown gives the impression of curvature to the upper neck. Therefore, the dorsal and ventral neck regions have not been subdivided into anterior and posterior parts. A small amount of fat is present in the cervical patagium, but it is minimal enough that the lateral boundaries of the dorsal region continue without interruption into the cervicoalar groove. This patagium is well shown in dorsal and ventral views (figs. 39 and 41). The boundaries of the four neck regions fit the same description that was applied to the birds described earlier, so need not be reiterated.

Trunk

The trunk (*truncus*), or body, of birds is built upon the same plan as that of mammals, namely, two major parts—thorax and abdomen. In their evolution from reptiles, however, birds did not attain the same degree of separation among the visceral organs as did the mammals. As a result, there can be no simple transverse plane in birds that will separate the thorax from the abdomen. For this reason, thorax and abdomen and, in addition, the pectoral and pelvic girdles are combined under one term, "trunk" (*truncus*).

The separation between appendages and body is partly arbitrary; the line of separation for the wing follows the angle between it and the body, whereas the boundary for the leg follows approximately the edge of the anterior and posterior thigh musculature.

There are four surfaces of the trunk of a bird—dorsal, ventral, right lateral, and left lateral. Each surface of the body has two parts—anterior and posterior. The authors considered the numerous names in the literature for the various parts of the avian trunk and concluded that there appeared to be no alternative than to introduce six new terms into the avian literature. These are short and self-evident:

Prodorsum	Postlatus (right and left)
Postdorsum	Proventer
Prolatus (right and left)	Postventer

These names do not exclude the use of synonyms when they are applicable, such as Coues' (1903:100) term "notaeum" described as follows:

> Beginning where the neck ends and ending where tail coverts begin . . . , this part of a bird is subdivided into *back* (Lat. *dorsum* . . .) and *rump* (Lat. *uropygium* . . .). These are in direct continuation of each other, and their limits are not precisely defined. . . . In general, we shall call the anterior two-thirds or three-fourths of notaeum 'back' and the rest 'rump'.

In reference to *Pteranodon*, a flying reptile, Eaton (1910) applied the term "notarium" to a group of eight vertebrae following the last cervical that were fused together by a supraneural plate and by paired osseous unions of the transverse processes. The term "dorsum" was applied to the vertebral members of the rib cage—all vertebrae caudal to the neck—except those of the tail and the bones of the pelvic girdle.

We have attempted to give exact criteria for the terms introduced here, based on the external shape of the deplumed bird and the use of underlying bones as palpable landmarks.

The term "dorsum" includes the surface of the back, beginning with the shoulder and ending with the caudal indentation (*incisura caudalis*), namely the constriction that marks the separation of body and tail. Dorsum, therefore, includes the interscapular neck and the interpelvic tail (fig. 27). The interscapular neck has already been defined as the caudal end of the neck beginning at the anterior end of the shoulders and ending at the last cervical vertebra, even when this vertebra is fused to the first thoracic vertebra.

It will be necessary to define the term "caudal vertebrae" before a definition can be given for the internal and external parts of the tail. These vertebrae lie immediately caudal to the sacrals. Some of them are fused with the ilia, but those beyond are free. Of the free group, some lie within the caudal boundary of the body; the others—those distal to the caudal indentation—lie beyond the trunk to form the tail proper. The authors arbitrarily name the first free vertebra that follows the synsacrum, the first coccygeal vertebra. The interpelvic tail (*cauda interpelvina*), or internal tail, is that area beyond the synsacrum but anterior to a line joining the tips of the iliocaudal spines. Laterally the internal tail is bounded by the ilia (figs. 25 and 27). The internal tail obviously is not an anatomical part of the caudal end of the trunk, just as the interscapular part of the neck is not part of the anterior end of the trunk. Of the birds we have examined, only the chicken has an internal tail. In most birds the internal tail is absent because the ilial bones end caudally at about the same level as the last synsacral vertebra.

The terminology is awkward, for under certain circumstances we may wish to refer to trunk and include the proximal neck and tail; in other circumstances, to exclude them. Rather than introduce new terms, it seems desirable to use the term "trunk" in the broad sense; when excluding neck and tail, then specifically to indicate that this is done. Fortunately, the problem arises only when dealing with the dorsal regions of the body. The lateral and ventral regions lie below the level of neck and tail and, therefore, are not involved.

Some variations occur in the shape of the body. In the chicken and in most birds, the body is laterally compressed. In the White Pekin Duck it is compressed dorsoventrally; in the Common Pigeon and domestic broad breasted turkey, it is approximately round in cross section.

The middorsal line (*linea mediana dorsalis*) of the trunk

FIGURE 29.—Ventral view of a male Single Comb White Leghorn Chicken showing regions. Abbreviations: b., bone; reg(s)., region(s); s., synonym.

is slightly humped at the junction between thoracic vertebrae and the anterior end of the ilial bones. In the American Woodcock (*Philohela minor*), the downward slope of the rump is about 10°, in the pigeon it is about 15°, and in the chicken and turkey about 20°. The curvature of the rump toward the external tail is variable; in the chicken and turkey it is nearly a flat plane, but in the Common Coturnix and Blue Jay (*Cyanocitta cristata*) it is clearly rounded.

Thus far, we have discussed the dorsum of the trunk (*dorsum trunci*) in general terms; the same type of discussion is needed for latus (*latus trunci*) and venter (*venter trunci*). The shoulder (*omus*) as seen in dorsal view is part of the wing, and as seen in ventral view it is part of the prolatal region (figs. 27 to 29). In these illustrations, the approximate location of the shoulder joint is shown by dashed lines, based on dissections and an examination of X-rays. For the placement of boundary lines around joints, the authors followed the rule that the enlargements of the head of bones participating in the joint should be included in the region. A comparison of figures 28 and 25 shows that the heads of the clavicle, coracoid, scapula, and humerus are included in the shoulder region. The situation here, in which the shoulder is part of the prolatal region (*regio prolateralis*) and also part of the wing, is similar to that of the hyoid region, which is part of the submalar and part of the lateral neck regions.

The thigh is not included as part of the postlatal region (*regio postlateralis*). This part of the leg covers most of the postlatal region except for a small area between the caudal border of the thigh and the tail. Included in the thigh are the hip region and hip joint. Boundaries for the thigh and postlatal region will be discussed under each species studied.

The ventral side of the trunk is divided into anterior and posterior parts. The proventer includes much of the clavicle and all of the sternum. The transverse boundary between proventer and postventer is determined by the caudal margin of the sternum. Because the sternum is large in chicken, turkey, and Common Coturnix, the abdomen is small. More details of these regions and boundaries will be given under the description of the chicken and other species.

When the legs (*membra posteriora*) are pulled backwards, the covering of skin is usually thrown up into folds or webs (*telae genus*). Those in the knee region (*regio genus*) are transient folds that dissappear when the leg is moved to another position. Webs, or folds, may not be important anatomical structures, but they have to be taken into account because they are often crossed by region boundaries. See page 63 for a further discussion of web and patagia.

The midventral line (*linea mediana ventralis*) of the trunk extends from the notch of the clavicles, at the hypocleidium, posteroventrally to the carinal apex, thence along the edge of the keel to its midcaudal point on the sternum, and then along the soft tissues of the abdomen across the vent by its

midsagittal plane to the base of the external tail (figs. 25 and 29).

The boundaries of the anterior and posterior halves of the back will be described first, including the interscapular neck and interpelvic tail; then the anterior and posterior boundaries will be redefined to exclude these two parts of the body. The Single Comb White Leghorn Chicken will be described, and this will be followed by a brief statement on how the other bird species studied differ from the chicken.

Chicken

The prodorsum extends from the anterior margins of the shoulders to the anterior ends of the ilial bones. At the shoulder the lateral boundary follows the cervicoalar groove (fig. 27); it extends from here along the line of attachment of metapatagium to the body, and thence directly toward the space between the trochanter of the femur (fig. 25) and the lateral crest of the ilium. The prodorsum includes the vertebral columns in the interscapular neck and thorax, the dorsal parts of the vertebral ribs, and most of the scapulae. The common transverse boundary between prodorsum and postdorsum is identified by the anterior end of the ilial bones (fig. 25). Each lateral boundary of the prodorsum is palpable as a slight depression between the m. *sartorius* and the m. *latissimus dorsi posterior* (fig. 26). The tip of the last uncinate process locates the point where the transverse boundary intersects the lateral boundary. The anatomical anterior boundary of the prodorsum is a transverse plane between the last cervical and first thoracic vertebrae; it meets the right and left lateral boundaries in the cervicoalar groove (fig. 27).

The postdorsum, or rump, includes the remainder of the back, namely, the entire dorsal plate; the lumbar, sacral, and caudal vertebrae of the synsacrum; and the interpelvic part of the tail. Its anterior boundary is the same as the caudal boundary of the prodorsum, which has already been described. The lateral boundary of the postdorsum is a caudal continuation of the lateral boundary of the prodorsum; it follows the dorsal margin of the hip region and continues along the lateral edge of the ilium to the iliocaudal spine (figs. 25, 27, and 28). The posterior boundary of the postdorsum is a transverse line that joins the right and left iliocaudal spines.

In a strict anatomical sense, the postdorsum has the same anterior and lateral boundaries already described, but the posterior boundary is different. From the iliocaudal spines this anatomical boundary extends forward along the iliococcygeal grooves to the space between last sacral and first coccygeal vertebrae as shown by dashed lines in figure 27.

The right and left sides of the trunk, namely the lata, extend from the anterior face of the breast to the caudal indentation (fig. 28). The continuity of each latus is interrupted by the thigh, flattened against the body. The prolata

→

FIGURE 30.—Dorsal view of a Bronze Turkey showing regions. Abbreviations: reg(s)., region(s); s., synonym.

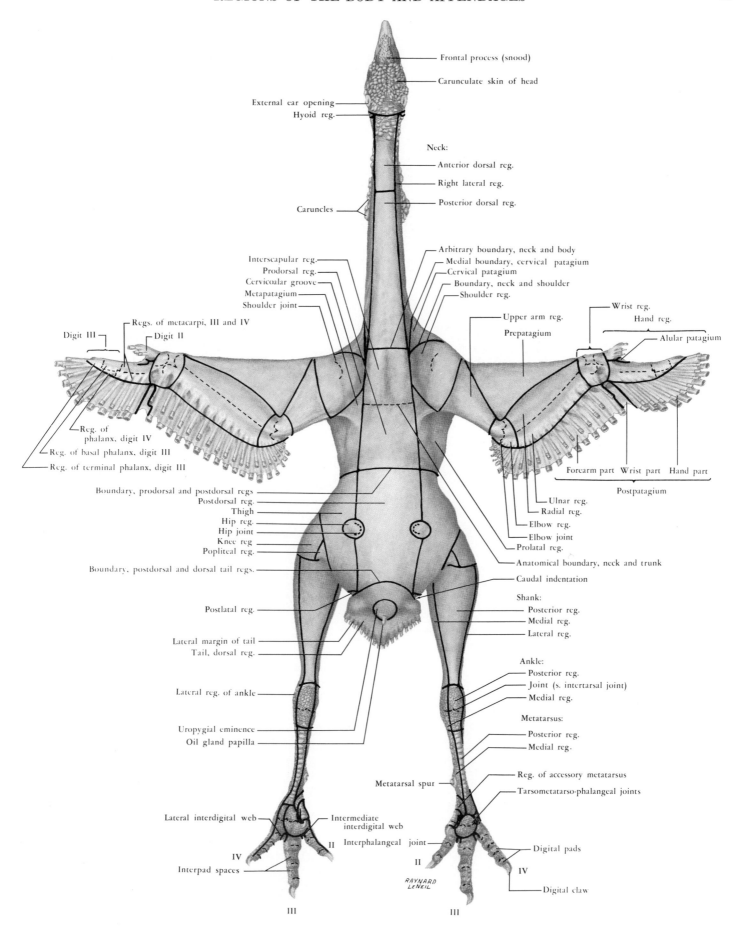

Frontal process (snood)

Carunculate skin of head

External ear opening

Hyoid reg.

Neck:

Anterior dorsal reg.

Right lateral reg.

Caruncles

Posterior dorsal reg.

Interscapular reg.

Prodorsal reg.

Cervicoalar groove

Metapatagium

Shoulder joint

Arbitrary boundary, neck and body

Medial boundary, cervical patagium

Cervical patagium

Boundary, neck and shoulder

Shoulder reg.

Wrist reg.

Hand reg.

Upper arm reg.

Prepatagium

Alular patagium

Regs. of metacarpi, III and IV

Digit III

Digit II

Reg. of
phalanx, digit IV

Reg. of basal phalanx, digit III

Reg. of terminal phalanx, digit III

Forearm part   Wrist part   Hand part

Postpatagium

Boundary, prodorsal and postdorsal regs.

Postdorsal reg.

Thigh

Hip reg.

Hip joint

Knee reg.

Popliteal reg.

Boundary, postdorsal and dorsal tail regs.

Postlatal reg.

Lateral margin of tail

Tail, dorsal reg.

Lateral reg. of ankle

Uropygial eminence

Oil gland papilla

Ulnar reg.

Radial reg.

Elbow reg.

Elbow joint

Prolatal reg.

Anatomical boundary, neck and trunk

Caudal indentation

Shank:

Posterior reg.

Medial reg.

Lateral reg.

Ankle:

Posterior reg.

Joint (s. intertarsal joint)

Medial reg.

Metatarsus:

Posterior reg.

Medial reg.

Metatarsal spur

Reg. of accessory metatarsus

Tarsometatarso-phalangeal joints

Lateral interdigital web

Intermediate
interdigital web

II

Interphalangeal joint

Digital pads

IV

Interpad spaces

II

IV

Digital claw

RAYNARD
LeNEIL

III

III

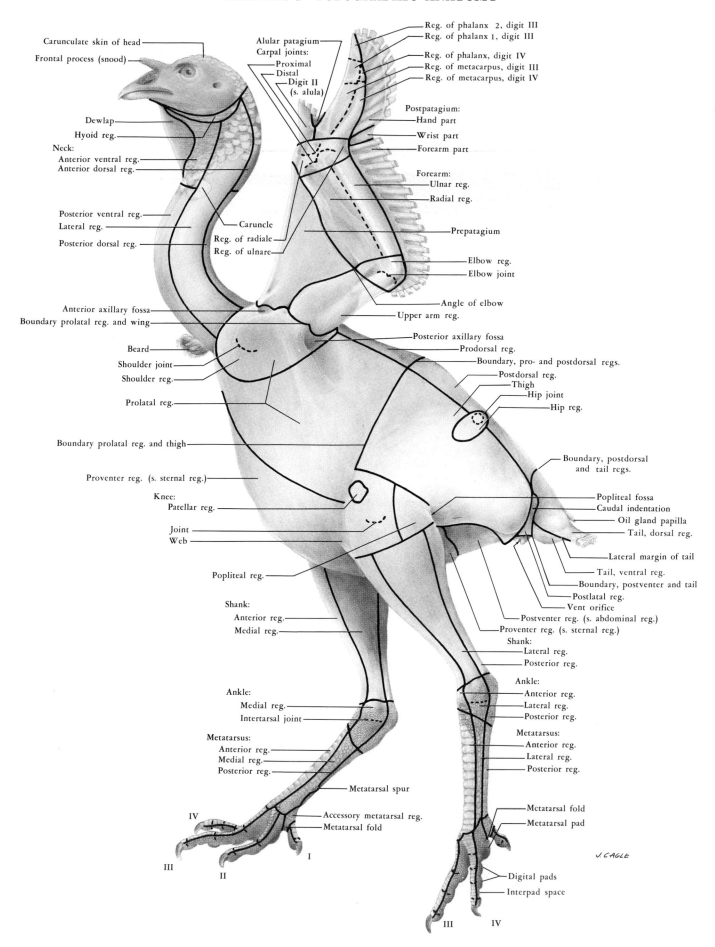

Carunculate skin of head

Frontal process (snood)

Dewlap

Hyoid reg.

Neck:
Anterior ventral reg.
Anterior dorsal reg.

Posterior ventral reg.
Lateral reg.
Posterior dorsal reg.

Anterior axillary fossa
Boundary prolatal reg. and wing

Beard
Shoulder joint
Shoulder reg.

Prolatal reg.

Boundary prolatal reg. and thigh

Proventer reg. (s. sternal reg.)

Knee:
Patellar reg.

Joint
Web

Popliteal reg.

Shank:
Anterior reg.
Medial reg.

Ankle:
Medial reg.
Intertarsal joint

Metatarsus:
Anterior reg.
Medial reg.
Posterior reg.

IV

III

II

I

Alular patagium
Carpal joints:
Proximal
Distal
Digit II
(s. alula)

Caruncle
Reg. of radiale
Reg. of ulnare

Reg. of phalanx 2, digit III
Reg. of phalanx 1, digit III
Reg. of phalanx, digit IV
Reg. of metacarpus, digit III
Reg. of metacarpus, digit IV

Postpatagium:
Hand part
Wrist part
Forearm part

Forearm:
Ulnar reg.
Radial reg.

Prepatagium

Elbow reg.
Elbow joint

Angle of elbow
Upper arm reg.

Posterior axillary fossa
Prodorsal reg.
Boundary, pro- and postdorsal regs.
Postdorsal reg.
Thigh
Hip joint
Hip reg.

Boundary, postdorsal
and tail regs.

Popliteal fossa
Caudal indentation
Oil gland papilla
Tail, dorsal reg.

Lateral margin of tail
Tail, ventral reg.
Boundary, postventer and tail
Postlatal reg.
Vent orifice
Postventer reg. (s. abdominal reg.)
Proventer reg. (s. sternal reg.)
Shank:
Lateral reg.
Posterior reg.

Ankle:
Anterior reg.
Lateral reg.
Posterior reg.

Metatarsus:
Anterior reg.
Lateral reg.
Posterior reg.

Metatarsal spur

Accessory metatarsal reg.
Metatarsal fold

Metatarsal fold
Metatarsal pad

Digital pads
Interpad space

J. CAGLE

III   IV

are fully exposed when the wings are extended but are partly covered when the wings are folded. Each prolatus has four boundaries—dorsal, ventral, anterior, and posterior. The base of the wing is inserted between the anterior part of the prodorsum and prolatus; thus in the wing region, no common boundary exists between these two adjacent areas.

The dorsal boundary of the prolatus begins at the groove between the ventral side of the wing and the body. On the skeleton this boundary falls at about the labeling line for the bicipital crest (fig. 25). The boundary continues along the line of attachment of prepatagium to the shoulder and to the groove between the brachial and pectoralis muscles.[11] It follows the groove formed by the junction of metapatagium to the body; the remainder of the dorsal boundary for the prolatus is shared in common with the lateral boundary of the prodorsum, and it terminates at the anterior edge of the sartorius muscle.

The ventral boundary of the prolatus begins anteriorly one-third of the distance ventrally from the head of the clavicle, and it extends downward as a curved line toward the groin groove (fossa inguinala) where it intersects the caudal boundary (figs. 28 and 29). The placement of this line is in part arbitrary, yet it does approximate the lateral edge of the sternal plate (fig. 25). The anterior boundary of the prolatus is the curved line that marks the junction of neck and trunk. The prolatus includes the shoulder region, and they both share the same anterior boundary.

The definitions for the caudal boundary of the prolatus and for most of the boundaries of the postlatus and postventer depend upon a fixed position of the hind limb. The position chosen is that of the limb fully extended with the limb axis at right angles to the body axis. The caudal boundary of the prolatus is a transverse plane at the cephalic end of the ilium. The boundary follows the anterior margin of the sartorius muscle across the knee web to the groin groove where it intersects the ventral boundary. In summary, the prolatus includes part of the shoulder and most of the rib cage located below the scapula and in front of the sartorius muscle, the upper parts of clavicle and coracoid bones, and the upper parts of the pectoral and supracoracoid muscles.

The postlatus is covered almost entirely by the flattened musculature of the thigh; only a small triangular area, as labeled in figure 28, is visible without removal of the thigh. In order to differentiate between postlatus and thigh it is

necessary to describe the latter. The thigh includes the hip region. The dorsal boundary of the thigh is the same as the lateral boundary of the postdorsum; the anterior boundary is the same as the caudal boundary of the prolatus; and the ventral boundary is an arbitrary line that separates the thigh and knee regions. The caudal boundary begins dorsally as a continuation of the transverse line that separates the trunk and external tail and follows the caudal margin of pelvic girdle from iliocaudal spine to the tip of the pubis. From this point anteroventrally, the caudal boundary swings along the lower margin of the pubis and then along the caudal margin of the semimembranosus muscle to the popliteal region of the knee. The caudal margin of the thigh is important in establishing the extent of the postlatus and the postventer.

The ventral boundary of the postlatus follows the groin groove across the knee and the groin web (tela inguinala) of skin that is produced by pulling the leg caudally. It continues along the caudal margin of the thigh to the end of the pubis and thence to the caudal indentation (incisura caudalis), where it ends (figs. 28 and 29).

The posterior boundary of the postlatal region forms two sides of a triangle. One side extends from the tip of the pubis dorsally along the side of the cloacal lips to the ventral junction of body and tail (fig. 28); the other side begins at this junction and continues dorsally along the base of the caudal indentation until it unites with the caudal boundary of the thigh. Beneath the externally visible part of the postlatus lie such muscles as the m. levator cloacae, m. transversus perinei (m. transversus cloacae, Knight (1967)), m. piriformis pars caudifemoralis, and m. depressor caudae (fig. 26).

In summary, the total postlatus includes the caudal part of the rib cage, the lateral face of the pelvic girdle, and the internal ramus of the posterolateral sternal process; the external ramus lies approximately at the boundary between prolatus and postlatus. The triangular posterior end of the postlatus covers the anterior wall of the caudal indentation.

The venter extends from the thoracic inlet to the base of the external tail. The anterior and posterior parts of the back and side are of about equal size, but the proventer (sternum) is much longer than the postventer (abdomen). The lateral boundary of the venter has already been described; it is the same as the ventral boundary of the latus. The anterior boundary of the proventer is the anterior margin of the breast and follows the contour of the clavicle to its junction at the hypocleidium. This boundary is shared with the ventral neck and has already been described.

The proventer region overlies the sternum, parts of some sternal processes, and the muscles that have their origin on the keel, namely mm. pectoralis et supracoracoideus. The posterior boundary is an arch that crosses the lateral and medial parts of the posterolateral sternal process, crosses the lateral and medial sternal notches to the edges of the sternal

---

[11] The line separating wing and body can be described in another way. When the wing is forceably elevated, two distinct pits, or depressions, associated with the underlying musculature are produced (figs. 24, 26, and 28). We named these depressions "anterior and posterior axillary fossae" (fossa axillaris anterior et fossa axillaris posterior). The separation of wing and body begins anteriorly as a line that crosses m. propatagialis longus et brevis. This line then curves into the anterior axillary fossa, crosses the pectoral muscle near its insertion, dips into the contour of the posterior axillary fossa, and follows the junction line between metapatagium and body.

←

FIGURE 31.—Left lateral view of a male Bronze Turkey showing regions. Abbreviations: reg(s)., region(s); s., synonym.

plate, and follows this to the caudal tip of the sternum (figs. 25 and 29). In the chicken the posterior boundary is strongly bowed because the sternum is pointed, but in the White Pekin Duck, which has a truncate sternum, the posterior boundary more nearly crosses the body at right angles to the body axis (fig. 38).

The postventer region or abdominal region is an irregular-shaped space that is small in chickens but large in some other birds. This region is soft and has no underlying bones except the tips of the pubic bones that project into this region. The lateral and anterior boundaries of the postventer region have been described. The posterior boundary is a slightly curved line that follows the angle between the dorsal lip of the cloaca and the ventral surface of the tail. This boundary at each end joins a lateral boundary of the abdomen.

Turkey

Specimens of the turkey vary considerably in conformation. Some are poorly fleshed (fig. 30). As a result the dorsum is rather narrow, whereas in other specimens it is broad. This variation in no way modifies the boundaries for prodorsum and postdorsum nor the location of arbitrary and antomical boundaries between neck and trunk. The turkey has but a single boundary between trunk and tail, because pelvic bones in turkey are shaped differently from those in the chicken. In the turkey the iliocaudal spine lies so near the same level as the junction between caudal and coccygeal vertebrae that practically all of the tail is external to the pelvis. As in the chicken, the hip region is included in the thigh. The caudal indentation is deep in the turkey. The cervicoalar groove is shallow in a turkey that has a large amount of fat in the cervical patagium, and the iliococcygeal groove is usually nonexistent.

The latus of the turkey, as in the chicken, is broad in the middle of the body and narrow at both ends. The axillary fossae of the turkey are deep and more distinct than in other birds examined (fig. 31). The thigh and postlatus are similar to those of the chicken.

The proventer of the turkey is broad, usually much more so than shown in figure 32. The postventer has an anterior part between sternum and interpubic space and a posterior part around the lips of the cloaca. The reference points are similar to those of the chicken except that the pubic bones are more robust. In the male these bones curve medially in front of the vent with the result that the area of the vent seems to be partially separated from the adjacent portion of the postventer. The width of the postlateral region and of the caudal indentation is variable in both the turkey and chicken.

Common Coturnix

The prodorsum of the quail has the same landmarks and pattern as it does in the chicken, except at the caudal end. Here the structure differs because there is no caudal indentation; the external tail lies within the contours of what is generally considered to be trunk, and behind the tail is a protruding cloacal eminence (figs. 33 and 34). The Common Coturnix has only one separation between postdorsum and tail, which is a compromise between an "anatomical" and an "arbitrary" boundary, but actually the two lie close together. This compromise separation is related to the fact that the caudal end of the ilial bones is shaped differently in the quail than in the chicken. In the chicken the pelvic girdle diverges toward the iliocaudal spines, leaving a space between the interpelvic vertebrae and the medial margins of the ilial bones. In the quail no such space exists and the iliocaudal spines rest against the transverse processes of the second coccygeal vertebra. In the chicken the caudal margin of the lateral plate of the girdle is nearly vertical (fig. 25), but in the quail it slopes backward at about a 45° angle, terminating at the ischiatic process.

The latus and its division into prolatal and postlatal regions in the quail are the same as those already described for the chicken, except that in the quail the caudal boundary for the narrow triangular portion of the postlatus behind the thigh is placed arbitrarily in figure 34 because there is no caudal indentation to serve as a landmark.

The venter boundaries of the quail have the same landmarks as those named in the chicken; the chief difference is that the external tail is absent in the quail so that the dorsal lip of the vent (*labium dorsalis cloacae*) is almost the most caudal structure of the ventral surface (fig. 35). The remiges of the tail are actually placed in nearly the same plane as the vent (fig. 34).

White Pekin Duck

The body surfaces and regional boundaries of the duck follow the reference points described for the chicken, but there is need for supplementary remarks on the skeletal system and its effect on these reference points.

Both the Mallard and the White Pekin Duck have seven ribs that articulate with the lateral edge of the sternum. There are no floating ribs caudal to these. The terminal three of this series lie beneath the anterior end of the ilium and articulate with the transverse processes of the vertebrae in this region.

The interscapular region is either a trapezoid (fig. 36) or is approximately square. The boundaries for this region have been described under the heading "Neck" (p. 38). The lateral boundaries of the prodorsum follow the metapatagium and trunk and then curve in the direction of the hip joint. The common dorsal boundary of prodorsum and postdorsum is more curved in the duck than in the other birds studied because the ilium in the median line extends farther forward than the anterior border of the anterior margin of the sarto-

---

→

FIGURE 32.—Ventral view of a male Bronze Turkey showing regions. Abbreviations: b., bone; reg(s)., region(s); s., synonym.

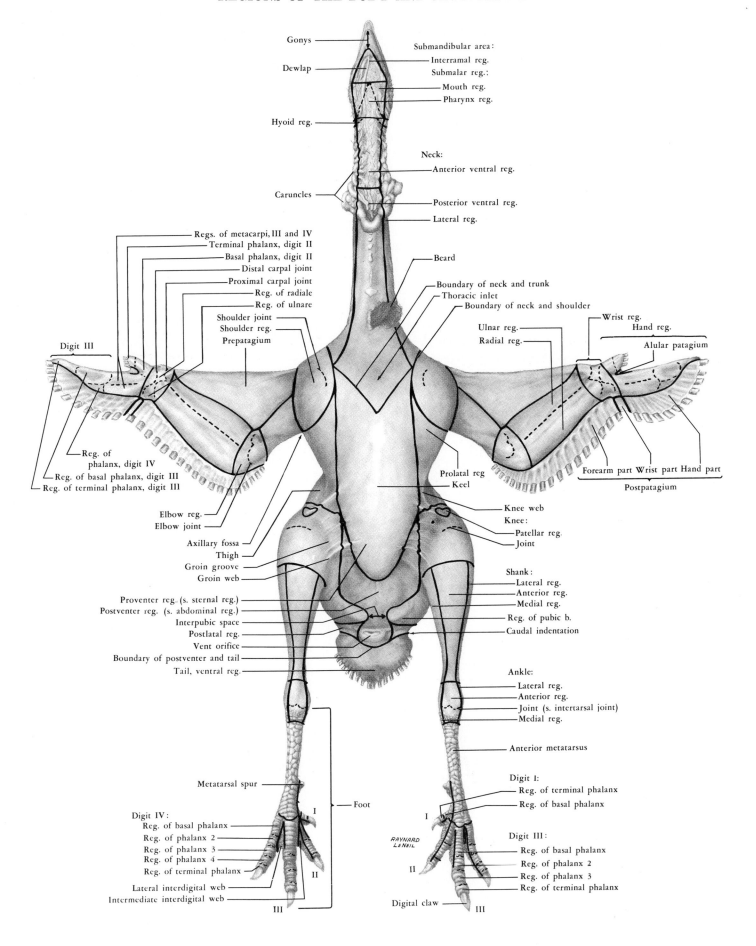

Gonys

Dewlap

Hyoid reg.

Caruncles

Submandibular area:
Interramal reg.
Submalar reg.:
Mouth reg.
Pharynx reg.

Neck:
Anterior ventral reg.

Posterior ventral reg.

Lateral reg.

Beard

Regs. of metacarpi, III and IV
Terminal phalanx, digit II
Basal phalanx, digit II
Distal carpal joint
Proximal carpal joint
Reg. of radiale
Reg. of ulnare
Shoulder joint
Shoulder reg.
Prepatagium

Boundary of neck and trunk
Thoracic inlet
Boundary of neck and shoulder

Ulnar reg.
Radial reg.

Wrist reg.
Hand reg.

Alular patagium

Digit III

Reg. of
phalanx, digit IV
Reg. of basal phalanx, digit III
Reg. of terminal phalanx, digit III

Forearm part Wrist part Hand part

Postpatagium

Elbow reg.
Elbow joint

Axillary fossa
Thigh
Groin groove
Groin web

Proventer reg. (s. sternal reg.)
Postventer reg. (s. abdominal reg.)
Interpubic space
Postlatal reg.
Vent orifice
Boundary of postventer and tail
Tail, ventral reg.

Prolatal reg
Keel

Knee web
Knee:
Patellar reg.
Joint

Shank:
Lateral reg.
Anterior reg.
Medial reg.
Reg. of pubic b.
Caudal indentation

Ankle:
Lateral reg.
Anterior reg.
Joint (s. intertarsal joint)
Medial reg.

Anterior metatarsus

Metatarsal spur

Foot

I

Digit I:
Reg. of terminal phalanx
Reg. of basal phalanx

Digit IV:
Reg. of basal phalanx
Reg. of phalanx 2
Reg. of phalanx 3
Reg. of phalanx 4
Reg. of terminal phalanx
Lateral interdigital web
Intermediate interdigital web

I

II

III

RAYNARD
LENEIL

Digit III:
Reg. of basal phalanx
Reg. of phalanx 2
Reg. of phalanx 3
Reg. of terminal phalanx

Digital claw

III

rius muscle, and these reference points (anterior margin of ilium and anterior margin of sartorius muscle) determine the placement of boundary between the prodorsum and postdorsum and the prolatus and thigh, respectively. The

postdorsum is narrow, which fact is in harmony with the narrow pelvic girdle.

Only a single transverse caudal boundary is shown for the duck in figure 36. As in other domestic birds except the

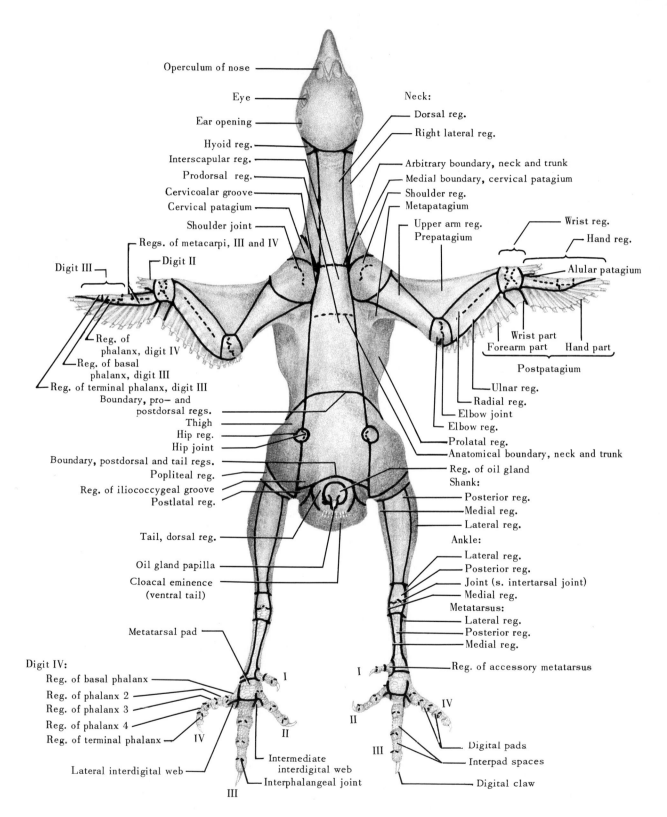

Operculum of nose

Eye

Ear opening

Hyoid reg.

Interscapular reg.

Prodorsal reg.

Cervicoalar groove

Cervical patagium

Shoulder joint

Regs. of metacarpi, III and IV

Digit II

Digit III

Reg. of phalanx, digit IV

Reg. of basal phalanx, digit III

Reg. of terminal phalanx, digit III

Boundary, pro— and postdorsal regs.

Thigh

Hip reg.

Hip joint

Boundary, postdorsal and tail regs.

Popliteal reg.

Reg. of iliococcygeal groove

Postlatal reg.

Tail, dorsal reg.

Oil gland papilla

Cloacal eminence (ventral tail)

Metatarsal pad

Digit IV:

Reg. of basal phalanx

Reg. of phalanx 2

Reg. of phalanx 3

Reg. of phalanx 4

Reg. of terminal phalanx

IV

Lateral interdigital web

III

I

II

Intermediate interdigital web

Interphalangeal joint

Neck:

Dorsal reg.

Right lateral reg.

Arbitrary boundary, neck and trunk

Medial boundary, cervical patagium

Shoulder reg.

Metapatagium

Upper arm reg.

Prepatagium

Wrist reg.

Hand reg.

Alular patagium

Wrist part

Forearm part   Hand part

Postpatagium

Ulnar reg.

Radial reg.

Elbow joint

Elbow reg.

Prolatal reg.

Anatomical boundary, neck and trunk

Reg. of oil gland

Shank:

Posterior reg.

Medial reg.

Lateral reg.

Ankle:

Lateral reg.

Posterior reg.

Joint (s. intertarsal joint)

Medial reg.

Metatarsus:

Lateral reg.

Posterior reg.

Medial reg.

Reg. of accessory metatarsus

I

IV

II

III

Digital pads

Interpad spaces

Digital claw

FIGURE 33.—Dorsal view of a male Common Coturnix showing regions. Abbreviations: reg(s)., region(s); s., synonym.

chicken, this boundary serves as both an "anatomical" and an "arbitrary" separation. As in the quail, the iliocaudal spine in the duck lies opposite the second coccygeal vertebra. This vertebra and the first coccygeal vertebra are fused to the ilia in the full grown Mallard; in the young White Pekin Duck, however, they are separated by a distinct space, and the iliocaudal spines lie opposite the third coccygeal vertebra. The caudal end of the lateral plate of the fused ilium and ischium spreads laterally about 45°, and all of it lies in a transverse plane, to give the pelvic girdle a truncate caudal end.

The broad proventer of the duck (fig. 38) gives the impression that the shoulder, as seen from the ventral side, is located differently than in other birds, but basically the location is the same. The impression of difference is due to the fact that the boundary between proventer and prolatus arises from the middle of the shoulder region (figs. 37 and 38) rather than from its medial margin (as it does in the chicken, figs. 28 and 29). The relationship of shoulder to wing and prolatus in the duck is the same as in other birds, namely, the dorsal surface of the shoulder region is part of the wing, whereas the ventral surface is part of the prolatus. Because of the broad expanse of the proventer, the width of the prolatus is restricted. The area, therefore, differs from that found in other birds examined where the shoulder region is broader (dorsoventrally) than the interior end of the prolatus (fig. 37).

The lateral boundary of the proventer (the ventral boundary of the prolatus) is placed so that it has the same relationship to the sternum and to other underlying osseous structures as it has in other birds.

The postlatal region is larger in the duck than in any of the other birds studied here. Its anterior boundary coincides with the pubic bone; the ventroposterior boundary curves caudally and ends at the lateral margin of the tail and is part of the line directed toward the side of the tail (fig. 37).

The truncate character of the caudal end of the sternum establishes the boundary common to proventer and postventer as a straight transverse line (fig. 38). The lateral boundaries of the proventers and postventers follow along the groin grooves and curve medially to the tip of the pubic bone, then around the end of the bone and upward to the lateral margin of the tail. Here a transverse line follows the groove between ventral tail and cloacal opening and establishes the caudal boundary of the postventer. The lips of the cloaca lie within a much larger area than in other kinds of birds studied.

Common Pigeon

The placement of regional boundaries for the pigeon follows closely in most respects that described for the chicken, except only one boundary is between the trunk and tail instead of two. The interscapular region is narrow at the arbitrary boundary of neck and trunk and is broad at the anatomical boundary. In the Common Pigeon about four and one-half caudal cervical vertebrae occur within the interscapular region. The last one is free from the four fused thoracic vertebrae that follow, but the cleft between last cervical and first thoracic vertebrae is bridged by a delicate ossified tendon. As a consequence, one has to press hard downward with a fingernail to feel the separation.

The pigeon's back is broad. The synsacrum ends abruptly in a nearly straight transverse line that turns backward slightly to form the iliocaudal processes. Below the spine is a small notch, and the caudal margin of the ischium gradually swings downward to meet the pubis. All vertebrae of the synsacrum are strongly fused with the ilia with the result that the transition to coccygeal vertebrae is abrupt. The latter vertebrae have well-developed neural spines and tranverse processes, whereas the neural spines of the synsacral vertebrae are fused to form a low, smooth, median ridge; therefore, it is relatively easy to palpate the junction. Because the pelvis of the pigeon is not shaped to form an interpelvic space, there can be no internal or interpelvic tail.

The breast of the pigeon is broad, thus both the prolatus and proventer are wide (figs. 40 and 41). The postlatal region is irregular and occupies all of the anterior wall of the caudal indentation. The latter terminates in a rounded curve that follows the shape of the caudal margin of the sternum. The space of the postventer in front of the interpubic space (fig. 41) is large, and the area behind the pubic bones is occupied almost entirely by the lips of the cloaca as in the chicken.

Tail

The tail of the chicken is atypical compared to that of other birds described here. In the chicken the iliocaudal spine extends caudally along each side of the tail vertebrae for a considerable distance and is separated from the vertebrae by an interpelvic space. The tail, enclosed within the space, has been named interpelvic, or internal tail, and may be considered as part of the trunk. The tail beyond the iliocaudal spine is named external tail. In the general discussion the authors pointed out that this was an arbitrary division of parts; however, of the species discussed here the division is applicable only to the chicken. In the turkey, Common Coturnix, the duck, and especially in the pigeon the internal tail is either too small to be differentiated from an external tail, or it does not exist.

Chicken

Three coccygeal vertebrae form the internal tail of the chicken, and the remaining three vertebrae plus the pygostyle are associated with the external tail. The interpelvic tail has a dorsal surface only, but the external tail has both dorsal and ventral surfaces (figs. 27 to 29). The interpelvic tail has an anterior boundary that is a transverse plane separating the last synsacral caudal from the first coccygeal vertebrae. As already mentioned, the posterior boundary of the interpelvic tail is a transverse line that joins the right and left iliocaudal spines (fig. 25). The lateral boundaries extend along the lines made by the iliococcygeal grooves associated with the space between ilia and the transverse processes of the vertebrae.

The anterior boundary of the external tail has already been described. Each lateral boundary begins at the upper end of the groove of the caudal indentation and follows the lateral margin of the external tail to the caudal tip of the pygostyle. Along much of this margin are implanted the rectrices.

The dorsal part of the external tail includes the region of the oil gland and its papilla. The gland is a bilobed rounded organ that may cause a distinct elevation on the dorsal surface, the uropygial eminence. Each gland unit drains caudally by an excretory duct through the oil gland papilla and thence

opens at its caudal tip. The chicken and other kinds of birds used in this study have two excretory ducts in the papilla.

The ventral surface of the tail is not as large as the dorsal surface. The anterior boundary of the ventral surface is shared with the caudal boundary of the abdomen, dorsal to the cloaca. The dorsal and ventral surfaces share a common lateral boundary.

Turkey

The tail of the turkey has the tip of the iliocaudal spines

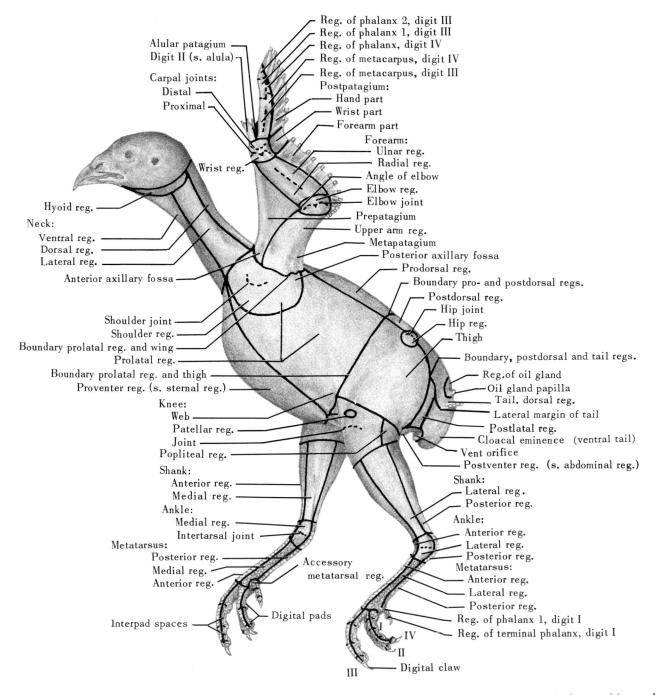

FIGURE 34.—Left lateral view of a male Common Coturnix showing regions. Abbreviations: mar., margin; reg(s)., region(s); s., synonym.

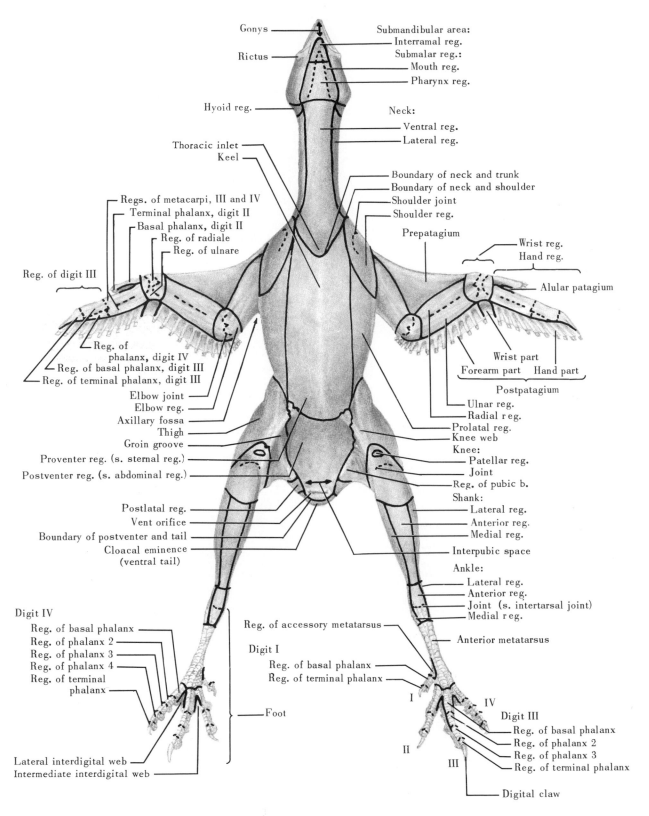

FIGURE 35.—Ventral view of a male Common Coturnix showing regions. Abbreviations: b., bone; reg(s)., region(s); s., synonym.

opposite the middle of the first coccygeal vertebra; therefore, the turkey cannot be assumed to have an interpelvic component of the tail. By drawing the line arching foward, as in figure 30, the entire external tail lies caudal to it. The place-ment of this line can easily be determined by palpation because the dorsal spines of the synsacral vertebrae are flat and broad; those of the coccygeal vertebrae are tall, narrow, and bifid.

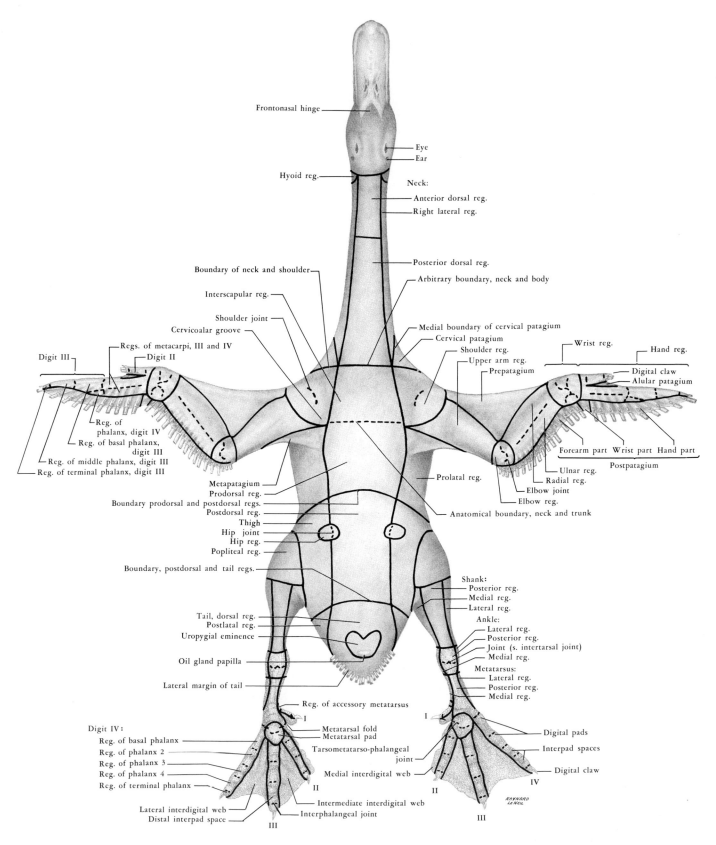

Frontonasal hinge

Eye
Ear

Hyoid reg.

Neck:
Anterior dorsal reg.
Right lateral reg.

Posterior dorsal reg.

Boundary of neck and shoulder
Arbitrary boundary, neck and body

Interscapular reg.

Medial boundary of cervical patagium
Cervical patagium
Shoulder reg.
Upper arm reg.
Prepatagium

Shoulder joint
Cervicoalar groove

Regs. of metacarpi, III and IV
Digit II

Wrist reg.
Hand reg.

Digit III

Digital claw
Alular patagium

Reg. of
phalanx, digit IV
Reg. of basal phalanx,
digit III
Reg. of middle phalanx, digit III
Reg. of terminal phalanx, digit III

Forearm part Wrist part Hand part
Postpatagium

Ulnar reg.
Radial reg.
Elbow joint
Elbow reg.

Metapatagium
Prodorsal reg.
Boundary prodorsal and postdorsal regs.
Postdorsal reg.
Thigh
Hip joint
Hip reg.
Popliteal reg.

Prolatal reg.

Anatomical boundary, neck and trunk

Boundary, postdorsal and tail regs.

Shank:
Posterior reg.
Medial reg.
Lateral reg.
Ankle:
Lateral reg.
Posterior reg.
Joint (s. intertarsal joint)
Medial reg.
Metatarsus:
Lateral reg.
Posterior reg.
Medial reg.

Tail, dorsal reg.
Postlatal reg.
Uropygial eminence

Oil gland papilla

Lateral margin of tail

Reg. of accessory metatarsus

Digit IV:
Reg. of basal phalanx
Reg. of phalanx 2
Reg. of phalanx 3
Reg. of phalanx 4
Reg. of terminal phalanx

I
Metatarsal fold
Metatarsal pad
Tarsometatarso-phalangeal
joint
Medial interdigital web

I
Digital pads

Interpad spaces

Digital claw

II

II

IV

Lateral interdigital web
Distal interpad space
III

Intermediate interdigital web
Interphalangeal joint

III

RAYNARD
LeNEIL

FIGURE 36.—Dorsal view of a White Pekin Duck showing regions. Abbreviations: reg(s)., region(s); s., synonym.

The caudal indentation is deep and broad in the turkey. The lateral processes of the coccygeal vertebrae are long, and laid over these are the caudal muscles of the tail. The lateral margin of the tail region begins in the middle of the caudal boundary of the postlatus, crosses the midlateral surface to the emergence of the last rectrix, and then crosses the open follicles of the rectrices, of which there are approximately 18 in the Bronze Turkey, to the tip of the pygostyle.

In the midline of the dorsal surface of the uropygial eminence is the erect muscular papilla of the oil gland. Lateral and slightly anterior to this, the small, underlying oil gland (fig. 390) slightly elevates the skin. Palpation is necessary to determine the full extent of the boundaries of the oil gland.

The ventral surface does not extend as far forward as the dorsal surface because the lips of the cloaca lie beneath some of the coccygeal vertebrae. Opposite the caudal indentation, caudal to the dorsal lip of the cloaca, is a deep depression. This pit and the groove formed by the dorsal lip mark the boundary that separates the postventer and ventral surface of the tail (fig. 32).

Common Coturnix

The tail region of the male coturnix differs from that in the chicken and turkey (figs. 33 to 35). There is a long caudal slope, half of which is the cloacal eminence. The dorsal surface of the tail is relatively small; it begins at the curved transverse line joining the iliocaudal spines as described on page 51 and continues to the rectrices, which project outward about half way down the caudal slope. The uropygial eminence is slight but with care can be palpated. The uropygial papilla lies at the caudal end of the eminence.

In the adult coturnix male there is no ventral surface as in other birds. This surface has been replaced by a protrusion of the dorsal lip of the cloaca and a gland that secretes material into the cloacal cavity, as previously discussed (page 48). Assignment of the cloacal eminence to the postventer brought us to the anomalous situation that part of the ventral surface can be seen looking down from above. However, this situation happens so rarely that it seems unnecessary to make any deviations of our reference points for coturnix. When the quail expells an egg, the open vent is the most caudal protrusion of the bird.

White Pekin Duck

The tail of the duck is a cone-shaped continuation of the trunk, without trace of caudal indentation (figs. 36 to 38). The tail of the duck appears to be relatively longer than the tail of the chicken because in the duck the caudal end of the synsacrum is truncate. Therefore, all free caudal vertebrae in the duck belong to a readily visible tail and are not subdivided into an internal and an external part of a tail as in the chicken. The smooth body contour is due to a pad of

thick fat at the posterior margin of the thigh. If the fat had been absent, this area of the thigh would have been occupied by a rather large caudal indentation. Because the tail of the duck is long, the postlatus beyond the thigh is larger than in other birds examined. The same is true of the postventer. This length is augmented by the fact that the sternum is not extended to a long pointed tip as in the chicken. The tips of the pubic bones indent the abdomen at about the middle of the postventer, relatively far anterior to the opening of the vent. Between the pubic bones and the vent is a large area that shares its lateral margin with the ventral margin of the large postlatal region. The ventral surface of the tail is a small triangle lying between the lateral margins and the caudal boundary of the postlatus, behind the lips of the cloaca.

The dorsal surface of the tail begins at the common boundary it shares with the postdorsum and broadens laterally, following the limits of the postlatus as far as the lateral margin of the tail (fig. 36). As in other birds, this margin in the duck is identified by the follicles of the rectrices. The apex of the lateral margin passes around the caudal tip of the pygostyle. The uropygial papilla of the duck has the shape of a flattened oval with its long axis placed transversely. The two lobes of the oil (uropygial) gland diverge anteriorly from the isthmus of the papilla (fig. 392); the outline of the glands can be determined by palpation. The glands are joined by an isthmus, but because this lies largely beneath the base of the papilla, the shape of the uropygial region in the duck differs from that in the chicken, turkey, and quail.

The ventral surface of the duck's tail is smaller than the dorsal surface (compare figs. 36 and 38). The anterior boundary of the ventral surface is a line arising in the groove that the dorsal lip of the cloaca makes with the ventral surface of the tail (figs. 37 and 38). As this boundary extends upward toward the lateral boundary of the tail, it shares a common boundary with the postlatal region for part of the distance.

Common Pigeon

The general appearance and shape of the tail of the pigeon are very similar to those of the turkey, even to the similarity in the wide angle between the right and left rows of rectrices, which is the extreme opposite from that in the duck (fig. 39). The pigeon has six rectrices in each half. The oil gland papilla is a broad cone that is little more than the caudal part of the uropygial eminence; most of the papilla does not elevate the skin (fig. 40). The oil gland is bilobed as in the duck, but the lobes are not spread so far apart. Each lobe is pointed at its anterior end as it runs lateral to a strong longitudinal tail muscle. The flatness of the oil gland and the fact that it lies in the plane of adjacent tail muscles make it practically impossible to palpate. The details of the ventral surface of the tail are similar enough to those of the turkey that they need not be redescribed (fig. 41).

Anterior Appendage

The wing (*ala*) is the avian form of the anterior appendage (*membrum anterius*) of the tetrapod plan. It has the parts of the forelimb of a quadruped, but these have become modified to serve primarily one function, namely, flight. In a few species of birds the wing has become specialized as a swimming organ, and in the young Hoatzin (*Opisthocomus hoazin*) it serves as a climbing organ. The wing may be long and slender or short and broad. It may be held outstretched and used primarily for gliding as in an albatross or it may beat

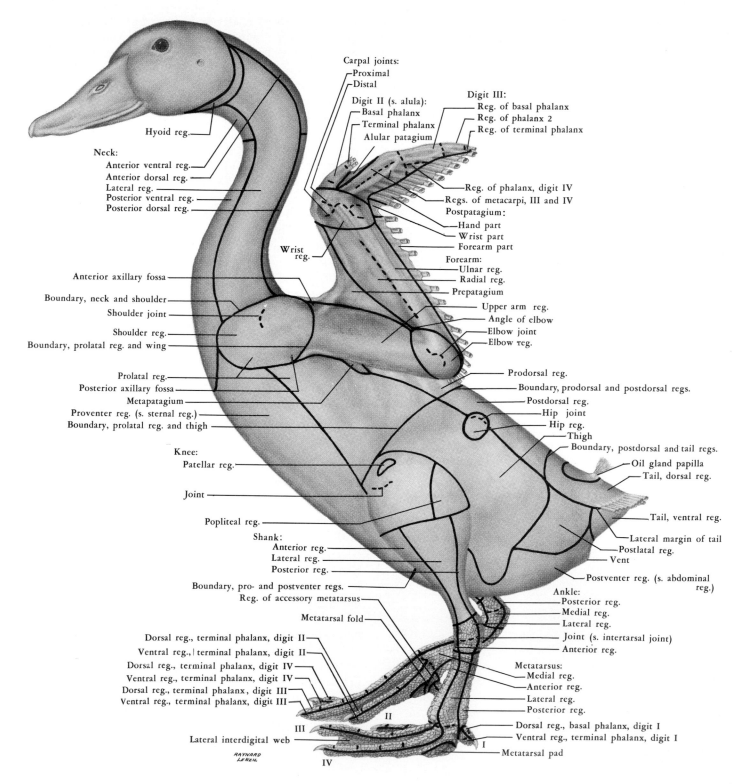

FIGURE 37.—Left lateral view of a White Pekin Duck showing regions. Abbreviations: mar., margin; reg(s)., region(s); s., synonym.

continuously as in a hummingbird. The wing has wide flexibility at the shoulder joint but only restricted movements at its other joints. Most of the bones of the wrist, as found in reptiles, have united with the metacarpals; only two movable bones remain in the joint.

The parts, surfaces, regions, and margins of the wing of the five kinds of birds considered here are similar in all points except size and proportions. These variables do not concern us at this time. Therefore, the following description, based primarily on the chicken, will apply to the remaining four domestic birds. A careful study of figures 27 to 41 will eliminate the need for extensive detailed description.

The placement of boundary lines for parts and regions of the wing and limb follows certain guidelines. The location of a joint is indicated in our illustrations by dashed lines, and some distance on each side of the joint are boundary lines for the region. These boundary lines enclose heads of the bones that enter into the joint. Most bones adjacent to a joint have enlargements to which ligaments and tendons are attached. The boundary lines are placed to enclose these enlargements. Dissections and the study of prepared skeletons and X-ray photographs made it possible to place these boundaries with fair accuracy.

Chicken and other species

In its extended position the wing has two surfaces—dorsal and ventral—and two edges—anterior and posterior. The anterior appendage of birds has the same component parts as the homologous structure in other vertebrates, namely, upper arm (*brachium*), forearm (*antebrachium*), and hand (*manus*). The hand is composed of wrist (*carpus*), metacarpus, and digits (*digiti manus*). However, the wrist and wrist region (*regio carpalis*) are often referred to separately from the hand and hand region. The base of the wing lies in a roughly fusiform space between the lateral edge of the prodorsum and the dorsal edge of the prolatus. These boundaries around the base of the wing are described on page 47.

Four patagia are usually present in the avian wing— prepatagium, metapatagium, postpatagium, and alular patagium. The cervical patagium, anterior to the shoulder in the angle between neck and shoulder, is not part of the wing. It belongs to the lateral neck (fig. 27).[12] The thin free edge of the prepatagium is directed anteriorly; the mediocaudal boundary is the anterior margin of the *m. biceps brachii;* and the distocaudal boundary is the forward edge of the *m. extensor metacarpi radialis* (fig. 26). These two boundaries intersect at the anterior angle of the elbow region.

The mediocaudal boundary crosses the *m. propatagialis longus et brevis, m. pectoralis propatagialis,* and *m. biceps propatagialis.*

The metapatagium has a triangular shape. Its free edge is directed caudally. Its medial margin joins the body and forms part of the separation between the back and side, namely between the prodorsum and prolatus. The edge attached to the wing does so along the caudal border of the *m. triceps humeralis.*

The postpatagium is a chevron-shaped skin web that lies caudal to forearm and hand, and it bears the primary and secondary remiges. It extends from the elbow to the tip of the longest finger. The patagium is narrow, forms a wide angle in the wrist region, and tapers to a point at the two ends. It is composed of three parts—forearm, wrist, and hand (*postpatagium partes antebrachialis, carpalis, et manualis*). The line of junction of postpatagium and forearm is the caudal margin of the *m. flexor carpi ulnaris* (fig. 26). The wrist part of the postpatagium lies posterior to the region of the wrist; in its junction with the hand, it follows the osseous tissues of the fourth metacarpus and the caudal edges of the fourth and third phalanges. In the carpal region are several small muscles—as the *m. ulnimetacarpalis dorsalis*—that serve to locate the junction of the wrist and postpatagium. In the hand region small muscles and bones of the third and fourth digits establish the junction between the hand and its postpatagium.

The alular patagium is a small web that lies between the *m. adductor indicis* (Hudson and Lanzillotti, 1955: 43) and the tendons to digit III. Its free edge is directed toward the tip of the wing (figs. 27 and 28).

The boundaries of the shoulder have already been described to some extent in establishing limits for prodorsum and prolatus, but as part of the wing it is necessary to review some of these points and the osseous structures involved. The shoulder includes the heads of the *clavicle, coracoid, scapula,* and *humerus;* the intervening spaces of the glenoid fossa and adjacent articulations; and the overlying musculature and integument. The upper portion of the shoulder joint—a deep notch between the acromion of the coracoid and the head of the humerus—is easily palpable.

The shoulder of a bird is large but has proved to be the most difficult part of the body for which to establish boundaries. The heavy musculature obscures osseous landmarks, but more than that, the boundaries on upper and lower surfaces do not lie opposite each other. In fact the plane that carries medial and lateral boundaries on the dorsal surface when the wings are extended lies almost at right angles to the plane on the under surface that carries the superior and inferior margins. The problem will be evident if the drawings of the three views are compared (figs. 27 to 29). This problem has been avoided in human anatomy by naming regions according to the underlying muscles and bones involved in the formation of the shoulder. In birds the axillary groove on the ventral side identifies the boundary between the base of the wing and the prolatus. When projected this line crosses the humerus at the distal edge of the deltoid crest.

---

[12] Several names have been used for these patagia of the wing and the one of the neck. Pycraft (1910:13) called the prepatagia and postpatagia, anterior and posterior patagian membranes. Lange (1931:443) referred to a prepatagialis muscle; Hudson and Lanzillotti (1964) designated the muscle as propatagialis; Thomson (1964) listed only the one term, propatagialis; Ede (1964:41) used prepatagium; and Wray (1887a:351 and 357) designated the postpatagium as *ala membrana.* The cervical patagium was referred to by Compton (1938) as the parapatagium. There has been general acceptance of the term "metapatagium."

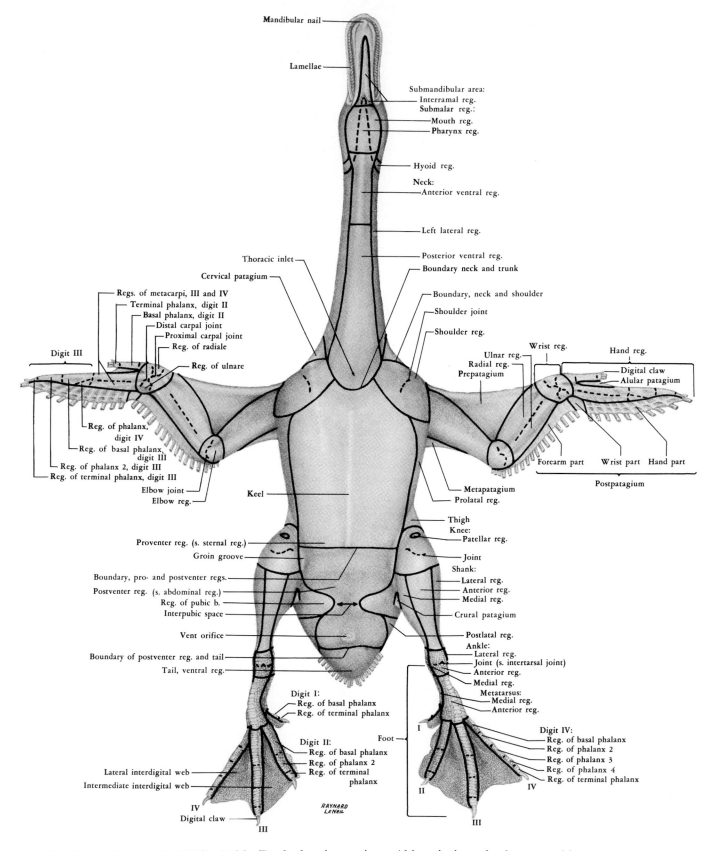

FIGURE 38.—Ventral view of a White Pekin Duck showing regions. Abbreviations: b., bone; reg(s)., region(s); s., synonym.

The line corresponds closely with the position of the equivalent boundary on the dorsal side of the wing; however, on the dorsal side it is slightly more distal. The shoulder has four boundaries in dorsal view (figs. 27, 30, 33, 36, and 39). One boundary follows the contour of the muscles that cross the anteromedial surface of the shoulder joint and separates cervical patagium from shoulder region; the second is the free edge of the shoulder; the third crosses the humerus; and the fourth is a common boundary with the interscapular region.

On the lateral wall, the shoulder region has three main boundaries (figs. 28, 31, 34, 37, and 40): (1) The line through the axillary fossae already described; (2) the anterior margin of the body that separates the neck and body; and (3) continuation of the anterior margin across the pectoral muscle and upward to the beginning of the metapatagium. This curved boundary of the shoulder may or may not touch the lateral boundary of the proventer. The shoulder joint lies near the center of the shoulder region and caudal to the articulation of clavicle and coracoid.

The elbow, or cubitus, includes the ectepicondyles and entepicondyles—protuberances on the distal end of the humerus (fig. 25)—and their processes; the heads of the ulna including the olecranon, the head of the radius; the elbow joint; and the overlying ligaments, muscles, tendons, and integument. The osseous structures mentioned are palpable, and the enlarged ends of the bones adjacent to the joint establish the location of the two converging lines that bound the triangular elbow region (figs. 27 to 41). The lines are farthest apart along the posterior margin of the elbow. On the dorsal and ventral sides of the wing, these lines converge to the angle of the elbow formed by the crossing of the anterior edges of the *mm. biceps brachii* and *extensor metacarpi radialis*.

The upper arm or brachium extends from the shoulder joint to the elbow joint, and thus it includes half of the shoulder region and half of the elbow region; it excludes the prepatagium and metapatagium. The upper arm region lies between the shoulder region and the elbow region. The entire dorsal surface of the humerus is palpable; much of the proximal part is covered by thin muscles, the distal part by integument only. The upper arm has dorsal and ventral surfaces; the anterior border of the upper arm is identified by the laterocaudal boundary of the prepatagium. The posterior boundary separates the metapatagium from the muscular part of the upper arm; the free margin of the forearm extends to the intercondylar space at the elbow. Sometimes it is convenient to refer to the posterior surface of the upper arm, especially when dissecting muscles of this area. It is impractical to attempt to establish boundary lines on the skin because it is difficult to define a posterior surface that in this case is clearly distinguishable from dorsal and ventral surfaces.

The forearm, or antebrachium, includes the area of the radius and ulna from their proximal ends at the elbow joint to their distal ends at the articulations with the radiale and ulnare. The forearm region is more restricted than the total forearm and lies between the elbow and wrist regions. The anterior boundary of the forearm is the anterior margin of forearm muscles; the posterior margin is the junction of forearm muscles. The forearm region has two surfaces—dorsal and ventral; each surface is rectangular in shape and is bisected longitudinally by dashed lines (figs. 27 to 41) into two nearly equal parts by a plane that passes dorsoventrally longitudinally between radius and ulna. The region of the radius (*regio radialis*) is the anterior half of the forearm, and that of the ulna (*regio ulnaris*) is the posterior half.

The wrist is relatively large, and its margins approximately form a four-sided figure when the wing is extended. The wrist region includes the enlarged distal ends of the radius and ulna; the anterior and posterior carpal bones; and the several proximal tuberosities of metacarpi II, III, and IV, all of which are palpable beneath the skin. The anterior margin of the wrist region is part of the leading edge of the wing. The posterior boundary is curved concentrically with the anterior margin and forms the carpal notch. It shares a common boundary with the postpatagium. One transverse boundary is just proximal to the enlarged ends of radius and ulna, and the other is just distal to the several palpable processes on the proximal end of the fused carpometacarpus,[13] II, III, and IV.

The hand, or manus, includes the wrist, the carpometacarpus, and the digits. It, therefore, has its proximal origin at the articulations of the anterior and posterior carpal bones with the radius and ulna. Because the wrist, or carpus, has already been described, description of the manus will be limited to the part distal to the wrist. The metacarpus is composed of three bones—II, III and IV—and their associated ligaments, tendons, muscles, and integument.[14] The term "metacarpus" is applied here to that part of the hand between wrist and digits and carpometacarpus to the underlying, supporting skeleton. At the proximal end, digits II, III, and IV in an adult chicken are fused into one osseous structure. At the opposite end, the metacarpi of III and IV are fused; II is short and scarcely extends beyond the region of the wrist. Dashed lines were used in figures 27 to 41 to show the regions encompassing these structures.

In the chicken, digits II and III each have two phalanges, and digit IV has one. The region of digit II extends from the metacarpophalangeal joint to the tip of the digital claw, and

---

[13] Carpometacarpus is written in the singular because the several bones of which it is composed are fused into one.

[14] The numbering of the digits on the avian manus has been presented by some as I, II, III and by others as II, III, IV. The latter sequence is generally supported by those who have studied the embryology of the wing, for example, Montagna (1945) and Holmgren (1955). Additional references on the subject are: Heilmann (1927) and Romanoff (1960).

it has dorsal and ventral surfaces. The proximal boundary follows the transverse line of the joint between metacarpus and basal phalanx, the anterior boundary is part of the leading edge of the wing, and the posterior boundary is the space between digits II and III. The distal half of the caudal edge has a free margin into which are inserted the alular remiges. Most of the terminal phalanx is a small conical bone that is covered by a straight or curved digital claw in the chicken, Common Coturnix, and White Pekin Duck. The claw is absent in the turkey and pigeon (Fisher, 1940).

The combined third and fourth metacarpal region at the skin surface corresponds in extent approximately to the underlying bones. The region is rectangular in shape (figs. 27 to 41); most of the landmarks are readily palpable, and in a bird with thin translucent skin they often are readily visible. Muscular tissue occupies the spindle-shaped space between metacarpus III and IV (figs. 25 and 26); in the illustration of the hand for the five species, dashed lines over this space mark the separation between the region of metacarpus III from metacarpus IV. The anterior margin of the metacarpus III region is the alular patagium and the leading edge of the wing; the posterior margin of metacarpus IV region is the caudal margin of the muscles of the hand. The calami of primary remiges protrude into this region.

A description of the region associated with each phalanx amounts to a reiteration of the bones of the hand. In the illustrations of the tips of the wings, the dashed lines locate the joints and the spaces between bones. Each region has a dorsal and a ventral surface and three or four boundaries. The number of regions depends on the number of phalanges

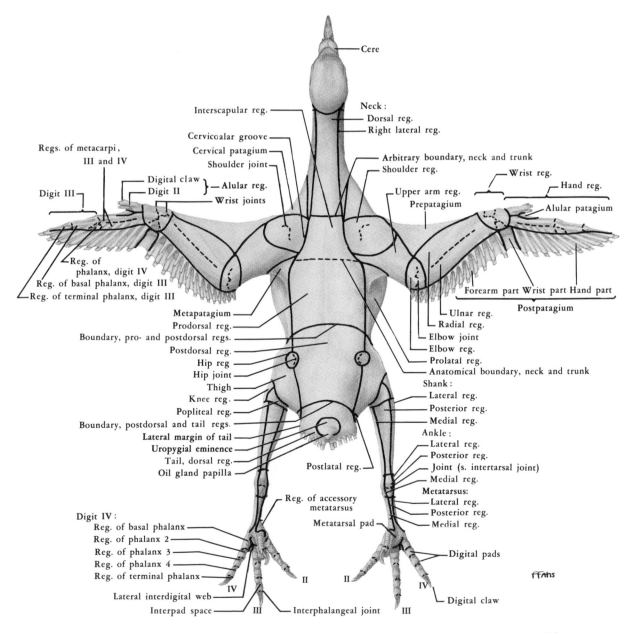

FIGURE 39.—Dorsal view of a Common Pigeon showing regions. Abbreviations: reg(s)., region(s); s., synonym.

and metacarpi; the phalangeal formula for the chicken, turkey, quail, and pigeon is 0, 2, 2, 1, 0; that for the duck is 0, 2, 3, 1, 0.

Posterior Appendage

Thigh and shank

Both anterior and posterior appendages of tetrapods are called limbs, but in birds the synonym "wing" is generally used for the anterior appendage. The hind limb is the poste-rior appendage. The effort has been made here to avoid the use of the word "leg" chiefly because it has both a general and a restricted meaning. The terms "leg" and "limb" are often used interchangeably, but in a strict sense, leg is that portion of the limb from knee to ankle; in restricted meaning it is often designated "lower leg," "leg proper," or *"crus"* to distinguish it from the upper leg. We have chosen the following common English terms because they are readily understood, monomial terms—"thigh" for upper leg and "shank" for lower leg.

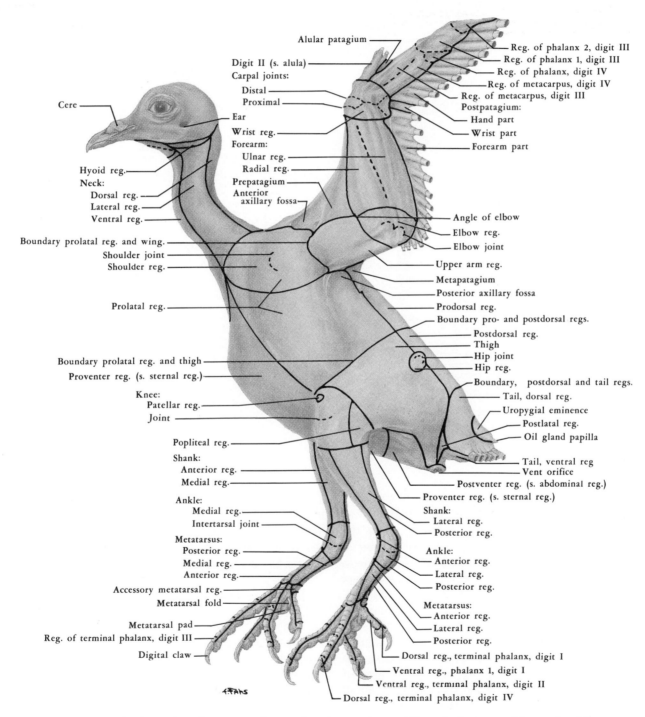

FIGURE 40.—Left lateral view of a Common Pigeon showing regions. Abbreviations: reg(s)., region(s); s., synonym.

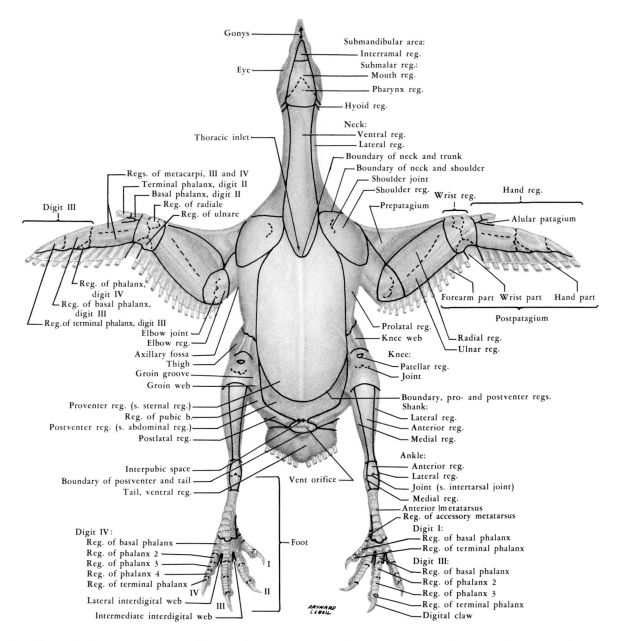

FIGURE 41.—Ventral view of a Common Pigeon showing regions. Abbreviations: b., bone; reg(s)., region(s); s., synonym.

In most ornithological literature the part of the foot that contains the tarsometatarsal bones is referred to as the tarsus. This seems inappropriate to us because the tarsal bones are those that border the intertarsal joint. Coues (1903:127) recognized the inaccuracy of the term as applied to the instep region of the foot. Its use here will be avoided. Instead the portion of the foot between intertarsal joint and base of the toes will be named "metatarsus" and the supporting skeleton, the "tarsometatarsal bone or bones."

The axis of each segment of the avian hind limb can move around a range of angles in respect to the axes of adjacent segments. Storer (1960b:20) presented a series of diagrams to show the significance of the relative lengths of segments and the direction of bending at the joints to the bird's center of gravity and to its maintenance of equilibrium.

Coues (1903:124) stated, "The modifications of the hind limb are more numerous, more diverse, and more important in their bearing on classification than those of either bill, wing, or tail; their study is consequently a matter of special interest."

Birds use their feet and legs in various ways on the land and in the water. They may use them to run, walk, hop, swim, perch, receive impact of descent, cling to rough vertical surfaces, scratch, grasp prey, and fight. Birds use feet with the beak to build nests, tie knots, hold or cover the egg during incubation, turn eggs, and scratch themselves. Figure 42, A–I illustrates nine modifications of feet that are described later.

Webs of skin between body and thigh are transitory structures that appear when the limbs are pulled apart laterally and extended caudally. They are described here because they sometimes are landmarks for boundaries and often break the continuity of other lines, as already mentioned on page 44. Because their existence is in a sense an artifact and depends upon the position of the limb, they are called webs and not patagia.[15] The skinfold that occurs most of the time in birds is the knee web. It stretches from the body to the knee. It appears at the boundary line between lateral and ventral surfaces of the body and reaches to the anterior face of the knee region. One or more folds of skin, called groin webs, extend from the sternal region to the medial surface of the thigh. These folds are highly variable in location and number; they may arise just behind the knee web or they may cross the groin groove near the posterior end of the sternum. Although artifacts, webs break the continuity of the groin groove and can sometimes be used as reference points.

Only the thigh and shank are described here. The introductory and general remarks for metatarsus and toes are given later because they are specialized and variable among birds, including the five described here.

Chicken.—The thigh extends from the lateral margin of the ilium to the knee joint, including the hip region (*regio coxendicis*) and half of the knee region (*regio genus*). The knee joint includes the femur, the musculature that arises from the lateral surface of the pelvic girdle, and the overlying integument. The boundaries for the outer surface of the thigh region are: The dorsal boundary is common with the lateral boundary of the postdorsum; the anterior boundary is the cephalic edge of the sartorius muscle, which is also the caudal boundary of the prolatus; the posterior boundary follows the caudal margin of the thigh musculature and is the same as the cephalic edge of the postlatal region. Distally, the thigh region ends at the knee region, but as a part of the body, the thigh extends to the knee joint. The upper boundary of the knee region lies in a transverse plane above the patella and the condyles of the femur. This boundary crosses the lateral and anterior surfaces of the thigh and as much of the medial surface as is separated from the lateral body wall. In a young, thin chicken the upper boundary line for the knee may encircle the leg.

The medial surface of the thigh is variable and in most specimens is not visible in an undissected bird. This is true for the chicken (fig. 29) where the caudal boundary line for the thigh crosses the knee web and then the groin web and then terminates in the groin groove at the junction with the lateral proventer border. We have not attempted to divide the thigh into lateral, medial, anterior, and posterior surfaces.

The knee includes the knee joint; the enlarged ends of the femur, tibia, and fibula; and the overlying ligaments, tendons, muscles, fascia, and integument. The osseous struc-

tures lie in the anterior two-thirds of the knee region, and only soft tissues are present in the posterior third. In man the tendons of the biceps femoris laterally and those of the semitendinosus and semimembranosus medially create the popliteal fossa. In the chicken the same tendons are present, but the fossa is not well defined because in the flattened thigh of the bird the hamstring muscles are more compressed. The posterior third of the knee is designated the "popliteal region" (*regio poplitea*) and the angle between thigh and shank, the "popliteal angle" (*angulus popliteus*).

The osseous reference points for the inferior margin of the knee are the inferior edges of the inner and outer cnemial crests of the tibiotarsus and the head of the fibula (fig. 25). The boundary line of the knee region encircles the shank at this level which, on the posterior side of the knee, is a short distance below the angle between thigh and shank. The depression in the region of this angle is the popliteal fossa (*fossa poplitea*).

The shank, or lower leg, is that portion of the limb between the knee joint and ankle joint; it includes the tibiotarsus, fibula, ligaments, muscles, tendons, and the integument covering these structures. The shank is divided into four surfaces or regions—anterior, posterior, lateral, and medial— and is bounded by four lines that extend lengthwise on the shank from the region of the knee joint to the region of the ankle joint. The boundaries for these surfaces are called anterolateral, anteromedial, posterolateral, and posteromedial. The proximal and distal boundaries for these regions are the knee and ankle regions respectively. The rudimentary character of the fibula and its closeness to the tibiotarsus make it impractical to establish tibial and fibular regions of the shank. The fore part of the shank is sometimes called shin; the posterior part, calf.

The ankle, or hock, is a rather extended region of the limb. The superior boundary encircles the shank proximal to the condyles and tibial cartilage, whereas the inferior boundary lies just distal to the heads of the fused tarsometatarsal bones on the anterior surface and is distal to the calcaneal ridges of the hypotarsus on the posterior surface (figs. 25, 27, and 28). These transverse boundaries are about twice as far apart on the posterior surface as on the anterior surface. The ankle region has anterior and posterior, lateral and medial surfaces, or regions. The edges of the condyles identify the lateral margins for these surfaces (figs. 25 and 28). The joint of the ankle lies approximately midway between the dorsal and ventral boundaries of the ankle region.

During embryonic and early posthatching development, most of the tarsal bones that are characteristic of the tetrapod limb can be identified. All tarsal bones eventually fuse either to the distal end of the tibia or to the proximal ends of the metatarsi II, III, and IV, thus forming a tibiotarsus and a tarsometatarsus. The ankle joint itself is an intertarsal joint. The portion of the foot from the ankle joint to the base of the toes is the metatarsus, a term already discussed.

Other species.—The thigh and shank of the turkey are large; yet the boundaries, surfaces, and parts are the same

---

[15] Unfortunately, it is not possible to be entirely consistent in using this criterion for the term "web." Through long, well-established usage, the term "web" has been applied to the skin stretched beneath the toes of birds, and because this usage is well understood by writers and readers, no change is suggested in this instance.

as in the chicken. This fact is illustrated by comparing figures 30 to 32 with figures 27 to 29.

The thigh is farther separated from the body in the Common Coturnix than in the chicken and turkey, as shown in a ventral view (fig. 35). All of the knee region and even a small part of the adjacent thigh are entirely separated from the body. In figure 35, therefore, the dorsal boundary of the knee region completely encircles the leg. In the popliteal region of the knee is a well-defined fat pad that makes the area of the fossa level with the remainder of the knee. As a consequence, the designation of a popliteal fossa for the Common Coturnix may not be justified. The remainder of the leg proximal to the foot is similar to that described for other galliforms.

Like many other swimming birds, the White Pekin Duck, has all of its thigh musculature and most of the knee region beneath the skin of the lateral body wall. The knee is situated higher on the side of the trunk than in nonaquatic birds. The broad patagium (named here the "crural patagium)" joins body and shank and eliminates the complete encirclement of the knee region by boundary lines; it also eliminates the popliteal fossa. A depression does exist in the skin that bridges the angle between shank and thigh, but it is too far caudal to be justifiably identified as a popliteal fossa.

The Common Pigeon (figs. 39 to 41) is somewhat like the Common Coturnix in that when the leg is extended the thigh is encircled by the upper boundary of the knee region. This line is not shown as completed in figure 41 because knee and thigh have been pushed forward in this illustration. Although the pigeons examined had a small fat pad below the popliteal fossa, a small pit remained in that area as in the chicken (fig. 28). The four surfaces and boundaries for the shank are shown on figures 39 to 41 and agree in the use of landmarks with the other species described.

Foot

The foot of a bird includes only the structures distal to the intertarsal joint; therefore, it contains only part of the ankle bones. In mammals, all of the ankle bones are included as part of the foot. This is another situation in which it is difficult to apply to a bird a definition developed for a mammal.

Poultrymen and ornithologists use the term "hock" as synonymous with ankle region (regio tarsi), and "hockjoint" with ankle joint. The term "heel" has been used for the same region, but a bird does not have a separate and well-developed calcaneum, which forms the heel of man.

Separate ankle bones (ossa tarsi) are lacking in adult birds although three or four bone complexes are present in the embryo. One or two of these bones disappear when they fuse with the lower end of the tibia and thereby form the tibiotarsus. The remaining bone (sometimes two) fuses with the metatarsus, thus forming a tarsometatarsus (Parker, 1891; Holmgren, 1955; Bellairs and Jenkin, 1960). In many perching birds, the integument that covers the heel is similar to that found on the remainder of the metatarsus, except

for the folding and wrinkling associated with the movement of loose skin over the joint. In the chicken, this region is thickened slightly, and the epidermis is roughened. However, according to Chasen (1923), about 16 families of birds, which include some owls (figs. 50 and 51), parrots, and numerous families in the Piciformes and Coraciiformes, have well-developed heelpads. These appear best developed in birds whose nests are made on the ground or in the interior of trees. The pads vary from smooth and cushiony to large elevated structures in which the scales are conical and may have needlelike points. They may be better developed in the recently hatched bird than in the adult. For example, in the woodpeckers observed by Chasen, the young bore elevated tubercles pointing backward, which were used for locomotion within the nest cavity, but later in development these specialized structures were lost.

The ankle joint is constructed so that the metatarsus can be extended enough to bring it into the same axis with the crus but no farther. In the opposite direction the ankle can be flexed so that the metatarsus rests against the anterior surface of the lower leg.

The metatarsus has four surfaces—anterior, posterior, lateral, and medial; the boundaries for these are described under the headings of the specific birds studied. The metatarsus includes the integument, tarsometatarsal bones, and tendons, many of which are ossified. In most birds the integument is modified to form scales, but in some the metatarsus and toes bear either feathers without scales or scales penetrated by feathers. The dorsal surface has sometimes been designated as the dorsum pedis and the ventral side as the sole, or plantar surface (planta pedis). Only a few birds like the loons and grebes normally stand on the full length of their feet, in a posture called plantigrade. Because most birds are digitigrade (they stand and walk on their toes only), it seems less confusing to use the term "anterior" and "posterior" for these regions of the metatarsus and limit use of the terms listed previously to the toes.

Some modifications of the foot among birds are illustrated in figure 42, A to I, which make it possible to discuss the different types of webbing between toes, the position of the toes, their loss and fusions, and variations in the phalangeal formulae. A flexible webbing exists between the toes of most aquatic and some terrestrial birds, but it is absent in passerines. The extreme condition is found in such totipalmate swimmers as the pelicans (fig. 42, A), boobies, and cormorants in which all four toes of each foot are united by webs to form medial, intermediate, and lateral interdigital webs. In the palmate foot of ducks (fig. 42, C), geese, swans, gulls, skuas, and skimmers, the intermediate and lateral webs involve the three forward-directed toes; a web is absent between digit II and the hallux. An equivalent situation exists in birds that have only three toes, such as loons and alcids.

The incised palmate type of foot has the attachment at the top of the toes as in the palmate type but there is a greater indentation of the free edge. Terns have this type of webbing. Semipalmate toes are common among the galliforms (fig. 42, D and E) where the webbing is limited to the angles between toes 2 and 3 and 3 and 4. The web may be limited to lobes on each side of the toes, a condition well developed in finfoots, less so in the grebes, and slightly in phalaropes. The thin fold of skin on the medial side of the second toe of the duck has only one attached edge. It partially fills the space between this toe and the hallux to form part of a medial web.

A special modification of the scales along the side of the toe occurs in the Ruffed Grouse (fig. 42, D) where a pectinate type of marginal scale projects downward and forms a fringe that makes walking on the snow more effective. The pectinate scales are shed in the spring (Bump et al., 1947).

The toes (*digiti*) in birds, typically four in number (figs. 42, A, C, D, E, H, and I), are homologous with digits I to IV of a pentadactyl appendage. No bird has more than four toes except chickens of the Dorking, Faverolle, Houdan, Sultan, and Non-bearded Silkie Bantam breeds, all of which have five toes. In these breeds the extra toe arises above the base of the hallux and projects upward, never touching the ground. In the Silkie, the extra toes often lie nearly in the same plane as the hallux; in addition, the number of extra toes ranges from zero to three, and the number of bones within an extra toe may also be variable. The extra toe has no relationship to the missing fifth toe of the pentadactyl foot. The diversity of form found in the skeleton of atypical toes, and the genetics of polydactyly and brachydactyly were reviewed by Hutt (1949).

Some birds, however, have only three toes. Among these are the rheas, cassowaries, auks and alcids, some petrels, most albatrosses (*Diomedea* spp.), most plovers, oyster-catchers, Sanderling (*Crocethia alba*), stilts (fig. 42, G), kittiwakes (*Rissa*), certain flamingos (*Phoenicoparrus* spp.), certain woodpeckers (*Picoides* spp., *Dinopium* spp.), and certain kingfishers (*Ceyx* spp.). Only the adult ostrich (fig. 42, B) has two toes. In some of these examples the bones of additional toes are present, but they are enclosed within the skin-covering and so are not visible, or they were formed during embryonic development and later disappeared (Duerden, 1920).

Coues (1903:134) classified avian feet according to the position of the first digit as elevated, insistent (the tip touches the ground), or incumbent (full length of first toe touches the surface on which bird rests). Galliforms have the elevated type of foot, on which the hallux is carried above the ground level at the end of a rudimentary accessory meta-tarsal bone. Various gradations occur in the transition first to the insistent type of toe and finally to the incumbent type of toe, as occurs in the pigeon and most perching birds. Often there is a correlation between the position of the first toe and the webbing. In general, the attachment of the hallux is elevated (insistent) in any bird with true webbing or lobing of the front toes except in herons and some birds of prey; thus all domestic fowl would be included in this group. Birds with the hallux resting on the ground for the full length and in the same plane with the other toes have no webbing between their toes.

In most birds three toes point forward (*digiti* II, III, and IV) and one toe points posteriorly, but in penguins all four toes are directed forward and laterally. The same is true of some species of woodpeckers when they are climbing (Bock and Miller, 1959). In some birds, notably owls, the hallux can be moved either into a forward or backward position, and in the African Mousebirds (*Colius* spp.) the hallux can be moved forward and the fourth toe backward. In parrots, cuckoos, woodpeckers (fig. 42, I), and trogons the toes are arranged in pairs—two forward and two backward (zygodac-tylous condition). In all of these except the trogons, the outer toe is directed backward, but in the trogons the digit adjacent to the first toe has moved backward. The evolutionary influence of perching and climbing on the zygodactylous foot has been extensively studied by Bock and Miller (1959).

In many passerine birds a scale crosses the angle formed by adjacent toes and produces a fusion for a short distance. In the syndactyl feet of kingfishers (fig. 42, H) fusion involves numerous scales and almost completely unites the third and fourth toes—an extreme condition. Fusion of toes by binding them together with scales occurs to a lesser extent in wrens, titmice, creepers, vireos and may occur in chickens as an anomaly. In woodpeckers, the basal phalanges of toes II and III are involved. A more extensive discussion of the foot of the bird is in the article by Reichenow (1871).

In poultry literature, booted and booting refer to feathering of the metatarsus rather than to a fusion of scales, which is what the term means in ornithological literature. We suggest that the term "ptilopody" coined by Danforth (1919) should be used in both poultry and ornithological literature to designate leg-feathering. Danforth stated (p. 587):

> Two terms, "leg-feathering" and "booting" have been employed to indicate the presence of feathers on the tarsus and toes. Both of these terms are inappropriate; the former because it is not the leg, but the tarsus and toes that is meant, the latter because the term is already in use to indicate a fusion of tarsal scutella. Since no other convenient term seems to be available the word ptilopody (πτιλον, feather; πους, foot) is used in this paper to designate the condition in which down or feathers tend to appear on the tarsus and toes.

Danforth used ptilopod as the adjective form of the noun, ptilopody. Unfortunately, these terms have not received general acceptance in the poultry husbandry literature nor were they included in "Webster's New International Dictionary," Second Edition, nor in the 1944 edition of Funk and Wagnall's "New Standard Dictionary of the English Language." Ptilopod is included in "Webster's Third New International Dictionary" (1965), but not ptilopody. The latter is listed in Thomson's (1964) "A New Dictionary of Birds." Van Tyne and Berger (1959:570) regarded the term "booted" for the smooth, undivided tarsal sheath as obsolete, and in their glossary recommended the term "holothecal."

Birds have retained the phalangeal formula of their bipedal reptilian ancestors, namely, 2, 3, 4, 5, —, for the first four digits, the fifth digit having been lost; in primitive reptiles the typical phalangeal number for the fifth digit is 4. Such formulae as the foregoing designate the number of phalanges on each digit presented in sequence from I to V. In the higher

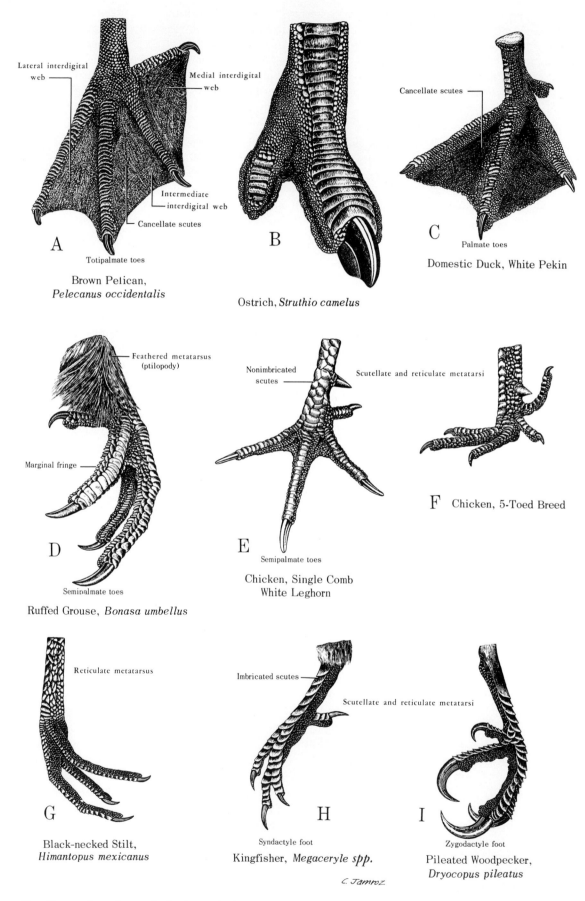

Lateral interdigital web

Medial interdigital web

Intermediate interdigital web

Cancellate scutes

Totipalmate toes

A

Brown Pelican,
Pelecanus occidentalis

B

Ostrich, *Struthio camelus*

Cancellate scutes

C

Palmate toes

Domestic Duck, White Pekin

Feathered metatarsus (ptilopody)

Marginal fringe

D

Semipalmate toes

Ruffed Grouse, *Bonasa umbellus*

Nonimbricated scutes

Scutellate and reticulate metatarsi

E

Semipalmate toes

Chicken, Single Comb
White Leghorn

Scutellate and reticulate metatarsi

F Chicken, 5-Toed Breed

Reticulate metatarsus

G

Black-necked Stilt,
Himantopus mexicanus

Imbricated scutes

Scutellate and reticulate metatarsi

H

Syndactyle foot

Kingfisher, *Megaceryle spp.*

I

Zygodactyle foot

Pileated Woodpecker,
Dryocopus pileatus

C. Jamroz

FIGURE 42.—Examples of morphologic variation in the toes and feet of some birds. Abbreviation: spp., species.

mammallike reptiles and in all mammals, the formula is 2, 3, 3, 3, 3. Among birds, Coues (1903:133) cited members of the swift family (Apodidae) as having 2, 3, 4, 4, —, and in some of the Procellariiformes the formula may be —, 3, 4, 5, — or 1, 3, 4, 5, —. The reasonable constancy of the phalangeal formula has made it easy to determine whether it was the second or the fourth toe that rotated backward to parallel the first toe. In woodpeckers (fig. 42, I) the fourth toe moved in a position to parallel the first toe.

The terminal phalanx of each toe carries a claw. This is true for practically all birds except the ostrich in which the outer toe carries no nail, or claw, or only a very rudimentary nail (fig. 42, B). The claws in chickens are relatively short and not greatly curved and serve the function of scratching. The claws of birds that perch are more strongly curved (fig. 42, I). The claws of birds are laterally compressed (figs. 50 and 51) except in grebes, where they are flattened dorsoventrally to form typical nails.

Scales of birds are homologous with those of reptiles and mammals. Structurally, scales are similar to the sheathing substance of beaks, claws, and spurs, and they may appear as small keratinized thickenings of the epidermis or as large overlapping plates. Scales (scutes and scutella) are found chiefly on the metatarsus and digits of the foot but also may cover part of the leg in birds whose plumage does not extend the full length of the crus. Scutes show their greatest development on the front surface of the metatarsus (acrometatarsium) and the dorsal surfaces of the digits (acropodium). (See footnote 24 in chapter 9 for a discussion of the name, acrometatarsium.) On the sides and on the palmar surface of the toes, scales are often small and form a reticulate type (Coues, 1903). In feet of the pelican, stilt (fig. 42, A and G), and plover, all scales on the metatarsus are reticulate. In numerous birds the metatarsus is both scutellate and reticulate; the scutes may be a single row of rectangular plates as in the ostrich or they may consist of two or more rows as in the chicken. The reticulate type is small and randomly distributed, as on the ventral surface of the toes and the lateral and posterior surfaces of the metatarsus. The extreme condition seen on webs of the pelican and duck is merely a roughness of the skin surface termed "cancellate" (fig. 42, A and C).

The scutes of most birds are nonimbricated, that is, no significant overlapping of scales, but kingfishers and woodpeckers (fig. 42, H and I) have overlapping scales.

Reduction in number of scutes on the dorsal and anterior surfaces of toes and the reduction on the metatarsus to a few plates that encircle this part of the foot are considered to be examples of specialization. Among such passerine birds as the thrushes, which includes the American Robin (Turdus migratorius), there is a fusion of all the scutes or all except a few at the distal end of the metatarsus. This extreme development produces a smooth metatarsus, which ornithologists call booted (holothecal). Coues (1903) listed nine genera in which a complete holothecal metatarsus occurs. The subject of scales has been reviewed here very briefly, but Boetticher (1929) described the scale pattern for all the

major groups of birds, including the chicken among the galliforms, and discussed types as well as phylogenetic relations based on his comparative study.

Chicken.—The metatarsus has four surfaces, but they are not of equal size and some have an irregular shape. The two to three rows of large scutes on the forward surface of the metatarsus aid in identifying the anterior surface. The marginal boundaries can be seen fully only in medial and lateral views (figs. 28 and 377), but the encircling proximal and distal boundaries can be seen in several views (figs. 27 to 29). The proximal boundary is common with the ankle region; the distal boundary is the caudal end of the tarsometatarsus at the junction with the basal end of toes II, III, and IV (fig. 25).

The posterior boundary follows the margins of the medium size scutella on the caudal surface of the metatarsus. The medial margin of the posterior surface bypasses the base of the metatarsal spur so that the spur is included in the medial surface (figs. 42, E and F; and 377, B). The inferior boundary of the posterior surface (fig. 27) was placed at the basal end of the accessory metatarsus.

The metatarsal spur, like the beak and claws, has two parts—the underlying osseous structure and the covering of heavily keratinized epidermis. The spurs in the chicken project from the axis of the metatarsus at an angle of about 90° and are pointed posteromedially at about a 45° angle. They are placed between the middle and distal thirds of the metatarsus. A more extended discussion of the metatarsal spur is in chapter 9, beginning with page 609.

The accessory metatarsal region (figs. 27 to 29) corresponds to metatarsal bone I (fig. 25) already mentioned. The proximal and distal joints are the reference landmarks for the region; the latter is more readily palpable. These joints are circular because the accessory metatarsus is rodlike. Below the accessory metatarsal is a thickening called the metatarsal fold; it lies between the metatarsal pad and the base of digit I. The metatarsal pad is at the end of the tarsometatarsal bone and is identified in figures 27; 28; 43, A; 44, A and C; and 377, G. Its boundary is well indicated by the crease on one side between fold and pad and on the other side between pad and bases of toes.

The joint between tarsometatarsus and the bases of third and fourth digits establishes the distal end of the medial surface of the metatarsus. The lateral surface, like the medial surface, is broad adjacent to the ankle, and it narrows distally to a point between accessory metatarsus and fourth digit. It contains reticulate scales.

The general remarks made earlier on the toes of birds apply to the chicken; the phalangeal formula is 2, 3, 4, 5, —. The first toe is the shortest, the third is the longest; the fourth toe has five phalanges and is only slightly longer than the second with three phalanges. In the chicken all phalanges are relatively long except the terminals and those of the fourth toe. Although round in cross section, the toes seem to be divided into dorsal and ventral surfaces, based chiefly on scale structure and placement of the interdigital webs. However, reference to the side of the toe is not excluded.

The location of joints is indicated by dashed lines across the toes in figures 27 to 29. The phalangeal bones are enlarged at each joint (fig. 25) and are readily palpable.

The chicken has an intermediate interdigital web joining toes II and III and a lateral interdigital web joining toes III and IV (fig. 43, *A*). The webs in the chicken extend no farther than the distal ends of the basal phalanges. The free edges of the webs are curved with the concavity outward. The webs are located at the junction of dorsal and ventral surfaces of the toes, and their surfaces are covered with small reticulate scales (fig. 42, *E*).

The digital claws of the chicken are short and only slightly curved and their bases are large and strong. They are adapted to cursorial locomotion and to the function of scratching. The claws have two surfaces—dorsal and ventral—which are called, respectively, dorsal plate (unguis) and ventral plate (subunguis). The dorsal surface curves downward laterally and medially to form the sides of each claw. The upper surface is composed of compact horn; the lower of sole horn, which is thinner and less dense than the compact horn. At the base of the claw is a fold of skin that borders the margin of the base. The fold involves the apical scale on the dorsal surface, the lateral scales on each side, and part of the terminal digital pad. Claw length is least in the hallux, intermediate in digits II and IV, and greatest in digit III (fig. 43, *C–F*). Curvature of the middorsal profile is greatest on the hallux, about equal on digits II and IV, and least on digit III. These comparisons are best made on the baby chick. In older birds the tips of the claws become broken and worn, and in some birds rotation of the phalanges makes the claw point sideways instead of downward. Claws may then become abnormally long because the usual abrasion is lacking.

In side view, part of the ventral contour is formed by the ventral margin of the dorsal plate, and part is formed by the downward protrusion of the body of the ventral plate. This downward protrusion is caused by the tubercle at the basal end of the terminal phalanx. In the young chicken, this protrusion of the ventral plate by the underlying bone continues to the tip of the bone, but in older birds it is masked by a proliferation of subungual laminae that parallel the plane of the ventral plate and have their free edges converging toward the midline (figs. 43, *G–I*). These thin plates are soft and opaque. The increase in number and extent of these laminae with age is indicated in these illustrations. At hatching only one or two laminae are present, and these lie in the angle between dorsal and ventral plates. In the young bird the laminae become more extensive; toward the tip laminae from the two sides meet, and the point of junction is marked by a line. In the adult chicken almost the entire ventral plate may be covered by these cornified laminae, so that the translucent underlying keratin is visible only at the basal end of the claw. These cornified laminae probably protect the underlying keratin from the abrasion associated with scratching and other cursorial activities. With use these laminae and the lateral edges of the dorsal plate may be almost completely worn away.

The proximal end of the dorsal plate passes under the terminal dorsal scale proximally almost to the level of the joint (fig. 380). The ventral plate arises on the distal side of the tubercle of the terminal phalanx and thus does not reach as far proximally as does the dorsal plate.

Other species.—Because of its large size, the turkey provides excellent material for study of the foot—regions, surfaces, and especially scale types. Pads and interpad spaces for other species have already been described. In spite of the large size of the turkey foot, there are but two rows of scales on the anterior surface of the metatarsus, whereas in the adult Plymouth Rock male there is a tendency to form three rows. The comments presented here on the turkey do not indicate differences from the chicken but point up some additional features that are common to both turkey and chicken.

The posterior surface of the turkey foot has two rows of rather broad scutella, the lateral of which restricts the width of the lateral surface with the result that its narrowest part is only two small scales wide. Both of these columns of scales converge toward the base of digit IV. The large scales on the anterior surface of the metatarsus overlap hardly at all near the proximal end of the foot, but near the tarsometatarso-phalangeal joints is considerable overlap, and this applies also to the scales on the dorsal surfaces of the toes. During strong flexion of the toes the overlap disappears.

A metatarsal fold is less dominant in the turkey than in the chicken. On the other hand, the metatarsal pad is particularly bulbous. The scales are sharply circumscribed, low flattened (macular) projections. The scales are of the same type, but smaller ones are present on the digital pads and interpad spaces.

The Common Coturnix has two rows of relatively large scales on the anterior surface of the metatarsus. The groove between the rows follows the median line of the anterior surface. Laterally the scales lie well up on the sides of the metatarsus. The two rows are continuous with those of the dorsal surface of toes III and IV.

No metatarsal spur is present in the Common Coturnix, and therefore the two rows of scales that occupy the posterior surface of the metatarsus extend the full length of this region and terminate at the base of the accessory metatarsus and metatarsal pad. The lateral surface has its narrowest part spanned by three small scales. The rows of small reticulate scales are directed toward the outer side of the last toe. The medial surface is directed toward the base of the second toe, and the adjacent space toward the hallux.

The Common Coturnix has long slender toes, and all pads are rather small and delicate; the metatarsal fold is absent, and the metatarsal pad is little more than a thickened layer of skin covering the tarsometatarso-phalangeal joints. All the claws are strongly curved.

The metatarsus of the White Pekin Duck (fig. 42, *C*) is flattened laterally with a rounded front surface and bears several rows of scales. Those along the leading edge are largest and are continuous with the dorsal surface of the middle toe; the two rows of scales near the lateral border are smaller and are continuous with the small dorsal scales of digit IV (fig. 38). The scales on the narrow posterior surface

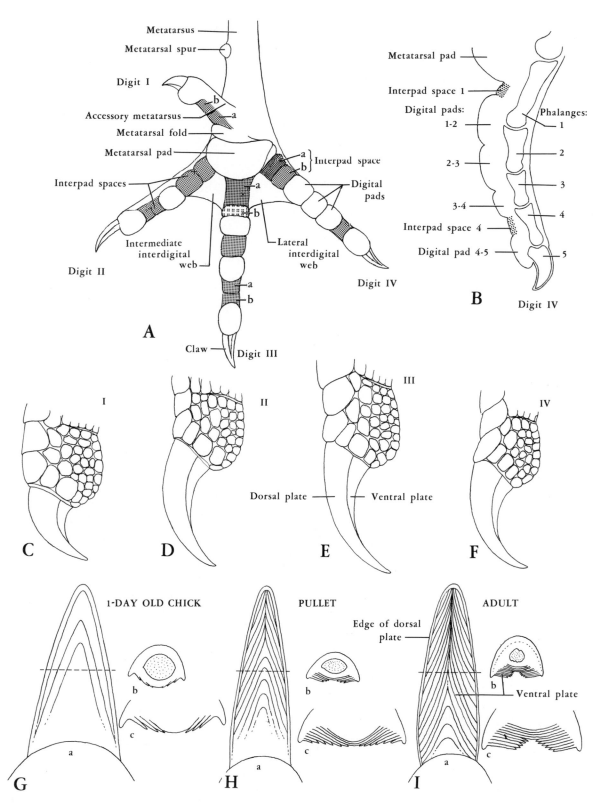

FIGURE 43.—Toes of the Single Comb White Leghorn Chicken (A, C–I) and Bronze Turkey (B).

A, view of the plantar surface of the toes showing digital pads (unshaded) and interpad spaces (shaded).

B, profile view of digit IV to show pads and interpad spaces of the Bronze Turkey.

C, D, E, and F, profile view of claws on digits I to IV, respectively, showing the size and arrangement of scales on the dorsal surface and terminal pad in the young chicken.

G, H, and I, ventral and cross section views of claws showing the increase in dehiscence of corneum to form laminae with increase in age. The level at which b and c sections were taken is indicated by the dashed line in a; c is a higher magnification of the ventral plate shown in b. (B drawn by Raynard LeNeil; all others by Casimir Jamroz.)

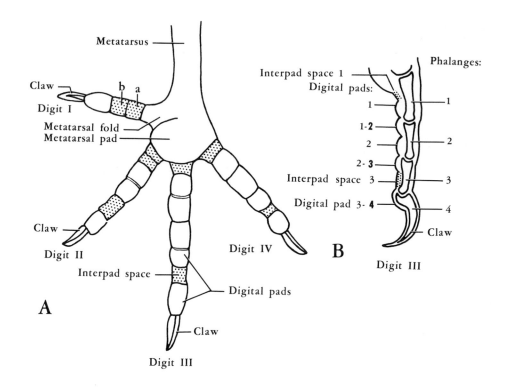

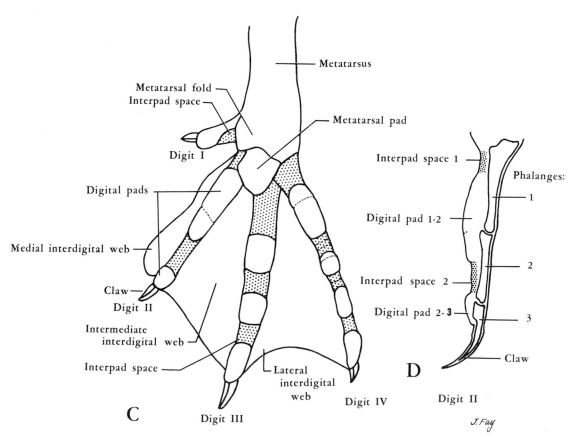

FIGURE 44.—Joints, digital pads, and interpad spaces of avian toes. Interpad spaces are indicated by stippling.

A, plantar surface of the toes of a Common Pigeon.
B, longitudinal section of the third digit of a Common Pigeon, showing the relationship of pad and interpad spaces to the joints. Numerals in regular type indicate that only a small portion of the pad overlays the phalanx bearing that numeral, and the numerals in boldface type indicate that most of the pad overlays the phalanx of that numeral. These agree with the data in table 1.
C, plantar surface of the toes and web of a White Pekin Duck.
D, longitudinal section of digit II of a White Pekin Duck.

are only slightly larger than those on the broad lateral and medial surfaces. In fact the boundaries separating these three surfaces are partially arbitrary; they begin below the hypotarsus and extend approximately parallel. One margin ends at the junction of metatarsal pad and last toe, the other shares the common boundary of the accessory metatarsus in its lower part and ends at the base of the metatarsal pad.

The medial surface of the metatarsus is broad, the proximal end is the diagonal lower boundary of the ankle region. The medial surface excludes the accessory metatarsal region and terminates distally at the level of the first joint of toes II and III. The small scales of the medial surface are continued onto the dorsal surface of the second toe, thus the middle toe is the only one having large dorsal scales. The lateral surface of the metatarsus has small scales also, and this surface terminates at the distal end of the tarsometatarsus.

The webs join the full length of toes II to IV. An incomplete medial interdigital web is attached to the medial side of digit II (fig. 44). The webs are thin and leathery, and the scales, designated as cancellate, are extremely small and are actually the denser areas between intersecting furrows. The scales of the webs adjacent to the digits are larger than those more centrally placed. The partial medial interdigital web is covered with scales similar to those of the dorsal surface of digit II; on the ventral surface, the scales are smaller, similar to those of cancellate areas. The metatarsal pad is well defined and extends forward on to the basal phalanx of the middle toe.

The claws are slightly arched, about to the same extent as in the chicken, but the dorsal plate is strongly curved circumferentially around the toe so that the ventral plate is reduced to a narrow band covered with many laminae.

The scales of the pigeon are large, red, and strongly outlined. The dorsal (anterior) surface of the metatarsus has fundamentally two rows of scales, but at the upper end those of the lateral side are large and those of the medial side are small or absent. Toward the base of the toes, the large scales become smaller as the row swings laterally toward the base of toe IV, and the scales of the medial row become larger as they pass toward the base of toe III (fig. 41). The scales on the posterior and lateral surfaces of the metatarsus are so slightly elevated and poorly delimited that the wrinkles in the thin red skin are more conspicuous than the scales. As a result, the boundaries that divide the posterior, medial, and lateral surfaces have no relationship to any pattern of scales.

The dorsal surface of each toe of the pigeon carries a single row of large scales. Adjacent to these, along the lateral edge of the dorsal scales, is an abrupt transition to a cancellate type of organization in the skin. The skin of the metatarsal pad, metatarsal fold, and ventral surfaces of all the toes is elevated into closely packed flattened papillae, which are separated by narrow sulci. On the free surface of most of the papillae is a shallow pit. The structure of the papillae enhances the grip of the feet when the bird perches.

The claws are moderately compressed laterally, though there is a large dorsal plate and a small ventral plate as in the chicken. The curvature on the claws for each of the toes

TABLE 1.—*Distribution of interpad spaces and digital pads on the toes of five species of domestic and laboratory birds*[1]

Bird	Digit I		Digit II		Digit III		Digit IV	
	IPS	DP	IPS	DP	IPS	DP	IPS	DP
Single Comb White Leghorn Chicken.	1 a–b	1–**2**	1 a–b 2 a–b	1–2 2–3	1 a–b 2 3 a–b	1–2 2–3 3–4	1 a–b 4	1–2 2–3 3–4 4–5
Bronze Turkey.	1	1–2	1 a–b 2	1–2 2–3	1 2 3	1–2 2–3 3–4	1 4	1–2 2–3 3–4 4–5
Common Coturnix.	1	2	1 2	1–2 3	1 2 3	1–2 2–3 4	1 2 3 4	1–2 2–3 3–4 5
White Pekin Duck.	1	1–2	1 2	1–2 2–3	1 2 3	1–2 2–3 3–4	1 2 3 4	1–2 2–3 3–4 4–5
Common Pigeon.	1 a–b	1–2	1	1–**2** 2 2–3	1 2 3	1 1–**2** 2 2–**3** 3–**4**	1 4	1–2 2–3 3–4 4–5

[1] Abbreviations: IPS, interpad space; DP, digital pad. See text for further explanation of numerical symbols, p. 72.

is about the same as shown in figures 43, *C–F*. Some partially desquamated laminae cover the ventral plate, but they are not as abundant in the pigeon as in the chicken.

Pads and interpad spaces.—Even a cursory examination shows that the plantar surface of the toes of birds has elevated digital pads and less elevated interpad spaces (fig. 43, *A*). Our search of the literature failed to reveal names for the individual pads and spaces. To fill this need, we selected names that seemed appropriate; later we revised, these names. Eventually we found that any set of names failed to have general applicability to species from different orders and even within orders. This is due chiefly to the fact that sometimes a pad covered parts of two phalanges and sometimes only of one. This difference is important; Lull (1904) discussed how the difference influences the interpretation of fossil footprints. We devised a system of coding the relationship of pads and interpad spaces for each phalanx and joint of each toe for the five kinds of birds (table 1). The system is described in the paragraphs that follow.

In table 1, under the heading for each digit, are two columns, IPS (interpad space) and DP (digital pad). The Arabic numerals in these two columns identify the phalanges. The pads and interpad spaces for the Single Comb White Leghorn Chicken (fig. 43, *A*) are as follows: Phalanx 1 of digit I has two interpad spaces, *a* and *b* separated by a furrow. Distal to these interpad spaces is a pad, the smaller part of which lies below phalanx 1 and the larger part of which is under phalanx 2. To indicate that the terminal pad is not equally distributed proximal and distal to the joint, the numeral 1 is shown in regular type and the **2** in boldface type. If both numerals are printed in regular type, the pad is distributed about equally distal and proximal to the joint.

On digit II, there is proximally an interpad space composed of two parts—a digital pad over the first joint, partly below phalanx 1 and partly below phalanx 2. Next is an interpad space composed of two parts that are associated entirely with phalanx 2, followed by the terminal pad that lies beneath the phalanges and the joint of 2 and 3.

Digit III begins with an interpad space having two parts; the distal of these is elevated almost to the level of the pad and is shown in figure 43, *A* by intermediate shading. The first pad covers the joint and adjacent phalanges of 1 and 2. The interpad distal to this lies entirely below phalanx 2; the pad beyond covers the joint. The third interpad space is long and is divided into two parts. The terminal digital pad covers the joint and parts of phalanges 3 and 4. It now should be relatively simple to correlate pads and spaces of digit IV (fig. 43, *A*) with the data in table 1.

For the foot of the turkey, an outline drawing was made only of the fourth digit (fig. 43, *B*). The digital pads are placed so that the joints proximally bisect each pad. Pad 3–4 is slightly asymmetric in relation to the joint.

The pattern for the Common Coturnix is similar to that for the chicken and turkey except for the fourth toe. The quail has a regular alternating sequence of interpad spaces and pads rather than a grouping of several pads. The coding is closely similar to that for the duck, but the general appearance of the foot of quail and duck differs partly because of differences in toe webbing. The pads of the latter are elongated, and both the pads and spaces may be crossed by very slight grooves indicated by dotted lines in figure 44, *C*. A longitudinal section of the second toe of the duck is diagramed in figure 44, *D*. This toe has a long first digital pad with a slight tendency to form a crease over the joint.

Pads and spaces in the pigeon (fig. 44, *A*) are arranged somewhat like those of the chicken except, as indicated in table 1, many of the pads lie more under the distal joint than under the proximal joint for digits II and III. This is diagramed in figure 44, *B*, a longitudinal section of digit III.

Associated with each terminal digital pad is a digital claw. At the sides of the toe, in line with the intermediate scales, are one or two truncate scales that fill the angle between the pad and dorsal scutes, similar to those shown for the chicken (figs. 43, *C–F*). These scales are placed diagonally and overlie the dorsal plate of the claw. By this arrangement the anterior ends of the terminal pads are limited almost entirely to the ventral surfaces, rather than to ventral and lateral surfaces.

The first toe has only a single pad, the terminal one; proximal to this and beneath the basal phalanx is the interpad space. In 11 of 23 newly hatched chickens, this area was undivided by transverse creases, in nine there were two parts, and in three there were three parts. (No adult chickens were found with three parts.) Basal to the interpad area of digit I and beneath the metatarsal bone of this digit is the metatarsal fold. When the hallux is flexed this fold may resemble a well-developed pad except for its narrow rectangular shape, but extension of the first digit may flatten this fold to approximately the level of the interpad space.

Our study of variations of pads and interpad spaces of the fourth toe among 100 11-day-old Single Comb White Leghorn Chicks, showed that one chick had a divided number 4 interpad space, and two chicks had double 3-4 and 2-3 pads. The 1 interpad space was single in 40 chicks and it was creased to form two parts in 60 chicks.

CHAPTER 2

Principles of Pterylosis

DEFINITIONS

Only a few 18th-century authors, whose studies were reviewed by Scherren (1903), recognized that most birds are not uniformly covered with feathers. Nitzsch completed much of the text and the copper plates for an extended monograph on the pterylosis of birds before his death, about 1837. His successor, H. Burmeister, compiled and translated the material from Latin into German. It was published in 1840. Later it was translated into English by W. S. Dallas and edited by P. L. Sclater (Nitzsch, 1867).

Nitzsch (1867) used the term "pterylography" to designate the pattern of feather tracts in birds. This term is still acceptable, but "pterylosis" is more commonly used. Miller (1915) introduced the term "ptilosis." At present all three terms, as well as the modified forms "pterylology" and "ptilology," are in use. May (1945) proposed that the term "ptilology" be used to cover the whole science of plumage, including the study of the microscopic structure of feathers (microptilology), and that the terms "pterylosis," "pterylography," and "pterylology" be limited to the morphology of or studies on feather tracts. Except as noted, this distinction is in harmony with the following definitions quoted from Webster's Third New International Dictionary (1965:1835):

Pterylography . . . . "The study or description of the pterylae of birds."
Pterylographer . . . . (Used by Heimerdinger (1964), not in the dictionary.)
Suggested definition: one who studies and records the pterylosis of a bird.
Pterylographic . . . . ". . . of or relating to pterylography."
Pterylological . . . . ". . . of or relating to pterylology."
Pterylology . . . . The study of pterylosis. (Not found in the dictionary.)
Pterylosis . . . . "Arrangement of feathers in definite areas of growth (pterylae)."
Ptilology . . . . "The study of ptilosis, a term meaning the plumage of birds, irrespective of pterylosis."
(Taken from May (1945), not in the dictionary.)
Ptilosis . . . . "Plumage, irrespective of pterylosis."

Heimerdinger (1964) did not define the term "pterylographer;" the definition suggested here was derived from the connotation taken from her text (p. 7).

Thomson (1964:670) considered ptilosis and plumage synonymous. Humphrey and Parkes (1959:30), however, restricted the term "plumage" to mean a single generation of feathers. They explained (p. 5) that previous workers had used the term in a broader, vaguer sense, meaning a stage in a sequence of the total appearance of a bird. These meanings are almost similar, but the context usually makes the intended meaning clear. Some confusion can be avoided by applying the term "ptilosis" to the feather coat only, as we have done in this study.

Birds in general appear to be covered with feathers over their entire body, except for feet, beak, and eyes. Naked or seemingly naked skin in birds, such as in the head region of turkeys and vultures, attracts attention because it is atypical. Yet a continuous distribution of feathers over the avian body is found almost exclusively in the "ratite" birds, which include the kiwis, cassowaries, emu, rheas, and ostrich. The small feathers on the head and neck of cassowaries may give the impression of naked skin. Among the "carinate" birds, the penguins have almost a complete feather coat, and DeMay (1942) has described such a condition in detail for the screamers. In all others the plumage is interrupted. The feathers are segregated into tracts or groups intermingled with featherless spaces over the body. The pattern of the feathered tracts and the featherless spaces was presented by Nitzsch (1867) for representatives of most of the major groups of birds. As a result of his extended studies, a basic plan was formulated for pterylosis of birds in general. He established criteria for the identification of a pteryla and for an apterium. The former was to be based on the presence of contour feathers only, and all the feathers were to be visible on the external surface of the plumage. The latter was identified by the absence of feathers or by the existence of down or semiplume feathers. In some adult birds, however, the complete gradation of types from down to pennaceous plumes makes it difficult to adhere closely to these criteria. Application of strict criteria produces some inconsistencies that are pointed out where the pterylosis of the chicken, turkey, and Common Coturnix is described in chapter 3.

PTERYLAE

Although Nitzsch's classification was used as a guide in compiling the key to feather tracts (*Pterylae*) (next column), the key contains some additions and changes in terminology established by common usage since 1900; also, some of Nitzsch's terms have been deleted. In the past, the need for subdividing most pterylae, especially the capital, spinal, and ventral tracts, has brought about the naming of tracts according to the region of the body on which the tract occurs.

Boulton's (1927) designation of these subdivisions of feather groups by the term "region," leads to some ambiguity of meaning because he did not clearly define the names either in terms of regions or of tracts. For example, we assume that if he had written a term out in full, it would have read "frontal region of the capital tract." We, on the other hand, have listed each region as a tract under the inclusive plural heading, "Capital tracts." Heimerdinger (1964) has avoided using the word "region" by subdividing the dorsal tract into anterior, saddle, and posterior elements and the ventral tract into flank and main elements.

It is certainly confusing to use the term "region" for both a feather tract (or part of a feather tract) and a circumscribed anatomical part of the body. The distribution of a group of feathers is often but not always identical with the body region of the same name, chiefly because the feathers may occupy only a small part of the particular region, the remainder being a featherless area. Also, a feather group having the name of one region may extend into an adjacent region. A tract, such as the loral, does not exist as a named anatomical region. The occipital tract approximates the parietal region in its placement on the head. It could not correspond in location to the occipital region because this region is fully covered by neck muscles. Therefore, to avoid possible ambiguity in this publication, we have termed all feather groups "tracts," and we have reserved the term "region" for areas of the body, independent of plumage. Nitzsch did not use the term "region" to indicate a subdivision of a tract, instead he called such subdivisions parts when they were linear in arrangement and he called them branches when they were offshoots from the main tract. Nitzsch used the term "tract," not only for large feathered areas but also for small groups as we have done here; an example is his use of the terms "anal tract" and "oil-gland tract." Nitzsch (1867) used the name "featherless space" in referring to an apterium.

During the course of preparing this chapter and the next, it soon became apparent that some new names had to be selected to designate groups of feathers not specifically mentioned in the literature. Also it seemed desirable to change a few names well established in the literature to those that would be less controversial or less ambiguous and that more specifically designated the group of feathers to which reference was being made. These changes, as well as all other names used throughout the text and illustrations, are listed in the key to the feather tracts that follows this paragraph. The changes are discussed throughout the text. Also, the list of featherless spaces on page 93 should be examined because featherless spaces are inseparably associated with the tracts; without the one, there cannot be the other. The lists of tracts and spaces can be confusing to those covering this subject for the first time without previous background, but they will be aided by the frequent references made to figures 50 to 52 of the Great Horned Owl and to the numerous illustrations in chapter 3. The old terminology reviewed and the new terminology introduced in this chapter are the tools we use in succeeding chapters to describe domestic birds.

In the following key to the feather tracts (*pterylae*) and subdivisions, some of the named tracts apply only to the owl; most of them, however, apply to the domestic birds discussed in this and the following chapter.

Capital tracts (*pterylae capitales*)
  Frontal tract (*pteryla frontalis*)
  Coronal tract (*pteryla coronalis*)
  Occipital tract (*pteryla occipitalis*)
  Auricular tract (*pteryla auricularis*)
  Postauricular tract (*pteryla postauricularis*)
  Temporal tract (*pteryla temporalis*)
  Loral tract (*pteryla lorata*)
  Superciliary tract (*pteryla supercilii*)
  Ocular tracts (*pterylae oculares*)
    Upper ocular tract (*pteryla ocularis superior*)
    Lower ocular tract (*pteryla ocularis inferior*)
  Genal tract (*pteryla genae*)
  Rictal tract (*pteryla rictus*)
  Malar tract (*pteryla malaris*)
Spinal tracts (*pterylae spinales*)
  Dorsal cervical tract (*pteryla cervicalis dorsalis*)
    Lateral cervical tract (*pteryla cervicalis lateralis*)
  Interscapular tract (*pteryla interscapularis*)
  Dorsal tract (*pteryla dorsalis*)
    Lateral scapular tract (*pteryla scapularis lateralis*)
  Pelvic tract (*pteryla pelvina*)
  Lateral pelvic tract (*pteryla pelvina lateralis*)
Lateral body tract (*pteryla corporalis lateralis*)
Ventral tracts (*pterylae ventrales*)
  Ventral cervical tract (*pteryla cervicalis ventralis*)
    Interramal tract (*pteryla interramalis*)
    Submalar tract (*pteryla submalaris*)
  Pectoral tract (*pteryla pectoralis*)
    Lateral pectoral tract (*pteryla pectoralis lateralis*)
    Medial pectoral tract (*pteryla pectoralis medialis*)
  Sternal tract (*pteryla sternalis*)
  Abdominal tract (*pterylae abdominales*)
    Lateral abdominal tract (*pteryla abdominalis lateralis*)
    Medial abdominal tract (*pteryla abdominalis medialis*)
    Cloacal tract (*pteryla cloacalis*)
    Cloacal circlet (*circulus cloacalis*)
Caudal tracts (*pterylae caudales*)
  Dorsal caudal tract (*pteryla caudalis dorsalis*)
  Lateral caudal tract (*pteryla caudalis lateralis*)
  Tail feather(s)—rectrix, rectrices (*rectrix, rectrices*)
  Upper major tail coverts (*tectrices caudales majores superiores*)
  Upper median tail coverts (*tectrices caudales medianae superiores*)
  Upper minor tail coverts (*tectrices caudales minores superiores*)
  Oil duct circlet (*circulus uropygialis*)
  Ventral caudal tract (*pteryla caudalis ventralis*)
  Under major tail coverts (*tectrices caudales majores inferiores*)

Caudal tracts (*pterylae caudales*)—Continued

Under median tail coverts (*tectrices caudales medianae inferiores*)
Under minor tail coverts (*tectrices caudales minores inferiores*)

Downs of the tail (*plumae caudae*)

Upper proximal downs of tail (*plumae proximales superiores caudae*)
Upper distal downs of tail (*plumae distales superiores caudae*)
Under distal downs of tail (*plumae distales inferiores caudae*)

Tracts of the anterior appendage (wing) (*pterylae membri anterioris (ala)*)

Brachial tracts (*pterylae brachiales*)

Humeral tract (*pteryla humeralis*)
Subhumeral tract (*pteryla subhumeralis*)
Posthumeral tract (*pteryla posthumeralis*)

Upper posthumeral coverts (*tectrices posthumerales superiores*)
Posthumeral quills (*pennae posthumerales*)
Under posthumeral coverts (*tectrices posthumerales inferiores*)

Alar tracts (*pterylae alares*)

Hand (*manus*)

Primary remiges (*remiges primariae*)
Upper primary coverts (*tectrices primariae superiores*)

Upper major primary coverts (*tectrices primariae majores superiores*)
Upper median primary coverts (*tectrices primariae medianae superiores*)
Upper minor primary coverts—first row (*tectrices primariae minores superiores—ordo primus*)
Upper minor primary coverts—second row (*tectrices primariae minores superiores—ordo secundus*)

Under primary coverts (*tectrices primariae inferiores*)

Under major primary coverts (*tectrices primariae majores inferiores*)
Under median primary coverts (*tectrices primariae medianae inferiores*)
Under minor primary coverts—first row (*tectrices primariae minores inferiores—ordo primus*)
Under minor primary coverts—second row (*tectrices primariae minores inferiores—ordo secundus*)

Alular remiges (*remiges alulae*)

Upper major alular coverts (*tectrices majores superiores alulae*)
Under major alular coverts (*tectrices majores inferiores alulae*)

Marginal coverts (*tectrices marginales*)

Upper marginal coverts of the hand (*tectrices marginales superiores mani*)
Upper marginal coverts of the alula (*tectrices marginales superiores alulae*)
Under marginal coverts of the hand (*tectrices marginales inferiores mani*)
Under marginal coverts of the alula (*tectrices marginales inferiores alulae*)

Wrist (*carpus*)

Carpal remex (*remex carpalis*)
Upper carpal coverts (*tectrices carpales superiores*)

Upper major carpal covert (*tectrix carpalis majoris superior*)
Upper median carpal covert (*tectrix carpalis medianae superior*)
Upper minor carpal covert (*tectrix carpalis minoris superior*)

Under carpal coverts (*tectrices carpales inferiores*)

Under major carpal covert (*tectrix carpalis majoris inferior*)
Under median carpal covert (*tectrix carpalis medianae inferior*)
Under minor carpal covert (*tectrix carpalis minoris inferior*)

Forearm (*antebrachium*)

Secondary remiges (*remiges secundarii*)
Upper secondary coverts (*tectrices secundariae superiores*)

Upper major secondary coverts (*tectrices secundariae majores superiores*)
Upper median secondary coverts (*tectrices secundariae medianae superiores*)
Upper minor secondary coverts—first row (*tectrices secundariae minores superiores—ordo primus*)

Tracts of the anterior appendage (wing) (*pterylae membri anteriores (ala)*)—Continued

Alar tracts (*pterylae alares*)—Continued

Forearm (*antebrachium*)—Continued

Upper secondary coverts (*tectrices secundariae superiores*)—Cont.

Upper minor secondary coverts—second row (*tectrices secundariae minores superiores—ordo secundus*)

Marginal coverts (*tectrices marginales*)

Upper marginal coverts of the prepatagium (*tectrices marginales superiores prepatagii*)
Under marginal coverts of the prepatagium (*tectrices marginales inferiores prepatagii*)

Under forearm tract (*pteryla antebrachialis inferior*)

Downs of the wing (*plumae alae*)

Hand (*manus*)

Upper primary downs (*plumae primariae superiores*)

Upper distal primary downs (*plumae primariae distales superiores*)
Upper median primary downs (*plumae primariae medianae superiores*)
Upper proximal primary downs (*plumae primariae proximales superiores*)

Under primary downs (*plumae primariae inferiores*)

Under distal primary downs (*plumae primariae distales inferiores*)
Under proximal primary downs (*plumae primariae proximales inferiores*)

Alular downs (*plumae alulae*)

Upper alular downs (*plumae superiores alulae*)
Lower alular downs (*plumae inferiores alulae*)

Wrist (*carpus*)

Upper carpal downs (*plumae carpales superiores*)

Upper distal carpal down (*pluma carpalis distalis superior*)
Upper proximal carpal down (*pluma carpalis proximalis superior*)

Under carpal downs (*plumae carpales inferiores*)

Under distal carpal down (*pluma carpalis distalis inferior*)
Under proximal carpal down (*pluma carpalis proximalis inferior*)

Forearm (*antebrachium*)

Upper secondary downs (*plumae secundariae superiores*)

Upper distal secondary downs (*plumae secundariae distales superiores*)
Upper median secondary downs (*plumae secundariae medianae superiores*)
Upper proximal secondary downs (*plumae secundariae proximales superiores*)

Under secondary downs (*plumae secundariae inferiores*)

Under distal secondary downs (*plumae secundariae distales inferiores*)
Under proximal secondary downs (*plumae secundariae proximales inferiores*)

Tracts of the posterior appendage (*pterylae membri posterioris*)

Femoral tract (*pteryla femoris*)

Anterosuperior angle (*angulus anterio superior*)
Posterosuperior angle (*angulus posterio superior*)
Inferior angle (*angulus inferior*)
Infracaudal margin (*margo infracaudalis*)
Tensor muscle of the femoral tract (*M. tensor pterylae femoralis*)

Crural tracts (*pterylae crurales*)

External crural tract (*pteryla cruralis externalis*)
Internal crural tract (*pteryla cruralis internalis*)
Crural flag (*vexillum crurale*)

Metatarsal tract (*pteryla metatarsalis*)
Digital tracts (*pterylae digitales*)

Some tracts in the deplumed bird are conspicuous because the feather follicles within the tract are large and close together. Usually the skin is thick, and the area of large feathers has sharply defined boundaries. These are named "strong tracts." Often associated with a strong tract is a subdermal body of fat that adds to the thickness of the skin in the area; the sharp margins of the fat body often coincide with the boundaries of the overlying tract. In contrast, other tracts have small feathers implanted in small follicles that are so far apart that the pterylae often have poorly defined boundaries. In these areas, subdermal fat bodies are usually absent or present in a small amount. These are named "weak tracts". The same tract may be strong in one part and weak in another.

The humeral tract and the cervical portion of the spinal tract are examples of strong tracts. The sternal tract may be weak in its anterior end and strong throughout the remainder of its length. The lateral abdominal tract is weak in the chicken; in the other species examined, it is replaced by an apterium. An interruption in the continuity of a tract may occur as either a real gap or a false gap, according to Nitzsch (1867:20). The former is a featherless area within a tract, the latter is an apparent space but is occupied by contour feathers. These feathers are smaller than those that form the main body of the tract and may resemble down feathers. In this study, large and small contour feathers were included as part of a tract. Tracts may be divided or double, and among various species a tract may be present in one species and absent in another, as described by Nitzsch (1867). Therefore, the pterylosis of a bird can be used as a taxonomic character (Heimerdinger, 1964:213).

Capital Tracts

The capital tract was named by Nitzsch (1867), who regarded it as a single tract. This tract has been subdivided by Boulton (1927), Burt (1929), Miller (1931), Compton (1938), Miller and Fisher (1938), Fisher (1943), and Pitelka (1945). In this publication we followed Compton (1938), who included the feathers of the malar region as a subdivision of the capital tract. Like Compton, we regard the interramal and submalar regions as anatomical parts of the head. Furthermore, in dealing with the pterylography, we agree with Compton that it is preferable to treat the interramal and submalar tracts as the two anterior parts of the ventral cervical tract. The authors listed above designated capital tract in the singular, as did Nitzsch, but we have chosen to use it in the plural as a term covering a group of tracts.

Nitzsch suggested that the term "head tract" be applied also to the upper cervical portions of the spinal and ventral tracts as far as the point where they separate at the lateral cervical apterium. However, since the point of origin of this space is highly variable among different species of birds, this criterion for the boundary would lead to confusion. Therefore, it seems desirable to limit the capital tracts to the feathers of the head in spite of their continuity with those of the neck.

Compton (1938) is one of the few who has been willing to indicate boundary lines for each of the capital tracts (fig 45). He showed nine tracts, including the interramal and submalar, whereas in the feather tract key we listed 12, with a subdivision of the ocular into upper and lower parts. This difference in number is due to the fact that we have

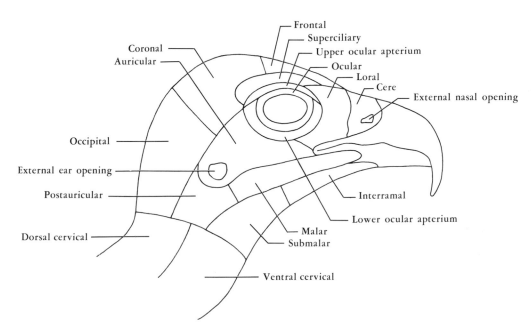

FIGURE 45.—Placement and boundaries for the capital tracts of the Osprey (*Pandion haliaetus*). (Redrawn from Compton, 1938, fig. 1).

included temporal, genal, and rictal tracts. If the location, size, and extent of tracts for the Osprey (*Pandion haliaetus*) (fig. 45) are compared with our application of this information to the chicken (figs. 53 and 54), the reason for these few differences becomes apparent; namely, in the Osprey (fig. 45) the auricular tract is outlined as an extensive area where-as in the chicken it is shown as a small area with a boundary enclosing the external ear opening (fig. 53). Compton, however, apparently established the boundaries for the auricular tract on the basis of the plumage arising from around the ear opening. If we circumscribe the auricular plumage in the chicken (fig. 54), we obtain a spread comparable to that shown for the Osprey. In the pigeon, the ptilosis of the auricular area is almost similar to that shown for the Osprey. The question, therefore, arises whether the boundaries for a tract should be based on the location of follicles on the skin or on the extent of the plumage that comes from those follicles? We have tried consistently to follow the former point of view in our studies of pterylosis and the latter point of view in our studies of ptilosis.

Spinal Tracts

Nitzsch (1867) used the term "spinal tract" to describe the location of the follicles on the dorsal surface of the body. We use the term "spinal tracts" (plural) and apply the term "tract" (singular) to each of its subdivisions. Nitzsch (1867: 21), in describing the spinal tract, stated, "This extends along the whole vertebral column, . . . from the nape of the neck to the tail, and is bounded by the lateral spaces of the neck and trunk."

Nitzsch listed only two subdivisions, whereas we have listed four that constantly occur and two that are found only in particular species. The four major subdivisions are dorsal cervical, interscapular, dorsal, and pelvic. Our terminology agrees with that of Humphrey and Butsch (1958) and Humphrey and Clark (1961) except that these workers used the term "regions" and we use "tracts." A lateral-scapular tract (region) was named by Compton (1938) and a lateral-pelvic tract (region) was named by Burt (1929) and by Compton (1938). As mentioned previously, we found it less confusing to place the origin of the dorsal cervical tract at the base of the head than to place it on the nape of the neck. As a synonym for Nitzsch's spinal tract, Heimerdinger (1964) suggested the term "dorsal tract," which she considered as extending from the capital tract to a point just anterior to the uropygial gland. We have used dorsal tract in the more limited sense of lying within the prodorsal region. The caudal termination is somewhat different from that given by Nitzsch and is discussed on page 78.

The term "lateral cervical tract" is not in common usage; in the two instances in the literature where it was used, it had different meanings. Actually, there is no true lateral cervical tract in birds, but Nitzsch (1867) applied the term to the condition found in herons, where, due to large dorsal and ventral cervical apteria, the two halves of the adjacent tracts are displaced laterally to such an extent that the lateral apteria are obliterated and a feather tract composed of the united halves of the dorsal and ventral tracts has come into existence on the side of the neck. On an entirely different basis, Burt (1929) applied the term in woodpeckers to a branch from the dorsal cervical tract that projected into the lateral cervical apterium.

The interscapular tract is an important part of the spinal tracts and was recognized as a distinct unit by Humphrey and Butsch (1958) and Humphrey and Clark (1961) in ducks, by Pycraft (1898) in owls, by Boulton (1927) in the House Wren (*Troglodytes aedon*), by Burt (1929) in woodpeckers, by Pitelka (1945) in the Scrub Jay (*Aphelocoma coerulescens*), and by others. In some species, such as the chicken, it stands apart as a group of follicles and feathers distinct from the anteriorly located dorsal cervical tract. In other species no natural boundary occurs between these two tracts and the separation is arbitrary; it is usually placed across the base of the neck at the anterior level of the shoulders. The interscapular tract then extends from this transverse line caudally to a level between the last cervical and the first thoracic vertebrae.

Heimerdinger (1964), like Nitzsch (1867), extended the capital tracts onto the dorsal neck; for Nitzsch the capital tract ended at the level where the lateral cervical apterium began, and for Heimerdinger it ended at the point of transition in the direction of rows from the midline. In the neck portion of the capital tract, as identified by Heimerdinger, the apexes of the pairs of rows are directed caudally, and the rows extend forward along the dorsal surface and side of the neck. Where the rows change direction and the apexes point forward, marks the beginning of Heimerdinger's dorsal tract. (We call this the interscapular tract.) This group of follicles is continuous with all those that follow it, as far as the oil gland papilla on the dorsal tail. Caudal to the interscapular tract is the dorsal tract and immediately posterior to this, the pelvic tract. What we have designated "dorsal tract," Heimerdinger has named "saddle element," and what we have named "pelvic tract," she has named "posterior element."

The dorsal and pelvic tracts are broadly continuous in the species we have examined, but in the passerines studied by Heimerdinger (1964) there is always a sharp discontinuity at the common boundary. Humphrey and Butsch (1958) found unbroken continuity between dorsal and pelvic tracts in the Labrador Duck (*Camptorhynchus labradorius*). In such a situation, for the sake of convenience, one may use the term "dorsopelvic tract" to designate these two combined as one. Similar continuity is present in the five kinds of domestic birds included in this study. When a natural boundary exists between dorsal and pelvic tracts, it should be used to separate the tracts, but if there is unbroken continuity, then the anterior end of the ilium should be utilized and accepted as an arbitrary boundary.

Most investigators extend the pelvic tract onto the dorsal tail so that all that remains to be included in the caudal tract are rectrices and their coverts. In our studies we have chosen to divide the pelvic and caudal tracts at the anatomical boundary between pelvis and tail. We have used the same boundary for separating the abdominal and ventral caudal tracts. Support for so doing is found in Nitzsch (1867: 31), who described the caudal tract as follows:

> This [the caudal tract] occurs on the true tail, or the last caudal vertebrae. From it originates the *rectrices*, and both the *upper* and *lower tail coverts* (*tegmina caudae superiora et inferiora*). It also includes the *oil-gland*, to which we shall refer more particularly hereafter. It likewise receives the posterior extremities of the spinal tract, the two truncal bands of the ventral tract, and the extreme portion of the lumbar tract.

Burt (1929), in his study of certain North American woodpeckers, designated a tract that lay lateral to the pelvic tract and parallel to it, as the lateral pelvic region (tract). This band of feathers continues on to the tail as far as the upper tail coverts (included in the feather tract key on page 74), but was not found in the five kinds of domestic birds under study. In the Red-tailed Hawk (*Buteo jamaicensis*), Compton (1938) identified a lateral pelvic region (tract) and also showed a group of three feathers on each side of the base of the tail that he labeled the postpelvic region, but this small group of feathers does not appear to be significant in his subsequent discussion of several species, and therefore it was omitted from the feather tract key.

Caudal Tracts

Included under caudal tracts in the feather tract key are 10 groups of feathers, among them are three rows of upper tail coverts and three rows of under tail coverts. In none of the birds that we have studied are all these rows present; often either the coverts are limited to upper and under major rows or the under covert rows are merely part of the ventral caudal tract.

A count of the rectrices is made by beginning at the midline and proceeding laterally. Although the number of rectrices is not constant within each species, the size, number, and arrangement are useful tools for taxonomic comparisons. Several authors have listed the number of rectrices among groups of birds (Nitzsch, 1867; Newton and Gadow, 1893–96; Miller, 1915, 1924b). Coues (1903: 124) diagrammed most of the tail types based on the whole tail and gave each a name. The shape is determined when the tail is closed or nearly closed. Chickens do not have a flat tail as do most birds. The name "vaulted type" is used to describe the arrangement of caudal feathers that resembles the roof of an A-frame house. The two medial feathers are commonly called deck feathers, a term that might erroneously lead one to believe they are coverts. In many species of birds the medial pair of rectrices lies at a different level than the remainder, as shown in the lateral view of the owl (fig. 51).

On the dorsal surface of some species is a circlet of small feathers at the tip of the uropygial papilla. The presence or absence of this oil gland circlet was previously considered to be of taxonomic value (Coues, 1903: 89).

Ventral Tracts

Nitzsch (1867: 26) gave a clear statement of the ventral tract and its subunits. He recognized three major divisions: a gular portion on the ventral side of the neck, a truncal portion on the breast and belly that is divided longitudinally, and a lateral offshoot of the truncal portion that he named the "lateral tract." To the first we have applied the term "ventral cervical tract," to the second, "sternal and abdominal tracts," and to the third, "pectoral tract."

Many of the names of the subdivisions of the ventral tract have been changed since Nitzsch developed his terminology for pterylography. We have followed closely those subdivision names used by Humphrey and Clark (1961), except for the substitution of the word "tract" for "region."

At the anterior end of the ventral cervical tract are two subdivisions, the interramal tract, corresponding in its boundaries to the interramal region, and the submalar tract, occupying the area of the submalar region. Generally, the ventral cervical tract divides to form two branches, one on each side of the midline. These have complete continuity with the pectoral tracts, and an arbitrary line of separation is placed at the anterior end of the shoulder.

Our use of the term "pectoral tract" is equivalent to the term "flank region," by Humphrey and Clark (1961) and to "flank element" by Heimerdinger (1964). Flank, in mammals, is defined as the side of the body between the ribs and pelvis and therefore would be equivalent to the lateral abdominal region; the pectoral tract, however, entirely overlies the rib cage and sternum ventral to the pectoral muscles. Our term, *"pteryla pectoralis,"* is similar to that used by Lowe (1925), *"pteryla ventralis pectoralis."*

The sternal tract lies on each side of the keel, sometimes close to it and sometimes far laterally. It may be narrow or wide, and it may have continuity with the pectoral tract, but in most species of birds, it does not.

The pectoral tract is often stronger than the sternal tract. In most species of birds the pectoral tract is single, but in the Great Horned Owl this tract has two parts, which are designated the medial and lateral pectoral tracts (figs. 51 and 52). The medial part is composed of large contour feathers, closely placed, but the feathers of the lateral part are farther apart; yet when observing the plucked bird, two distinct tracts are apparent.

Sometimes the pectoral and sternal tracts are confluent, thereby eliminating the pectoral apterium. Examples are the Northern Gannet (*Morus bassanus* (=*Dysporus bassanus*)), Nitzsch (1867: pl. 10); the White Pekin Duck, the Common Pigeon; and all passerines studied by Heimerdinger (1964). In some birds, as in the Great Bustard (*Otis tarda*) and the California Condor (*Gymnogyps californianus*), the tract of the pectoral region extends posteriorly and unites with the sternal tract, leaving an insular space, which Miller and Fisher (1938) designated as the "sternal apterium." In this study we have designated the space between the pectoral and sternal tracts as the "medial pectoral apterium" and that between the medial and lateral pectoral tracts as the "lateral pectoral apterium" (figs. 51 and 52). Generally, however, the apterium lateral to the pectoral tract has continuity with the lateral body apterium and therefore is not designated by a different name. Apteria are discussed more fully beginning on page 92.

The abdominal tract is continuous with the sternal tract and extends to and includes the vent. Most authors agree that the line of separation between the abdominal and sternal tracts is the posterior margin of the sternum. Burt (1929) used about the same names for subdivisions of the ventral tracts but applied them differently. The ventral tracts include the cloacal circlet, composed usually of a single row of small feathers surrounding the vent. When the cloacal circlet is not distinctly separated from the abdominal feathers on the anterior and posterior surfaces of the vent, then the feathers on the lip of the vent are included with the abdominal tract or its subdivision, the cloacal tract.

Four possible subdivisions are mentioned under abdominal tracts in the feather tract key on page 74; of these, the cloacal circlet and the cloacal tract have already been discussed. Of the remaining medial and lateral abdominal tracts, the medial abdominal is the only tract usually present. But in some birds, such as female chickens, where the "fluff" is large and covers the entire abdominal area, it seems too arbitrary to imply that the fluff feathers on the strong portion of the tract are the complete abdominal tract and that identical fluff feathers lateral to these belong to an apterium. In the chicken, the lateral abdominal tract is a weak tract composed of semi-plumes. In the turkey, however, the laterally placed feathers are downlike and far apart, and in this bird the position of the lateral abdominal tract of the chicken is occupied by a lateral abdominal apterium.

Lateral Body Tract

The lateral body tract is composed of feathers found on the lateral body surface. The only feathers conspicuous enough to constitute a tract are found below the axillary region within the prolatus. The lateral body tract is absent in the Great Horned Owl but is present in the domestic chicken, turkey, duck, Common Coturnix, and Common Pigeon. The feathers of the lateral body tract are covered by the folded wing.

Anterior Appendage Tracts

Brachial tracts

The tracts of the wing are divided into two groups—brachial tracts and alar tracts. The former are on the upper arm and, therefore, in a broad sense, might also be considered as alar tracts. Although the terminology given in the feather tract key departs from the time-honored precedent for naming tracts on the upper arm, the need for terms that specifically identify the location of these feather tracts seems to justify the change. We have substituted the term "subhumeral" for "axillar" and "axillary" and the term "posthumeral" for "tertiary" and "tertial." On the upper arm, therefore, are three tracts—the humeral tract on the dorsal

surface, the subhumeral on the ventral surface, and the posthumeral on the posterior margin.

The humeral tract is present in all birds illustrated by Nitzsch (1867); it is usually a strong tract and has well-defined boundaries. It forms a band that extends from the anterior edge of the shoulder and proximal corner of the prepatagium, across the arm, to the caudal edge of the metapatagium. The feathers of the humeral tract produce a lanceolate group of feathers that lies above the base of the wing, over part of the back, and extends beyond the posterior margin to fill the space between the wing and the body. Usually the anterior end of the tract crosses part of the shoulder joint, as already mentioned for the Great Horned Owl, but it may be located more distally on the arm as in the plantain-eaters (*Musophaga* spp.) or in the European Cuckoo (*Cuculus canorus*). Occasionally, the humeral tract may be double as in the Blue Coua (*Coua caerulea*) (Berger, 1953: 13), the Green Woodpecker (*Picus viridis*) (Shufeldt, 1888), and the Brown-throated Parrot (*Aratinga pertinax*). Burt (1929) named these two parts the "inner" and "outer humeral tracts" in the Pileated Woodpecker (*Dryocopus pileatus* (= *Ceophloeus pileatus*)). The humeral tract, or at least its posterior part, has also been designated the "scapulohumeral tract" by Humphrey and Clark (1961) and by Heimerdinger (1964).

The humeral tract is separated from adjacent tracts by featherless spaces—medially by the scapular apterium and distally by a space we have named the "humeral apterium." In some birds the humeral tract may be joined at its anterior end by one or more rows of feathers of the ventral cervical tract, as in the chicken (fig. 60). In the Northern Gannet, a lateral extension of the interscapular tract joins the medial side of the humeral tract thereby covering the dorsal shoulder (Nitzsch, 1867: pl. 10). In the Great Horned Owl, a few scattered contour feathers on the dorsal surface of the back—called the lateral-scapular region by Compton (1938)—form a small band joining the dorsal and humeral tracts (fig. 50). On the distal side of the humeral tract, the feathers of the upper marginal coverts of prepatagium may be so widely distributed that they extend to the edge of the humeral tract and thereby eliminate the humeral apterium, as in a Mousebird (*Colius colius* (= *C. capensis*)) and the Common Sandgrouse (*Pterocles exustus*), as illustrated by Nitzsch (1867: pls. 6 and 7). Only a small humeral apterium exists in the Bronze Turkey (fig. 73). In many species the proximal end of the posthumeral tract is joined to the caudal part of the humeral tract.

On the ventral side of the upper arm, in some species, is a group of large contour feathers, which are particularly apparent in the White Pekin Duck (Compton, 1938), the Red-tailed Hawk (*Buteo jamaicensis*), the Great Horned Owl (figs. 51 and 52), the chicken, and other domestic and laboratory birds (figs. 61, 75, 82, 90, and 97). Compton designated this group of feathers the "subaxillar region." This group has also been designated "axillars," which is probably the term most commonly used today. Thompson (1901) applied the term "hypopteron" to this same group of feathers. We propose that the terms "subhumeral tract" and "subhumeral feathers" be used instead. On the ventral surface of the brachium the group is equivalent anatomically to the humeral tract on the dorsal surface. Our objection to using "subaxillar" or "axillar" is that these terms do not accurately designate the region in which the feathers are implanted. The axilla, according to both Dorland's (1957) and Stedman's (1961) medical dictionaries, is the axillary fossa or armpit. The bird has an armpit which, as in man, is the fossa created by the junction of an arm to the side of the body and is bounded by adjacent muscles,[1] but these feathers are not located there; instead, they lie on the ventral surface of the upper arm, forming one or more longitudinal rows between the elbow joint region and the axillary fossae.

The feathers of the third group on the upper arm have been designated "tertiary remiges," "tertials," or "tertiaries" by many authors who have described the alar tracts of birds. Berger and Lunk (1954: 124) reviewed the synonyms and significance of this group of feathers and mentioned the term "parapteron" used by Degen (1894: xxi). These feathers are on the posterior margin of the upper arm between elbow and humeral tract and may be limited to a few at the elbow joint as illustrated by Berger (1953) in the Blue Coua (*Coua caerulea*), or they may be spread along half the length of the arm. Where present, they are usually slender contour feathers, which lack the rigidity that characterizes primary and secondary remiges. Occasionally the tertiaries are smaller and shorter than their coverts. This depends, however, on which rows are designated as tertials and which as coverts. We have assumed that the longest feathers should be designated "tertials" or "posthumeral quills" and the shorter ones above and below this row should be named the "upper" and "under tertial" or "posthumeral coverts." The name "posthumeral quills" has been used in labeling figures 46 to 49. The term "remiges" has been avoided, and the term "quills" is used instead.

The feathers of the most inferior row of the posthumeral tract, by their position, appear to be continuous with the secondary remiges, and are often downlike and generally small. In our study, wherever a group of feathers is found on the posterior region of the upper arm and the group is clearly not a continuation of the secondary remiges, the term "posthumeral tract" is used. These feathers are shown in the Great Horned Owl (fig. 50) but not in the same detail as in four other species of wild birds (figs. 46 to 49).

The posthumeral tract is commonly composed of two to four rows of feathers. These feathers differ from the primary and secondary remiges in four respects: (1) They are not pressed against the humerus; (2) the longest ones usually are not the most posterior row of feathers in the tract; (3) they are generally smaller and more flexible than primary or secondary remiges; and (4) if it is typical for afterfeathers to be present in contour feathers of the species, they will be present here on the quills as well as on the coverts, in contrast to their absence on remiges and rectrices.

---

[1] The musculature on the ventral side of the wing produces both an anterior and a posterior axillary fossa (see the turkey, fig. 31).

Some authors (for example, Burt, 1929) have applied the name "tertiaries" to all the rows of feathers. The term "parapteron" has likewise been used both for the remexlike feathers (Beddard, 1898: 9) and for the entire tract (Pycraft, 1898: 232, 237, pl. 24). The name *"parapterum"* was first applied to this tract of feathers by Nitzsch (1867: 31). The feathers have also been called humeral coverts (Reichling, 1915: 239).

The name "tertiary" or "tertial" was originally intended to show that the remexlike feathers on the upper arm were in a series with the primary and secondary remiges. It has long been recognized that these feathers are not continuous, and that tertiary or tertial, therefore, is an inappropriate term, a conclusion maintained by Degen (1894: xxi) many years ago.

The feathers of the posthumeral tract often merge with those at the posterodistal corner of the humeral tract and with the secondary remiges and their coverts. Distinctions between these groups may be arbitrary, as pointed out by Humphrey and Clark (1961: 376).

While it is often clear that the posthumeral quills are not in series with the secondary remiges, the covert row with which they have true continuity, if any, is not so evident. The posthumeral quills have been considered to be continuous with either the upper minor or the upper major secondary coverts (summarized by Humphrey and Clark, 1961: 376). It is frequently impossible, however, to follow the rows with certainty; if there is any continuity at all between the secondary remiges and one of the rows of the posthumeral tract, it is with the under major posthumeral coverts, but as mentioned earlier, these are often small and downy. In the Falconiformes (Compton, 1938) there is a sharp change in feather type from secondaries to posthumerals and, as Compton has pointed out (p. 20), "The tertiaries are not a continuation of the secondaries but are homologous with the lesser upper secondary coverts. The row that is homologous to the secondaries is the second row of under tertial coverts (middle under tertial coverts)." Some of the difficulties inherent in placing an exact line of demarcation between secondaries and tertiaries are indicated by Miller (1925) in his study in the male Mandarin Duck (*Aix galericulata*) of a large fan-shaped feather located at about this point of junction.

We have chosen the point of demarcation between secondaries and posthumerals as the proximal end of the ulna. The follicles joined to the ulna by a ligament or those unattached but directed toward the ulna are regarded as secondaries; those having a juxtaposition to the humerus are designated as posthumerals or tertials. When the proximal secondaries differ morphologically from the remainder of the secondaries, some authors (Newton and Gadow, 1893–96: 957; Dwight, 1900a: 89; Kortright, 1942: 16) applied to these proximal secondaries the name "tertials." Van Tyne and Berger (1959: 83) pointed out a problem that can arise when this is done, ". . . we are completely lost when making comparisons with species in which these feathers do not differ morphologically."

We have attempted to present evidence and reasons for avoiding the ambiguity and connotations of tertiary or tertial and, as already stated, have suggested the term "posthumeral

TABLE 2.—*Summary of feather rows found in the posthumeral tracts of several species of wild birds*

Figure No.	Species and reference	Upper posthumeral coverts	Posthumeral quills	Under posthumeral coverts	
				1st row	2d row
46....	Horned Grebe (original data)................	x	x	x	
47....	Mallard (Humphrey and Clark, 1961: 376) and (original data)........	x	x	x	
	Falconiform birds (Compton, 1938: 202)..	x	x	x	x
48....	Red-tailed Hawk (original data)........	x	x	x	
	Woodpeckers (Burt, 1929: 431)............	x	x		
	Common Starling (original data)........		x	x	
49....	Common Crow (original data)........	x	x	x	x

tract" for feathers on the posterior margin of the upper arm that clearly are not secondary remiges or their coverts. The listing of rows found in certain birds is shown in table 2.

The text thus far has dealt with general terminology for the feather groups on the upper arm and particularly the posthumeral tract. It seems desirable to amplify the description of the four species of wild birds beyond that given in table 2 and to discuss figures 46 to 49 in more detail.

The Horned Grebe (*Podiceps auritus*) (fig. 46), representing a podicipediform, has the last of its 20 secondary remiges located around the curvature of the cubitus. Dorsal to the secondary remiges are three barely distinguishable rows of coverts, which have been labeled major, median, and minor upper secondary coverts.

The feathers of the posthumeral tract are shown between the proximal end of the series of secondary remiges and the posterior end of the tract. The row having the largest feathers is labeled posthumeral quills (there are nine of these), those dorsal to this row are called upper posthumeral coverts, and those inferior to it, the under posthumeral coverts. A small feather is present between the first posthumeral quill and the humeral tract. This feather might be the first in the series of posthumeral quills. Not every posthumeral quill has an upper covert. In the specimen examined, feathers overlaid quills 3 to 9 so that quills 1 and 2 were without coverts. The upper posthumeral coverts, 3' to 9', were separated farther from the quills than were the under coverts. In the latter series, under major posthumeral coverts began with 3″ and continued to 8″. In this species the rows are curved together, but it appears as if the row of under posthumeral coverts was in line with the secondary remiges.

The Mallard is representative of the Anseriformes. Dorsal to the secondaries of the Mallard are three distinct rows— upper major, median, and minor secondary coverts (fig. 47). The pterylosis of the proximal end of the secondaries in the Mallard is similar to that in the White Pekin Duck (figs. 91 and 94). The remiges each have an under major secondary covert, except the last one, in this case the 19th. The shafts of the coverts extend somewhat diagonally across the shafts of the remiges.

The posthumerals, 1 to 7, are relatively large, widely spaced feathers. Dorsal to them lies a single row of upper posthumeral coverts, 2' to 7'; 1' of the series is absent. Beneath the posthumeral quills is a single row, the under posthumeral coverts, from 1″ to 6″. Proximal to these, additional feathers extend along the same margin as the posthumeral quills but lie entirely under the large feathers of the humeral tract and therefore are not included as part of the posthumeral tract. Any conclusions in regard to continuity between a particular row of the posthumerals and the secondary remiges are purely speculation when based only on the adult bird. In figures 47 and 91 the upper posthumeral coverts appear to be contin-

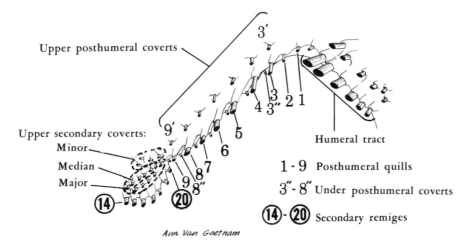

Ann Van Goetham

FIGURE 46.—Posthumeral tract and adjacent feathers in the Horned Grebe (*Podiceps auritus*). Dorsal view of left wing.

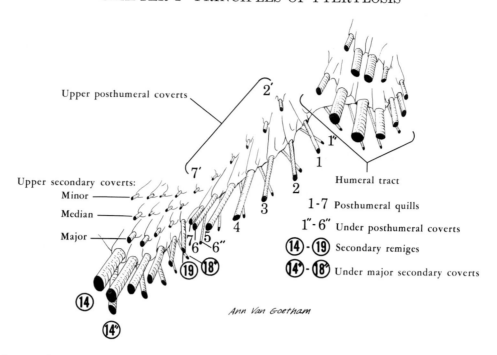

FIGURE 47.—Posthumeral tract and adjacent feathers in the Mallard (*Anas platyrhynchos*). Dorsal view of left wing.

uous with either the upper minor or median secondary covert rows.

In the Red-tailed Hawk, a falconiform, the arrangement of feathers on the posthumeral tract (fig. 48) is similar to that already mentioned in the podicipediforms and anseriforms. There are 15 large secondary remiges and two additional ones, the 16th and 17th, that are distinctly smaller and rather more widely spaced. Probably the 16th and 17th,

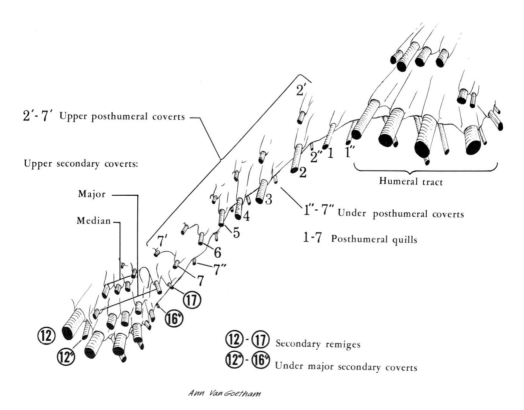

FIGURE 48.—Posthumeral tract and adjacent feathers in the Red-tailed Hawk (*Buteo jamaicensis*). Dorsal view of left wing.

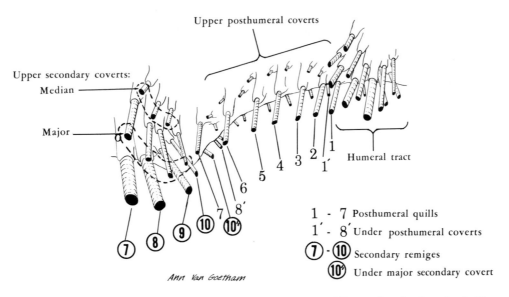

FIGURE 49.—Posthumeral tract and adjacent feathers in the Common Crow (*Corvus brachyrhynchos*). Dorsal view of left wing.

but certainly the 17th, lie on the humerus rather than on the forearm. In fact it is doubtful if the 17th is a secondary remex. The upper major secondary coverts form a distinct group whose feathers are relatively large.

The axis of the row for the posthumeral quills cuts diagonally toward the upper median secondary coverts and perhaps even to a higher level. These quills are numbered 1 to 7, and above them lie the upper posthumeral coverts 2' to 7'. The under posthumeral coverts, 1″ to 7″, are shown lying on the proximal side of each posthumeral quill. In the hawk there may be some question as to whether 1″ is actually the first under posthumeral covert or if it should be assigned to the group of small contour feathers immediately below the humeral tract. We observed a total of three rows in the posthumeral tract of the Red-tailed Hawk (fig. 48 and table 2). Compton (1938: 202) stated that in falconiforms there were two rows of under coverts and one row of upper coverts. These, added to a row of quills, make a total of four rows. This difference in the number of rows may be due to variability among individual birds of this order.

Passerine birds are represented by the Common Crow (*Corvus brachyrhynchos*), in which 10 secondary remiges have been identified. In figure 49, the last four of the 10 are shown. Immediately above them are four upper major secondary coverts, each corresponding to its equivalent remex. The group is circled by dashed lines for easy identification. Dashed lines also enclose three upper median coverts, which probably represent 8, 9, and 10.

It is difficult to draw a line clearly distinguishing the last feather at the distal edge of the humeral tract from the first feather at the proximal end of the posthumeral tract. Figure 49 shows seven posthumeral quills but this could vary by one. In this as in the other examples shown in this series of drawings, the direction taken by the row of posthumeral quills is toward the upper minor or median secondary coverts. The

row of seven upper posthumeral coverts has at the distal end of the row an additional feather that may be number 8, corresponding to a missing quill. Each under posthumeral covert lies on the proximal side of its posthumeral quill.

Alar tracts

The alar tracts have been studied more than any other plumage group. Out of these studies has come a large number of subdivisions, as indicated by the length of the list on page 75. These subdivisions have many synonyms, some of which were compared in a table by Wray (1887a). The large, stiff, pennaceous feathers that project posteriorly from the postpatagium in a single row are called the flight feathers or remiges. Above and below these are several overlapping rows of feathers called coverts. The feathers on the ventral side are often smaller and less numerous than those on the dorsal side. A plan whereby only two edges, leading and trailing, converge to a point at the distal tip of the wing, would seem to predicate a simple organization, but actually the pattern of wing feathering is highly complex and can be resolved into something meaningful only when the embryology of the wing has been taken into account.

When the wing first develops, the anterior and posterior borders are rounded and the feather primordia are implanted on these rounded surfaces as well as on the dorsal and ventral surfaces (Wray, 1887a). With continued differentiation and growth, the wing flattens and the rounded margin reorganizes into the flattened upper and lower surfaces of the postpatagium. Some of the feathers now located on the bird's underside were at one time in the phylogenetic past located on the dorsal surface. To what extent there is actual rotational migration of feather follicles from dorsal to ventral surface during the development of the individual, has not been determined. Steiner (1917 and 1956), from his extensive study of feather development on the wing, was emphatic in his opinion that the pattern of the adult is clearly set forth in the earliest appearance of the follicles and that migration of feather groups and rows is phylogenetic rather than ontogenetic. The earlier studies of Pycraft (1899 and 1904) demonstrated that shifting of the rows could be clearly followed when the feather buds were forming on the wing. This shifting of feather rows from dorsal to ventral surface will by chance catch certain feathers on the edge of the growing patagium. These become the remiges, and it is obvious that they might not all have been in the same embryonic row of feather buds. Those not caught on the edge become coverts, and, depending on the relationships of the species, some coverts of one may be homologous with certain remiges of another. Even in the same species all remiges in a row may not be homologous. A further discussion of this point is presented (p. 88) after some definitions of terms have been given.

The remiges on the hand are called primaries or pinion feathers and those on the forearm, secondaries or cubitals. The vestigial digit II (often called digit I) of birds usually bears remiges called alular feathers or alulars. There is some question whether these should be called remiges or quills, but since they have an association with the skeleton, as do the primaries and secondaries, we have designated them as remiges. Sometimes the primaries are classified into two groups, the digitals and metacarpals, depending on the bones with which the bases of the quills are associated. The digitals are subdivided into three subgroups (Wray, 1887a)—predigital, middigital, and addigital. The location of each primary remex with respect to a particular phalanx of digit III is highly constant among most bird species.

The feather arising at the wrist joint is called the carpal remex (a term coined by Degen, 1894), and it may be fully developed, rudimentary, or absent. If absent, its location may be indicated by the presence of a carpal covert as in the House Wren (*Troglodytes aedon*) (Boulton, 1927). Sometimes only the carpal remex is present and the corresponding coverts are lacking, as in the woodpeckers (Burt, 1929). The location of a carpal remex and its upper covert is shown in the nestling of the Common Coucal (*Centropus sinensis*). These feathers lie in the row of upper major coverts between the hand and forearm (Shelford, 1900). Pycraft (1899, fig. 1, pl. 15), for the pigeon (*Columbia livia*), shows the carpal remex in the row between the primary and secondary remiges. The secondaries are remiges located in the forearm region; their number varies among species and is approximately associated with the length of the wing. The basal ends of the calami are attached by ligaments to the ulna.

The primary remiges are numbered from the carpal region outward by American workers, but in the opposite direction by most European workers. The American system of numbering the primary remiges has acceptability because the terminal feather is often small or absent; when absent it shifts the numbering one place with the result that homo-

logous feathers in closely related genera have different numbers. The term "remicle" has been given to the outermost primary when it is very small. The number of primaries is relatively constant for the various species and has taxonomic value. The number in various families of birds has been presented by Sundevall (1886), Gadow (1888), Jeffries (1891), and Miller (1924b). The ostrich has the greatest number, 16; the rheas have 12; and the storks, ibises, flamingoes, and grebes each have 11 primaries and one remicle. Most other birds have either 10 primaries and one remicle or 10 primaries alone without a vestigial feather. The chicken and Common Coturnix may have 11 as a variation from the normal number of 10. The Great Horned Owl has 10 primaries but is said to have a rudimentary 11th (Pycraft, 1898). In some passerine groups the number is further reduced to nine primaries without a 10th vestigial. Gadow (1888) suggested that the reduction from 12 to 11 took place by reduction of the metacarpal quills from seven to six, and that the reduction from 11 to 10 was in all cases brought about by a loss of the terminal primary.

Numbering of the secondaries begins at the wrist and continues to the elbow. In contrast to the primaries, which have a relatively constant number, the remiges on the forearm are highly variable as indicated by the fact that there are six in a hummingbird (Coues, 1903:118), 18 in the chicken, and 40 in an albatross (Coues, 1903:118). According to Steiner (1917), among the Galliformes, Cracidae have 15; Megapodii (Megapodiidae), 16; Gallidae (Phasianidae), 16 to 18; and Tetraoninae (Tetraonidae), 22. The Great Horned Owl has 19 secondaries (Pycraft, 1898), excluding the fifth secondary from the count. This is in agreement with our own observations (figs. 50 to 52). The presence or seeming absence of a fifth secondary will be discussed later in this chapter. Sundevall (1886) tabulated the number of secondaries and posthumerals for many orders and species of birds. Excluding posthumerals, he listed 18 for turkeys, 10 for the domestic chicken, and 11 for the Common Pigeon. Our counts for turkey, chicken, and pigeon are greater than Sundevall's.

The axial feather in the "American Standard of Perfection" (1953:30) was defined as "The short feather growing between the primaries and secondaries of the wing." On page 31 it was stated that key-feather is the "same as axial feather." In this case, reference was being made to the outermost remex on the ulna and not to the carpal remex. In our opinion the axial feather (of the poultryman) is the first secondary. Exactly which shall be designated as the first secondary feather has led to some lack of uniformity; Mitchell (1899) suggested that the carpal remex is the first secondary. This is a small feather located in the region of the wrist, between the proximal end of the primaries and the distal end of the secondaries. In Webster's Third New International Dictionary (Gove, 1965:153) axial feather is defined as: ". . . a small feather between the primary and secondary wing feathers of some

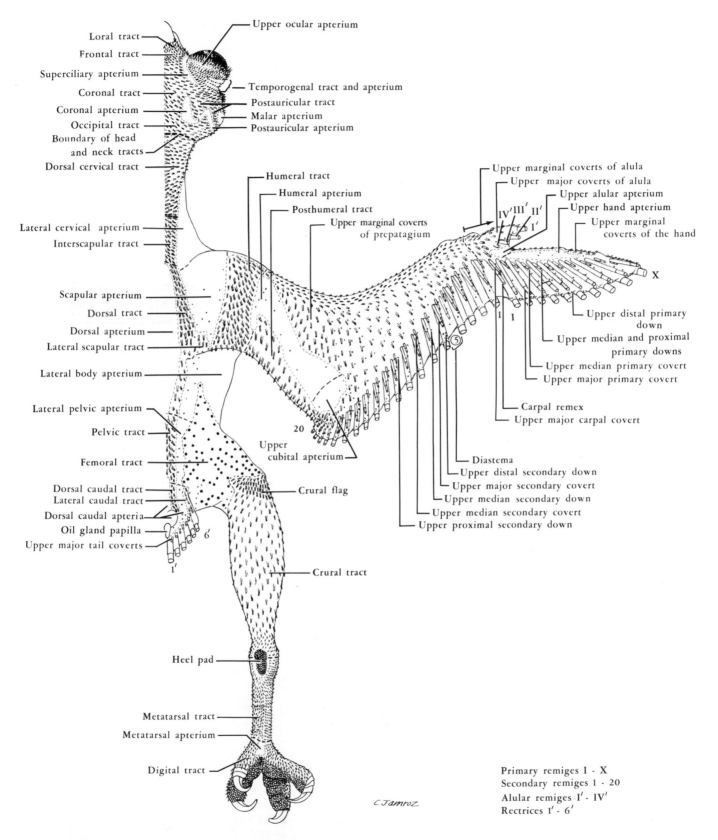

Figure 50.—Pterylosis of the Great Horned Owl (*Bubo virginianus*)—dorsal view. Follicles of down and semiplume feathers represented by dots. (Modified by Raynard LeNeil.)

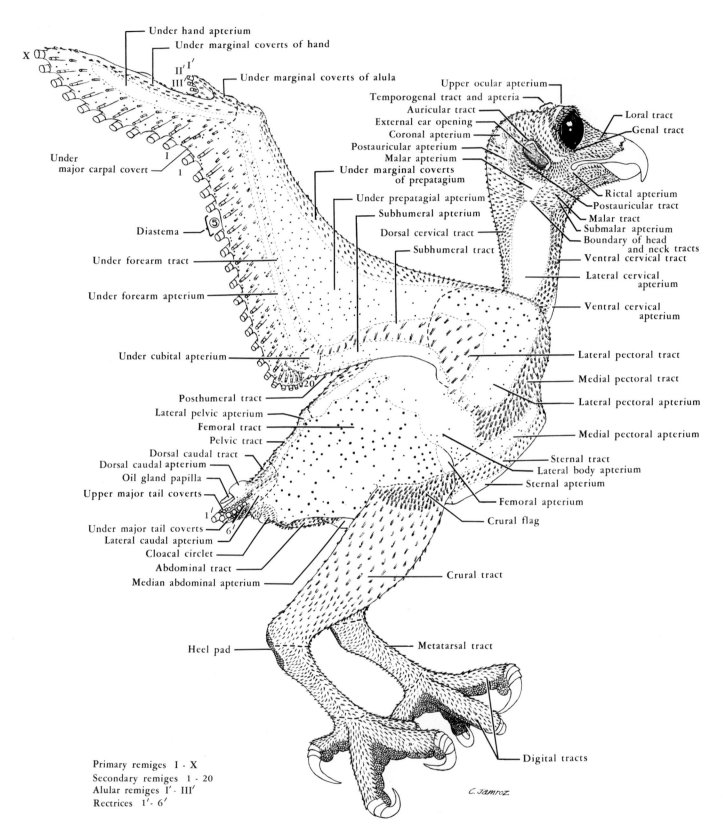

FIGURE 51.—Pterylosis of the Great Horned Owl (*Bubo virginianus*)—right lateral view. Follicles of down and semiplume feathers represented by dots. (Modified by Raynard LeNeil.)

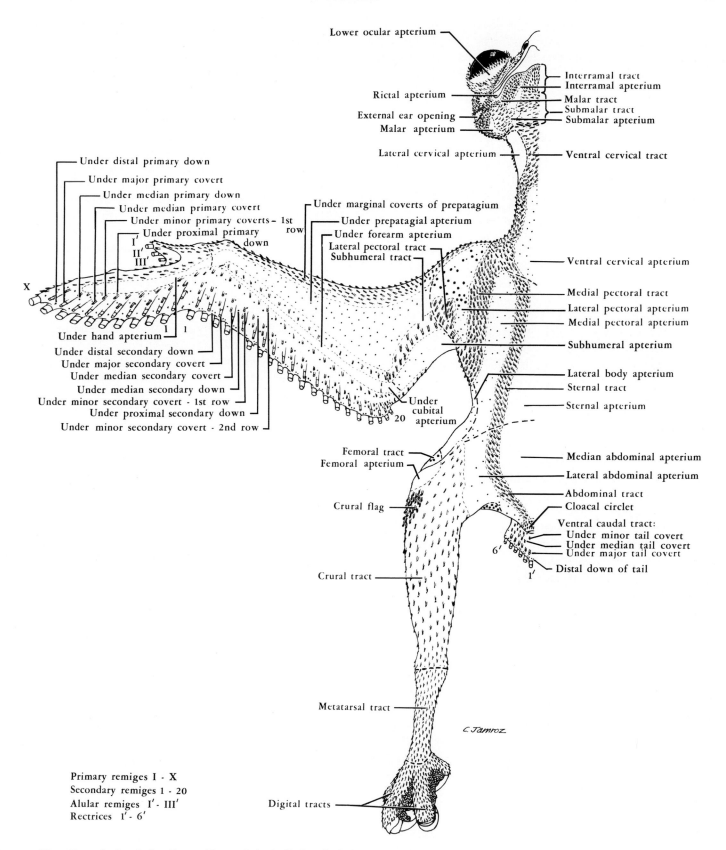

Lower ocular apterium
Interramal tract
Interramal apterium
Rictal apterium
Malar tract
External ear opening
Submalar tract
Malar apterium
Submalar apterium
Lateral cervical apterium
Ventral cervical tract

Under distal primary down
Under major primary covert
Under median primary down
Under median primary covert
Under minor primary coverts - 1st row
Under proximal primary down
I'
II'
III'

Under marginal coverts of prepatagium
Under prepatagial apterium
Under forearm apterium
Lateral pectoral tract
Subhumeral tract

Ventral cervical apterium
Medial pectoral tract
Lateral pectoral apterium
Medial pectoral apterium

X

Under hand apterium
Under distal secondary down
Under major secondary covert
Under median secondary covert
Under median secondary down
Under minor secondary covert - 1st row
Under proximal secondary down
Under minor secondary covert - 2nd row

Subhumeral apterium
Lateral body apterium
Sternal tract
Sternal apterium

Under cubital apterium
20

Femoral tract
Femoral apterium

Median abdominal apterium
Lateral abdominal apterium
Abdominal tract
Cloacal circlet
Ventral caudal tract:
Under minor tail covert
Under median tail covert
Under major tail covert
Distal down of tail

Crural flag

Crural tract

6'
1'

Metatarsal tract

C. Jamroz

Primary remiges I - X
Secondary remiges 1 - 20
Alular remiges I' - III'
Rectrices 1' - 6'

Digital tracts

FIGURE 52.—Pterylosis of the Great Horned Owl (*Bubo virginianus*)—ventral view. Follicles of down and semiplume feathers represented by dots. (Modified by Raynard LeNeil.)

birds." From this definition it is not possible to determine if Mitchell's "carpal remex" is intended or the poultryman's "axial feather." Pycraft (1899: 245) discussed both the carpal remex and the rudimentary first secondary as follows:

> . . . I think the probability is that the [carpal] "remex" is really correctly so named, and that it represents a feather more or less completely dwarfed and in course of disappearance. Its office—as a remex—has not entirely ceased. It is probably being slowly crushed out of existence by reason of its position, which is in the angle of the wing caused by the folding of the band on the forearm. The first cubital remex of the Gallinae is, like the carpal remex, and for the same reason, undergoing a similar process of reduction.

A gap, known as a diastema, is present in birds of many species between the fourth secondary and the secondary just proximal to it. This is shown in an owl (fig. 50) and a duck (figs. 88, 90, and 91). The condition was first noted by Gerbe (1877), who concluded that it was due to the absence of the fifth secondary. It was hence designated aquintocubitalism in contrast to quintocubitalism where the fifth secondary was present. Wray (1887a), Newton and Gadow (1893–96), and other workers of their time accepted the idea that a feather had been lost and that the secondary just proximal to a diastema was equivalent to the sixth in a quintocubital series.

Independently, but a few years later, Mitchell (1899) from his studies of adult anatomy and Pycraft (1899 and 1904) from his studies on embryos arrived at the idea that the space was not due to the loss of the fifth secondary but had resulted from the shifting of rows of feather follicles. Pycraft (1899) regarded eutaxism as typical of the primitive condition. Instead of the old terms, Mitchell suggested the terms "diastataxic" and "eutaxic," which are in general use today. A diastataxic wing has a diastema and a eutaxic wing does not. The evolution and selective advantage for the diastataxic wing are still controversial.

In our text and illustrations for owl, duck, and pigeon, the material has been treated as if there were a missing fifth. Until some of the differences of opinion are definitely resolved, it seems desirable to do this; if we number and label according to Pycraft, we will be wrong in respect to Steiner. It may be confusing to some who have followed this phase of pterylosis with painstaking exactitude (for example, Humphrey and Clark, 1961), but the plotting of feathers in the adult for the three species mentioned has failed to indicate the shifts others have described, the direction taken, and the presence of intercalary rows. The subject is discussed again in chapter 3 and even more thoroughly in chapter 8 after the feather musculature has been examined. Mitchell (1899) and Steiner (1917) have expressed the opinion that the diastataxic condition was the most primitive one and that subsequently the gap closed due to a shifting of adjacent feathers. Van Tyne and Berger (1959: 82) noted that "Many of the more primitive groups of birds are diastataxic; . . ." Steiner (1917 and 1956) strongly advocated this point of view. He regarded *Archaeopteryx* as diastataxic and stated that there was evidence for this type of feather development in the rhea embryos. He listed a table of many families to support his idea that diastataxy occurred more frequently among lower orders

of birds. His table should be compared with the groups listed below.

Later writers have also come to regard the origin of the space as due to a slippage of feather rows past each other in such a way that the portion of the original embryonic row from the fifth to the last secondary has rotated around the edge of the wing and become the under major coverts for the feathers that took their places and hence became the definitive secondary remiges. Steiner also was of the opinion that during the course of many generations there has been a slippage but in the opposite direction. The "catching" of dorsal feathers on the ventral side of the wing was well illustrated by Bates' (1918) study of under coverts. The inversion of feathers was noted earlier by Pycraft (1899). If an extension of the excellent studies of Holmes (1935) on the development of feathers in general could be combined with the newer techniques of the experimental embryologists and applied in detail to the wing of a diastataxic embryo, perhaps further information on the subject might be obtained.

Miller (1924b) carefully reviewed the distribution of eutaxic and diastataxic conditions among birds. This distribution is shown in the following tabulation taken from his work.[2] We changed many of the names to bring them up to date based on Wetmore's (1960) classification and on suggestions by Van Tyne (1959). In addition, we have done some regrouping.

Universally Diastataxic Forms

Gaviiformes	Loons.
Podicipediformes	Grebes.
Procellariiformes	Petrels, albatrosses, shearwaters.
Ciconiiformes	Herons, storks, ibises, flamingoes.
Anseriformes	Swans, ducks, geese, screamers.
Falconiformes	Hawks, vultures, falcons, osprey, secretary bird.
Charadriidae	Plovers.
Laridae	Gulls, terns.
Alcidae	Auks, puffins.
Pteroclidae	Sandgrouse.
Psittaciformes	Parrots, lories, macaws.
Strigiformes	Owls.
Caprimulgiformes	Oilbird, frogmouths, nightjars, goatsuckers, potoos.
Coraciidae	Rollers.

Both Eutaxic and Diastataxic Forms

Pelecaniformes	Snakebirds, pelicans, boobies (all diastataxic except one genus of cormorants).
Megapodiidae	Megapodes.
Gruiformes	Cranes, rails, limpkin, trumpeters, coots, gallinules, bustards.
Scolopacidae	Woodcocks, snipes, sandpipers (all diastataxic except *Philohela*).
Columbidae	Pigeons.
Apodiformes	Swifts, hummingbirds.
Alcedinidae	Kingfishers.

---

[2] Antedating Miller's tabulation is a shorter one by Pycraft (1899). A more recent list was presented by J. M. Harrison (*In* Thomson, 1964: 641).

Universally Eutaxic Forms

Struthioniformes................Ostrich.
Rheiformes....................Rheas.
Tinamiformes.................Tinamous.
Cracidae......................Curassows.
Phasianidae...................Pheasants, chicken, peafowl.
Numididae....................Guineafowl.
Meleagrididae................Turkeys.
Opisthocomidae...............Hoatzin.
Cuculiformes..................Cuckoos, turacos.
Coliiformes...................Colies.
Trogoniformes................Trogons.
Meropidae....................Bee-eaters.
Momotidae....................Motmots.
Todidae......................Todies.
Bucerotidae...................Hornbills.
Piciformes....................Jacamars, barbets, woodpeckers.
Passeriformes.................Broadbills, tyrant flycatchers, song-
                             birds.

The upper coverts (tectrices) fall typically into three groups—major (greater), median (middle), and minor (lesser). The under wing coverts fall into these same three groups. Coverts on the dorsal side of the wing are designated as "upper" and those below as "under".

The major and median coverts on both upper and under surfaces of the wing are each represented by a single row of feathers, whereas the minor coverts may be composed of more than one row. The major coverts lie adjacent to the remiges and cover their calami, the downy portions of the feathers, and the spaces between them. According to Wray (1887a: 345), there is supposed to be one major covert for each remex as follows: "Each remex is serial with the covert proximal to it, the cubital coverts crossing over the bases of the remiges. . . ." The next row in an anterior direction is formed by the median coverts, and the third row and perhaps the fourth is formed by the minor coverts. In a wing more primitive than that which exists in birds today, one would expect to find all rows complete from wrist to humeral tract, but in no living bird is this the case. During the evolution of the wing there has been a loss of the distal-most ends of these rows so that no definite statements can be made concerning feathers present or absent.

Among different kinds of birds, the presence or absence of certain parts of a row of under coverts—major, median, or minor—varies even more than it does in the upper coverts. This is because the plumage on the underside of the wing is not developed to the same high degree as it is on the upper side. Also, the feather primordia supposedly have migrated from the dorsal to the ventral surface. As a result of this migration, a row, which in the primitive bird may have represented the under major coverts, has been pushed forward, after moving around the edge, to become a row of under median or of under minor coverts. An illuminating discussion of this problem was given by Bates (1918), who cited as evidence the fact that the major and median rows of under coverts have the same orientation as the remiges. Thus, in relation to the under minor coverts, these under major and median coverts are seemingly reversed, and the term "re-

versed coverts" is applied to them. Bates (p. 530) cited the following interesting example:

> The reversed under coverts in the large Plantain-eater, *Corythaeola cristata*, have their dorsal surfaces of the same beautiful blue color as those of the remiges, though these surfaces lie flat against the bases of the remiges and upper coverts and are never exposed to the light, while the exposed ventral surfaces are dull black like those of the remiges, and like other feathers of the underside of the wing: thus the reversed coverts are brightly colored exactly like the upper wing feathers even though in their case the bright color is never seen.

The reversal of coverts on the under surface of the wing was mentioned briefly by Wray (1887a: 345) as follows:

> The tectrices majores and mediae on the ventral surface have at first sight an anomalous position. Being on the ventral side of the adult wing, one would expect the backs of the feathers to look ventralwards, whereas they look dorsalwards just as do the remiges.

Sundevall, a year earlier (1886: 118) had also noted reversed feathers.

Another point of diversity among different species of birds is the direction of overlap. The overlap in the remiges is constant and is the same in all birds, namely, the outer vane of one remex overlaps the inner vane of the next more distal remex. Some upper coverts of the major and median rows have the same orientation as the remiges and these are designated as "overlap conforming," whereas those tipped in the opposite direction are called "overlap contrary" or "overlap nonconforming." Part of a row may conform and the remainder may not conform. The feathers may be disturbed by mechanical means but ruffling returns the feathers to their established positions. Accidental disturbance of overlap pattern is not as big a factor as might be anticipated, and overlap is remarkably constant for various species (Goodchild, 1886 and 1891; Bates, 1918).

Just as the distal ends of the covert rows tend to be suppressed or to be shifted near the tip of the wing on the upper surface, the same is true for the under surface. This is clearly illustrated by Pitelka (1945) in a photograph of the wing of the Scrub Jay (*Aphelocoma coerulescens*), where the primary coverts are composed of only major and minor rows, the under median row of the arm ending in the carpal region. A similar absence of the under median primary coverts occurs in the House Wren (*Troglodytes aedon*) (Boulton, 1927). A detailed study of coverts was made by Bates (1918) for many species of birds representing numerous orders.

The alular remiges are attached on the distal margin of digit II (see p. 59 for the basis of naming the first digit as digit II). In some birds the alulars are said to be absent, but the point was questioned by Miller (1915). Among species, the number of alulars may vary from two to six but commonly is four. The alular feathers have a great range in size but are usually smaller than the primaries. Compton (1938) in his study of pterylosis in falconiforms did not indicate the order for numbering the alular quills, yet mentioned a vestigial fifth as being present or absent in association with the presence or absence of a claw on the pollex, so we assume the most posterior was counted as the first. Van Tyne and

Berger (1959: 83) spoke emphatically on the subject of numbering the alular quills as follows:

> Alula quills should be numbered from the innermost to the outer-most, since in the known cases of reduction in number within a taxonomic group, it is the outermost quills that are lost (see, e.g., Compton, 1938: 202–204); also, this order agrees with the order of molt (Mayaud, 1950: 59). Unfortunately, the practice has not been standardized, and such an eminent student of ptilosis as W. DeW. Miller (1924b: 318) numbered alula quills in the opposite order.

In all the material we have examined, the system of num-bering quills from anterior to posterior, as proposed by DeW. Miller, seems to assure homologous identification of quill I. The presence of a rudimentary quill appears to exist at the posterior rather than at the anterior end of the row and, therefore, in this study, number I is given as the most an-terior (nearest the tip) feather and in doing this, the presence or absence of a rudimentary feather does not then change the homologies of feathers having the same number.

Degen (1894: xxix) offered several reasons why the alula feathers should be called remiges: (1) They are closely as-sociated with underlying bones, (2) they have upper and under coverts, and (3) the under coverts are reversed in orientation as they are beneath the secondaries. He stated: "This . . . will show that the feather-quills of the *ala spuria* or *pennae pollicis* are true remiges."

The down feathers have generally been ignored, yet, on the wing in the region of the coverts, they are not merely scattered plumes; rather, they form definite rows and lie in definite positions relative to the follicles of remiges and coverts. Terms resulting from the classification system de-veloped in this study are listed in the key to the feather tracts on page 75. The pattern is definite and precise for the chicken. In other species the arrangement in rows may be much less definite. In the duck the downs are so abundant, no classifica-tion is applicable. A terminology of general applicability is as follows: Those downs near the free margin of the post-patagium are called upper distal primary and upper distal secondary down feathers; those lying near the middle of the remex calami are called upper median primary and upper median secondary down feathers; and those at the basal ends of the calami are called upper proximal primary and upper proximal secondary down feathers. On the ventral side of the wing, the word "under" precedes the above names for the downs. In the Great Horned Owl, the upper proximal primary down feathers are absent. In the chicken there are fewer rows than in the owl and the rows of down feathers are much more distinct, some of them showing a transition to small contour-type feathers.

Our examination of the ventral surface of the wing has led us to identify a small tract not previously named in the literature, namely, the under forearm tract. In the Great Horned Owl (fig. 51) it is a single row of feathers between the under coverts and the under marginals and separated from both of these groups by apteria. In the Common Coturnix (figs. 81, 82, and 86) this tract is also a single row. In the turkey (figs. 74, 75, and 79) it includes a group of several rows of feathers, randomly scattered.

The remaining feathers of the alar tract are the marginal coverts, which are small, contour-type plumes located largely on the prepatagium from the minor covert row to the free forward edge. It is often difficult to determine where the minor coverts end and the marginal coverts begin. Lack of distinction between upper marginal and upper minor coverts is discussed further in chapters 3 and 8.

Marginal coverts are present also on the hand. Those of the prepatagium may extend proximally along the leading edge as a narrow row to join the humeral tract at its forward edge. Marginal coverts of prepatagium form two major groups (1) those on the surface and (2) those, closely placed, on and near the leading edge.

The under marginal coverts are not as numerous as are those on the dorsal surface (the upper marginal coverts). Some of them possibly are derived from the dorsal integu-ment, which has rolled across the leading edge to the ventral side. This point, however, needs further study. The arrange-ment of marginal feathers gives the leading edge of the wing a rounded contour, which has been duplicated in the leading edge of the airplane wing. This arrangement functions in such a way as to create lift and prevent turbulence. In con-trast, the trailing margins of the wings of both birds and air-planes have thin edges. Even the bony structure of the hand carries out this same pattern. The Great Horned Owl shows the same adaptation to the mechanics of flight in the leading edge of the first primary remex; the barbs are short, stiff, curved bows, which give this edge a slightly rounded contour.

Posterior Appendage Tracts

The only tracts on the posterior appendage are femoral, crural, and in some birds, metatarsal and digital. The femoral tract is on the integument covering the thigh. In many birds it is a narrow, strong band with clearly defined margins, but this is not always the case; for example, in the chicken and in Great Horned Owl the femoral tract is spread over most of the surface of the thigh and extends forward onto the adjacent prolatus. The plumage from the infracaudal margin of this tract may extend backward beyond the appendage and merge with the sparse plumage covering the postlatus; only the margin adjacent to the crus is sharply defined.

The only part of the thigh visible from the medial side is the inner surface of the knee region. The feathers in this area tend to be more downy than those on the outer surface and are not considered to be part of the femoral tract. The femoral tract in woodpeckers is weak, consisting of a single row of feathers (Burt, 1929). On the other hand, Shufeldt (1888), working on the same group, depicted the thigh as nearly covered with feathers, some of which form a narrow, strong band. This lack of agreement on what should be included in the femoral tract is evident in the works of other authors also, although the problem as such has not been discussed. The form of the femoral tract may vary among species. This is indicated in the following examples: Boulton (1927) found that in the House Wren the femoral tract was limited to a narrow band on the boundary between postdorsum and thigh regions. Berger (1953 and 1957) depicted the feathers distributed over the entire external surface of the thigh region in a Blue Coua (*Coua caerulea*) and in an extinct starling (*Fregilupus varius*).

In certain species the rows of the femoral tract lie close together along the infracaudal margin, as illustrated by Berger (1953) for the Blue Coua and as shown in the chicken (figs. 64, *C*, and 265, *A*) and in the turkey (fig. 74). The contour feathers from these rows are long and well developed. In the chicken they produce a caudal extension of the femoral tract plumage that partially covers the rear body feathers, but these long feathers do not appear in the owl. A comparable function in the Great Horned Owl is met by the plumage of the crural flag. Beebe (1915) applied the terms "pelvic wing" and "pelvic alar tract" to this group of feathers. He observed in the squab, during the first 3 weeks, that the quills from the infracaudal margin of the femoral tract, including those of the crural flag, were unusually large. He suggested that phylogenetically this represented a pelvic wing and identified remiges and coverts. The usefulness of a wing in this location, even in the gliding of the primitive bird, *Archaeopteryx* (Nopcsa, 1923; de Beer, 1954), has been questioned.

The crural tract encircles the lower leg from the knee to the ankle joint. It may end short of the ankle joint as it does in herons, cranes, storks, flamingoes, rails, sandpipers, bustards, and others. The feathers in the crural tract are relatively far apart and do not as a rule form a dense plumage. The tract has been subdivided into external and internal tracts, corresponding to the external and internal surfaces of the crus; the plumage is weaker on the internal tract than it is on the external, and the feathers tend to be more downy. These statements imply that the external and internal tracts are well defined, but in reality any division line between them is arbitrary. In the chicken, where the feather muscles were studied, we found that the so-called "external tract" encompassed about three-quarters of the circumference and the "internal tract" was nearly devoid of feathers; this space has been named the intracrural apterium (fig. 266, *A*). For this reason the terms "external" and "internal" were not applied to the crural tract of the chicken and other species studied, including the Great Horned Owl, but they are listed in the key to the feather tracts because there may be some species for which these terms are applicable.

In some birds, such as hawks, owls, and many cuckoos, there may be a specialized group of large feathers called a crural flag in the knee region, just below the knee joint. The crural flag in the pigeon has already been mentioned. In the owl the crural flag is separated from the femoral tract by a femoral apterium (figs. 50 to 52). The follicles of the flag are close together and support large, long contour feathers, similar to those arising from the infracaudal margin of the femoral tract. There may be continuity between the two tracts, as Beebe (1915) found in the pigeon.

In grouse, owls, many hawks, and in numerous breeds of chickens, the feathers of the crural tract may continue down the leg onto the foot. Where these feathers extend but a short distance onto the metatarsus, they are included as part of the crural tract, as Compton (1938) reported for the Red-tailed Hawk. The term "crural flag," however, seems inappropriate where the feathering extends as far as the metatarsophalangeal joints and onto the surface of the toes as far as the claws, as in the Great Horned Owl (figs. 50 to 52). The terms "metatarsal tract" and "digital tract" are used when the feathers extend into these respective regions. The metatarsal tract may show complete feathering of the metatarsal portion of the foot, as in certain owls and in ptarmigans, or the feathering may extend only for varying distances down the metatarsus. Likewise, there are differences among species in the lateral and ventral extensions of the tract. In the Great Horned Owl the tract completely encircles the metatarsus except for the posterior surface of the ankle, which is occupied by the heel pad and a narrow longitudinal band, the metatarsal apterium. In the Ruffed Grouse, Cooper's Hawk (*Accipiter cooperii*), Red-tailed Hawk, and many of their allies, feathering is limited to the dorsal and lateral surfaces, and the ventral surface is bare and covered with scales. Plumage on the metartarsus is called continuous, because feathered and nonfeathered areas do not alternate, except for the Bank Swallow (*Riparia riparia*) in which the tract is interrupted, there being feathers on the upper end and a small tuft at the lower end just above the hind toe.

Feathering on the digital tracts is always limited to the dorsal surfaces, where the scutes are usually large; reticulate scales are present on the ventral surfaces. Wherever feathes and scales meet at the lateral margins of the toes there is a slight overlapping of the two types of integumentary structures, and each feather protrudes through or from beneath the lower margin of the scale. The first scale above the lowest feather is almost as tough and hard as the one below it, but each succeeding scale upward into the plumage is softer and less keratinized. By about the third or fourth scale, the structure has changed and the scales have merged into the general character of the integument. Blaszyk (1935) has described the relationship of feathers and scales for several species of birds, including the Tawny Owl (*Strix aluco*).

The feathering on the metatarsus and toes has long been thought to aid in keeping these parts of the posterior appendage warm. In order to arrive at a more scientific opinion on this subject, Kelso and Kelso (1936) studied the relationship of extent of foot feathering in owls to the environment. Although there was wide overlapping of toe and metatarsal feathering in relation to climatic zones, species with bare appendages tend to be present in tropical, subtropical, and temperate zones. Lack of foot plumage was associated also with humid environments. Those species of owls with metatarsus and toes fully covered with long, dense plumage were found predominantly in the cooler temperate to Arctic regions.

POWDER DOWN PATCHES

The existence of powder down patches has aroused the curiosity of many, but relatively few investigators have given them serious study. A summary of literature, as well as an original study of birds in which powder downs occur, was reported by Schüz (1927). Typically, a patch is recognized as a matted clump of waxy, down or semiplume feathers, hidden in part or completely by the longer surrounding contour feathers. There may be a transition to typical contour feathers as described in chapter 6 for the pigeon. See chapter 6, page 335, for a detailed description of powder-producing feathers as observed in the pigeon. The powder downs have been described as producing a powder-like talc that makes the powder down feathers slippery.

It has been difficult to establish clearly which species have powder down feathers and how these feathers are distributed over the body for the following reasons: (1) In some species the powder-bearing feathers are not grouped in patches but are scattered and isolated; (2) powder downs exist in all stages of transition from a typical contour feather that produces a little powder on its basal, plumulaceous portion to the truly distinct powder down feather; and (3) the small size of the powder particles and absence of identifying features.

As far as we know, powder feathers have not been reported for gallinaceous birds. The only suggestion of their presence is a statement by Schüz (1927) that, at the boundary between the downy base and the pennaceous part of contour feathers of francolins, large granules are scattered, and that a finer powder of homologous substance can be found in the domestic chicken. No details were given, however, and we have been unable to confirm the finding in chickens.

The number of pairs of patches varies from one to five, in addition to the diffused condition found in some birds. Murie's (1871 and 1872) terminology for classifying powder down patches according to their location on the body is as follows:

Dorsal patches
    Scapular portion
    Lumbar portion
    Iliac portion
    Caudal portion
Carino-ventral patches
    Sternal portion
    Abdominal portion
    Cloacal portion
Lateral sterno-ventral patches
    Pectoral portion
    Gastric portion
Coracoid patches
    Furcular portion
Costo-thoracic patches

Cranio-nuchal patches
    Head portion
    Nape portion
    Throat portion
Lateral neck patches
Humeral patches
    Brachial portion
    Axillary portion
    Cubital portion
    Alar portion
      Anterior
      Posterior
Femoral patches
Crural patches

Murie applied the foregoing terminology to the Kagu (*Rhynochetos jubatus*) (illustrations in Murie, 1871). Apparently there has been no significant attempt to re-evaluate these terms. The names that he gave to the patches and to their subdivisions, which he called portions, indicate the area or region of the body to which they applied. Not all authors have followed Murie's terminology. For example, Lowe (1924), in his description of the five pairs of powder down patches in the mesite (*Mesoenas unicolor*), used names that also described patch locations, but only a few were the same as those given by Murie. We have not given Latin name equivalents in Appendix B to powder down patches. We believe that this area needs extensive restudy and a re-evaluation of existing terminology. This has not been attempted here because there was insufficient time to digress from our study of domestic birds to those wild birds in which powder downs are well developed.

Murie (1872) described in some detail the location of each of the patches found in the Kagu. Although no classification of the patches would be fully applicable to all birds, Murie's principle of choosing terms corresponding to the regions of the body does seem to have general applicability. Another problem arises—establishing a boundary for each patch and portion. As brought out in figure 226, page 336, many patches are diffuse and spread over a relatively large area without sharply defined limits.

APTERIA

The featherless spaces (apteria) are not as appropriately named or well defined as are the tracts. Featherless spaces may exist due to the absence of a tract, or they may appear within tracts as insular spaces, or as spaces between the two parts of a divided tract, or as spaces between adjacent tracts. The attitude of most observers has been to regard the apteria as merely the spaces left after the tracts have been described, and to a certain extent this is true; as a result, a fully satisfactory terminology for the apteria is lacking. Based on the assumption that a featherless space may occur within any of the body regions—either as part of a region, if the remainder is occupied by a feather tract, or as filling the whole region, if feathers are entirely absent or the space is occupied by down feathers—we present the following list of featherless spaces (*apteria*). On this basis the boundaries of the capital apteria are the same as those for the tracts and have the same names as the tracts.

Capital apteria (*apteria capitalia*)
 Frontal apterium (*apterium frontale*)
 Coronal apterium (*apterium coronale*)
 Occipital apterium (*apterium occipitale*)
 Auricular apterium (*apterium auriculare*)
 Postauricular apterium (*apterium postauriculare*)
 Temporal apterium (*apterium temporale*)
 Loral apterium (*apterium loratum*)
 Superciliary apterium (*apterium supercilii*)
 Ocular apteria (*apteria ocularia*)
  Upper ocular apterium (*apterium oculares superius*)
  Lower ocular apterium (*apterium oculares inferius*)
 Genal apterium (*apterium genae*)
 Rictal apterium (*apterium ricti*)
 Malar apterium (*apterium malare*)
Spinal apteria (*apteria spinalia*)
 Dorsal cervical apterium (*apterium cervicale dorsale*)
 Interscapular apterium (*apterium interscapulare*)
 Scapular apterium (*apterium scapulare*)
 Dorsal apterium (*apterium dorsale*)
 Pelvic apteria (*apteria pelvina*)
  Median pelvic apterium (*apterium pelvinum medianum*)
  Lateral pelvic apterium (*apterium pelvinum laterale*)
Ventral apteria (*apteria ventralia*)
 Ventral cervical apterium (*apterium cervicale ventrale*)
  Interramal apterium (*apterium interramale*)
  Submalar apterium (*apterium submalare*)
 Sternal apterium (*apterium sternale*)
 Pectoral apteria (*apteria pectoralia*)
  Medial pectoral apterium (*apterium pectorale mediale*)
  Lateral pectoral apterium (*apterium pectorale laterale*)
 Abdominal apteria (*apteria abdominalia*)
  Median abdominal apterium (*apterium abdominale medianum*)
  Lateral abdominal apterium (*apterium abdominale laterale*)
  Cloacal apterium (*apterium cloacale*)
Lateral apteria (*apteria lateralia*)
 Lateral cervical apterium (*apterium cervicale laterale*)
 Lateral body apterium (*apterium corporale laterale*)
Caudal apteria (*apteria caudalia*)
 Dorsal caudal apterium (*apterium caudale dorsale*)
 Ventral caudal apterium (*apterium caudale ventrale*)
 Lateral caudal apterium (*apterium caudale laterale*)
Anterior appendage apteria (wing) (*apteria membri anterioris (ala)*)
 Brachial apteria (*apteria brachialia*)
  Humeral apterium (*apterium humerale*)
  Subhumeral apterium (*apterium subhumerale*)
 Alar apteria (*apteria alaria*)
 Upper alar apteria (*apteria alaria superiora*)
  Upper cubital apterium (*apterium cubitale superius*)
  Upper forearm apterium (*apterium antebrachiale superius*)
  Upper alular apterium (*apterium alulae superioris*)
  Upper hand apterium (*apterium mani superioris*)
 Under alar apteria (*apteria alaria inferiora*)
  Under cubital apterium (*apterium cubitale inferiorius*)
  Under forearm apterium (*apterium antebrachiale inferiorius*)
  Under prepatagial apterium (*apterium prepatagiale inferiorius*)
  Under alular apterium (*apterium alulae inferioris*)
  Under hand apterium (*apterium mani inferioris*)
Posterior appendage apteria (*apteria membri anterioris*)
 Crural apteria (*apteria cruralia*)
  Crural apterium (*apterium crurale*)
  Intracrural apterium (*apterium intracrurale*)
 Metatarsal apteria (*apteria metatarsalia*)
  Anterior metatarsal apterium (*apterium metatarsale anterius*)
  Posterior metatarsal apterium (*apterium metatarsale posterius*)

A few additional names have been coined to fit special apteria. Burt (1929) used "median capital apterium" to designate a narrow featherless space along the dorsal midsagittal line of the head. This apterium is found in woodpeckers and hummingbirds, birds that have extended terminal processes of the hyoid that curve dorsally over the skull. Berger (1953) described a small triangular apterium in the midline of the frontal region in the Blue Coua (*Coua caerulea*). In the Great Horned Owl (figs. 50–52) there are apteria in the coronal, auricular, postauricular, ocular, malar, and rictal regions. The question, "Why are there apteria?" has never been satisfactorily answered. Nitzsch (1867:17) suggested (1) that the total feather weight, which is considerable, was reduced by having featherless areas, (2) that a drain on the metabolism to produce feathers was reduced by having some areas devoid of feathers, and (3) that greater freedom of wing and limb movements was possible if joint areas were not crowded with large contour feathers. Nitzsch noted also that species with small apteria generally had small contour feathers in those same areas whereas species with broad apteria bore large contour feathers. Our own observations on the head of the turkey (p. 101) substantiate the idea that small feathers are associated with reduced or complete absence of apteria.

Nitzsch (1867) named the following apteria: head spaces, lateral neck-space, lateral space of the trunk, inferior space, spinal space, upper wing-space, lower wing-space, and crural space. He did not, however, subdivide these into lesser units, as we have done in the foregoing list. But with these subdivisions, it should be possible to describe the apteria for a large number of species.

The spinal apteria are a series of featherless spaces along the middorsal back and within the spinal tracts. The part of the body where a space occurs determines the regional name applied to it. For example, dorsal cervical apterium, interscapular apterium, dorsal apterium, and pelvic apterium. One of these, the dorsal, is present in the Great Horned Owl (fig. 50). Other examples of middorsal apteria were given by Heimerdinger (1964). Spinal apteria are absent in a number of birds. Among these are the chicken, the House Wren (Boulton, 1927), an extinct starling (*Fregilupus varius*) (Berger, 1957), and the House Sparrow (Heimerdinger, 1964).

When the spinal tracts are narrow, there are often broad bare dorsal surfaces on each side of the individual tracts. Such spaces have never received special names but may be included as part of the lateral apterium. We suggest the term "scapular apterium" for the space between the interscapular portion of the spinal tract and the humeral tract, and "lateral pelvic apterium" for the space on each side of the back (fig. 50) between the pelvic and femoral tracts.

The name "ventral apteria," is given to the succession of spaces between the paired units of the ventral tracts. Probably every carinate species has at least some part or parts of the ventral apteria, except possibly penguins, which have almost a continuous distribution of feathers over the body. The ventral apteria are very narrow in the White Pekin Duck.

The regions in which the spaces appear are indicated by the names—"interramal," "submalar," "ventral cervical," "pectoral," "sternal," and "abdominal apteria." In addition, there are dorsal and ventral caudal apteria. Some of these apteria are shown in the ventral view of the Great Horned Owl (fig. 52). The locations of the first two are indicated by their names. A submalar apterium is shown by Berger (1953) in the Blue Coua and by Compton (1938) in the Red-tailed Hawk, where it extends forward into the interramal region. The sternal apterium is the space covering the keel; it is present in all birds but varies widely in width among species. The pectoral apterium is the space between the sternal tract and the pectoral tract and between the pectoral tract and the shoulder joint. In the Great Horned Owl the pectoral apterium is logically divisible into medial and lateral pectoral apteria, respectively (figs. 51 and 52). However, in birds such as chicken, turkey, and Common Coturnix, where the pectoral tract is broad, the lateral component does not exist. Where the space is small, it is included with an adjacent apterium, usually the lateral body apterium.

The abdominal apteria begin at the posterior end of the sternum and extend to the proximal margin of the vent. The median abdominal apterium lies between the right and left branches of the abdominal portions of the ventral tracts. The lateral abdominal apterium is in the area of the groin groove. Both abdominal apteria in the Great Horned Owl (fig. 52) are broad. The terms "median abdominal apterium" and "lateral abdominal apterium" apply to the situation illustrated by Berger (1953) for the Blue Coua (*Coua caerulea*), and by Burt (1929) for the Eastern Pileated Woodpecker (*Dryocopus pilcatus = Ceophloeus pileatus*). In the Bronze Turkey (fig. 75), Common Coturnix (fig. 82), White Pekin Duck (fig. 90), Common Pigeon (fig. 97), and Great Horned Owl (fig. 52), both abdominal apteria are present. In the Single Comb White Leghorn Chicken the area of the lateral abdominal apterium bears feathers that form the lateral abdominal tract. A small cloacal apterium is shown on the upper lip of the cloaca of the chicken (fig. 66). This apterium separates the caudal end of the right and left halves of the abdominal tract and could be considered as an extension of the median abdominal apterium.

Lateral apteria on the right and left surface planes of the body, begin at the base of the head and extend to the thigh On each side there are two subdivisions—the lateral cervical apterium and the lateral body apterium. The length-to-width ratio of the lateral cervical apteria varies widely. In most birds they are well developed, usually more so than either the dorsal or ventral cervical apteria, but their cephalic extension varies. In over half the birds whose pterylosis has been described by Nitzsch (1867), the lateral cervical apteria extend as far rostrally as the head, as exemplified by the owl (fig. 51). In some aquatic birds and some galliforms, including

the chicken, these apteria begin at various distances away from the head along the length of the neck, and thus the dorsal cervical and ventral cervical tracts adjacent to the head are fused. The White Pekin Duck and Common Pigeon (figs. 89 and 96) lack lateral cervical apteria because the dorsal and ventral tracts have fused throughout the length of the neck. Continuous plumage of the neck is approached in the Great Bustard (*Otis tarda*), a flamingo (*Phoenicopterus ruber = P. antiquorum*), and a gannet (*Morus bassanus = Dysporus bassanus*) (Nitzsch, 1867).

The opposite condition—where the four apteria of the neck are broad and extend the full length of the neck—is found in the Hammerhead (*Scopus umbretta*). The lateral cervical apteria in the Great Horned Owl are even broader than they appear to be in figure 51 because the dorsal cervical tract is carried on a horizontal, loose fold of skin that in part hangs down over the lateral apterium.

The lateral body apterium is limited to the prolatus; it bears a few downs and the contours of the lateral body tract. In the Great Horned Owl this is an extensive nonfeathered area.

In our illustrations we used dashed lines to separate apteria that are continuous from one body region to another and to separate named tracts.

Caudal apteria that may be present on dorsal, ventral, and lateral surfaces of the tail are the dorsal caudal apterium, the ventral caudal apterium, and the lateral caudal apterium. They represent the nonfeathered areas between the coverts and the base of the tail or nonfeathered areas within the dorsal and ventral caudal tracts. The dorsal caudal apteria lie on the uropygial eminence and the adjacent area (fig. 50). A small ventral caudal apterium is present in the owl but is not labeled, is distinct in the chicken, and has continuity with the lateral caudal apteria in the turkey. The lateral caudal apterium is generally a large, bare area of thin skin over the base of the last rectrix on the lateral margin of the tail.

Apteria are more abundant on the under surface of the wing than on the upper. Most of the apteria for both surfaces are found in the Great Horned Owl and the remainder in domestic birds. Generally, apteria fall into two groups—brachial apteria and alar apteria. Each group has subdivisions, however, these are distinct enough so that assigning names to them seems justified even where there may be continuity between adjacent spaces.

The humeral apterium on the upper surface of the brachium lies distal to the humeral tract. The space may be T-shaped, L-shaped, or irregular. It may be small as in the turkey or large as in the Great Horned Owl (fig. 50.) In the owl it is continuous with the upper cubital apterium. This space over the elbow is the only apterium on the dorsal surface of the forearm. The upper hand apterium is an elongated narrow space paralleling the trailing edge. A small upper alular apterium may be present in some species and is often continuous with the upper hand apterium.

The only under brachial apterium, the subhumeral, lies

in the space between the subhumeral tract and the posterior margin of the upper arm. It is often continuous with the under forearm apterium. There are five under alar apteria. An under cubital apterium is frequently present in the elbow region. It often has continuity with either the subhumeral apterium or the under forearm apterium, or both. The under forearm apterium exists only if an under forearm tract is present; otherwise there is continuity with the under prepatagial apterium. The latter space covers much of the triangle between the upper arm and forearm and is bounded by three tracts—under forearm, under marginal coverts of prepatagium, and subhumeral tracts.

Two small apteria are present on the ventral surface of the hand—(1) the under hand apterium, which extends lengthwise between marginal and remigial coverts and (2) the under alular apterium, which is the small space on the ventral surface of the alula. The latter is featherless perhaps because when the alula is adducted, this surface presses against the forward edge of the metacarpus.

There are usually two apteria on the leg, four at the most. One space is between the pelvic and the femoral tracts, along the lateral margin of the pelvis. It has often been called the femoral apterium, but we prefer to call it the pelvic apterium. It has already been discussed under spinal apteria. In many species there are no crural apteria because this area is occupied by the crural flag, as it is in the Great Horned Owl (fig. 51). In this owl there is featherless space above the patella, which we have named the "femoral apterium," but we have not applied this term to any of the domestic birds studied. The femoral apterium of the Great Horned Owl is not the same as the lateral pelvic apterium, which, as mentioned previously, others had named the "femoral apterium."

A crural apterium is found in the three galliforms studied here. It is small in the pigeon, absent in the duck. When present, it is usually continuous with the intracrural apterium that lies on the caudal or medial surface of the crus. "Intracrural apterium" is a new term, introduced in these studies. This featherless space generally has continuity with the crural apterium and extends variable distances toward the angle.

It would probably be logical to continue down the foot and identify metatarsal and digital apteria, except for the fact that featherless metatarsi and toes are characteristic for most birds. However, where feathering occurs below the ankle, we have named the featherless spaces. In the owl (fig. 50) the metatarsal apterium (p. 85) is shown as an elongated space on the posterior surface of the metatarsus. In the pigeon the crural tract continues on to the upper metatarsus except for some spaces that we have named the "anterior metatarsal apteria" and "posterior metatarsal apteria" (figs. 96 and 97).

CHAPTER 3

Pterylosis and Ptilosis of Domestic Birds

Pterylosis is the arrangement of feathers within tracts over the body of the bird. Most descriptions of pterylosis deal with the location of the feather follicles. Ptilosis is the total plumage associated with these follicles. Generally, there has not been much confusion in meaning associated with terms used in pterylography. As pointed out in the first chapter, names for feather groups used in describing ptilosis have produced some confusion, in that authors often apply the same name to plumage groups that they apply to breast, abdomen, and other anatomical parts with little effort to associate each name with the correct anatomical counterpart. On the head, where feathers are short, agreement is often close between the boundaries of each capital tract and the feathers that come from each tract; in other cases the feathers may be long and give no indication of the boundaries of the tract. An example is the auricular plumage that extends far beyond the auricular tract, which is a narrow circle of follicles around the external ear opening.

Frequently color or markings of feathers are used to determine what should be included in a particular ptilosis group, for example, the superciliary feathers extend rostrally and caudally beyond the eye. Other examples are groups of feathers that are part of a pattern of coloration, such as eyeline and whisker mark and stripes on the crown. For these, no equivalent pterylosis terms are available. An appreciation of the innumerable variations that may occur in head plumage and appendages is readily gained by a perusal of such illustrated books as those by Gilliard (1958) and Austin and Singer (1961). It is, therefore, impossible to build a description of capital tracts upon the color of the plumage; likewise, it is impossible to build the pterylosis of the head strictly on the regions of the head.

Practically all other investigators who have described pterylosis of the head have given the term "region" to the various tracts, with the understanding that the region of the head and of the tract on the head were synonymous. However, in our studies we have attempted to define and determine a plan for the regions of the head based on surface and underlying anatomical structures. We have done the same for the remainder of the body, and we early found that it was impossible to correlate anatomical regions with distribution of feather tracts except in an occasional situation and in broad general terms. Therefore, the terms that we have selected to define and identify tracts may or may not be the same as those applied to a region, and the use of a term may or may not indicate an agreement in extent of boundaries. Also, some names are given to regions not duplicated in the subdivisions of pterylosis and the reverse is also true.

The key to the feather tracts (p. 74) lists 12 pterylae under a general heading of capital tracts. One of these, the ocular tract, is subdivided into upper and lower parts. The capital tracts depicted by Compton (1938) for the Osprey (*Pandion haliaetus*) are reproduced in figure 45. Each tract is fully outlined because we feel that this is a helpful practice. In many illustrations of pterylosis, other authors have extended lines to the center of an area that they felt unequivocally identified a particular tract without attempting to draw boundary lines between adjacent tracts. Without boundary lines, however, it is difficult to interpret the extent of a tract. Figures 53 and 54, respectively, show pterylosis and ptilosis for the chicken, and it is apparent that the boundary lines enclosing the areas where feathers are implanted are not in complete agreement with the boundaries of plumage areas.

PTERYLOSIS OF THE HEAD

Capital Tracts and Apteria

Chicken

The capital tracts of the chicken are discussed in the same order in which they are presented in the key to the feather tracts.

Frontal tract.—The frontal tract lies in the general area of the forehead, but the tract and forehead do not have identical boundaries. The boundaries as shown in figures 53 and 54 apply to the Single Comb White Leghorn Chicken, but the general location of the tract is applicable to all birds. In the chicken, the feather coat of this tract is rather sparse, the feathers are short and moderately erect. In the male, the comb is well developed, and the tract is restricted to one or two rows of feathers that project laterally and only slightly posteriorly. In the female, the comb is smaller, and the feathers are more numerous, and more of them point directly caudally. If we had drawn the boundary between the frontal

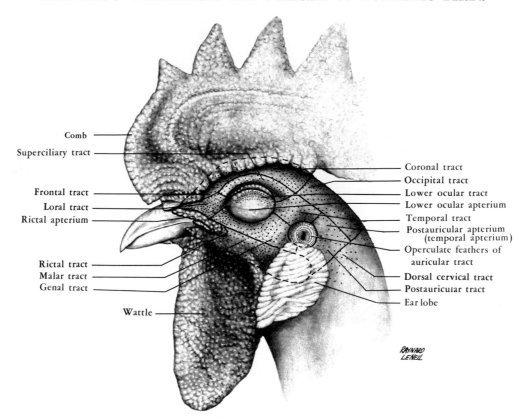

Comb
Superciliary tract
Frontal tract
Loral tract
Rictal apterium
Rictal tract
Malar tract
Genal tract
Wattle

Coronal tract
Occipital tract
Lower ocular tract
Lower ocular apterium
Temporal tract
Postauricular apterium
(temporal apterium)
Operculate feathers of
auricular tract
Dorsal cervical tract
Postauricular tract
Ear lobe

FIGURE 53.—Capital tracts and apteria of the male Single Comb White Leghorn Chicken. Each feather follicle is represented by a black dot. Individual tracts are bounded by solid or dashed lines.

tract and coronal tract to agree with the regional boundary, we would have cut across a group of feathers that are similar in character, directed caudally, and flattened against each other; all these feathers are considered here to belong to the coronal tract. The frontal tract and coronal tract share a common boundary with the superciliary tract.

Coronal tract.—Figure 53 shows the coronal tract lying on each side of the base of the comb and extending posteriorly to the caudal attachment of the comb to the head. The feathers of the coronal tract form a rather narrow band in the anterior part and broaden caudally. Figure 54 shows the feathers spreading upward beyond the point of their origin on the head and covering the basal portion of the comb. The feathers in this area have the same sexual dimorphism as do the hackle feathers of the dorsal neck. Extensive development of head plumage is found in all breeds that have V-shaped combs. Within each sex, the hackles and crests have the same feather type.

Occipital tract.—The occipital tract includes feathers implanted on the caudal part of the dorsal surface of the head. The tract terminates at the junction with the neck. The lateral boundary of the occipital tract is shown in figures 53 and 54. We regard it in the chicken as a continuation of the dorsal margin of the superciliary tract, whereas Compton (1938) brought the coronal tract of the Osprey backward from the corner of the eye. To do this in the chicken would be rather artificial as far as feather structure is concerned,

and we have attempted here to place the occipital tract so that it encloses natural plumage groups. As seen in figure 53, follicles are not differentiated among the tracts of the head. The feathers caudal to the comb are directed backward but the shafts tend to curve toward the midline. There is no natural differentiation between the feather coat of occipital and dorsal cervical tracts. The row pattern of follicles shows the same lack of a natural boundary between the two tracts.

Auricular tract.—In the deplumed bird, the auricular tract is limited to the circlet of feathers that surrounds the external ear opening. The barbs of these feathers are farther apart than they are in body contour feathers. (See page 308 for a description of their detailed structure.) The feathers on the anteroventral third of the rim, called operculate feathers, are longer than the others and are directed dorsoposteriorly, covering the external ear opening (fig. 55). The remainder of the circlet is composed of short feathers that project directly perpendicular to the surface, forming a cup or auricle. The operculate feathers impinge against the tips of these auricular feathers, thereby screening the opening and minimizing the entrance of dust and insects. The passage of sound would also be obstructed by this closure were it not for the open structure, peculiar to the feathers of this region.

In many birds, the feathers that cover the external opening of the ear are barely distinguishable from the adjacent contour feathers of the head and face; but in some, the

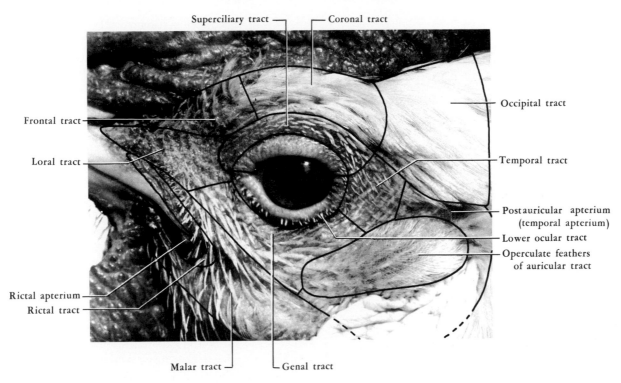

Superciliary tract — — Coronal tract

Occipital tract

Frontal tract —

Loral tract —

Temporal tract

Postauricular apterium
(temporal apterium)

Lower ocular tract

Operculate feathers
of auricular tract

Rictal apterium —
Rictal tract —

Malar tract — — Genal tract

FIGURE 54.—Ptilosis of head of female Single Comb White Leghorn Chicken, showing feathers from 10 capital tracts bounded by solid or dashed lines.

auricular plumage is prominently developed. The extent of the operculate feathers is shown in figure 54 for the chicken and in figure 56 (labeled auricular plumage) for the Ruffed Grouse. The operculate feathers of the Ruffed Grouse extend far caudal to their origin, thereby covering the postauricular tract. In the Osprey, Compton (1938) has shown the auricular tract as extending forward to the eye, with the external ear opening at the caudal end of the auricular tract. This is the situation in birds such as the Mockingbird (*Mimus polyglottos*), Catbird (*Dumetella carolinensis*), and Common

Pigeon. Note that the follicles where the feathers are implanted are limited to several rows encircling the external ear opening (fig. 53).

Postauricular tract.—The feathers behind the auricular feathers and between the occipital tract and the malar tract, from the facial region to the base of the head, represent the postauricular tract (fig. 53). The feather coat of this area merges with that of the upper neck as the feathers become longer posteriorly. Many of the short feathers of the postauricular tract are covered by the extended operculate

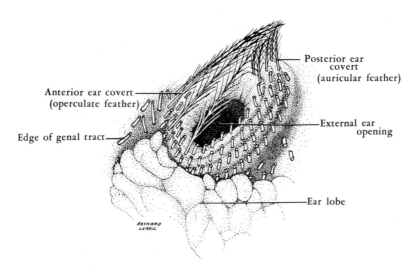

Posterior ear
covert
(auricular feather)

Anterior ear covert —
(operculate feather)

External ear
opening

Edge of genal tract —

Ear lobe

RAYNARD
LENEIL

FIGURE 55.—Pterylosis and ptilosis of the auricular tract of the left ear of Single Comb White Leghorn Chicken. (Modified from a drawing by Casimir Jamroz.)

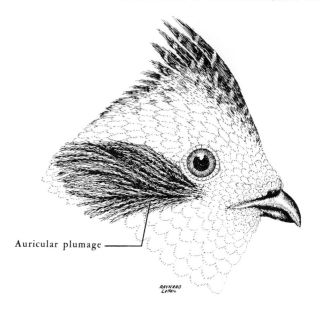

FIGURE 56.—Head of Ruffed Grouse (*Bonasa umbellus*), showing opercular feathers of the auricular tract. These feathers extend beyond the base of the head. Feathers of the frontal and coronal tracts form a small crest.

feathers. Above and slightly caudal to the external ear opening is the postauricular apterium. The skin of the apterium is smooth, extremely thin, and devoid of down as well as contour feathers.

Temporal tract.—Although we have not designated a temporal region of the head, we have applied the name "temporal tract" to those feathers located between the eye and ear and between the occipital and genal tracts. These feathers are located in the upper part of the postorbital region (compare figs. 3 and 4 for regions with figs. 53 and 54 for tracts). The feathers of the temporal tract are short and are similar to those of the loral tract and to part of the superciliary tract.

Loral tract.—The loral tract is usually considered to be a band of feathers extending from the region of the nose to the anterior corner of the eye. In a white chicken there is no particular coloration or structural character of these feathers to distinguish them from adjacent feathers. The same is true in the Ruffed Grouse (*Bonasa umbellus*) (fig. 56); however, there is distinct coloration of this group of feathers in such birds as the Blue Jay (*Cyanocitta cristata*), Cardinal (*Cardinalis cardinalis*), House Sparrow (*Passer domesticus*), and Common Coturnix, which, of course, makes the tract easy to identify. In the chicken this tract is bounded by frontal, superciliary, and genal tracts above and caudally (figs. 53 and 54). Below it is bounded by the rictal apterium or the malar tract. Feathers on the upper margin of the loral tract parallel the direction of those in the frontal tract, and the remainder of the loral feathers spread out like a fan; those dorsally point above the eye; those in the midloral region point backward toward the corner of the eye; and those ventrally point along the margin of the malar tract.

Superciliary tract.—The superciliary tract occupies the region of the upper stationary lid and overlies the edge of the frontal bone in the chicken, turkey, and other galliforms. It lies partly on the crown and partly in the upper orbital region. The tract extends from the anterior end to the caudal end of the eye and is a narrow band concentric with the line where the mobile part of the lid folds under the overlying margin of the stationary lid. The feathers in this tract are directed caudally. In many birds the plumage from this tract is distinguished by its color and may include an area of uniform color in the loral plumage. If such colored plumage extends caudally to the base of the head, as in certain wrens, warblers, vireos, and in the House Sparrow (*Passer domesticus*), it may be named "superciliary line" or "eyebrow."

Ocular tracts.—The ocular tracts do not cover the total orbital region. They are equivalent to the upper and lower mobile lids only. The tracts are divisible into upper and lower portions. The upper ocular tract is shown in figure 57. The upper lid must be closed in order to expose the several rows of feathers paralleling the edge of the lid. Dorsal to this is a space devoid of feathers, the upper ocular apterium. The lower lid is well exposed when it is closed. Several rows of feathers form the lower ocular tract (figs. 53 and 57). Ventral to the tract is a large lower ocular apterium. The feathers of the ocular tracts are short, so that the feather coat (ptilosis) agrees with the pterylosis in the location of boundaries.

Genal tract.—The genal tract is largely equivalent to the suborbital region and probably represents as much of "cheek feathers" as birds possess. The tract extends from the loral to the temporal tracts, from the lower ocular tract to the malar and auricular tracts. It includes the lower stationary lid as well as the suborbital region (figs. 53 and 54). In this tract the feathers in the chicken are fairly uniform and rather sparsely distributed so that the characteristic red color of the underlying skin shows through among them.

Rictal tract.—The rictal tract is relatively small. The rictal

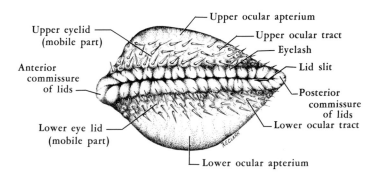

FIGURE 57.—Tracts and apteria of the upper and lower eye lids—left eye of the Single Comb White Leghorn Chicken. The feathers of the ocular tracts are represented as narrow cones, but under magnification each has, in simple form, the basic structure of a contour feather. The attached boundaries of the mobile lids merge into the skin of the stationary lids. (Modified from a drawing by Casimir Jamroz.)

apterium is larger than the tract. Together, they occupy the region designated as the rictus. The rictal tract is that portion of the rictus caudal to the bare area of the gape. The caudal extent of the rictus is discussed in chapter 1 and depends on the spread of the gape. The feathers included in the rictal tract are identical with those that cross the malar tract and, in the chicken, are similar to those in the genal tract and are sparsely distributed (fig. 54).

Malar tract.—The malar tract has the same boundaries as the malar region. Its sparsely distributed feathers continue down to the interramal region on the outer surface of the wattle. Caudally the feathers of the malar tract become small and widely separated and disappear altogether at the level of the earlobe. Therefore, the earlobe in the chicken occupies part of the malar tract. This area could justifiably be called an apterium, but it seems better to identify it merely as an earlobe since it is a specialized structure. The boundaries of the malar tract of the chicken, as shown in figures 53 and 54, agree closely with those outlined by Compton (1938) for the Osprey (fig. 45).

The earlobe is an ovate or disk-shaped area of modified skin containing only a few feather follicles around the perimeter. In young birds it is a flat disk over the posterior end of the jaws, but in older chickens, especially males, it becomes pendulous and forms a double-layered flap of skin. The lobe can attain the form of a flattened plate suspended from a short stalk having nearly the same diameter as the plate. The earlobe is continuous with the lateral submalar skin and ventrally with the base of the wattle. The pale iridescent blue found in small earlobes in the Single Comb White Leghorn Chicken changes to a chalky white in large lobes. The carunculate texture is formed by sulci and rugae which in general extend from the posterodorsal boundary of the earlobe diagonally forward to its anteroventral margin. The larger rugae are interrupted by numerous shallow transverse sulci. In old males with large lobes, the texture and color of the lobe extend to the adjacent skin of the face and neck.

Turkey

The turkey head when viewed superficially is often considered to be devoid of feathers because of the conspicuous carunculate character of the skin of the head, face, jaws, dewlap, and upper neck. However, even a reasonably close examination will show that small bristle feathers (figs. 5, p. 10, and 217, p. 324) project outward from follicles implanted either in the crevices between the carunculate rugosities or on the crests of the folds. This is particularly well shown in dark-colored varieties of the Bronze Turkey. The pattern of these feathers agrees with that found in the young poult. It is possible that bristle feathers of the adult agree in number with those of the poult, but that growth of the head has moved the feathers apart.

The head of the turkey lacks apteria, which seems rather strange in view of the extensive reduction that has occurred in the size and structure of the feathers. Perhaps this gives us a clue to one of the principles involved in pterylosis,

namely that the feather covering is complete where the overlapping of feathers is minimal. Where feathers extend well beyond their area of implantation, apteria arise, thereby relieving the overcrowded condition.

In the young poult the ptilosis is complete; no bare skin is visible. In a poult of intermediate age (74 days) some natal feathers remain on the head, but as the next generation of feathers comes in, carunculate skin appears on the top of the head. The new feathers of the genal and malar regions are short, intermediate to the ultimate bristle type. The head feathers of the third and subsequent generations are definitely bristles, having a shaft that is devoid of barbs except at the base. Transitions from a contour to a bristle feather are described in chapter 6. Figure 5 of the head of a turkey shows the distribution of bristle feathers, but in this illustration the lines are boundaries for regions rather than for tracts.

Frontal tract.—All the ptilosis of the frontal process (snood) is included within the frontal tract, although part of the frontal process lies on the nasal arch. The frontal process contains bristle feathers distributed most densely at the base and tip. Those at about the midlength of the frontal process are farthest apart, but obviously this varies with the degree of extension of the frontal process (fig. 5). In an old tom, carunculate skin on top of the head is extensive, and the coloration characteristic of this carunculate skin is found over the entire head. The bristle feathers on the frontal tract are far apart. Laterally, the density of the implantation of follicles becomes somewhat greater. The midline may show either a dense concentration of bristles separating the carunculate mass into right and left halves, or there may be so few bristles that the entire crown appears to be a continuous layer of carunculate skin. Such variables are probably related to age and to differences between individuals.

Coronal tract.—The coronal tract is a continuation of the frontal tract, and the character, density, and distribution of the bristle feathers are the same. As in the frontal tract, a median concentration of bristle feathers may be present or absent.

Occipital tract.—In the occipital tract, particularly at or near the midline, there is a transition in character from bristle feathers to the typical contour type. The barbs of the feathers are lost near the tips, exposing a bare rachis both on the primary shaft and the afterfeather. On some specimens the transition takes place nearly at the caudal end of the carunculate skin.

Auricular tract.—The auricular tract is the area immediately encircling the external ear opening that contains several rows of follicles. The general arrangement of the feathers of the auricular tract is similar to that in the chicken except that the opercular feathers are not nearly as long, but they retain the same wide spacing of barbs found in the chicken. The anterior feathers point dorsocaudally. Those at the opposite margin of the ear opening are erect but actually do not contribute much to the support of the distal ends of the opercular feathers; in some cases the opercular feathers are not long enough to touch them.

Postauricular tract.—The bristles in the postauricular area are rather widely distributed and apteria are absent. Many bristles come from the surface of the carunculate folds and others come from the depressions between them.

Temporal tract.—The feathers of the temporal tract are similar to those of the areas immediately above and below this tract. At the upper part of the temporal tract the feathers are somewhat widely dispersed, whereas in the lower part of the temporal tract they are implanted somewhat more closely.

Loral tract.—The bristle feathers are closely placed in the upper half of the loral tract. This is similar to the nearby base of the frontal process and to the adjacent superciliary tract. In the lower part of the loral tract the bristles are sparse.

Superciliary tract.—The superciliary tract, along with the tracts on the eyelids, has the greatest density of bristle feathers of any tract area on the head. The structure of the bristle feathers is typical; some are long and some are short. The area where the bristle feathers are close together extends from the loral tract well back onto the edge of the temporal tract. Those immediately adjacent to the upper eyelid are worn to the extent that they are very short and would be difficult to distinguish without their black color.

Ocular tracts.—The upper and lower eyelids are entirely covered with rows of bristle feathers. Those on the upper lid are more closely placed than are those on the lower lid; neither lid has an apterium. On both lids the row adjacent to the slit is prominent. Under a hand lens of moderate magnification, it can be observed that black eyelashes parallel this last row and arise from the fleshy edge of the lid, close to the last row of the tract.

On the lower lid some of the feathers of the tract are not typical bristle feathers but retain some of the main features of the small contour feather. This is a transitional area in which feather structure varies from contour type to bristle.

Genal tract.—The genal tract has no distinctive features. At the anterior end, the tract is continuous with and similar to the lower half of the loral tract. Adajcent to the eye it is like the lower ocular tract. At the caudal end it is somewhat like the superciliary tract. Immediately in front of the auricular tract the bristle feathers are moderately dispersed. Adjacent to the malar tract, their distribution is somewhat denser.

Rictal tract.—The pattern for the rictus in the turkey is similar to that of the chicken, namely, there is a rictal apterium that is more extensive adjacent to the lower jaw than it is toward the upper jaw. In the part covering the upper jaw a few bristle feathers constitute a small, weak rictal tract.

Malar tract.—The malar tract has a moderately dense distribution of typical bristle feathers in the anterior part. Caudally, beneath the ear there is development of carunculate skin with a more sparse distribution of the bristle feathers. Bristle feathers extend into the interramal and submalar regions and are also present on the dewlap.

Poult ptilosis.—The head of the 2-week-old poult of the Bronze Turkey is fully feathered; no evidence of carunculate skin is apparent. Most of the feathers, whether considerably long as on the frontal, coronal, and occipital tracts, or short as on the upper and lower ocular tracts, the loral region, and the genal region, are more of a contour than a bristle type. Except for the rictal apterium near the edge of the gape, apteria are absent from the head.

Common Coturnix

All the feathers of the head of the Common Coturnix are contours ranging in size from small to medium large. However, the barbs of these feathers are widely spaced, like teeth on a comb. This is true of many of the feathers over the body of coturnix.

The feathers of the frontal tract extend caudally. The lateral margins of the tract are overlapped by feathers of somewhat greater length sweeping up from the edge of the loral tract. The coronal and occipital tracts cover the remainder of the head with no particular significant features. No apteria are on the dorsal tracts of the head.

The auricular tract is similar to that in birds described previously. The follicles are arranged in several concentric rows surrounding the external ear opening. The feathers arising from the anterior margin of the tract extend backward over the opening. These opercular feathers have the widely spaced barbs observed in the chicken. The auricular group, constituting the remainder of the tract, is composed of feathers considerably shorter than those of the opercular group, but both are similar in structure. The auricular feathers, instead of extending directly outward from the surface of the head as in the chicken, point caudally; therefore, they do not provide a significant support for the ends of the opercular feathers. The feather coat of the postauricular tract is similar to that of the dorsal region of the head and adjacent neck regions except that the feathers are somewhat shorter. Among the feathers in the upper part of the tract, there is no space of sufficient magnitude to be considered as an apterium.

The feathers of the temporal tract are shorter than those of the postauricular. This tract is relatively small because of the close proximity between the ear opening and the caudal margin of the eye.

The dorsal half of the loral tract bears feathers that sweep upward and merge with those of the superciliary tract and overlie the marginal feathers of the frontal tract. The ventral half of this tract contains short contour feathers that in general turn downward and backward to follow the direction of the rictal apterium.

The genal tract supports feathers that are uniformly distributed, directed caudally, and that increase in length from the forward to the caudal end of the tract. They merge with those of the malar tract and take on the character of the feathers in the malar tract.

The rictal margin is darkly pigmented and well defined. The feathers of this tract overlie the bare edge of the rictus. The apterium, which lies behind the margin, is not visible unless the mouth is opened and the feathers in that area are pushed backward (fig. 12, p. 20).

The plumage of the malar tract shows no features of particular significance. The feathers are directed caudally toward the interramal and submalar tracts; in these two tracts of the neck the feathers are directed downward.

The feathers of the superciliary tract are directed upward and caudally. The coloration of feathers in coturnix makes the superciliary tract conspicuous because they are tan in contrast to the dark brown of the frontal tract. The feathers are longer than those on the upper and lower eyelids.

The upper ocular tract contains many rows of small feathers. The row adjacent to the free margin of the upper lid has the most conspicuous feathers; in the rows above this the feathers decrease in length. As far as we can determine, there is no apterium on the upper lid. The pattern of the lower ocular tract is similar to that of the upper. However, toward the lower part of the lid the feathers are farther apart, and at the point where the mobile lid folds behind the stationary lid there is a band where feathers are absent. This band could be designated the lower ocular apterium, but it is so narrow that it seems hardly appropriate to assign a name to it. On both upper and lower lids along the free margin are black eyelashes, which are exceedingly small and barely visible when examined under low magnification.

White Pekin Duck

The pterylosis of the head of the White Pekin Duck is shown in figure 58. As may be noted, the follicles are uniformly distributed and closely placed. They form a pattern of rows oriented in various directions. There is no evidence of apteria in any of the capital tracts except along the margin of the rictus. The uniform white plumage of this variety of White Pekin Duck makes it almost illogical to attempt to subdivide the tracts of head into various named subdivisions. The label lines in figure 58 merely indicate the general area of each tract.

Only about two regions have any distinctive characteristics, namely, the upper and lower ocular tracts and the auricular

tract. The upper and lower lids of the eye are uniformly covered with small contour feathers. The narrow upper mobile lid and the larger lower lid are entirely covered with feathers. Toward the basal edge of the lid, an apterium is absent. We have not found eyelashes along the slit margin on either lid.

Externally there is no evidence of operculate feathers because the feather coat from the malar and genal tracts extends backward and completely obscures the operculate and other feathers of the auricular tract. However, if the feathers of adjacent tracts are pushed forward to expose the ear opening, the feathers around the external ear opening of the duck have the same characteristics as those found in the other species described, namely, a distinct rachis with barbs widely spaced. The operculate feathers are indefinite; the coverts on the caudal side of the auricular tract point caudally so that they merge with the adjacent contour feathers of the other tract areas, and therefore do not furnish a support that would elevate the tips of the operculate feathers.

Our studies on this variety of Pekin Duck revealed that although the feathers were small, their structure was of the contour type. Occasionally a down feather might be found, but the head lacked the extensive down plumage characteristic of the lower neck and trunk. The situation is different in the Mallard where Humphrey and Clark (1961: 382) noted: "Body downs are present over the entire head although their presence may be far from obvious to the unaided eye in examination of a pickled specimen."

Common Pigeon

It would appear from a comparison of figures 58 and 59 that the feathers are much more closely placed on the head of the duck than on the pigeon. Actually, the duck has a larger head; the drawing of it was reduced more in reproduction and therefore the feathers seem closer together.

The feathers of the frontal tract of the pigeon begin im-

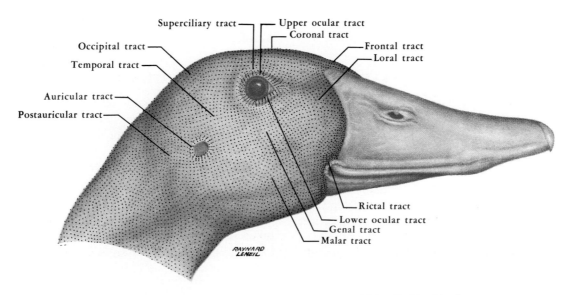

FIGURE 58.—Pterylosis of the head of the White Pekin Duck.

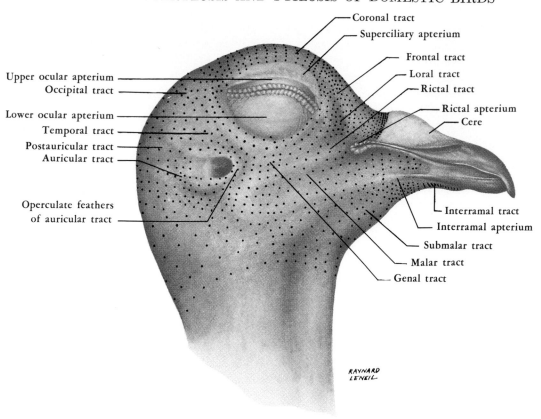

FIGURE 59.—Pterylosis of the head of the Common Pigeon.

mediately caudal to the cere. The feather rachises project directly outward, perpendicular to the skin, and their tips curve caudally. The same is true for the feathers implanted on coronal and occipital tracts. The curvature of the rachis applies also to most of the feathers on the dorsal neck.

The feathers of the auricular tract are distinguished by the fact that their barbs are more widely spaced than those of surrounding feathers. The area covered by feathers of the auricular tract is similar to that shown for the Osprey (fig. 45) and differs from that of the chicken in that the tract originates under the eye.

The postauricular tract has no distinctive features and the feathers merge into those of the upper neck. The feathers of the loral and maxillary malar tracts are directed across the rictus, obscuring it from view when the mouth is closed. The rictal tract is represented by only a few short feathers behind the rictal apterium.

The upper stationary lid is bare. The lid covers the edge of the frontal bone, which is the area usually occupied by the superciliary tract; in this case the area is designated the superciliary apterium (fig. 59).

The feathers of the genal and malar tracts, as well as the interramal and submalar tracts, although short, are fluffed outward like those of the neck and breast, giving the effect of a ruff.

PTERYLOSIS EXCLUDING THE HEAD

Introduction

In describing the feather coat of the head we have tried to distinguish between pterylosis and ptilosis. Because the feathers of the head are often short and because the outlines of tracts and feather groups usually coincide, this distinction has not been made in all cases. On the remainder of the body, however, the feathers usually extend far beyond the follicles from which they arise. Therefore, wherever possible, we will first describe the pterylosis and then the ptilosis of the domestic birds. Sometimes, however, because the identifi-

cation of a tract depends on the character of the feathers it may contain, we have had to describe feathers together with their tracts. A section of this chapter will follow devoted to ptilosis alone.

Three views of each of the five kinds of birds under study are presented here. The follicles are indicated by black dots (figs. 60–62, 73–75, 80–82, 88–90, and 95–97). This has been done as accurately and carefully as possible, and we have taken into account the influence of perspective as the rows follow the curvatures of surfaces. Dots have been used to

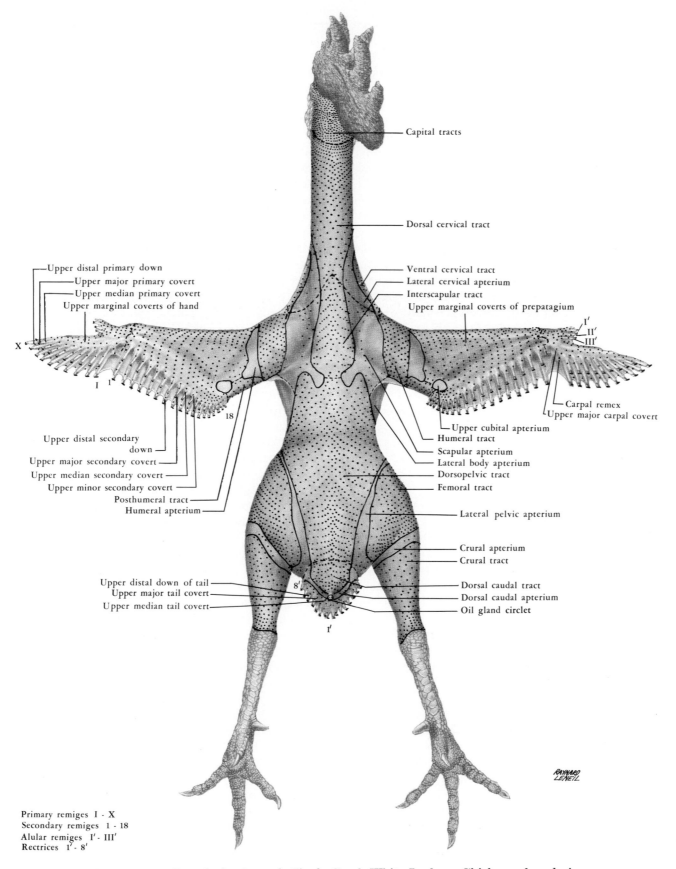

Capital tracts

Dorsal cervical tract

Ventral cervical tract
Lateral cervical apterium
Interscapular tract
Upper marginal coverts of prepatagium

Upper distal primary down
Upper major primary covert
Upper median primary covert
Upper marginal coverts of hand

I′
II′
III′

X

I   1

Carpal remex
Upper major carpal covert

18

Upper cubital apterium
Humeral tract
Scapular apterium
Lateral body apterium
Dorsopelvic tract
Femoral tract

Upper distal secondary
down
Upper major secondary covert
Upper median secondary covert
Upper minor secondary covert
Posthumeral tract
Humeral apterium

Lateral pelvic apterium

Crural apterium
Crural tract

Upper distal down of tail
Upper major tail covert
Upper median tail covert

8′

Dorsal caudal tract
Dorsal caudal apterium
Oil gland circlet

I′

Primary remiges I - X
Secondary remiges 1 - 18
Alular remiges I′ - III′
Rectrices 1′ - 8′

FIGURE 60.—Pterylosis of a male Single Comb White Leghorn Chicken—dorsal view.

represent all follicles, whether these contained large contour feathers or tiny downs. This applies particularly to the chicken, turkey, coturnix, and pigeon. In the duck the down feathers are so numerous that they have been represented by red rather than black dots. All the downs on the duck have not been shown, only those in representative areas. We found it impractical to vary the size of the dot according to the size of the follicle; therefore, in the finished illustration the entire body appears to be covered with contour feathers. After the drawings were finished, feathered specimens were examined and, on overlays, feather tracts were separated from feather spaces by boundary lines. We adhered to the rule that semiplumes be included within the boundaries of a tract along with the contour feathers and that down feathers be excluded from a tract and included in an apterium. The rule worked well for the chicken; but in the turkey some feathers located within obvious apteria were more like semiplumes than like down feathers, and in the Common Coturnix some feathers included within tracts were almost like typical down feathers. Our observations confirm those of Heimerdinger (1964: 17) who stated in her definition that "Apteria generally are bare but they may contain plumulaceous or downy feathers."

There was not enough room on the drawings of the whole birds for us to adequately show and label all the feathers of the upper and lower surfaces of the wing. Therefore, four drawings were prepared of the wing of each species. The procedures for preparing these are given in detail in chapter 10.

Chicken

Spinal tracts and apteria

The middorsal feather tract is continuous from the base of the comb to the oil duct (fig. 60), but throughout this length, the width of the tract, the curvature of the rows, and the morphology of the feathers change. In figure 60 a transverse dashed line drawn at the boundary of head and neck establishes a boundary between capital tracts and cervical tracts. Likewise, a dashed line drawn in the form of a chevron separates the cervical and the interscapular tracts. A transverse dashed line separates the interscapular from the combined dorsal and pelvic tracts, and a dashed line separates the pelvic tract from the upper caudal tract. In a sense these are arbitrary boundaries; nevertheless, they are precisely placed.

Dorsal cervical tract.—The dorsal cervical tract begins as a continuation of the capital tracts and covers the lateral as well as the dorsal surfaces of the neck in the anterior region as shown in figures 60 and 61. In this area, immediately behind the earlobe and at the anterior end of the tract, the dorsal and ventral cervical tracts merge. The lateral cervical apterium, characteristic of the side of the neck, does not extend as far forward as the head. In the caudal half or two-

thirds of the dorsal cervical tract, where the apterium lies adjacent to it, the boundary between the tract and the apterium is abrupt. The tract narrows caudally in the region that marks the junction between the cervical and interscapular tracts.

As we discuss the various tracts in the chicken, we will have occasion to refer frequently to figures 63 and 64. In this series of diagrams we attempted to represent the arrangement of rows in the tracts by lines. Much of this pattern may be illusionary; nevertheless, examination of the arrangement of feather muscles on the inner surface of the skin (ch. 8) confirms in most cases the pattern of follicle rows approximately as we have shown it.

As observed in the adult bird the rows fail to provide information about the sequence of steps taken in the embryological development of these tracts; yet it is the succession of changes during development that ultimately produces the adult pattern, especially the adult rows. In the embryo, feather ridges arise lengthwise on the neck and over most of the body (Holmes, 1935). Each ridge as it develops is broken up into separate focal points, the primordia of the feather papillae. The intervening ridge tissue migrates laterally and forms new longitudinal ridges on each side of the first-formed ridges. This next generation of ridges, like the first, breaks up into rows of feather germs, and the mesenchymal condensations lie opposite the spaces between the papillae of the original row. This alternate placement of feather primorida in adjacent rows produces the illusion that the feather follicles of an area are arranged predominantly in diagonal rows, and the primary arrangement in longitudinal rows is often rather inconspicuous. The reader is referred to chapter 7 for further details on the succession of morphological changes during development. Thus, the dorsal cervical tract when viewed from above appears to be made up of two sets of diagonal rows arranged like chevrons with their apices pointed posteriorly (fig. 63, *A*). The intersecting longitudinal and transverse rows are far apart at the base of the neck and close together toward the head. This is also shown by the actual specimen (fig. 60). The side view of the dorsal cervical tract is diagramed in figure 63, *B*. The arms of the chevrons shown in figure 63, *A*, extend laterally across the side of the neck and forward to produce the pattern shown in figure 63, *B*. The longitudinal lines are still present, diverging toward the base of the neck and converging toward the earlobe.

Interscapular tract.—In many birds the interscapular tract is distinguished more or less arbitrarily from the cervical and dorsal tracts. In the chicken, however, the interscapular tract differs enough morphologically from the tracts anterior and posterior to it so that the separation is natural rather than artificial. In figure 60, at the level where the dashed lines separate the interscapular and cervical tracts, feather follicles are disorganized; caudally, they become reoriented and organized so that the apices of the chevrons project forward

→

FIGURE 61.—Pterylosis of a male Single Comb White Leghorn Chicken—left lateral view.

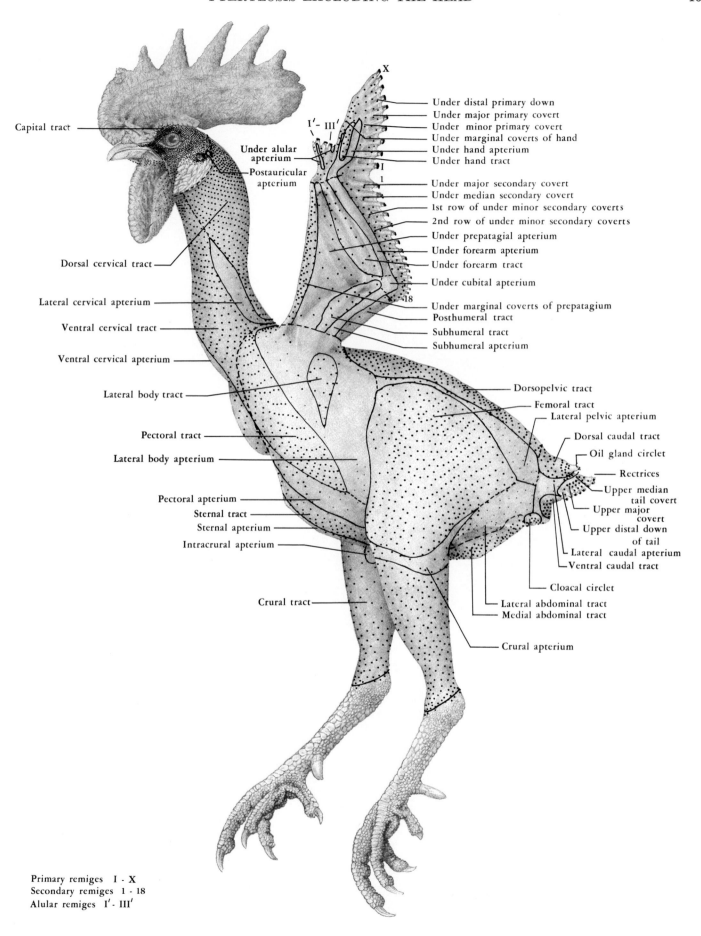

Capital tract

I' - III'

Under alular apterium

Postauricular apterium

Dorsal cervical tract

Lateral cervical apterium

Ventral cervical tract

Ventral cervical apterium

Lateral body tract

Pectoral tract

Lateral body apterium

Pectoral apterium

Sternal tract

Sternal apterium

Intracrural apterium

Crural tract

X

Under distal primary down
Under major primary covert
Under minor primary covert
Under marginal coverts of hand
Under hand apterium
Under hand tract
I
1
Under major secondary covert
Under median secondary covert
1st row of under minor secondary coverts
2nd row of under minor secondary coverts
Under prepatagial apterium
Under forearm apterium
Under forearm tract
Under cubital apterium
18
Under marginal coverts of prepatagium
Posthumeral tract
Subhumeral tract
Subhumeral apterium

Dorsopelvic tract
Femoral tract
Lateral pelvic apterium
Dorsal caudal tract
Oil gland circlet
Rectrices
Upper median tail covert
Upper major covert
Upper distal down of tail
Lateral caudal apterium
Ventral caudal tract
Cloacal circlet
Lateral abdominal tract
Medial abdominal tract

Crural apterium

Primary remiges   I - X
Secondary remiges 1 - 18
Alular remiges I' - III'

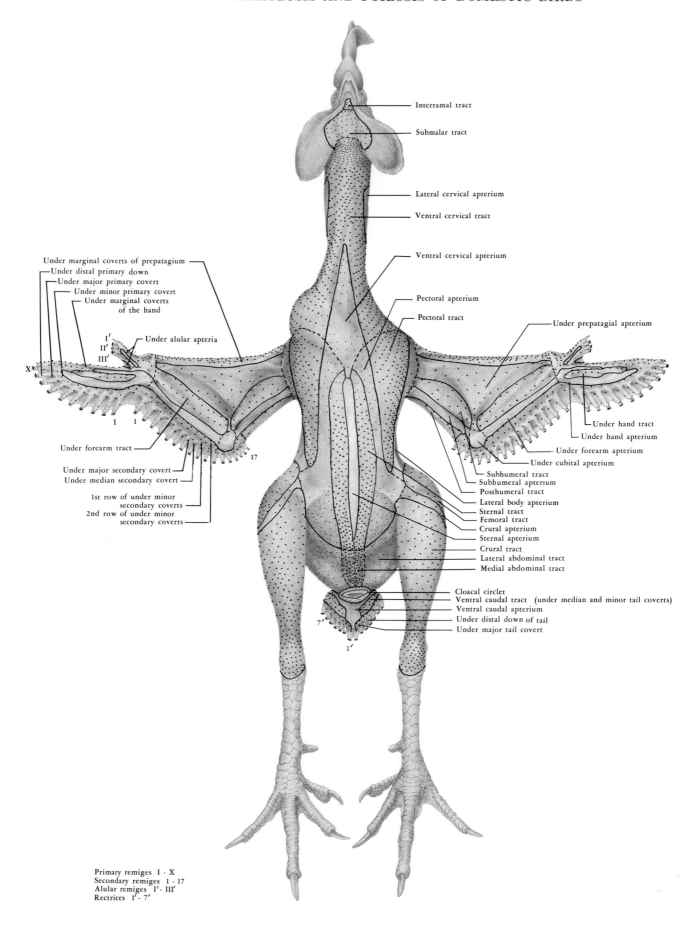

Interramal tract

Submalar tract

Lateral cervical apterium

Ventral cervical tract

Ventral cervical apterium

Under marginal coverts of prepatagium
Under distal primary down
Under major primary covert
Under minor primary covert
Under marginal coverts of the hand

Pectoral apterium

Pectoral tract

Under prepatagial apterium

I'
II'
III'

Under alular apteria

X

I   1

Under forearm tract

Under hand tract

Under hand apterium

Under forearm apterium

Under cubital apterium

Subhumeral tract

Subhumeral apterium

Posthumeral tract

Lateral body apterium

Sternal tract

Femoral tract

Crural apterium

Sternal apterium

Crural tract

Lateral abdominal tract

Medial abdominal tract

17

Under major secondary covert
Under median secondary covert

1st row of under minor secondary coverts
2nd row of under minor secondary coverts

Cloacal circlet
Ventral caudal tract (under median and minor tail coverts)
Ventral caudal apterium
Under distal down of tail
Under major tail covert

7'

1'

Primary remiges I - X
Secondary remiges 1 - 17
Alular remiges I' - III'
Rectrices 1' - 7'

FIGURE 62.—Pterylosis of a male Single Comb White Leghorn Chicken—ventral view.

instead of caudally. This transition is shown schematically in figure 63, C. At the caudal end of the tract the radius of the arc formed by each lateral row is relatively short, whereas at the anterior end of the tract the radii that form the rows are relatively long. At the point of transition between dorsal cervical and interscapular tracts, the arcs are carried forward and cross those from the opposite side. This disturbs the row pattern and seems to be the only way by which the direction of rows can be changed during development. Also, at the level of the interscapular tract, the longitudinal rows are approximately parallel, whereas in the dorsal cervical tract the longitudinal rows represented in figure 63, A and B, converge toward the head. Behind the interscapular tract, the longitudinal rows converge toward the tail (fig. 63, D). The longitudinal rows between head and tail are spindle-shaped. Therefore, it would be expected that somewhere along the length of the spindle, the rows would be nearly parallel to one another. This occurs at the level of the interscapular tract (fig. 63, C).

Dorsopelvic tract.—Behind the interscapular tract is a constriction in the boundary of the tract, and following this the tract broadens considerably within a short distance to form the dorsal tract. There is no natural interruption between the dorsal and pelvic tracts so we have grouped these two together under a combined name, the dorsopelvic tract (fig. 60). This compound term is useful sometimes when referring to the feathered area covering the dorsal surface of the body, but when one designates the dorsal and pelvic tracts individually, it is useful to have a specific name for each tract. The transverse boundary between the two tracts is the same as that used to separate the dorsal and pelvic regions, namely, at the anterior margins of the ilia.

At the anterolateral corner of the dorsal tract the follicles continue forward toward the scapular apterium. Usually these rows of contour feathers are continuous with the row of down feathers, which are located in the scapular apterium and extend into the lateral cervical apterium.

The feathers in the anterior end of the dorsal tract are widely separated. At first glance they may not seem to be organized in rows, but close observation of several specimens indicates that there is a pattern for this tract, as shown schematically in figure 63, D. Like the pattern in figure 63, C, there is in the dorsopelvic tract a changing length of radius and the position of the center for scribing the successive rows. Thus, at the anterior end, the junction of the rows in the midline forms a small angle, whereas this angle increases progressively down the pelvic tract until, at the caudal end, the rows diverge from the center at a wide angle.

The lateral boundary of the dorsal tract is established by the lateral body apterium. The lateral boundary of the pelvic tract is established by the lateral pelvic apterium (figs. 60 and 61). The pattern of rows, characteristic of the feathers of the pelvic tract, continues on to the uropygial eminence. These rows end at the base of the oil gland papilla (figs. 65, 388, p. 614). On the tail they constitute the dorsal caudal tract.

Ventral tracts and apteria

The ventral tracts of the body extend from the symphysis of the lower jaw to the base of the tail. Some subdivisions of these tracts can be seen in the lateral view (fig. 61); all are visible in the ventral view (fig. 62). The subdivisions of the ventral tract are described in the order given in the key to the feather tracts (p. 74), except for those not present in domestic birds.

Ventral cervical tract.—The ventral cervical tract is composed of three tracts—the interramal, submalar, and ventral cervical proper. The follicles of the interramal tract are small and closely placed. This pattern merges gradually into that of the submalar tract. In the latter, the feathers are longer and more widely spaced than in the interramal tract (fig. 62). In older birds with large wattles, the skin at the upper end of the wattle on the medial surface bears feathers. These feathers belong also to the submalar tract. At the caudal end of the wattles, there is a moderately abrupt transition to the closely placed follicles on the ventral surface of the neck. These follicles are arranged in chevron-shaped rows with the apices directed forward. The lateral ends of the rows curve upward and merge with the rows from the dorsal cervical tract that descend toward them across the side of the neck (fig. 61). Continuity of rows in the anterior part of the neck is sufficiently precise so that there is no natural boundary between the dorsal and ventral cervical tracts. Thus, in figure 61, an arbitrary dashed line was drawn from the earlobe to the anterior end of the lateral cervical apterium.

At about the midlength of the ventral cervical tract, the ventral cervical apterium begins, producing a bifurcation of the ventral cervical tract. At this point there appears to be a change in direction of the rows as shown in figure 62, but examination of several specimens indicates a pattern of rows as diagramed in figure 64, A. These two examples seem to be contrary to each other, but actually both are correct. The reason for the seeming difference is that when the dots lie close together, they give the visual effect of a row running in a certain direction. In the diagram, therefore, at the anterior end of the ventral cervical tract, the dots were so placed that the rows seem to extend forward toward the midline, but in the caudal part of the ventral cervical tract they seem to run in the opposite direction. Actually, there are two sets of rows that cross each other as shown in figure 64, A, and the symmetry of the arrangement at the anterior end of the tract indicates a third row shown as transverse rows by dotted lines in figure 64, A.

As the rows on the ventral cervical tract approach the region of the shoulder, they are farther apart, although the follicles within each row remain close together. When the crop is filled, the overlying skin of this area distends and pushes the rows as well as the follicles within the rows far apart. The ventral cervical tract covers the ventral surface of the cervical patagium and extends a short distance onto the dorsal surface (fig. 60). It is by this narrow band of follicles that continuity between the ventral cervical tract and the anterior end of the humeral tract is established.

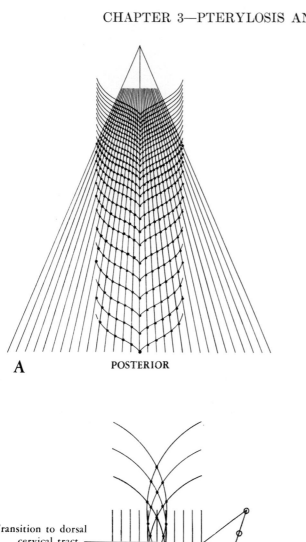

A

POSTERIOR

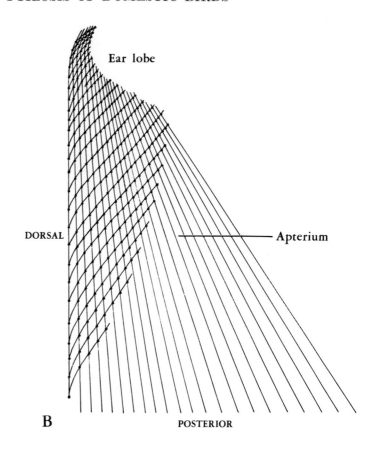

Ear lobe

DORSAL

Apterium

B

POSTERIOR

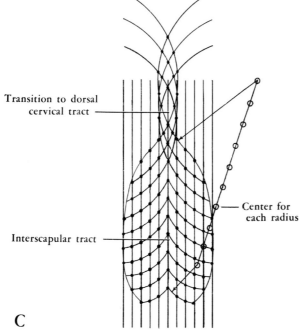

Transition to dorsal
cervical tract

Center for
each radius

Interscapular tract

C

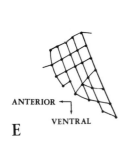

ANTERIOR

VENTRAL

E

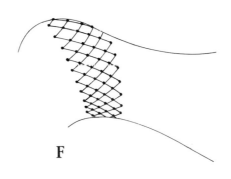

F

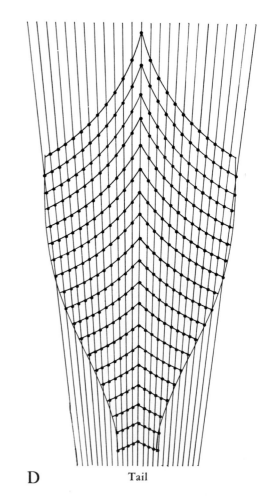

D   Tail

Pectoral tract.—The pectoral tract is broadly continuous with the ventral cervical tract, and the pattern of rows remains unchanged from one tract to the other (fig. 64, *A*). Therefore, an arbitrary line was drawn at the anterior shoulder boundary to separate these two tracts (fig. 61). The dashed lines of the shoulder are continued down along the margin of the thoracic inlet to separate the ventral cervical apterium from the pectoral apterium (fig. 62).

The pectoral tract is strong and the skin is elevated by subcutaneous adipose tissue. The margins of the tract are well defined. The rows and the follicles in the rows are more closely placed at the caudal end of the tract than at the anterior end. The caudal tip lies approximately opposite the middle of the keel.

The ventral cervical apterium, pointed at its anterior end, extends caudally. In the region of the keel, it passes along each side of the sternal tract, between this and the pectoral tract. Downy feathers are present in the apterium and, although widely scattered, follow the rows established by the contour feathers of the adjacent tracts on each side. One cannot help asking the question: Do the downy feathers of the apterium have the potential of developing into larger feathers, semiplumes, and contours, thus forming a tract, if the adjacent strong tracts are absent? It might be possible to answer this question experimentally if one repeatedly plucked the feathers of the tracts on each side of the apterium and observed if this led to the development of larger feathers in the apterium. The results of such an experiment might help answer the question discussed on page 93: "Why do apteria exist?"

Sternal and abdominal tracts.—The sternal and abdominal tracts are strong tracts. The sternal tract is divided by a medial apterium that lies on the ventral edge of the keel. The follicles at the anterior end of the sternal tract are rather widely spaced in the rows and the rows are far apart (fig. 62). Toward the caudal end, follicles and rows are gradually crowded together. At about the level where the two arms of the sternal tract unite, the medial abdominal tract begins. We arbitrarily placed the transverse boundary between the sternal tract and the abdominal tract at the junction between breast and abdomen at the posterior end of the sternum.

Close examination of the sternal and abdominal tracts reveals a complex pattern of rows (fig. 64, *B*). Diagonal rows crisscross as seen in figures 62 and 64. Crisscrossing is also seen in figure 259 (p. 428) by the arrangement of feather muscles joining follicles. In addition, the follicles are arranged so that they can be connected by longitudinal lines. The solid lines in figure 64, *B*, indicate the existence of feather muscles, and the dotted lines give the illusion of continuity in rows without definite connecting muscles.

At the anterior end of the sternal tract, the widely spaced rows swing across the apterium and are alined with the rows of the pectoral tract. The follicles of these rows that cross the apterium contain down feathers, but at the caudal end of the same apterium, lateral to the medial abdominal tract, the feathers on these rows are semiplumes. The important point is the definite continuity by rows between the scattered apterial feathers and feathers of the adjacent tract. This continuity makes it difficult to decide what is tract and what is apterium where the decision is based exclusively on the study of empty follicles. Much of the difficulty is removed when the feather and apterial muscles are studied, a subject given attention in chapter 8. We decided to designate the space between the sternal and pectoral tracts as the *pectoral apterium*, but the continuity of this space lateral to the abdominal tract and the caudal part of the sternal tract as the *lateral abdominal tract*. The abdominal tract region, together with the feathers of the medial abdominal tract, constitutes the fluff of the abdomen of the chicken, especially of the laying hen. The feathers that form the fluff are similar on both the strong medial abdominal tract and the weak lateral abdominal tract. The similarity in feather type is a strong argument for designating both as tracts.

It has been a question whether the abdominal tract should be terminated in front of the cloacal orifice, or should include the feathers of the cloacal circlet, namely the feathers bordering the two lips of the cloaca. In figure 66, we have shown the cloacal circlet as part of the medial abdominal tract. The few feathers shown on the dorsal lip on each side of the cloacal apterium have been named the cloacal tract. This tract also is a subdivision of the medial abdominal tract.

Cloacal circlet.—Immediately adjacent to the fleshy margin of the lips is a row of small feathers that constitute the cloacal circlet (fig. 66). On the dorsal lip, the cloacal circlet consists of a single row, whereas on the ventral lip approximately two rows are present but they are irregularly arranged.

Caudal tracts and apteria

The pterylosis of the tail is divided into three groups of feathers as follows: the continuation of the pelvic tract on the dorsal side and of the abdominal tract on the ventral side, the rectrices that lie on the caudal margins of the tail, and the tail coverts both on the dorsal and ventral surfaces. Several apteria separate some of these feather groups.

Dorsal caudal tract.—The dorsal caudal tract is a continuation of the pelvic tract. An arbitrary line drawn at the level

---

FIGURE 63.—Arrangement of feather follicles in rows.

A, dorsal cervical tract—dorsal view.

B, dorsal cervical tract—right lateral view.

C, interscapular tract and transition to dorsal cervical tract. Each transverse row of the interscapular tract has a radius of different length. The longitudinal alinement is parallel.

D, dorsal pelvic and caudal tracts. Like *C*, each transverse row has a different radius. The longitudinal alinement diverges in the cephalic direction.

E, lateral body tract—left side.

F, humeral tract—right wing.

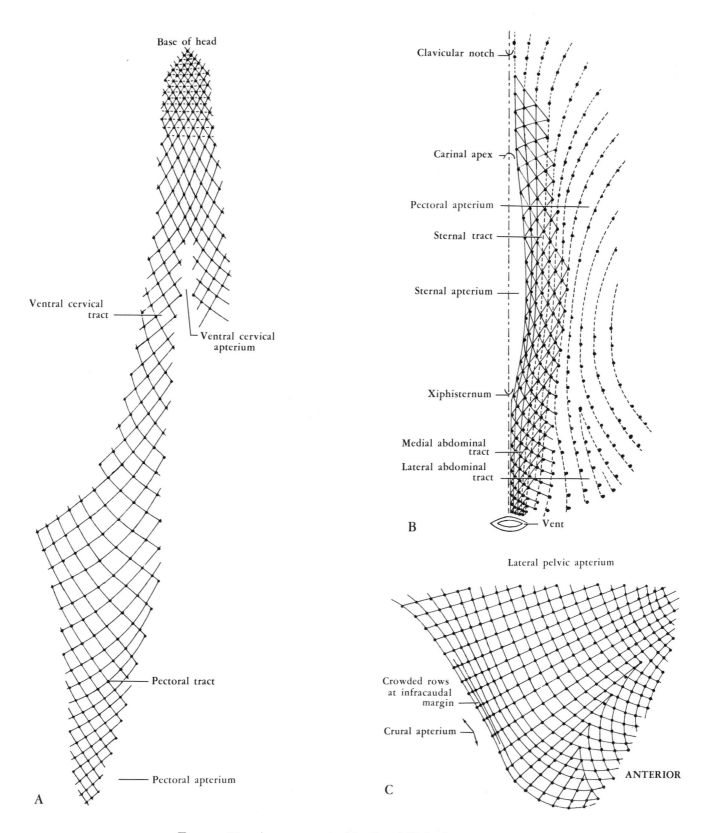

FIGURE 64.—Arrangement of feather follicles in rows.

A, ventral cervical and pectoral tracts.
B, sternal, abdominal, and under caudal tracts. The sternal and medial abdominal are strong tracts, the lateral abdominal is a weak tract in the chicken and is a lateral abdominal apterium in most species.
C, femoral tract—right side.

of the caudal indentation separates these two tracts (figs. 60 and 61). As shown in figures 65 and 388 (p. 614), the terminal end of the dorsal caudal tract lies on the uropygial eminence. A pair of small, isolated feathers within the dorsal caudal apterium and lateral to the uropygial papilla (fig. 65 near the end of the bracket) seems to occur frequently in the Single Comb White Leghorn Chicken.

Oil gland circlet.—Protruding from the caudal end of the oil gland is the uropygial papilla at the tip of which are the openings through which drain the secretions produced by the gland. Around each opening is a circlet of three or four small feathers. Their arrangement is shown in figure 65 and the character of the plumage, in figure 388. The detailed description of these feathers is given in chapter 6.

Ventral caudal tract.—The ventral caudal tract in the chicken is limited to a few rows of small, irregularly scattered feathers adjacent to the under tail coverts (fig. 62). A ventral caudal apterium separates right and left halves of the ventral caudal tract. The continuation of the apterium along the margin of the dorsal lip provides a natural separation between the abdominal and ventral caudal tracts.

There is no natural distinction between the feathers of the ventral caudal tract and those of under tail coverts. In discussing these feathers collectively, we have found it less confusing to list them all as under tail coverts.

Rectrices.—The rectrices are along the lateral margin of the tail. Those of the medial pair are larger than the others and lie at a slightly higher plane close to the pygostyle. In many birds the medial pair appear to be part of the row of major coverts. In the cock these are designated the main sickles (fig. 67). The chicken often has 14 rectrices, seven on each side, as indicated in figures 62 and 67; however, the number of tail feathers varies and is discussed in greater detail on page 161.

Upper tail coverts.—The key to the feather tracts (p. 74) lists upper major, median, and minor tail coverts. These three rows occur in some birds, but in the chicken only two rows are found—the upper major and median. They parallel the rectrices. At the lateral ends of these rows some feathers may be missing, so that the rows are not always complete.

Under tail coverts.—As with the upper tail coverts, the under tail coverts are listed in the key to the feather tracts as forming three rows—under major, median, and minor. In the chicken only the under major row is identifiable. In figure 62, these and any additional feathers adjacent to the rectrices have been labeled collectively as under tail coverts.

Lateral body tract and apterium

There is only one lateral body tract on the side of the body. This group of feathers exists as a small island in the midst of a large lateral body apterium (fig. 61). The tract extends ventrally from the junction of the wing and body toward the pectoral tract, but among individuals, the size and pattern of feather arrangement varies. On one pattern shown in figure 63, *E*, crossing of rows has produced squares, diamonds, and triangles.

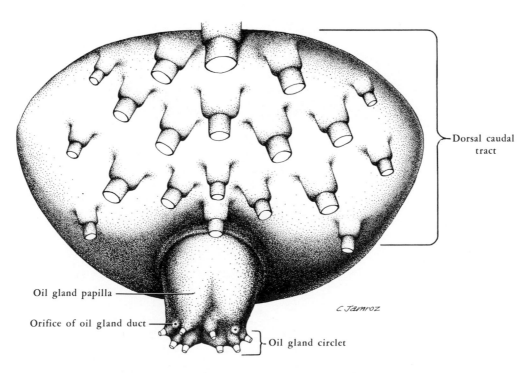

Dorsal caudal tract

Oil gland papilla

Orifice of oil gland duct

Oil gland circlet

C Jamroz

FIGURE 65.—Feather distribution on the uropygial eminence. The seemingly sharp margins merge into the adjacent dorsal surface of the tail. See figure 388 for additional details in this area. (Modified by K. E. Clark.)

Brachial tracts (upper arm)

A discussion of the terminology used here for the brachial tracts has been given in chapter 2 at some length, chiefly because we introduced two new terms, "subhumeral tracts" and "posthumeral tracts," as substitutes for axillary tract and tertiary remiges, respectively. Also we have used the term "humeral tract" rather than "scapulohumeral tract."

Humeral tract.—The humeral tract is a strong, moderately narrow tract with parallel sides; in the area of the tract the skin is considerably thickened. The follicles are arranged in crisscrossing rows (figs. 60 and 63, *F*). The tract has sharp medial and lateral boundaries. On the medial side is the broad scapular apterium, and on the lateral side is the broad humeral apterium. There may be continuity on the medial side of the humeral tract at the anterior end with the ventral cervical tract, on the lateral side with the upper marginal coverts of the prepatagium, and caudally with the posthumeral tract. The posterior edge of the tract lies at the junction of upper arm and metapatagium.

Subhumeral tract.—The subhumeral tract is a band of narrow, typically contour feathers, extending the length of the upper arm (figs. 61 and 62). The number of rows varies, but generally three are present (table 3).

TABLE 3.—*Counts on the subhumeral tracts of small chickens*

Chicken	Side	Rows	No. and relative size of feathers per row
1........	Right..........	Anterior....	Five small.
		Middle.....	Four large and three small.
		Posterior...	Four small.
	Left..........	Anterior....	Five small.
		Middle.....	Four large and three small.
		Posterior...	Four small.
2........	Right..........	Two rows...	....
	Left..........	Three rows.	....
3........	Right and left...	Three rows.	....
4........	Right and left...	Three rows.	Variable.
5........	Right and left...	Three rows.	Do.
6........	Right and left...	Three rows.	Do.

The subhumerals may be separated from the under forearm tract as shown in figures 61 and 62, but in most specimens there is continuity of the two tracts at the elbow.

Posthumeral tract.—The details of the posthumeral tract, shown for wild birds in figures 46 to 49, are not shown for

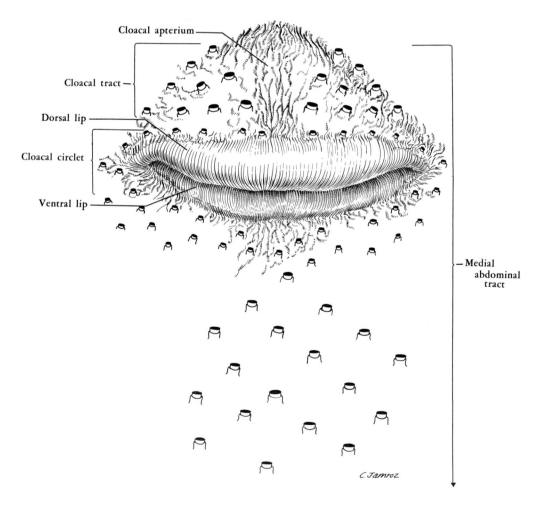

FIGURE 66.—Feather follicles around the cloaca merge with the follicles of the medial abdominal tract.
(Modified by R. B. Ewing.)

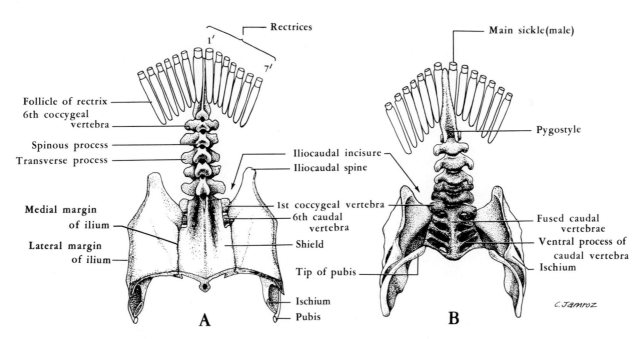

FIGURE 67.—Relationship of the rectrices to the pygostyle in the Single Comb White Leghorn Chicken. (Modified by J. Cagle.)

A, dorsal view of rectrices, coccygeal vertebrae, and caudal half of the pelvic girdle and shield.

B, ventral view of A.

the domestic birds, but the general plan of organization is the same. The posthumeral tract is usually composed of three rows of feathers. The middle row carries the longest ones, which are designated posthumeral quills; those in the rows in front of and behind the quills are called upper and under posthumeral coverts. The posthumeral tract lies between the secondary remiges and the humeral tract without separation by spaces from these two groups.

Alar tracts and apteria (lower arm and hand)

The list given under the heading of alar tracts in the key to the feather tracts is extensive because the rows of coverts (tectrices) associated with the primary and secondary remiges have each received names. When feathers are arranged in definite rows, as they are on the wing and the margins of the tail, they are not usually spoken of as tracts. Many, but not all the rows listed in the key to the feather tracts are present in the chicken. Also, under the heading of alar tracts, we have listed the rows of down feathers on the wing. These actually do not form tracts, but because they form rows like coverts and remiges, there seemed no other convenient category in which down feathers of this type could be placed. Because apteria are so intimately related to the tracts, we describe them together. Our purpose is to describe the location of the feathers rather than their size or appearance. The topic of ptilosis is discussed later in the chapter.

In the following text we describe all the feathers on the dorsal surface of the hand and forearm, and then those on the ventral surface of the hand and forearm; we have already described those associated with the upper arm. As explained in

the introduction to the section "Pterylosis—Excluding the Head" we could not show all the feathers of the wing in the total views of pterylosis (figs. 60 to 62); therefore, the wing had to be enlarged so that the details could be shown (figs. 68 to 71). The following description is based on these four figures.

Upper surface of the hand.—The 10 primary remiges of the manus are implanted in the hand portion of the postpatagium (figs. 69 and 70). The remiges are the most rigid feathers of the body, and the axes of the follicles in which they are implanted extend from the free edge of the postpatagium to the bones of the hand. Figures 111 and 112 show the location of the remiges from the tip of the middle finger to the wrist. We have followed Wray (1887a: 344), Steiner (1917: 224), and others in naming remiges according to the bones of the hand and fingers with which the remiges are associated. The 10th is the predigital, the ninth and eighth are the middigitals, the seventh is the addigital, and the sixth to first are the metacarpals.

We have examined several Single Comb White Leghorn Chickens that had 11 primary remiges. The most distal feather of the series was nearly as large as the adjacent 10th. It was not as small as the 11th primary remex of the duck. The 11th remex may be present in both wings or one. No data have been collected on the incidence of this anomaly. From the material examined, an 11th remex occurs more frequently in the Common Coturnix than in chickens. Its occurrence in coturnix is discussed on page 134.

There are at least nine upper major primary coverts; each is placed on the distal side of its corresponding remex. At first we were uncertain about which covert should be designated as the beginning of the series. What we labeled carpal remex in figure 69 closely resembled an upper major carpal covert, except that it was placed somewhat more anteriorly than the others. The answer to the problem came from an examination of the upper major primary coverts and carpal remex of the turkey (fig. 77). In the Bronze Turkey there is a full complement of 10 upper major primary coverts in addition to the carpal remex; also the carpal remex is short and placed near the basal end of the first primary remex so that it could not readily be considered a major covert.

Occasionally a chicken can be found with a 10th upper major primary covert. Each upper major primary covert is approximately two-thirds to three-fourths as long as its equivalent remex. The basal ends of the follicles of this row of coverts and those of the remex follicles coincide closely.

In the chicken there is poor positional continuity between the upper median coverts of the hand (fig. 69) and those of the forearm (fig. 68), whereas in the turkey the arrangement of rows suggests greater continuity (figs. 76 and 77). In the chicken, the distal end of the row of upper median secondary coverts curves anteriorly toward the base of the index finger rather than toward the beginning of the upper median primary covert row of the hand. The first upper median primary covert lies on the dorsal surface of the remex follicle. Number 2 in the series was absent in the material we studied and illustrated (fig. 69); the series begins again with number 3 and continues to number 10.

Upper minor primary coverts are composed of two rows: the first row begins with the third feather of the series and continues uninterruptedly to the ninth. The second row begins with the first feather, misses the second, and continues with the third feather to at least the eighth. Figure 69 shows another feather distal to the eighth that might be the ninth, but this one cannot be separated with certainty from the marginal coverts.

Small apteria separate the second row of minor coverts from the marginals located along the leading edge of the wing. The several parts of the upper hand apteria are separated by isolated feathers located between the second row of minor coverts and the marginals.

The upper marginal coverts of the hand are usually arranged in one row at the distal end as shown in figure 69, but the tract broadens to several rows in the region of the index finger. Our illustration does not show the follicles of the feathers that lay directly on the leading edge of the hand.

Four alular remiges are present. The first is the largest of the series and lies at the tip of the index finger. Each succeeding one is somewhat smaller and is placed farther from the free edge.

Among the species of birds studied here, there is no natural boundary between the follicles for the feathers that compose the marginal coverts and those that by their relation to the alular remiges should function as alular coverts. In figure 69, these follicles are labeled upper marginal coverts of the alula, and are separated by a dashed line from the marginal coverts on the prepatagium. The feathers adjacent to the alular remiges are somewhat longer than those more proximally placed, but the transition is gradual. The feathers illustrated

in figure 109, page 168, are labeled alular coverts because they appear to serve the function of coverts.

The chicken has more clearly organized rows of down feathers than has any other domestic and laboratory species we examined. One row of nine, the upper distal primary downs, lies near the free edge of the postpatagium of the hand between the remiges. The 10 follicles of the second row, the upper proximal primary downs, lie between the follicle openings of major and median coverts. Although these are designated as downs, some in a row have the characteristics of miniature contour feathers.

Upper surface of the carpal region.—The carpal remex of a chicken is similar in size and character to the first of the upper major primary coverts; like these coverts, it parallels the adjacent remex follicle. It has been customary to call this feather a remex, although in none of the specimens or species we have examined did we ever observe this feather at the free margin of the postpatagium. In the embryo it may lie close to the margin (Pycraft, 1899, pl. 15, fig. 1). Steiner (1956) depicted in the Tawny Owl, *Strix aluco*, and in the pigeon, *Columba livia*, that the carpal remex lies at the anterior end of the row of secondaries in line with the upper major primary coverts. What we have shown in the chicken is closely similar to the situation pictured by Steiner (1917: 381) for the Purple Heron (*Ardea purpurea*). As in the heron, the chicken has a feather that cuts across the dorsal surface of the carpal remex near its basal end; this feather is the upper major carpal covert. Anterior to this is a small feather on a line that continues from the upper median secondary coverts. We have designated it the upper median carpal covert (figs. 69 and 263, *A*, p. 434). Close by and anterior to it is a feather that from its location and its connection by muscles to other carpal coverts, has been named the "upper minor carpal covert" (fig. 263, *A*). Because there have been uncertainties in determining the number of carpal coverts, there needs to be made, unbiased by theory, a detailed, careful study of feathers in the carpal and adjacent areas, both embryologically and morphologically.

The rows of downs on the hand and forearm are represented on the carpus but have shifted anteriorly as have the carpal remex and its coverts. The single upper distal carpal down is at the same level as the proximal downs of the hand and the distal downs of the forearm (figs. 68 and 69). There are two upper proximal carpal downs, which lie at the same level as the proximal secondary downs.

Upper surface of the forearm.—The Single Comb White Leghorn Chickens that we have examined usually had 18 secondary remiges. Some chickens had 17 (fig. 62) and occasionally we suspected a 19th, but the last feather is small and similar to the adjacent posthumerals. A fifth secondary remex is present in chickens; the wing is thus of the eutaxic type. There is no evidence of irregularities in the arrangement of the covert rows.

There may be some question as to the identity of the coverts that belong to a particular remex, but we have followed Steiner (1917) and Humphrey and Clark (1961) in assuming that, basically, corresponding feathers in adjacent rows are inclined distally on the dorsal side of the wing. A minor covert is slightly closer to the tip of the wing than is a median covert, and a major covert has the most proximal position of the three. This was assumed to apply to the upper coverts on the hand as well as on the forearm. The typical plan is shown schematically in figure 72. It is this arrangement that Wray (1887a) depicted for the duck.

The 18 upper major secondary coverts form a complete row, and the bases of the feathers lie on about the same line as the bases of the remiges. Each of these coverts, up to about feather 15, crosses dorsally over its remex; but at the cubital end of the row, where all the feathers are small and crowded, the axes of feathers of adjacent rows parallel each other. In this area the basic pattern shows best that each row toward the leading edge is slightly more distally placed than the corresponding feather toward the trailing edge. This pattern carries upward into the marginals (fig. 68).

Each of the 18 upper median secondary coverts lies on the distal side of its remex and its major covert. The follicles for these feathers are much smaller than those of the major coverts, yet they form a complete row. Each upper minor secondary covert lies on the distal side of a medial covert and is only very slightly closer to the leading edge of the wing. The minor coverts, like the median coverts, form a complete row from 1 to 18.

We have labeled only one row of minor coverts (fig. 68); we could readily designate a second and a third minor row as Steiner (1917) has done, but it seems arbitrary because there is no natural boundary between these rows and the marginal coverts. Sundevall (Dallas, 1886: 396), Wray (1887a), Goodchild (1891), Steiner (1917), and others considered that several minor rows were present, but they based their decisions on the plumage rather than the pterylosis, as we have done here. The anteroposterior rows of the upper marginal coverts of the prepatagium follow an arc with the concavity toward the proximal end of the forearm. In forming this concavity, the direction of the follicle rows changes about 90°.

The upper cubital apterium overlies the elbow joint and is the only featherless space on the upper surface of the forearm. The upper distal (anterior) row of secondary downs lies either on the dorsal surface of the remex follicles or on their distal sides. The row begins with the first in the series; in the specimen shown in figure 68, it ended with the 13th. The upper proximal (posterior) secondary downs are placed on the carpal side of the major coverts. The row is relatively short, beginning with 1 and ending with 10 or 11.

Under surface of the wing (direction of rows).—The anteroposterior direction of the rows on the upper surface of the hand inclines distally from the trailing edge of the wing toward the leading edge (fig. 72, A). On the under surface of the wing, the rows incline in the opposite direction, which agrees with Steiner (1917) and Humphrey and Clark (1961). The postpatagial tissues in figure 72, A, are shown as semitransparent. The solid lines join the follicles on the dorsal surface and the dashed lines join the follicles on the ventral surface. The dorsal and ventral lines make **U** turns at the level

of the mouths of the remex follicles. This graphically shows that rows are inclined distally on the dorsal surface and proximally on the ventral surface. Figure 72, B, shows how the rows would look if the surfaces of the wings were unfolded. This type of diagram is used mostly by authors who have studied the arrangement of follicles in eutaxic and diastataxic wings. This pattern is easy to follow on the dorsal surface but becomes somewhat more difficult on the ventral surface because the feathering here is less complete.

Under surface of the hand.—There are 10 under major primary coverts, each on the proximal side of its corresponding remex. The follicles of the major coverts are only about a third as long as those of the primary remiges and are located near the middle of the calami of the remiges.

At the basal ends of the remiges are two rows of minor coverts (fig. 70). The first row is composed of 10 feathers, and the first in the series lies in the anterior part of the carpal region. The last in the series lies ventral to the 10th remex. The second row has only two follicles at the beginning of the row; each of these lie proximal to the minor coverts of 1 and 2 in the first row.

Extensive apteria spread over the ventral surface of the hand. The largest one is the underhand apterium. In the wrist region this apterium is continuous with the under forearm apterium (fig. 70). A small apterium in the hand region cuts into the tract of marginal feathers, and two small under alular apteria in the region of the under alular patagium are separated by a row of three feathers. These spaces vary in their extent, connections, and placements. The remaining surface along the leading edge of the wing, including the surface beneath the alula and along its margins, is occupied by under marginal coverts of the hand.

The under distal primary downs, one for each remex, form a row anterior to the ligamentous band that parallels the edge of the postpatagium. An under proximal primary down is sometimes present near the basal end of the first primary remex. Two downs are on the under surface of the alular quills, but these are inconstant in their occurrence.

Under surface of the carpal region.—An under major carpal covert is clearly evident near the anterior part of the carpal postpatagium. A question may be raised whether there should be included in the carpal group one feather from each of the two minor covert rows. In figure 70 these two feathers have been grouped together under the label, under minor carpal coverts. If the scheme depicted in figure 72 is followed closely, then these two feathers might be regarded as 1 in the first and 1 in the second under minor primary covert rows. The latter alternative seems unlikely since a 10th under minor primary covert—first row—is present, and if the one from the carpal region were included also, this would result in a total of 11 feathers, one more than the number of primary remiges. Pitelka (1945) demonstrated that in the Scrub Jay (*Aphelocoma coerulescens*) the under median coverts were present in the forearm but absent in the hand.

Under surface of the forearm.—Each under major secondary covert lies on the proximal side of its remex (fig. 71). The row

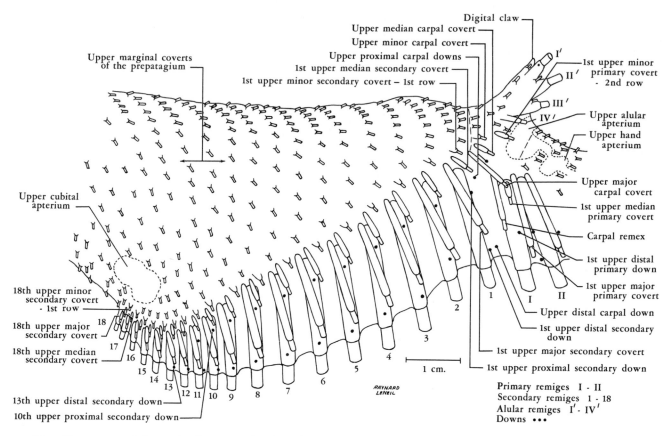

FIGURE 68.—Contour and down feathers on the dorsal surface of the forearm of the Single Comb White Leghorn Chicken.

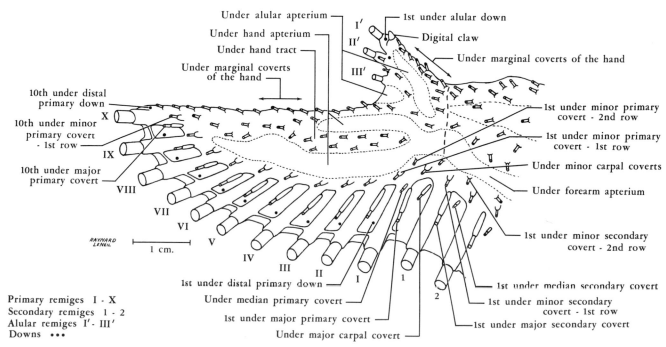

FIGURE 70.—Contour and down feathers on the ventral surface of the hand of the Single Comb White Leghorn Chicken.

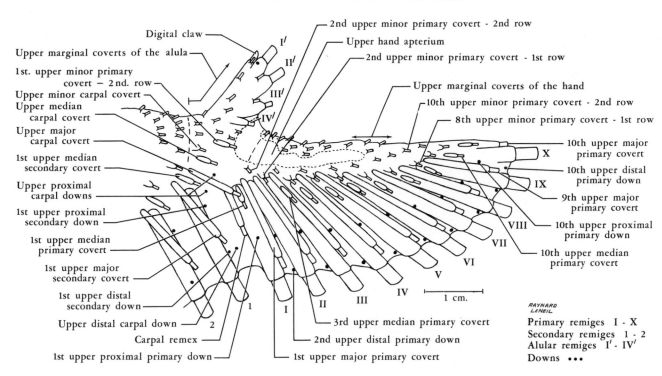

FIGURE 69.—Contour and down feathers on the dorsal surface of the hand of the Single Comb White Leghorn Chicken.

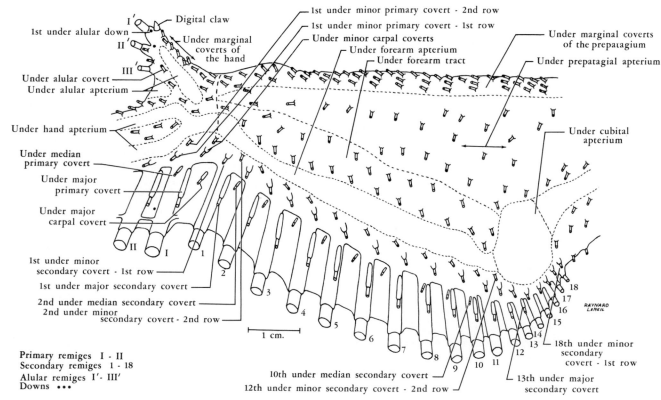

FIGURE 71.—Contour and down feathers on the ventral surface of the forearm of the Single Comb White Leghorn Chicken.

begins with 1 and ends with 13; absent for remiges 14 to 18.

The under median secondary coverts also form an incomplete row. The row begins with the second feather in the series and continues through the 10th. Only at the distal end do the median coverts have a close association with remex follicles of corresponding numbers. At the proximal end the

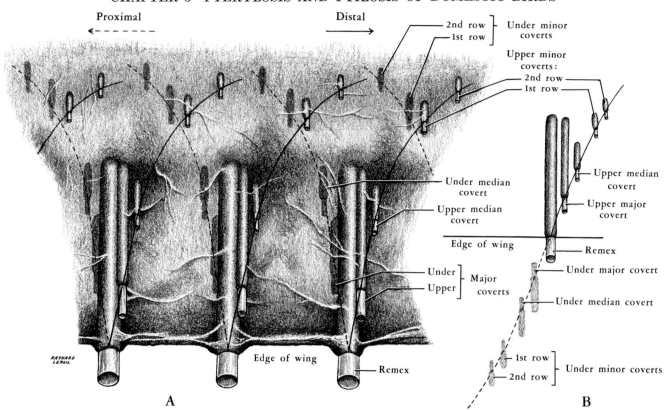

FIGURE 72.—Arrangement of the rows of coverts on the upper and under surface of hand and forearm. Lines join the rows of coverts with the remiges.

A, coverts are shown on a wing represented as semitransparent. The rows on the upper surface are inclined distally, and those on the under surface are inclined proximally.

B, illustrates the continuity that would exist if the surfaces could be laid out in a single plane.

follicles lie in the web of the postpatagium between adjacent remiges. In this position it might be assumed that what has been labeled 2 in the row (fig. 71) actually belonged to the first remex and therefore should be designated as 1. Support for choosing the labels presented here comes from an examination of the under forearm of the turkey (fig. 79), where each under median secondary covert retains a close association with its remex. In the Common Coturnix (fig. 86), the first under median secondary covert lies on the distal side of the first secondary and the second median covert lies on the proximal side of the next secondary. This same relationship of under median coverts to the follicles of secondary remiges applies also to the White Pekin Duck (fig. 94) and the Common Pigeon (fig. 101).

The first row of under minor secondary coverts is located well anterior to the under major and median coverts. The row begins with 1 and continues uninterrupted to 18. The first follicle lies directly anterior to its remex. Follicles 2 through 10 lie proximal to the remex of the corresponding number, some even to the extent of a full interremex space. Beginning with 11, a crowding together takes place so that at the end of the series, 18 lies in a direct line with its remex.

The second row of under minor coverts is an incomplete row beginning with 2 and ending with 12.

The under forearm apterium is continuous at the distal end with the under hand apterium, and at the proximal end with the cubital apterium. Anterior to the narrow, long apterium are two rows of follicles that represent the under forearm tract. Anterior to the tract are scattered down and delicate semiplume feathers located within the under prepatagial apterium. Close to the leading edge of the wing are three to four rows of short, stiff contour feathers placed closely together that constitute the under marginal coverts of the prepatagium.

Under distal and proximal secondary downs are absent from the forearm.

Femoral tract

The feathers of the femoral tract form a pattern of crisscrossing rows that produce squares, particularly near the center of the tract (fig. 64, C). The dorsal edge of the tract borders the lateral pelvic apterium (fig. 61). The rows of follicles in the tract curve from the dorsal to the anterior margin, which merges into the lateral body apterium. Along the infracaudal margin the rows lie close together, and the feather follicles may have an alternating arrangement. In figure 64, C, however, the follicles are shown one behind another. The alternating arrangement is demonstrated by the feather muscles (fig. 265, *A*, p. 438).

The arrangement of the rows varies considerably in the anterior part of the tract adjacent to the lateral body apterium, and the diagram in figure 64, *C*, does not apply to all the specimens examined. However, the condensation of rows adjacent to the infracaudal margin and the presence of a crural apterium, the space between femoral and crural tracts, is characteristic of all specimens we have seen.

Because the squares in the central part of the tract are large and uniform, the skin from this area has often served admirably for studies on the musculature, blood supply, and nerve supply of feather tracts.

Crural tract and apteria

The crural tract can be subdivided into three parts, as listed in the key to the feather tracts. In the chicken it seems valid to consider the tract as a continuous entity, both on the medial and outside surfaces of the leg. This becomes apparent when the smooth musculature of these feathers is studied, as illustrated in figure 266, *A*. The crural apterium is a transverse space across the knee region that separates the crural and femoral tracts. The follicles of the crural tract are rather widely separated. They are arranged in rows that crisscross in two directions; the pattern is relatively regular, with some condensations and terminations of rows as the intertarsal joint is approached. On the medial surface of the crus is a longitudinal area devoid of contour feathers, which is called the intracrural apterium. This apterium is continuous with the crural apterium (figs. 61 and 266, *A*).

Metatarsal and digital tracts and apteria

We will not discuss the metatarsal and digital tracts and apteria since the Single Comb White Leghorn Chicken, utilized as the type, has a metatarsus and digits covered with scales. In a number of breeds these parts are covered with feathers, and the terminology would be that essentially given for the Great Horned Owl in chapter 2. Usually, in certain parts of the tract there is an intermingling of feathers and scales, a situation discussed in chapter 9 and illustrated in figure 379, page 600.

Turkey

Our pterylosis studies on the turkey are based entirely on the Bronze variety. The description of this fowl is not as detailed as that given for the chicken; instead the approach is comparative. The turkey is the largest bird used in this series. In the chicken a tract may often contain some semiplumes at the margin transitional to the downs of an adjoining apterium, but in the turkey contour feathers appear at the margin and semiplumes appear in the apteria. Therefore, semiplumes and small contours were often excluded in outlining the tracts and were included with adjacent apteria. If distinction between tract and apterium had been made

strictly on the basis of feather type, there would have been an unnatural dissimilarity in the pterylosis of chicken and turkey. Perhaps future studies will indicate in the down-semiplume-contour feather series that proportionally more feathers remain at the lower end of the series in small birds than in large birds.

Spinal tracts and apteria

The dorsal cervical tract begins caudal to the carunculate skin of the head and upper neck (fig. 73). Because the origin of the tract is farther down the neck than it is in the chicken, the rows are not concentrated at the anterior end of the tract as they are in the chicken, and the tract may or may not join the ventral cervical tract (fig. 74). If there is continuity between dorsal and ventral tracts, it is limited to a few rows of feathers between the carunculate skin and the lateral cervical apterium. The tract extends farther forward on the dorsal surface of the neck than it does on the ventral.

In the turkey, the dominant direction of the medial ends of the rows is anterior (fig. 73), whereas in the chicken it is posterior (fig. 60). A change in the direction of rows on the dorsal neck is absent; therefore, there is no natural separation between dorsal cervical and interscapular tracts. The arbitrary separation of these tracts is indicated in figure 73 by a dashed line placed at the anterior margin of the shoulder.

The interscapular tract is particularly strong in the turkey; the skin beneath these feathers is greatly thickened. Along the midline, in the caudal two-thirds to three-fourths of the tract, there is a narrow but distinct interscapular apterium. Here the skin is thin. At the transition between the interscapular and dorsopelvic tracts, the feathers are relatively far apart, and in a full grown turkey there may be sufficient separation to suggest a small, transverse apterium.

The dorsopelvic tract in the turkey, as in the chicken, is an uninterrupted broad, longitudinal band of feathers. It may be divided into its separate parts by placing an arbitrary transverse boundary at the anterior end of the ilium; the follicles anterior to this would then belong to the dorsal tract and those over the ilia and synsacrum, to the pelvic tract. The dorsal tract is broad, covering scapulae and most of the dorsal ribs.

The pattern of rows in the dorsopelvic tract is similar to the diagram (fig. 63, *D*). In figure 73 the rows seem to be irregularly arranged, but we tried to place every follicle in its exact position. When every follicle was identified, it appeared that partial rows were present that sometimes influenced the direction of adjoining rows. This same situation is treated in chapter 8, for example, see figure 271. At the caudal end of the pelvic region, we placed an arbitrary transverse dashed line to separate the pelvic tract from the dorsal caudal tract.

Ventral tracts and apteria

Ventral tracts and apteria are shown in part in the lateral view (fig. 74) but most clearly in ventral view (fig. 75). The rows of the ventral cervical tract are directed caudally toward the midline, as one would expect if a basic continuity existed

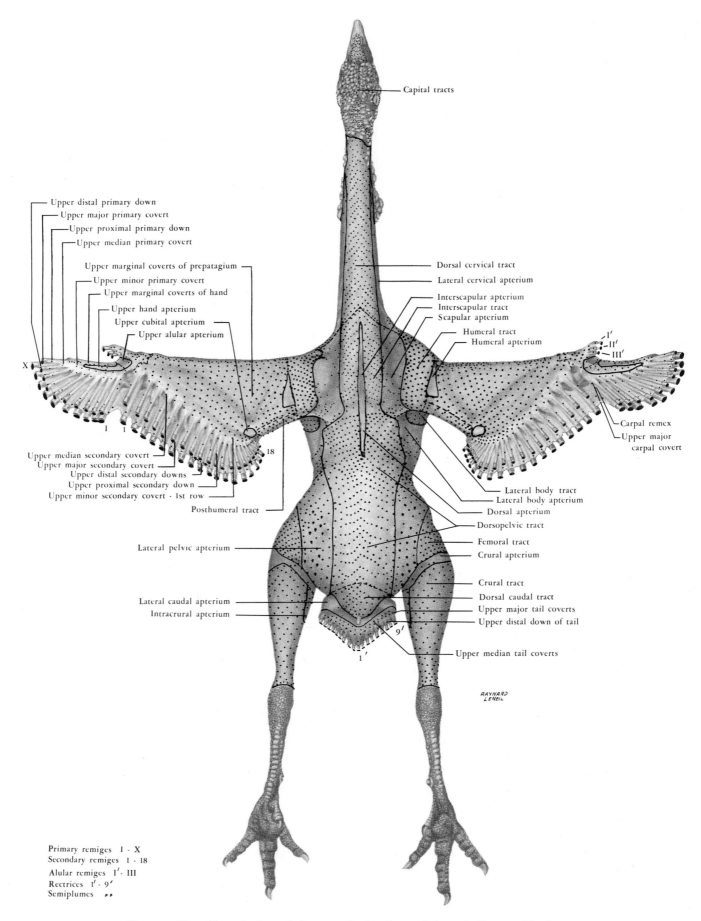

Capital tracts

Upper distal primary down
Upper major primary covert
Upper proximal primary down
Upper median primary covert
Upper marginal coverts of prepatagium
Upper minor primary covert
Upper marginal coverts of hand
Upper hand apterium
Upper cubital apterium
Upper alular apterium
X

Dorsal cervical tract
Lateral cervical apterium
Interscapular apterium
Interscapular tract
Scapular apterium
Humeral tract
Humeral apterium
I'
II'
III'

Carpal remex
Upper major carpal covert

Upper median secondary covert
Upper major secondary covert
Upper distal secondary downs
Upper proximal secondary down
Upper minor secondary covert - 1st row
Posthumeral tract

Lateral body tract
Lateral body apterium
Dorsal apterium
Dorsopelvic tract
Femoral tract
Crural apterium

Lateral pelvic apterium

Crural tract
Dorsal caudal tract
Upper major tail coverts
Upper distal down of tail

Lateral caudal apterium
Intracrural apterium

9'
1'

Upper median tail coverts

RAYNARD LENEIL

Primary remiges I - X
Secondary remiges 1 - 18
Alular remiges I'- III
Rectrices 1'- 9'
Semiplumes ,,

FIGURE 73.—Dorsal view of the pterylosis of an adult male Bronze Turkey.

between the rows of the dorsal and ventral cervical tracts. It is nearly impossible to determine if the tracts are continuous because they are separated by the great width of the lateral cervical apterium.

A narrow ventral cervical apterium in a full-grown tom begins at the carunculate skin (fig. 75). In half-grown turkeys, the anterior end of the apterium may lie about half way between the carunculate skin and beard. In still younger individuals the anterior end of the apterium may be located at the level of the beard. The featherless space extends posteriad to the level of the thoracic inlet, where it is continuous with right and left pectoral apteria. This pattern is similar to that in the chicken. As in the chicken, the ventral cervical and pectoral tracts are arbitrarily separated by dashed lines that begin on the anterior end of the shoulder and follow the margins of the thoracic inlet to the anterior end of the keel (fig. 62—chicken; fig. 75—turkey). The rows of contour feathers within the ventral cervical tract have continuity with rows of down feathers in the ventral cervical apterium. The pectoral apterium, separating the pectoral and sternal tracts, contains numerous semiplumes which, by their arrangement, give an impression of continuity between these two ventral tracts. The pectoral tract does not extend as far toward the groin region in the turkey as it does in the chicken. The tract is relatively broader in the turkey. The rows within the tract cross at right angles and give the effect of a geometrical arrangement of feathers as diagramed for the chicken in figure 64, A.

Feathers at the anterior end of the sternal tract are widely spaced and transitional toward feathers of the adjacent pectoral and ventral cervical apteria. The remainder of the sternal tract is strong, as is its continuation caudally where it becomes the medial abdominal tract. The sternal tract is divided by the sternal apterium located on the ventral edge of the keel. This space, entirely devoid of down feathers, continues into the abdominal region where it is continuous with the medial abdominal apterium.[1] Separation of the sternal and abdominal tracts is arbitrary, as indicated (fig. 75) by the dashed lines placed at the anatomical boundary between the sternum and the abdomen.

The sternal and abdominal tracts have an approximately uniform width throughout their length (fig. 75). The follicles lateral to the medial abdomial tract are widely spaced; the feathers of the apterium are small, as explained in footnote 1. The area where they are located is designated the lateral abdominal apterium.

The abdominal tract includes the feathers around the cloaca, but the abdominal tract proper is separated from the ventral lip of the cloaca by a narrow featherless space. The ventral

lip does not protrude as much in the turkey as it does in the chicken. Toward the corners of the dorsal lip are a few feathers that are separated from the remainder of the abdominal tract. They may be regarded as part of the cloacal tract. On the median part of the dorsal lip is a conspicuous cloacal apterium that continues without interruption to the soft, fleshy tissues of the cloacal margin. The feathers of the last row of the cloacal tract (adjacent to the vent opening) are slightly smaller than those of the adjacent row but appear to be part of the cloacal tract rather than a separate and distinct row forming a circlet.

Caudal tracts and apteria

The dorsal caudal tract is located on the dorsal surface of the tail and extends caudally to the oil gland papilla. The remainder of the dorsal surface of the tail is occupied largely by a dorsal caudal apterium. There are eight or nine pairs of rectrices in the male turkey.

Dorsal to the rectrices is a row of large upper major tail coverts, one for each rectrix (fig. 73). The shafts of these coverts parallel those of the rectrices. A row of from eight to nine upper median tail coverts lies parallel and anterior to each row of major coverts. The central members of the row have small contour feathers, but those more laterally placed are plumulaceous.

The uropygial eminence is covered with many feathers at the posterior of the dorsal caudal tract. These follicles of the feathers end at the base of the uropygial papilla. An oil gland circlet is not shown in figures 73 and 74; but small, short feathers are often present, especially in young turkeys. They seem to be abraded rather frequently in the turkey so that often the end of the papilla seems bare.

The bare surface covering the most laterally placed rectrix is called the lateral caudal apterium. It extends forward to the caudal indentation and is confluent with the dorsal and ventral caudal apteria.

The ventral caudal tract is larger in the turkey than it is in the chicken and occupies the space posterior to the caudal indentation as far as the rectrices (fig. 75). There are about four transverse rows and these are grouped together as a ventral caudal tract, but it would be equally accurate to label them under major, under median, and under minor tail coverts—the last having two rows. In the midline a ventral caudal apterium widely separates the two halves of the tract and is continuous with a transverse part of the same tract. At the posterior end, the apterium is continuous with a narrow space separating the ventral caudal tract and rectrices.

There are two distinct rows of down feathers, one on the upper surface and one on the lower (figs. 73 and 75). The upper down feathers of the tail lie nearly midway between the rectrices and upper major coverts, but slightly closer to the rectrices. There are about seven on each side. The under down feathers of the tail also lie close to the collars of the rectrix follicles. A few scattered downs are on the dorsal caudal apterium.

---

[1] In the chicken the feathers of the lateral abdominal tract are similar to and nearly as long as those of the medial abdominal tract so that both tracts contribute to the fluff. In the turkey, however, typical feathers of a fluff are limited to the medial abdominal tract, and the area of the lateral abdominal tract is more appropriately called an apterium.

Lateral body tract and apterium

The lateral body tract is a small group of feathers extending from the base of the wing, diagonally across the lateral body apterium toward the pectoral tract (fig. 74). Anterior to it are small scattered downs. All the feathers are large and of the semiplume rather than contour type, as in the chicken and duck.

Brachial tracts and apteria

The humeral tract on the dorsal side of the upper arm is a strong tract. It has a moderately well-defined boundary adjacent to the large scapular apterium, with some transitional small feathers, and a very sharp boundary adjacent to the humeral apterium (fig. 73). A narrow band of feathers provides continuity between the anterior medial corner of the humeral tract and the ventral cervical tract. Three rows of feathers extend along the posterior margin of the upper arm and fill the space between the secondary coverts and the humeral tract; these are the posthumerals. Among these the longest feathers are in the middle of the three rows. There is continuity between this tract and the upper marginal coverts of the prepatagium; however, the width of this continuity is restricted by the humeral and the cubital apteria. The upper cubital apterium is thin, featherless skin, covering the elbow joint (figs. 73 and 76).

The subhumeral tract is composed of a band of contour feathers on the under side of the upper arm. It extends from the lateral body tract almost to the elbow (figs. 74 and 75). The feathers of the caudal row are the largest; those anterior to it are much smaller, and anterior to these are scattered feathers similar to those of the under prepatagial apterium.

Alar tracts and apteria

The description of the feathers on the hand and forearm of the turkey are less detailed than those given for the chicken. The pterylosis patterns for turkey and chicken are similar, and, except for minor details, the description of one closely fits that of the other.

Upper surface of the hand.—There are 10 primary remiges, large and equally spaced, on the upper surface of the hand. Each upper major primary covert lies on the distal side of its remex; the 10th is large enough so that it is clearly a major covert and not one of the marginal coverts (fig. 77). As mentioned earlier, this fact enabled us to number correctly the major coverts of the chicken and the Common Coturnix.

The upper median primary coverts lie on the distal side of the major coverts, beginning with the second feather in the series and ending with the ninth. Squeezed in between the median coverts and the upper hand apterium is a partial first row of upper minor primary coverts, from the third

through the eighth feather. In some specimens it included only five feathers, the fourth through the eighth.

Down feathers, represented by black dots in figure 77, fill the upper hand apterium. This space extends from near the tip of the wing to the base of the index finger, where it merges with the upper alular apterium, and is arbitrarily separated from it by a dashed line. Because the upper hand apterium is broad, the upper marginal coverts are restricted to one or two rows of feathers. There are four alular remiges, and several smaller feathers on both sides of the fourth. The upper marginal coverts on digit II are numerous. Those adjacent to the alular remiges can be considered as alular coverts, but a one-to-one relationship does not exist between these remiges and their coverts.

Upper surface of the carpal region.—The carpal remex and its upper major covert are small. They lie close together on the dorsal surface of the first primary, near its basal end (figs. 76 and 77). The term "carpal" implies that these feathers are associated with the wrist. Soft X-ray radiographs of this area show that the carpal feather, closely associated as it is with the first primary, actually lies above the carpometacarpus, whereas the base of the first secondary or axial feather points toward the cuneiform (ulnare) bone of the wrist. These facts in no way change the well-established concept that the small feather on the proximal side of the first primary is a carpal remex and that the axial feather is the first secondary. The seeming differences between observations on fresh or dried specimens and X-ray pictures are discussed again on page 171.

Several down feathers lie on the postpatagium of the wrist. We have considered the down closest to the edge as the first upper distal primary down, anterior to this is the upper distal carpal down, and the remaining two are the first upper distal and upper proximal secondary down feathers. Variability in the placement of these down feathers renders this terminology subject to change.

Upper surface of the forearm.—There are 18 secondary remiges on the upper surface of the forearm in the turkey, as there are in the chicken. The first, the axial feather, is shorter than the second in the series. Each of the 18 upper major secondary coverts almost parallels but crosses slightly the corresponding remex (fig. 76). Each of the 18 upper median secondary coverts lies near the basal end of each major covert and on the distal side of it. Only the first row of upper minor secondary coverts is labeled; a complete series of these is present from 1 to 18. In the young turkey, the feathers in the more anterior rows are downy or semiplumulaceous, whereas in the old bird they are typically contour in type. No natural separation exists between minor coverts and marginals, and the lines joining the rows of secondaries and coverts could be extended smoothly to the marginal coverts. No apteria are present on the upper forearm

$\longrightarrow$

FIGURE 74.—Left lateral view of the pterylosis of an adult male Bronze Turkey.

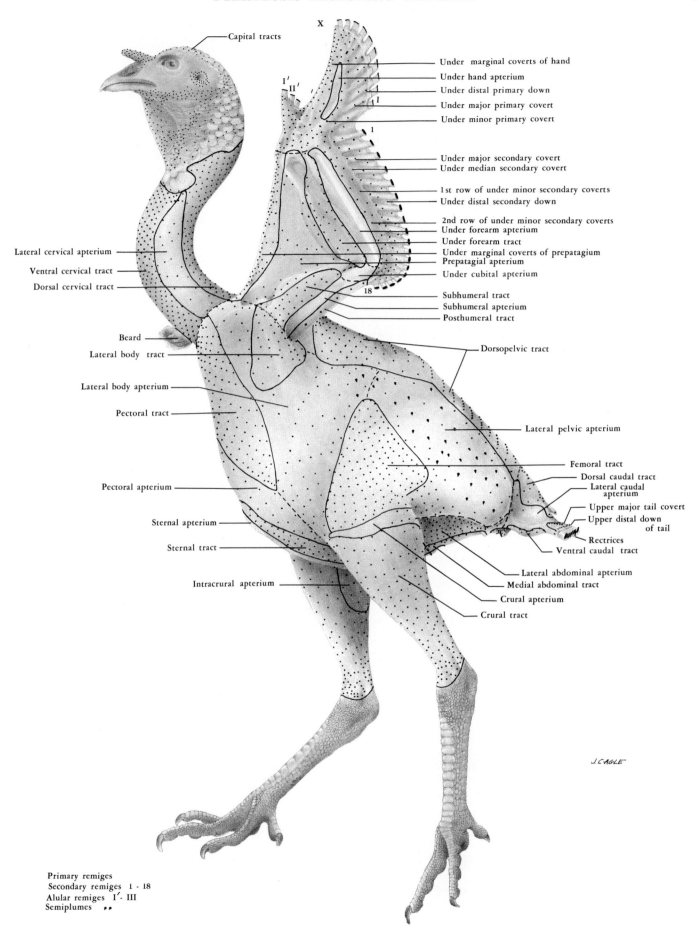

Capital tracts

X

I′
II′

Under marginal coverts of hand
Under hand apterium
Under distal primary down
Under major primary covert
Under minor primary covert

I

Under major secondary covert
Under median secondary covert

1st row of under minor secondary coverts
Under distal secondary down

2nd row of under minor secondary coverts
Under forearm apterium
Under forearm tract
Under marginal coverts of prepatagium
Prepatagial apterium
Under cubital apterium

18

Subhumeral tract
Subhumeral apterium
Posthumeral tract

Lateral cervical apterium
Ventral cervical tract
Dorsal cervical tract

Dorsopelvic tract

Beard
Lateral body tract

Lateral body apterium

Pectoral tract

Lateral pelvic apterium

Femoral tract

Dorsal caudal tract
Lateral caudal apterium

Pectoral apterium

Upper major tail covert
Upper distal down of tail

Rectrices

Sternal apterium

Ventral caudal tract

Sternal tract

Lateral abdominal apterium
Medial abdominal tract
Crural apterium
Crural tract

Intracrural apterium

J. CAGLE

Primary remiges
Secondary remiges 1 - 18
Alular remiges I′- III
Semiplumes

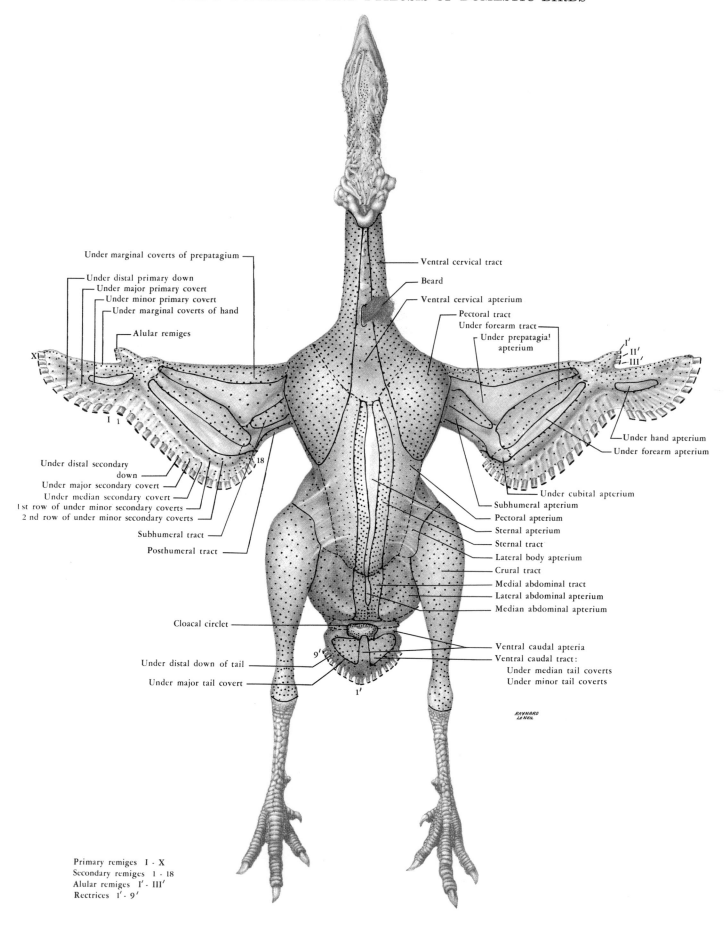

Under marginal coverts of prepatagium

Under distal primary down
Under major primary covert
Under minor primary covert
Under marginal coverts of hand

Alular remiges

XI
III

I 1

Under distal secondary down
Under major secondary covert
Under median secondary covert
1st row of under minor secondary coverts
2nd row of under minor secondary coverts

Subhumeral tract

Posthumeral tract

18

Cloacal circlet

Under distal down of tail

Under major tail covert

9'

1'

Ventral cervical tract

Beard

Ventral cervical apterium

Pectoral tract
Under forearm tract
Under prepatagia!
apterium

I'
II'
III'

Under hand apterium
Under forearm apterium

Under cubital apterium
Subhumeral apterium
Pectoral apterium
Sternal apterium
Sternal tract
Lateral body apterium
Crural tract
Medial abdominal tract
Lateral abdominal apterium
Median abdominal apterium

Ventral caudal apteria
Ventral caudal tract:
    Under median tail coverts
    Under minor tail coverts

RAYNARD
LeNEIL

Primary remiges I - X
Secondary remiges 1 - 18
Alular remiges I' - III'
Rectrices 1' - 9'

surface of the turkey, except for the upper cubital apterium located above the elbow joint.

There is a complete row of upper distal secondary down feathers; the first one lies at a higher level on the post-patagium of the wrist than do those in the remainder of the rows (fig. 76). The implantation of downs 2 to 18 varies; some seem to be attached to the webs between follicles of the secondaries and others spring from the skin overlying these follicles. We found that stretching the skin often produces differences in the placement of the down feathers. The upper proximal secondary down feathers begin with the first and continue along a straight line to the twelfth. The down feathers of this row are between the major and median coverts, as in the chicken.

Under surface of the hand.—On the under surface of the hand, the first under major primary covert lies on the proximal side of the first primary (fig. 78). A line joining the first under median and first under minor coverts should curve in a proximal direction, according to the scheme in figure 72. Instead, a line joining these three feathers curves in a distal direction. Irregularities of this sort occur more frequently on the under than on the upper surface of the wing.

There are 10 under major primary coverts. The under median primary coverts formed an incomplete row, from 1 to 7, in one specimen we examined. In seven specimens there was only a single feather of this row, as shown in figure 78, and in two specimens there were two feathers in this row. Anterior to the one or two under median coverts are 10 under minor primary coverts in the first row. At the end of the row is an additional feather that we consider to belong to the under marginal coverts. A second row of under minor primary coverts does not exist, its position having been taken by the under hand apterium. At the two ends of the apterium the follicles of the minor coverts seem to be part of the under marginal coverts of the hand, but the regularity of rows is less precise than on the dorsal surface.

Only three of the four alular remiges are visible from the ventral side. In the turkey a digital claw is absent. The under marginal coverts of the hand are scattered on the ventral surface of digit II, and presumably those adjacent to the alular remiges can be regarded as under major alular coverts.

Under surface of the carpal region.—Only one carpal feather is present on the under surface of the carpal region. It is labeled under major carpal covert, although it is clearly in line with the adjacent under median secondary and primary coverts (figs. 78 and 79).

Under surface of the forearm.—There are 17 under major secondary coverts, the 18th in the series being absent (fig.

79). Each of these lies on the proximal side of its adjacent remex, but the under median secondary coverts lie directly above the remex follicles having the same numbers. According to the scheme diagramed in figure 72, an under median secondary covert should lie proximal to its remex and to its under major secondary covert. The row of under median secondary coverts begins with follicle 1 on the ventral surface of the first secondary remex. This position is retained by other members of the row to the 15th, which is the last feather in the sequence. There are two rows of under minor secondary coverts. The first row is complete from 1 to 18. The second row begins with feather 1, and, in the specimen illustrated (fig. 78), the row continued through the 16th.

Anterior to the minor coverts is an elongated and relatively broad under forearm apterium beginning at the wrist region and extending to the elbow, where it is widely confluent with the under cubital apterium and, beyond that, with the humeral apterium.

The under forearm tract has a nearly complete posterior row of contour feathers. Anterior to these are two incomplete rows. Anterior to the under forearm tract are plumulaceous feathers within the under prepatagial apterium. Beyond the apterium are the two or three rows of under marginal coverts of the prepatagium.

Under secondary downs are limited to an incomplete distal row beginning with the third and ending with the 11th feather. Each is on the web between remiges (fig. 79).

Femoral tract

Relative to the size of the thigh, the femoral tract in the turkey is small compared to that in the chicken. The organization is the same in both birds, namely, the shape is triangular, the rows are irregular along the anterior margin, and several rows are compressed along the infracaudal margin (fig. 74). The follicles along the dorsal edge of the tract are large and sharply distinguished from the scattered follicles of the pelvic apterium. The pelvic apterium is much broader in the turkey than it is in the chicken. Many of the feathers are semiplumes rather than downs. Each semiplume is represented in figure 74 by a dot with an attached straight line.

Crural tract and apteria

The follicles of the crural tract are rather far apart but are uniformly distributed on the lateral, anterior, and posterior surfaces of the shank. On the medial surface the feathers are smaller and irregularly spaced. The rows of follicles are close together in the region of the ankle and the feathers are short. A small intracrural apterium, on the medial surface of the crus, is confluent with the crural apterium.

←

FIGURE 75.—Ventral view of the pterylosis of an adult male Bronze Turkey.

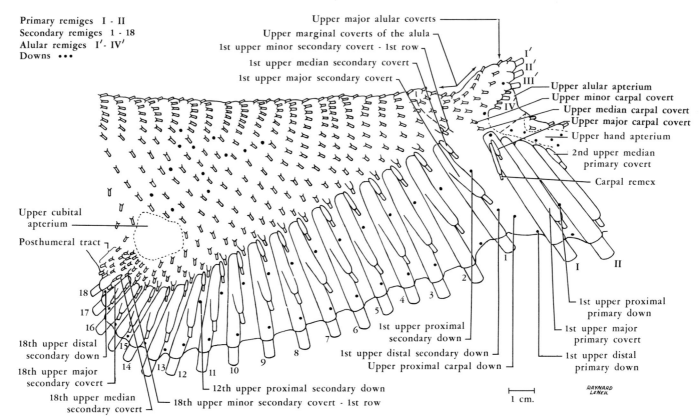

FIGURE 76.—Contour and down feathers on the dorsal surface of the forearm of the Bronze Turkey.

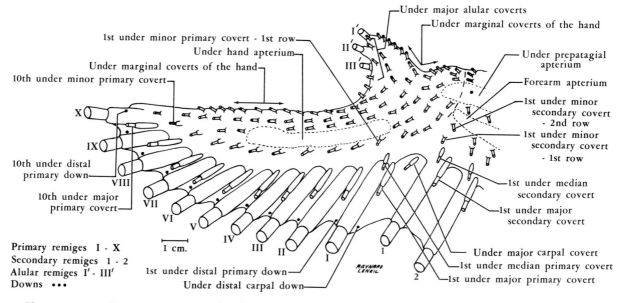

FIGURE 78.—Contour and down feathers on the ventral surface of the hand of the Bronze Turkey.

Common Coturnix

The pterylosis of the Common Coturnix is similar to that of the galliform species previously described. The chief technical problem in a study of pterylosis of coturnix is difficulty in seeing the empty follicles.

Spinal tracts and apteria

The anterior end of the slender neck broadens to meet the base of the head. In this area the short contour feathers project outward, almost at right angles to the skin. Farther down the neck, where the feathers are longer, they lie close

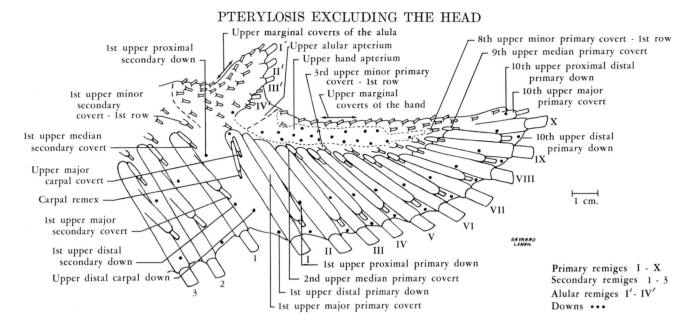

FIGURE 77.—Contour and down feathers on the dorsal surface of the hand of the Bronze Turkey.

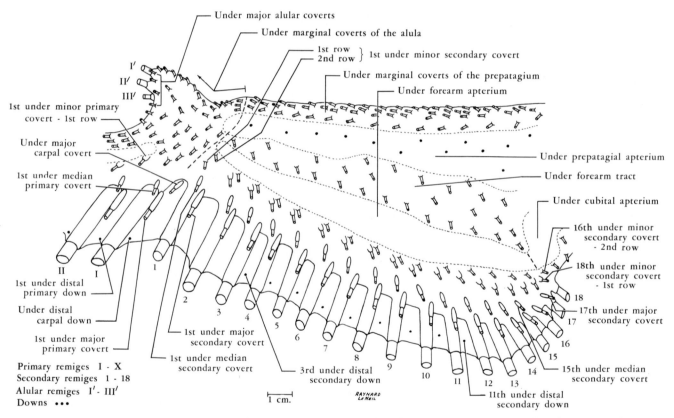

FIGURE 79.—Contour and down feathers on the ventral surface of the forearm of the Bronze Turkey.

to the skin and overlap one another. Adjacent to the head, the follicles are so small that the rows are poorly defined (fig. 80). Any suggestion of rows is obtained only after stretching the thin skin. In this region the dorsal cervical tract continues laterally so that it joins the ventral cervical tract (fig. 81). The area of junction is relatively small—about

four or five rows of feathers between the caudal end of the malar tract and the beginning of the lateral cervical apterium.

The skin of the dorsal neck, from the upper third of the neck to the interscapular region, is stretched like a cord suspending the lower flexure of the neck. This characteristic is not shown in figures 80 and 81 because in the drawings this band of skin has been stretched laterally to show the arrangement of follicles. When this is done, it is apparent that the follicles are arranged in chevron-shaped rows with the apices forward (fig. 80). The skin is so thin that the underlying smooth muscles moving the follicles can be seen clearly. The intersecting of these rows of muscles produces diamond-shaped spaces with a follicle at each corner.

The dorsal cervical band continues posteriorly into the interscapular tract. When the skin of the cervical band is stretched laterally, the feather tract it bears is approxi-

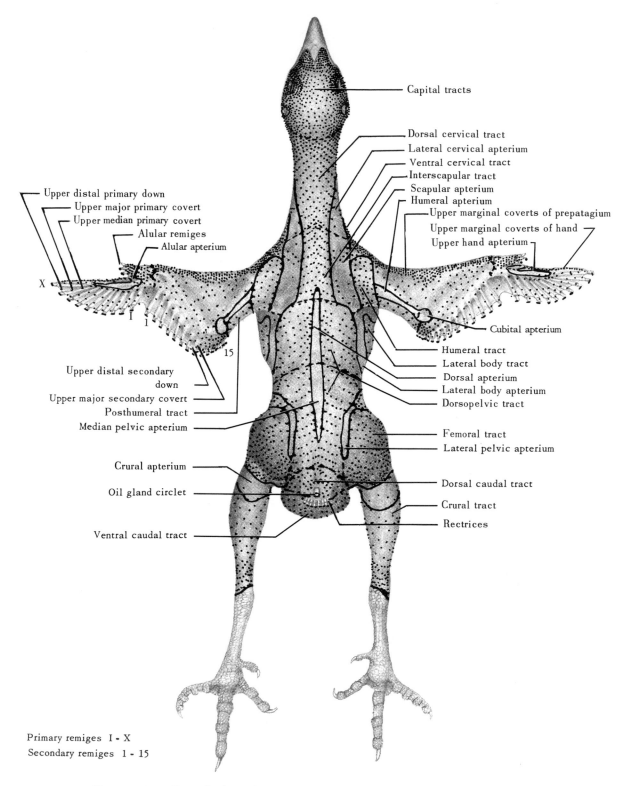

Capital tracts

Dorsal cervical tract
Lateral cervical apterium
Ventral cervical tract
Interscapular tract
Scapular apterium
Humeral apterium
Upper marginal coverts of prepatagium
Upper marginal coverts of hand
Upper hand apterium

Upper distal primary down
Upper major primary covert
Upper median primary covert
Alular remiges
Alular apterium

X

I 1

15

Cubital apterium

Humeral tract
Lateral body tract
Dorsal apterium
Lateral body apterium
Dorsopelvic tract

Upper distal secondary down
Upper major secondary covert
Posthumeral tract
Median pelvic apterium

Femoral tract
Lateral pelvic apterium

Crural apterium
Oil gland circlet

Dorsal caudal tract
Crural tract
Rectrices

Ventral caudal tract

Primary remiges I - X
Secondary remiges 1 - 15

FIGURE 80.—Dorsal view of the pterylosis of the male Common Coturnix.

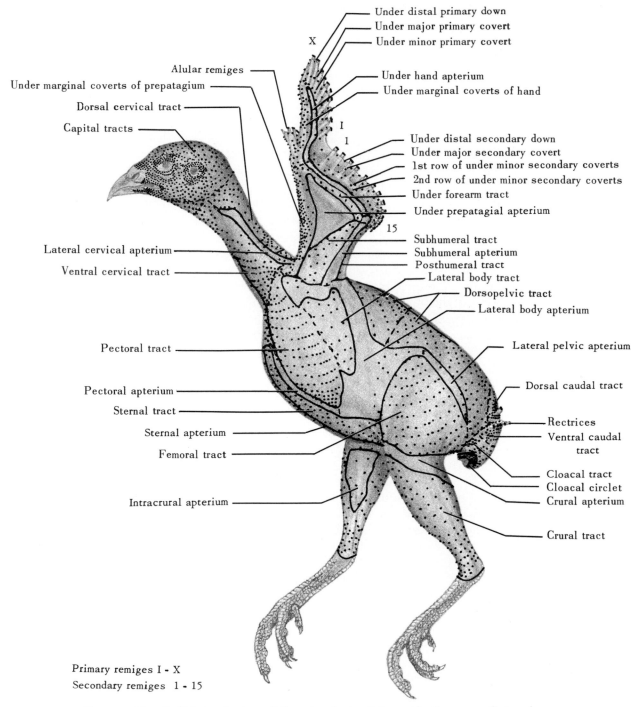

Under distal primary down
Under major primary covert
Under minor primary covert

X

Alular remiges
Under marginal coverts of prepatagium
Dorsal cervical tract
Capital tracts

Under hand apterium
Under marginal coverts of hand

I

1

Under distal secondary down
Under major secondary covert
1st row of under minor secondary coverts
2nd row of under minor secondary coverts
Under forearm tract
Under prepatagial apterium

15

Lateral cervical apterium
Ventral cervical tract

Subhumeral tract
Subhumeral apterium
Posthumeral tract
Lateral body tract
Dorsopelvic tract
Lateral body apterium

Lateral pelvic apterium

Pectoral tract

Dorsal caudal tract

Pectoral apterium
Sternal tract

Rectrices
Ventral caudal tract

Sternal apterium
Femoral tract

Cloacal tract
Cloacal circlet
Crural apterium

Intracrural apterium

Crural tract

Primary remiges I - X
Secondary remiges 1 - 15

FIGURE 81.—Left lateral view of the pterylosis of the male Common Coturnix.

mately the same width as the unstretched interscapular tract (fig. 80). The arrangement and character of the rows are the same in the dorsal and interscapular tracts; therefore, the boundary at shoulder level is indicated by a dashed line, representing an arbitrary boundary.

A lateral cervical apterium lies between the dorsal and ventral cervical tracts. At the anterior end, it begins as a narrow pointed space but expands uniformly as it approaches the shoulder, where it broadens greatly (compare figs. 80

and 81). In figure 81 the apterium appears to be of uniform width because the skin bearing the dorsal cervical tract has been stretched laterally. The dorsal surface of the cervical patagium is part of the lateral cervical apterium, and its feather coat is limited to a few scattered downs. The ventral surface of this patagium carries the feathers of the ventral cervical tract. The free edge folds upward rather than laterally, as suggested by figure 80; it thus folds the lateral cervical apterium on itself and produces a deep featherless pocket. This folding of the skin brings the feathers of the ventral cervical tract adjacent to those of the dorsal cervical tract. The feather color and pattern around the base of the neck are so well blended that no interruption in the transition from dorsal to ventral tracts is indicated.

There is only slight evidence of a transition between interscapular and dorsal tracts, not in the interruption of the rows but rather by the broadening of the dorsal tract (fig. 80). The feather rows have the same arrangement and slope in the area of the dorsal tract as they have in the interscapular, except that the rows in the dorsal tract are longer. The follicles near the midline and the muscles that move them are large but become smaller toward the ends of the rows. The strongest muscle bands follow the chevron-shaped rows, but delicate longitudinal muscles are visible through the thin skin.

An apterium runs along the middorsal line from the caudal end of the interscapular tract through the dorsal tract and well into the pelvic tract. The apteria in these three regions, although continuous, take the name of the tract within which each part is located. The skin of the apterium is elevated above the adjacent level by the neural spines of the vertebrae. Lateral to the interscapular tract is a broad scapular apterium that is continuous with the lateral cervical apterium at the anterior end and the lateral body apterium at the posterior end.

The dorsopelvic tract narrows gradually and in the pelvic region passes medial to the hip joints. Beyond the hips the pelvic tract tapers abruptly so that the tract is no wider than the transverse processes of the coccygeal vertebrae. As in other birds examined, the tract continues without interruption on to the dorsal and lateral surfaces of the uropygial eminence. In figure 80, a dashed line at the level of the slight caudal indentation marks the boundary of pelvic and dorsal caudal tracts. The rows, caudally, throughout the length of these tracts are increasingly closer together. On the uropygial eminence the rows lose their chevron arrangement and are transversely oriented. Also there is some disorganization of follicles within rows.

The lateral pelvic apterium is a narrow featherless space between the pelvic and femoral tracts (figs. 80 and 81). Within the space are a few scattered minute contour feathers that are entirely covered by the long feathers from the back.

Ventral tracts and apteria

The interramal tract, the most anterior of the ventral tracts, begins immediately behind the gonys. It is a triangular group of follicles, with short, close feathers, as indicated by the dots in figure 82. Close examination reveals that the feathers are regularly arranged into chevron-shaped rows with the apices directed forward. The angle made by the two rami of a row is relatively large. The pattern continues in the submalar region, but the limbs of each row enclose a smaller angle. The rows continue into the ventral cervical region, where the limbs swing sharply forward at the midline

to make a small angle at the apex of the chevron. About midway along the length of the neck, the rows change direction so that they now slope anterolaterally from the ventral cervical apterium to the side of the neck. At about the level of the lower flexure of the neck, the ventral cervical tract is split along the midventral line by the narrow ventral cervical apterium. The apterium continues caudally beyond the thoracic inlet by a pectoral apterium that separates the pectoral and sternal tracts and a sternal apterium along the edge of the keel that separates the two halves of the sternal tract.

The rows of the pectoral tract lie increasingly closer together at the caudal tip, which is located in front of the knee when the bird stands erect.

The sternal and abdominal tracts are weak in the Common Coturnix, and their contour feathers, although moderately numerous, are short. The lateral boundaries of the sternal and abdominal tracts are clearly defined because the contour feathers, although small, do not show a band of transitional feathers, semiplumes and downs, at the edge of the pectoral and lateral abdominal apteria. The pectoral apterium is narrow at the anterior end and relatively broad at the posterior end.

There is a gradual change in the character of feathers from the sternal to medial abdominal tract, and a dashed line (fig. 82) placed at the caudal end of the sternum represents an arbitrary separation. The feathers become increasingly long as the rows near the vent. Those immediately in front of the ventral lip stand erect and project vertically downward.

The Common Coturnix, like the turkey, in a normal standing position has the legs relatively close together and pressed against the abdomen. Where the inner surface of the thigh rubs against the abdomen, the feathers are few in number and are reduced in size so that a lateral abdominal tract is not present, but instead a lateral abdominal apterium occupies this area. This featherless space includes all the side of the abdomen caudal to the thigh.

The abdominal tract includes the cloacal tract and cloacal circlet, which is well developed (fig. 82). On the ventral (anterior) lip, the circlet stands apart from adjacent feathers of the abdominal tract, but on the dorsal (posterior) lip the short feathers of the circlet are the last transverse row of the cloacal tract, and the transition is uninterrupted.

Caudal tracts and apteria

The reduced tail is entirely covered with feathers, and no well-defined apteria can be observed. The feathers of the pelvic tract continue to the uropygial eminence. The oil gland circlet has approximately 12 feathers, but the papilla may appear nude if these feathers are broken and abraded. There are 10 rectrices (five on each side), and the median pair lies in the same plane as the remainder of the row (fig. 81). There are 10 upper major coverts for the rectrices, and these are almost as large as the rectrices with which each one corresponds. A row of upper median coverts consisting of small, short feathers is located close to the bases of the upper major coverts. The feathers and follicles are so small that we had to examine several specimens to make certain that the row exists; we have not determined the normal number of such feathers.

The under tail coverts form part of the large group of feathers covering the upper half of the cloacal protuberance. One can identify the large feathers adjacent to the rectrices as the under major coverts of the tail and those of the next row as the under median coverts.

The elimination of a distinct external tail in the male and the absence of a caudal indentation require that tract identi-

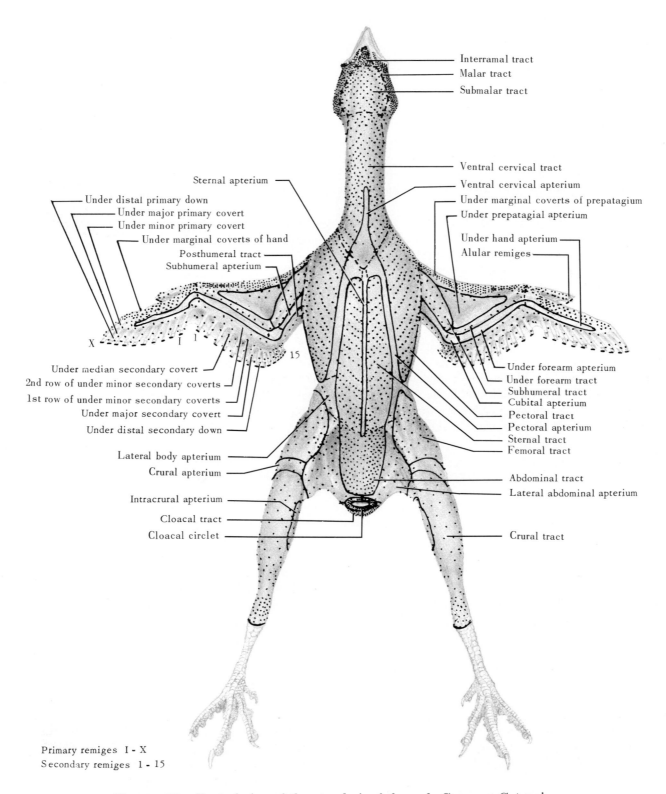

Interramal tract
Malar tract
Submalar tract

Ventral cervical tract
Ventral cervical apterium
Under marginal coverts of prepatagium
Under prepatagial apterium

Under hand apterium
Alular remiges

Sternal apterium

Under distal primary down
Under major primary covert
Under minor primary covert
Under marginal coverts of hand
Posthumeral tract
Subhumeral apterium

X   I   1

15

Under forearm apterium
Under forearm tract
Subhumeral tract
Cubital apterium
Pectoral tract
Pectoral apterium
Sternal tract
Femoral tract

Under median secondary covert
2nd row of under minor secondary coverts
1st row of under minor secondary coverts
Under major secondary covert
Under distal secondary down

Lateral body apterium
Crural apterium

Intracrural apterium
Cloacal tract
Cloacal circlet

Abdominal tract
Lateral abdominal apterium

Crural tract

Primary remiges I - X
Secondary remiges 1 - 15

FIGURE 82.—Ventral view of the pterylosis of the male Common Coturnix.

fication be dependent upon the use of guide points applied to the chicken and turkey. In simple terms, the ventral caudal tract lies below the rectrices and the dorsal caudal tract, above the rectrices (fig. 81). In the absence of constrictions around the tail, there is uninterrupted continuity between the cloacal and ventral caudal tracts and between the pelvic and dorsal caudal tracts.

Lateral body tract and apterium

The lateral body tract in the Common Coturnix consists of only a few feathers. It lies along the lateral edge of the pectoral tract (fig. 81). The feathers of the lateral body tract are smaller than those of the pectoral tract, a criterion that aids in arbitrarily placing a boundary between the tracts.

The lateral body apterium is most definite in the area of the prolatus, extending from the lateral body tract to the thigh and from the base of the wing and dorsal tract to the caudal part of the pectoral tract. At the anterior end of the femoral tract are several rows of short feathers that reach to the dorsal tract.

Based solely on a pterylosis study, it appeared that there was continuity between the pelvic and femoral tracts, but examination of the feather musculature revealed that the two tracts were fully separated by a lateral pelvic apterium, and figures 80 and 81 conform to these observations.

Brachial tracts and apteria

Humeral tract.—The humeral tract is strong. It lies on the dorsal surface of the wing and extends as a narrow band across the upper arm. Caudally, the feathers increase in length and extend beyond the wing to fill the space between the wing and the body. More specifically, the tract begins at the anterior lateral peak of the shoulder and extends diagonally to the posterior margin of the upper arm and to the distal half of the metapatagium (fig. 80). The proximal portion of the metapatagium is bare and is continuous with the scapular apterium. The band is about three feathers wide at the anterior end and about five feathers wide at the posterior margin. The feathers at the anterior end of the tract resemble those of the ventral cervical tract in color and pattern. Most of the feathers, however, resemble those of the interscapular tract and blend with the adjacent secondary remiges and coverts.

Subhumeral tract.—The subhumeral tract is limited to about three rows of feathers on the ventral surface of the upper arm (figs. 81 and 82); the most posterior of the rows bears the longest feathers. There are six to seven feathers in the posterior row; those at each end of the row are short, and about four in the center of the row are long. The proximal end of the first or second rows is at the junction of the prolatus and the wing and may be contiguous with the feathers of the lateral body tract.

The short subhumeral feathers on the anterior rows are borne on a narrow fold of thin skin that runs parallel to the axis of the upper arm. The free edge of the fold is caudal. The middle row is composed of medium-size feathers and

the anterior row, of small feathers. There are about four feathers each in the first and second rows.

A small apterium (part of the under prepatagial apterium) separates the feathers of the subhumeral tract from the under marginals, and a wide featherless space (subhumeral apterium) separates the feathers of the subhumeral tract from the posthumerals.

Posthumeral tract.—The posthumeral tract consists of three rows of feathers. The middle row composed of the largest feathers, has about six; the most proximal feather of the series is beneath the overhanging large feathers of the humerals. The feathers become larger toward the middle of the tract; those adjacent to the end of the secondaries are small. In figures 80 to 82 two rows lie on the dorsal surface of the wing and one on the ventral surface. The feathers on the ventral side of the wing are small semiplumes on the distal part of the row and are small down feathers on the proximal part. On the dorsal side of the wing there are about four feathers in the anterior row. These are in the center of the tract. Anterior to these there may be part of an additional row present. The posthumeral tract is separated from the upper marginal coverts of the prepatagium by the upper humeral apterium.

Alar tracts and apteria

Upper surface of the hand.—The pterylosis of the wing is more difficult to study in coturnix than it is in large birds. Many of the feathers are small and plumulaceous. In wings of large birds, equivalent feathers are typical contours.

Usually there are 10 remiges, but in the colony from which we obtained birds, 11 remiges were found in about 30 percent of the specimens. Specifically, in two specimens examined closely, there were 11 fully developed remiges on the right wings, as shown in figure 84, and 10 on the left. The 11th is not a remicle or a rudimentary feather but a feather as large as the adjacent 10th. A completely formed 11th remex has also been found in chickens but less frequently than in this stock of Common Coturnix. When 10 remiges are present, they have the same associations with the bones of the hand as described by Wray (1887a) for the duck.

Since there were 11 primaries instead of the usual 10 (figs. 84 and 85), an X-ray study of the coturnix wing (fig. 87) was made to show the position of each of the 11 remiges in relation to the bones of the hand. The 11th remex is associated with the terminal phalanx of digit III; the basal phalanx of the same digit bears the next two remiges, namely, the 10th and ninth; the phalanx of digit IV bears the eighth remex and the remaining seven are associated with the carpometacarpus. We have not studied the embryology of the development of the remiges; therefore, we cannot state definitely that the extra primary develops at the proximal end of the series, although this would seem to be the case.

Wray (1887a) studied the implantation of remiges on the wing of the "Wild Duck." Here also 11 primaries are present, the 11th being very small and called a remicle. In this bird both the 11th and 10th primaries were implanted on the second phalanx of digit III. Remiges 9 and 8 were implanted on the basal phalanx of the same digit, remex 7 on digit IV, and the first six remiges on the distal end of the carpometacarpus. In the duck there is a rather wide space between the first primary and the carpal joint. The first remex of an 11-primary coturnix is similarly located.

This perhaps is only slight evidence that the first primary in a coturnix with 11 remiges is not homologous with the first primary in a coturnix with 10 remiges, but instead is homologous with the second. Restated, the 11th feather of ducks is carried at the distal end of the series and in the Common Coturnix it seems to be proximal to the first.

Table 4 summarizes observations on the wings of five adult males and five adult females of the Common Coturnix. There proved to be no sex effect in this small population. Consideration is therefore given not only to the fact that the primaries might be either 10 or 11, but also that there were effects on the feathering of the forearm associated with the number of primaries on the hand. In specimen 2, there were 11 primaries on the left wing and 10 on the right; specimen 1 had 11 on both wings. When 11 are present there are 10 upper major primary coverts, but with the usual number of 10 primaries, the upper major primary coverts are reduced to nine. On the under surface of the hand, 11 primaries are associated with 11 under major coverts and 10 primaries, with 10 coverts.

When 11 primaries are present there may be 17 secondaries, whereas with 10 primaries there are generally 16 secondaries. In the two 11-primary specimens, there were 17 upper major secondary coverts. In the 10-primary specimens, there were 16 coverts with the 16 secondaries. Although they varied between 13 and 14, the under major coverts were not affected by either the number of primaries or the number of secondaries.

Only two rows of coverts are present on the dorsal side, the upper major and upper median primary coverts; the upper minor coverts were entirely absent in the specimen from which figure 84 was drawn, but in others there may be nearly a complete row of eight or nine feathers. Only eight upper median primary coverts are shown in figure 84. In another specimen there were but two, located above remiges 3 and 4. The question is how they should be numbered. Since each of them lies directly dorsal to the remex, it is assumed that they would be numbered correspondingly, namely, the median covert above the remex IV would also be 4. If, however, there is validity to the pattern that the equivalent members of rows arch distally from posterior to anterior, as diagramed in figure 72 and as found in the turkey (fig. 77), then an upper median covert lying upon the fourth remex is not the fourth upper median primary covert but is upper median covert 3. The labels applied to figure 84 agree with the latter assumption, and the feathers can be joined by lines on this basis. If each upper median covert were given the same number as the underlying remex, then a line joining the follicles would be strongly S-shaped, which could happen only if during development each succeeding row shifted one way and then the other.

TABLE 4.—*Variation in number of primary remiges in the Common Coturnix and its effects on feather number in other parts of the wing*

Pterylae	Specimens										
	♂	♀ 1	♀ 2	♂	♀	♀	♂	♀	♂	♂	♀
Primaries	11	11	10	10	10	10	10	10	10	10	10
Upper major primary coverts	10	10	9	9	9	9	9	9	9	9	9
Under major primary coverts	11	11	10	10	10	10	10	10	10	10	10
Secondaries	17	16	16	16	16	16	16	16	16	16	16
Upper major secondary coverts	17	17	16	16	16	16	16	16	16	16	16
Under major secondary coverts	14	14	14	14	14	14	14	14	13	13	13

[1] Right wing.
[2] Left wing.

An upper hand apterium is present beginning about half way between the tip of the wing and the alula and continuing proximally to establish continuity with the upper alular apterium. Dashed lines on figure 84 indicate an arbitrary separation.

Two rows of upper marginal coverts lie along the free edge of digit III and the metacarpus distal to the upper hand apterium (fig. 84). Proximal to that point there is but a single row between the apterium and leading edge. On the alula and proximal to it, upper marginal coverts consist of several rows that are continuous with those on the prepatagium. These groups are arbitrarily separated by a dashed line (fig. 84).

On the alula, there are three large remiges, I' to III', the fourth is small, and there may be a still smaller fifth remex. In some individuals another small feather lies between the third remex and the free edge. These details, of course, vary. It seems unrealistic to specifically designate upper alular coverts; nevertheless, those adjacent to the remiges serve that function.

There appear to be no upper distal primary downs. The row that does exist is identified as upper proximal primary downs because it lies between the openings of major and median follicles. In the specimen illustrated (fig. 84), there are six of these downs, 2 through 7. In other specimens, they varied from a few to a nearly complete row.

Upper surface of the carpal region.—A well-developed carpal remex stands well apart from the adjacent primary remex 1 (figs. 83 and 84). It is relatively smaller than the carpal remex of the chicken and relatively larger than this remex in the turkey. The upper major carpal covert of the chicken

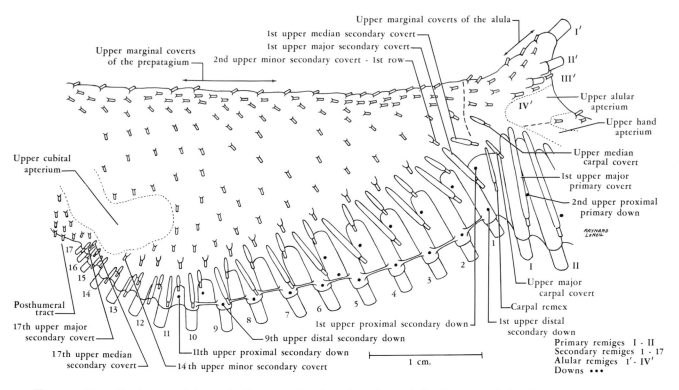

FIGURE 83.—Contour and down feathers on the dorsal surface of the forearm of the Common Coturnix.

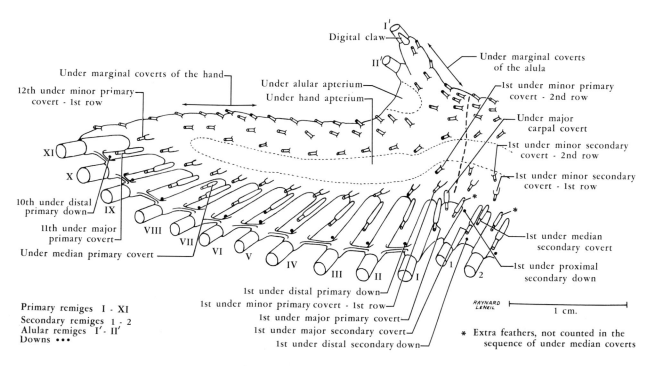

FIGURE 85.—Contour and down feathers on the ventral surface of the hand of the Common Coturnix. See figure 84 for names associated with numbers.

and turkey projects proximally, but in coturnix it points distally and does not overlap the carpal remex. Anterior to the carpal remex and its major covert and distal to the first upper median secondary covert is the upper median carpal covert (figs. 83 and 84). This feather holds the same

position in the Common Coturnix that it does in the chicken (fig. 68). No other coverts or downs are associated with the carpal region.

Upper surface of the forearm.—There are at least 12 large secondary remiges, and proximal to them are small feathers

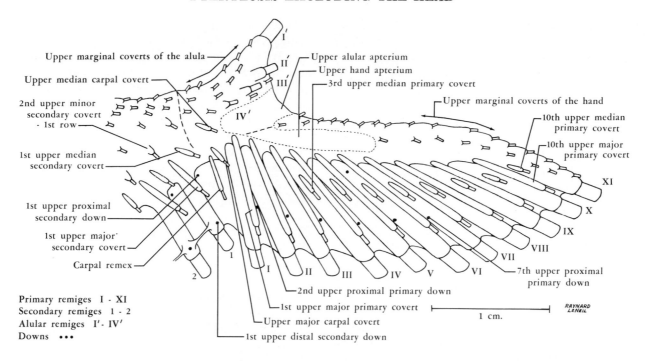

FIGURE 84.—Contour and down feathers on the dorsal surface of the hand of the Common Coturnix.

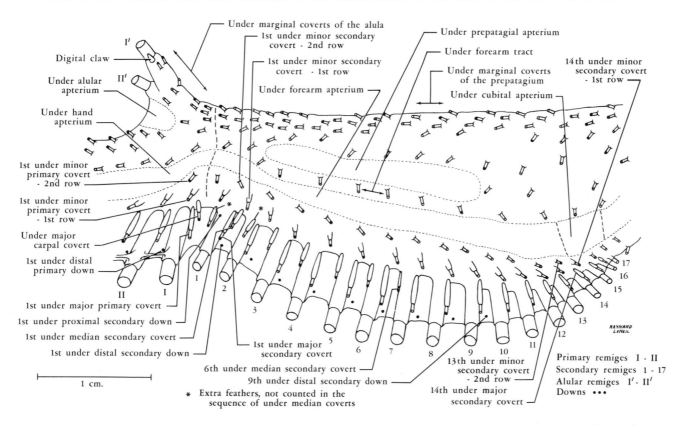

FIGURE 86.—Contour and down feathers on the ventral surface of the forearm of the Common Coturnix.

at the margin of the elbow. If all these feathers are included, the number of secondaries may be 16 or 17 (table 4). The upper major secondary coverts extend from 1 to 17 in figure 83. The follicles of the upper major secondary coverts at the carpal end of the row have their openings at about the midlength of the primary follicle but at the proximal end of the row the openings of follicles for major covert and remex are practically at the same level. At the carpal end of the row the major coverts are directed distally, but proximally beyond the ninth feather they closely parallel the remiges and tend to lie on the distal side rather than on the dorsal surface.

The upper median secondary coverts form a distinct row with follicles of intermediate size between major and minor coverts. The row begins with 1 and continues to 17. Each one lies about midway between adjacent upper major secondary coverts. All of the covert rows toward the carpal end swing anteriorly and thus are far apart, in contrast to the cubital end where all rows are crowded together.

The upper minor secondary coverts form an incomplete row, which begins probably with the first feather (fig. 83) and certainly with the second. It ends with about the 14th at the upper cubital apterium. The upper minor secondary coverts are similar to the upper marginal coverts of the prepatagium.

The upper marginal coverts of the prepatagium are arranged with curved rows across the face of the wing (fig. 83). As the rows approach the leading edge they swing proximally, and the feathers are oriented so that they point distally. On the prepatagium are spaces where feathers appear to be absent. The presence of these spaces were confirmed by the study of the feather musculature on the upper surface of the wing of the chicken (fig. 262, p. 433).

Downs are less abundant on the wing of coturnix than they are on the chicken. A partial row of upper distal secondary downs is present, ending with about the ninth, but these downs are so small that some may easily be overlooked. The upper proximal row begins at the carpal region, but after including in the count some missing feathers, ends at about the 11th.

Under surface of the hand.—Individuals with 11 remiges also have 11 under major primary coverts, as shown in table 4 and in figure 85; usually there are but 10 of each. The under major covert follicles are about half the length of the remex follicles and lie proximal to them. A row of under median primary coverts is lacking, but as shown in the illustration, one covert was present on the ventral side of remex 8, near its basal end. Usually when one or two under median primary coverts are present, they are located near the carpus. The under median secondary coverts, whenever present, are downy.

There is a single row of under minor primary coverts, forming a complete row from first to 12th. They are more closely placed than the remiges which may account for the 12th feather. Alternatively, this most distal feather may properly be one of the under marginal coverts of the hand. The second row of under minor primary coverts is often represented by one or two feathers adjacent to the carpal region (fig. 85).

An under hand apterium separates the under minor coverts from the under marginal coverts of the hand. The latter group is limited to two or three rows of feathers, the follicles of the row adjacent to the apterium point forward and downward so that the feathers cover the apterium. The shafts in the remaining two rows point directly toward the tip of the wing.

Only two of the four alular remiges are visible from the ventral side of the hand. A few feathers are implanted on digit II and the skin covering its extensor process. These are continuous with the under marginal coverts of the prepatagium and are arbitrarily separated by a dashed line (fig. 85). A small under alular apterium is present.

Under surface of the carpal region.—A small under major carpal covert is present and, as shown in figures 85 and 86, there is another feather at about the same level marked by an asterisk. The more proximal of the two may possibly represent an additional under carpal covert, but a definite identification is not possible at this time.

Under surface of the forearm.—The row of under major secondary coverts begins at the carpal region and ends at the 16th feather (fig. 86). The row of under median secondary coverts extends from about 1 through 6. These are exceedingly small plumulaceous feathers with small follicles. The asterisk marked above the second remex in figure 86 may represent an extra under median secondary covert. This row of feathers is entirely covered by the under minor secondary coverts–first row, which extends from 1 through 14. A second row of small under minor secondary coverts ends at the 13th feather.

A narrow apterium extends most of the length of the under side of the wing. It crosses the elbow region and ends at the subhumeral tract. Distally it is called the under hand apterium, and proximally, the under forearm apterium. On the forearm another shorter apterium parallels this one and is the under prepatagial apterium (fig. 86). Between the two apteria is a single row of feathers, the under forearm tract, which, at both its ends, is continuous with feathers of the under marginal coverts of the prepatagium. The under marginals are a scattered group, small and downy, and only the several rows along the free margin show distinct contour structure and definite organization of contour feathers.

The under distal secondary downs are located on the web of the postpatagium between the remiges (fig. 86) and extend from 1 through 9. They are exceedingly small. The under proximal secondary downs are absent on the forearm and also on the hand.

Femoral tract

The longest feathers of the femoral tract are on the infracaudal margin, and here the last two rows are close together. The feathers become smaller toward the anterior and dorsal margins of the tract. The transition to the crural apterium is abrupt. The dorsal margin of the femoral tract is separated from the pelvic tract by a narrow lateral pelvic apterium (figs. 80 and 81).

Crural tract and apteria

The crural apterium separates the femoral and crural tracts; the featherless space is especially wide in the popliteal region (fig. 80). The barbs of the feathers of the crural tract are widely spaced, giving a shaggy effect to the plumage covering the shank. The feathers of the crural tract are more

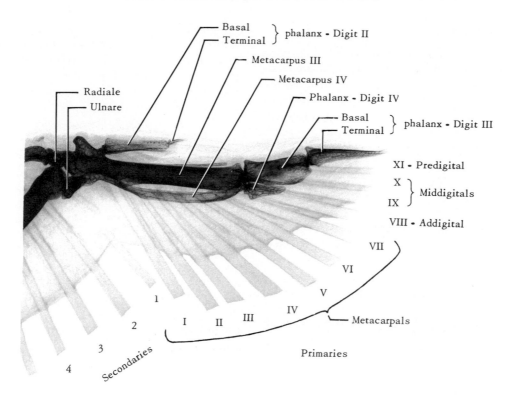

FIGURE 87.—Positive radiograph of the manus of a Common Coturnix having 11 remiges. The first secondary appears to be directed toward the ulnare.

widely spaced than on the femoral tract, but toward the ankle region they are close together and small.

A definite intracrural apterium is present on the medial surface of the crus of the Common Coturnix. At its upper end it joins the crural apterium. The lower end of the apterium tapers to a point and thus ends at about the midlength of the crus.

White Pekin Duck

The pterylosis of anseriforms is often very difficult to delineate because of the mingling of the down feathers with contour feathers. The pterylosis of the Great Horned Owl presents the same difficulty but to a much lesser degree. Both contour and down feathers have follicles, and when the study began, it seemed likely that there would be considerable confusion and difficulty in distinguishing these two types. At first the several down feathers surrounding each contour feather were plucked individually, leaving the contour feathers. This was indeed time consuming. Data collecting was speeded when we discovered later that the size difference for the neck opening of the contour and down follicles was sufficiently great that for most tracts there were no difficulties in distinguishing follicles for each feather type. Another useful technique was to shave the bird with animal clippers and singe away the plumulaceous barbs. This usually left bare the short shafts of the contour feathers and removed fluffy distal ends of the downs. The singeing left enough of the basal end of the downs to determine that no rachis existed. Using this technique to supplement the complete removal of the feathers with wax, we were able to make drawings of the pterylosis (figs. 88 to 90), which we feel are reasonably reliable. Supplementary information on these patterns became available from a study of the feather and apterial muscles.

One characteristic of feathering that could not be shown in these figures is the difference in size of contour feathers. This difference is associated with the identification of strong and weak tracts. Feather size is mentioned in the text, but it was found impractical to vary the size of dots on the drawings; it is for this reason that the dots for down feathers are shown in red. We have not attempted to depict all the down feathers, only those from sample areas, particularly to show the placement of the down feathers around and between the contour feathers and in the apteria.

The skin of the duck is far more extensively covered with contour feathers than is that of any other kinds of domestic birds studied thus far. Consequently, some apteria are reduced in size or are absent. Wherever tracts are not separated by apteria, the estimated boundaries are indicated on the drawings by dashed lines.

Humphrey and Butsch (1958) and Humphrey and Clark (1961) used soft and hard X-rays on the skin with the calami still retained by the follicles in order to study the pterylosis of ducks. Our observations on the White Pekin Duck do not completely agree with theirs on the wild Mallard and the Labrador Duck. In view of the close affinity between wild Mallard and White Pekin Duck, one might assume that the differences in pterylosis would be minimal.

Spinal tracts and apteria

There is complete continuity between the capital tracts and the dorsal cervical tract (fig. 88). The transverse boundary line has been placed at the same location as the region boundary, namely, between the base of the head and the beginning of the neck. In this area the feathers are small and the follicles close together, as they are on the head. Almost the entire surface of the neck bears contour feathers except for small apteria along the middorsal and midventral lines. The broad lateral cervical apterium, characteristic of domestic galliform birds, is absent in the White Pekin Duck except for a small terminal portion remaining on the dorsal surface of the cervical patagium. Therefore, an arbitrarily placed dashed line, as shown in figure 89, marks the boundary between dorsal and ventral cervical tracts. As in the chicken, it is located so that it begins at the caudal tip of the lower jaw and then moves into a position about midway between the dorsal and ventral surfaces. At the caudal end of the neck the line shifts slightly onto the dorsal surface of the cervical patagium and extends along the cervicoalar groove.

The small lateral cervical apterium (fig. 88) is continuous with the narrow, more caudally placed, scapular apterium. The posterior boundary of the dorsal cervical tract and the anterior boundary of the interscapular tract form a V-shaped line, the apex of which lies anterior to the shoulder. From the apex the lines slope laterally toward the shoulder margin. This approximately duplicates the pattern of the feather rows at the caudal end of the neck.

Near the base of the head the feather rows are arranged transversely or curved slightly forward, but caudal to this the rows swing downward and backward from the midline. This situation is essentially similar to that in the turkey and coturnix in that there is no natural boundary between the dorsal cervical and interscapular tracts, at least on the basis of a change in direction of rows as in the chicken.

Humphrey and Butsch (1958) and Humphrey and Clark (1961) used the term "spinal apterium" for the featherless space on the dorsal midline of the neck. We have used a different name because we regard spinal tracts and spinal apteria as being broadly inclusive terms applicable to the entire dorsal surface from head to tail and as having several subdivisions. We agree with Humphrey and Butsch (1958) and Humphrey and Clark (1961) in designating the feathers on the dorsal surface (one of the subdivisions) as the dorsal cervical tract. For the same reason we choose to designate the apterium on the dorsal surface of the neck, the dorsal cervical apterium, and its continuation caudally, the interscapular apterium. In both the Mallard and the Labrador Duck the authors mentioned above found that the apterium extends caudally, separating entirely the right and left halves of the interscapular tract. In the White Pekin Duck it may separate only the front half of this tract. We also found that the interscapular tract is about as broad as it is long, instead of narrow as in the wild ducks referred to.

The anterior end of the interscapular tract begins at an arbitrary chevron-shaped line established as the posterior boundary of the dorsal cervical tract. The interscapular tract extends caudally to another arbitrary boundary, placed at the anatomical junction of neck and thorax; this, therefore, agrees with the region boundary in figure 36, page 54. As already stated, the interscapular tract is broad, and its lateral margins are established by the right and left scapular apteria. Again our terminology differs somewhat from that used by Humphrey and Butsch (1958) and Humphrey and Clark (1961); we have called scapular apterium what they named "interscapular apterium." We have assigned the term "interscapular" to the space along the middorsal line where the two halves of the interscapular tract are separated, as they are in the turkey and in the White Pekin Duck. The scapular apterium is narrow in the domestic duck, whereas it is wide in the chicken and turkey.

The dorsopelvic tract (fig. 88) is large. The dorsal or thoracic part of this tract is about the same length and width as the interscapular tract. It extends from the interscapular tract as far caudally as the anterior margin of the ilium and thus has the same reference point as was used to separate the prodorsum and postdorsum. The lateral margins of the dorsal tract are established by the lateral body apteria. A narrow lateral pelvic apterium separates the pelvic and femoral tracts from the region of the hip joint forward. Behind this point the separation between these two tracts is an arbitrary one (figs. 88 and 89). The pelvic tract ends caudally at a V-shaped arbitrary line marking the anterior boundary of the tail region.

Humphrey and Clark (1961) showed in the Mallard a narrow apterium in the midline of the pelvic tract near the anterior end that they labeled "spinal apterium." To this apterium, present also in the White Pekin Duck, we have applied the name "median pelvic apterium."

Ventral tracts and apteria

The ventral cervical tract begins immediately caudal to the membranous, soft, leathery tissues that join the two rami of the lower jaw. The interramal tract is a small triangular area bounded by this membranous tissue and by an arbitrary line at the level of the rictus that separates the interramal from the submalar tract (fig. 90). The feathers in the interramal tract are small but increase in size caudally.

The submalar tract is arbitrarily separated from surrounding pterylae by dashed lines in figure 90. The lateral boundaries coincide with the inferior margins of the lower jaw; the posterior boundary joins the caudal tips of the jaw and, like the region boundary, lies at the junction of the ventral head and neck. The entire ventral surface of the neck is feathered except for a distinct ventral cervical apterium at the caudal end of the ventral tract. This apterium maintains nearly the same width along the midventral line as far as the vent opening and is arbitrarily divided into the ventral cervical apterium already mentioned, the sternal

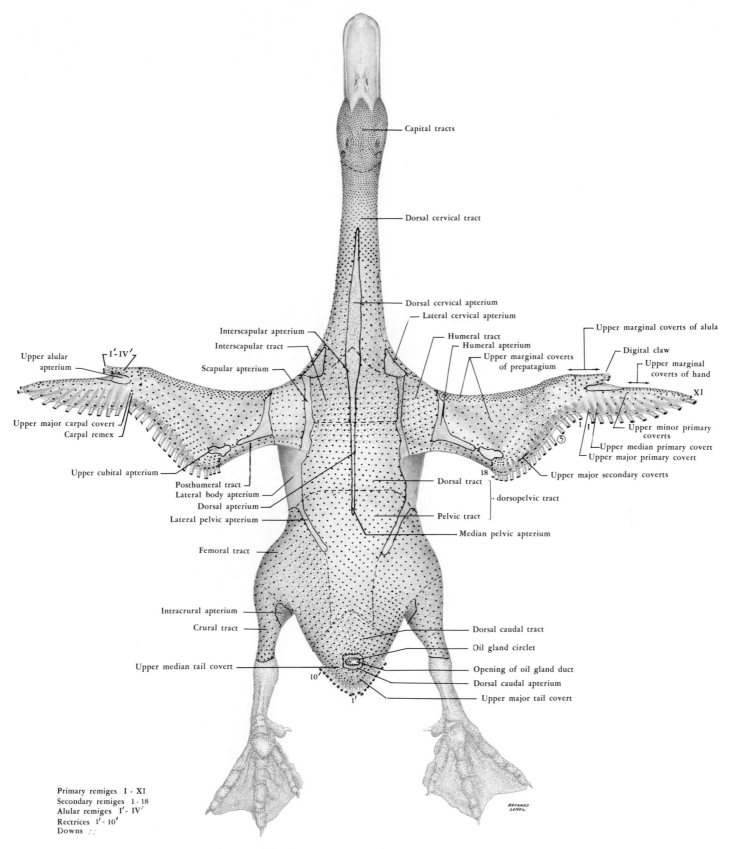

Primary remiges I - XI
Secondary remiges 1 - 18
Alular remiges I′ - IV′
Rectrices 1′ - 10′
Downs

FIGURE 88.—Pterylosis of an adult White Pekin Duck—dorsal view. Down feathers in selected areas are represented by red dots.

apterium, and the median abdominal apterium. Humphrey and Clark (1961) designated the full length of this featherless space as the midventral apterium.

The posterior boundary of the ventral cervical tract is an arbitrary one beginning at the anterior margin of the shoulder and curving downward and backward toward the midline following the margins of the clavicles. The boundary utilizes the same landmarks in the duck as those applied to the chicken and turkey, but because the shape of the clavicle is not the same as that for the galliforms mentioned, the

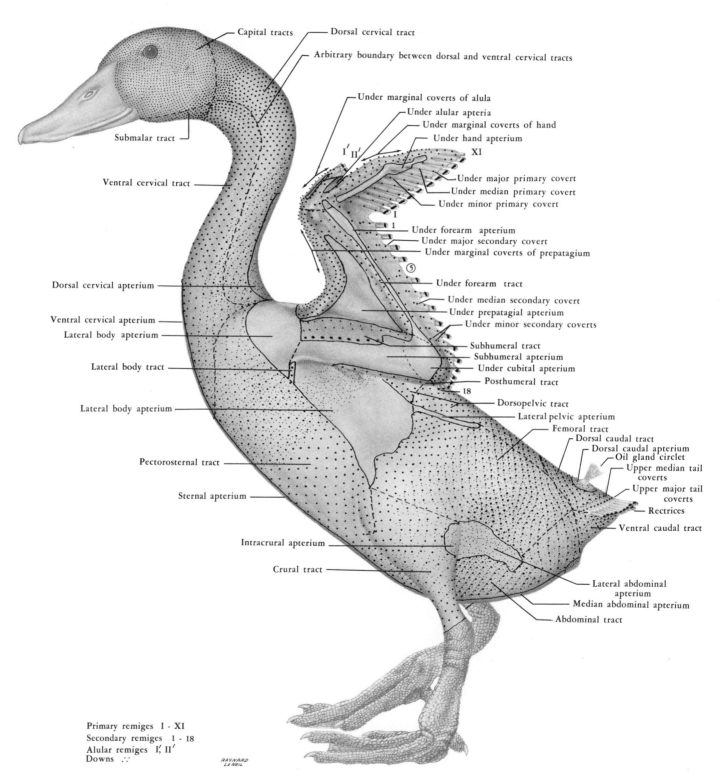

Primary remiges I - XI
Secondary remiges 1 - 18
Alular remiges I', II'
Downs ∴

FIGURE 89.—Pterylosis of an adult White Pekin Duck—left lateral view. Down feathers in selected areas are represented by red dots.

contour of the boundary line around the thoracic inlet appears somewhat different.

The placement of the arbitrary boundary line between the dorsal and ventral cervical tracts (fig. 89) has already been described.

The feathers on the proventer form a continuous group covering all the breast and sternum. Because there is no distinct separation between these tracts, the feathers on each half of the breast have been called a pectorosternal tract (fig. 90). However, when the feather muscles on the inner surface of the skin are examined, one can identify as separate entities, sternal, pectoral, and lateral body tracts. The anterior boundary of the combined tracts begins at the clavicle and extends to the caudal end of the proventer region, namely, to the truncate end of the keel. Two reference points identify the lateral boundary. In the anterior and middle thirds, it is the ventral edge of the lateral body apterium, and in the caudal third, it is the groin groove (figs. 89 and 90).

The halves of the pectorosternal tract are separated along the keel ridge by the narrow sternal apterium. It extends the full length of the tract, having throughout almost uniform width. The apterium is continuous with the ventral cervical apterium at the anterior end and the median abdominal apterium at the caudal end. In the illustrations, the separations between the parts of this continuous apterium are established by arbitrary lines drawn transversely from adjacent tract boundaries.

The abdominal tract lies caudal to the pectorosternal tract, separated from the latter by an arbitrary boundary. The abdominal tract surrounds the vent. The follicle pattern of the abdomen continues onto the ventral surface of the tail. Because a caudal indentation is absent, we established an arbitrary boundary to separate abdomen from tail (figs. 88 to 90).

The abdominal and femoral tracts are separated in part by the lateral abdominal apterium. In the duck, tracts are large and apteria are small so that there is wide continuity between tracts. No attempt has been made to circumscribe a postlateral body area. The postlatus in ducks is relatively large; nevertheless, since there are no known apteria in other species of birds that tend to set apart a tract of feathers in this region, it seems to us best to extend the femoral tract area somewhat farther caudally than it is extended when apteria are present and to meet it by extending forward the boundary of the abdominal area (fig. 89).

The vent of the White Pekin Duck is not surrounded by a cloacal circlet; the feathers on the lips of the vent are downs. The rows adjacent to the vent diverge away from the lip rather than pass around it. The relatively large lateral abdominal apterium already mentioned is an irregularly shaped space that extends to the medial surface of the crus (fig. 89), and the latter continues as a narrow space to the ventral limits of the crural tract as the intracrural apterium (fig. 90).

Caudal tracts and apteria

The boundaries that separate trunk and tail have already been described and are illustrated in figures 88 through 90. The dorsal caudal tract has continuity with the pelvic and femoral tracts. A small dorsal caudal apterium lies in the area of the uropygial eminence but does not extend forward in the White Pekin Duck as described by Humphrey and Clark (1961) for the Mallard. To such a pair of elongated featherless spaces they gave the name "postpelvic apteria". We have found this space to be very small, limited to the area closely surrounding the oil gland papilla. This we have designated dorsal caudal apterium. There is a possible explanation for the apparent large U-shaped space in the Mallard; if it is like the White Pekin Duck, there exist in this area small contour feathers with delicate rachises and widely spaced barbs. It is possible that similar short, narrow calami, if present in the Mallard, failed to produce an image in the X-ray print as used by Humphrey and Clark with sufficient clarity to demonstrate that contour feathers were present.

Two rows of upper tail coverts are present, and following the designations used in other kinds of birds used in this study, they would be major and median rows.

The 10 pairs of rectrices arranged along the caudal margin of the tail identify the boundary between the dorsal and ventral caudal tracts. The central pair of rectrices lies at a higher level than the ones lateral to them. Twenty rectrices appear to be a maximum number reported for the Mallard as well as for the White Pekin Duck. Humphrey and Clark (1961: 383) found this number in two adult Mallards and one juvenile Mallard. The under major tail coverts are not distinctly set apart from the feathers of the under caudal tract (fig. 90), and there seems no value in designating a median and a minor row.

Lateral body tract and apterium

The lateral body tract is small in the duck. It consists of a few feathers arranged in a row across the lateral body apterium from the shoulder end of the subhumeral tract to the edge of the pectorosternal tract. In figure 89 only two of these feathers are shown, but in some specimens four and five were observed.

Brachial tracts and apteria

The humeral tract is broad and extends from the anterior margin of the shoulder to the metapatagium. It is slightly wider at the middle than at either end. The rows are regularly arranged as shown in figure 88. The humeral tract is separated from the interscapular tract by a narrow scapular apterium. On the distal side the humeral apterium is narrow also, except posteriorly where it widens and extends parallel to the posthumeral tract.

The posthumeral tract is a group of several feather rows, visible in both dorsal and ventral views. The posthumerals begin at the humeral tract and extend nearly to the elbow

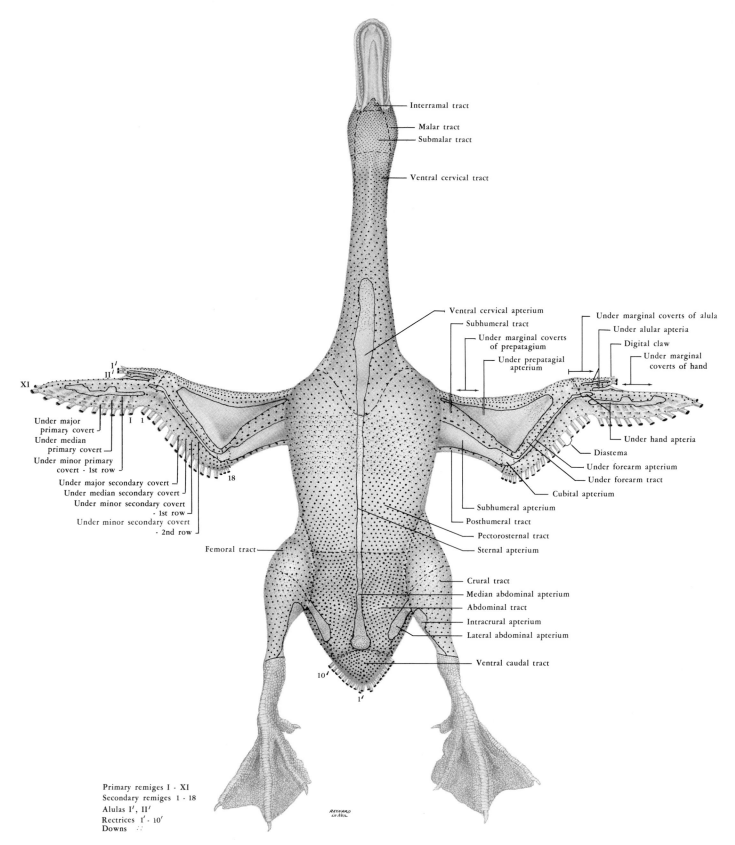

Primary remiges I - XI
Secondary remiges 1 - 18
Alulas I′, II′
Rectrices 1′ - 10′
Downs

FIGURE 90.—Pterylosis of an adult White Pekin Duck—ventral view. Down feathers in selected areas are represented by red dots.

joint. Portions of this tract are shown in figures 91 and 94. On the dorsal surface are three rows; the largest follicles and feathers, called quills, arise from the middle row. Near the basal tips of the quill follicles is a row of upper posthumeral coverts. The very small follicles between the quills, shown in figure 91, represent a row of under posthumeral coverts. The second row belonging to the same group lies entirely in the ventral surface (fig. 94).

The subhumeral tract is visible only in ventral view. The feathers of the posterior subhumeral row are large with typical contour shapes, whereas in some kinds of birds studied these feathers were small. In the duck also, the subhumeral feathers are small anterior to the first row. Between the posthumeral and subhumeral tracts is the subhumeral apterium, and as shown in figure 89, there may be continuity between the lateral body and under alar apteria.

Alar tracts and apteria

The down feathers of the duck are so numerous that samples of their distribution are shown in red (figs. 88 to 90) to reduce confusion with the contour feathers.

Upper surface of the hand.—The wing of the duck is long and narrow; its shape has had some effect on the pterylosis, particularly of the hand. The duck has 10 well-developed primary remiges; at the tip of the hand is a very small 11th, called the remicle (figs. 92 and 93). The first upper major primary covert lies in the space between the first and second primary remiges. These feathers continue in unbroken sequence to the 11th upper major primary covert, which lies close to the anterior margin of the hand but is sufficiently distinctive to be separated from the adjacent marginal coverts. The upper major covert of the remicle is smaller than the others in the series.

The upper median primary coverts are small feathers implanted near the bases of the remiges. The series begins with the third and ends with the 11th. Above these are two rows of minor coverts, the first row extends from fourth to 11th, and the second row from third to 11th. The spacing of these feathers is not uniform, and the 11th feather of the first row and the last five feathers of the second row might be considered as belonging to the marginal coverts. The number of minor coverts varies considerably.

The upper marginal coverts of the hand are restricted to a single row along the leading edge of the phalanges for the third digit. A large upper alular apterium overlies the carpometacarpus. Four alular remiges are present. About 9 or 10 feathers constitute the upper marginal coverts of digit II.

Upper surface of the carpal region.—The carpal remex and its upper major covert lie close together, the latter is the longer of the two. Anterior to this is an upper median carpal covert; it lies in the same row as the upper median coverts of the forearm but is definitely distal to the beginning of the row.

Upper surface of the forearm.—The typical number of secondaries is 18 if a "missing" fifth is included in the count.

The duck has a diastataxic wing that contains a definite space or diastema between the fourth and sixth remiges (fig. 91). Goodchild (1891) regarded the fifth as missing and numbered the remiges on each side of the diastema as 4 and 6. Following the 18th is a small feather that might represent a 19th remex. It is separated from the posthumeral tract and is overlaid by feathers representing each of the covert rows.

The upper major and median coverts are represented by complete rows, 1 to 18, but the sixth upper minor covert is missing in the row of 1 to 18. The first four upper median secondary coverts are supposed to belong to an intercalary row, on the assumption that the first four remiges belong embryologically to a different row than the remaining remiges, beginning with the sixth. The evidence for this is brought out by Goodchild (1891), Wray (1887), Steiner (1917 and 1956), Humphrey and Clark (1964), and others and is based largely on the study of the plumage and not on the discontinuities of follicle groups. The follicles of the coverts on both sides of the diastema show such complete continuity that it becomes impossible to identify an intercalary row. The only atypical feature is the large size of the upper median fifth covert and the missing sixth upper minor secondary covert–first row. This could be a compensatory development to fill and close the gap left by the "absence" of the fifth remex.

Only a single row of upper minor secondary coverts is clearly identifiable; beyond that, the feathers are part of the upper marginal coverts of the prepatagium. Within this group there is a shift in direction of rows so that they no longer run parallel to those of the first row of minor coverts.

Under surface of the hand.—The under major primary coverts are much smaller than the corresponding coverts on the upper side, but there is a complete row of 11 (fig. 93). The row of under median primary coverts begins with the first. The specimen illustrated ended with the eighth. There is only a single row of under minor primary coverts, beginning with the first and continuing unbroken to the sixth. Then follows a gap and the row begins with the ninth feather and continues to the 11th. Here, again, specimens vary widely.

The under hand apterium separates the coverts of the remiges from the marginal coverts. On the under side of digit II, groups of marginal feathers are separated by small under alular apteria. One of these has continuity with the under forearm apterium.

Under surface of the carpal region.—No under carpal coverts are present. The feather we labeled the first under median primary covert (fig. 93) lies in the position one would anticipate for the under carpal covert, but there may be a question whether it is correctly identified. An unlabeled follicle lies just to the left of the dashed line, anterior to the carpal region. This may possibly be an under minor carpal covert.

Under surface of the forearm.—The rows of under coverts

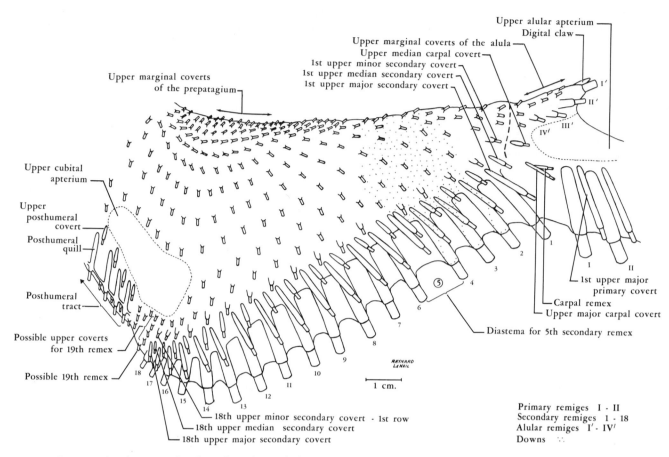

FIGURE 91.—Contour feathers on the dorsal surface of the forearm of the White Pekin Duck. Down feathers in selected areas are represented by red dots.

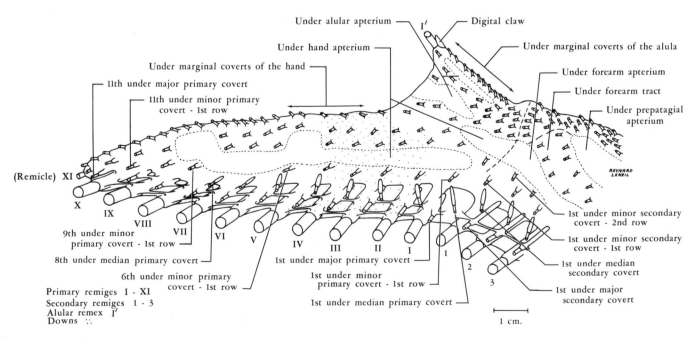

FIGURE 93.—Contour feathers on the ventral surface of the hand of the White Pekin Duck. Down feathers in selected areas are represented by red dots.

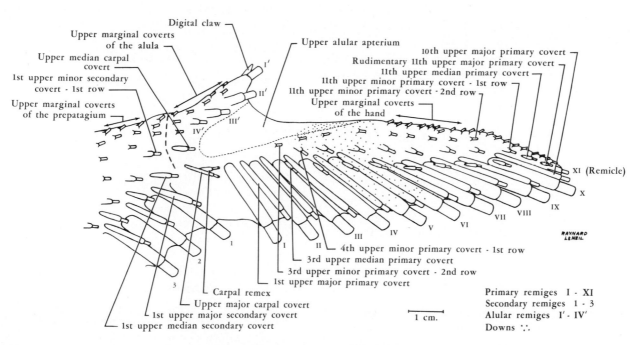

FIGURE 92.—Contour feathers on the dorsal surface of the hand of the White Pekin Duck. Down feathers in selected areas are represented by red dots.

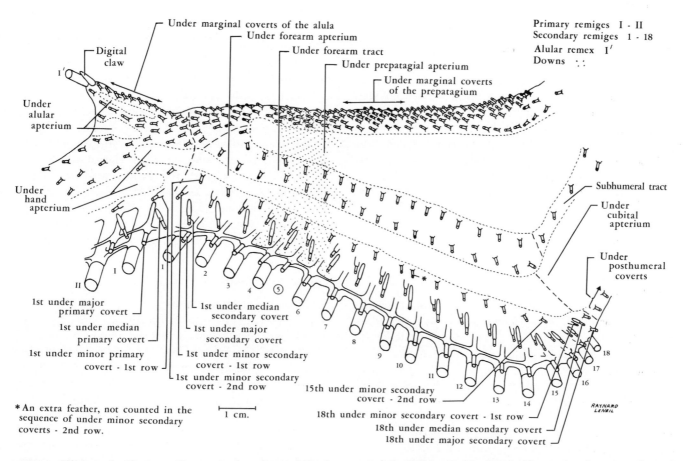

FIGURE 94.—Contour feathers on the ventral surface of the forearm of the White Pekin Duck. Down feathers in selected areas are represented by red dots.

when looked at longitudinally have a regular arrangement, but the alinement of rows at right angles to these produces many irregularities. This is evident in what has been labeled the first feather in each successive longitudinal row, and their positions obviously do not closely follow the schematic pattern shown in figure 72. The majors, medians, and first row of minors are complete, but the feathers of the second minor row are irregular. An extra feather, marked by an asterisk, was not included in the count. Variability of feather number is to be expected in this row.

The under forearm apterium is long and narrow; it is continuous distally with an under alular apterium and proximally with the under cubital apterium. An under forearm tract may be present or absent; in the duck, it is well defined by the under forearm and under prepatagial apteria. Anterior to the latter apterium is a rather broad, well-defined band of under marginal coverts of the prepatagium, close to and parallel with the leading edge of the wing.

Downs.—Samples of the distribution of down feathers are shown by red dots on figures 88 to 94. They do not have the specific relationship to the contour feathers, particularly remiges, found in the chicken and turkey. Instead, they are closely placed and are distributed the full width of the wing from margin to margin as well as the entire length of the wing on both surfaces.

Posterior appendage tracts and apteria

The femoral tract is more extensive in the duck than in any other species of bird we have examined thus far (fig. 89). It has a natural boundary at the anterior end of the tract and at the infracaudal margin. Throughout most of the broad lateral surface of the tract the rows crisscross at about 90° to form numerous squares, a pattern characteristic of the femoral tract in other kinds of birds studied.

In species where the femoral tract has been entirely circumscribed by apteria, the rows are crowded together along the infracaudal margin. This is indicated in the duck by a decreased spacing between rows adjacent to the dorsal margin of the lateral abdominal apterium (fig. 89). The concentration of rows in this part of the femoral tract produces an irregularity in the pattern of the rows.

The crural tract is a continuation of the femoral tract. In figure 89, an arbitrary line of separation has been placed at the knee joint. The line does not completely encircle the knee because it is interrupted on the medial surface by a large fold of skin stretched between leg and body. The crural tract covers the posterior, lateral, and medial surfaces of the shank and ends distally at the upper edge of the ankle region. On the medial surface of the ankle region is a small apterium, narrow at the distal end and wider at the proximal end. There is a question whether the apterium on the medial surface of the crus should be labeled crural or intracrural apterium. We reject the former name because the space does not effectively separate femoral and crural tracts. We prefer the latter name because the apterium extends length-

wise in the crural tract as it does in the other domestic birds.

Common Pigeon

A study of pterylosis in the pigeon provides a comparison of a columbiform with a galliform and an anseriform. Nitzsch (1867) and others who succeeded Nitzsch have sought to utilize pterylosis patterns as a means of establishing phylogenetic relations. Heimerdinger (1964) demonstrated the value of pterylosis data for a study of taxonomic relationships within an order, the passerines. In pterylography the technical difficulties are great, and the variation in description for the same species by different investigators sometimes makes comparative studies unsatisfactory. This is not a reflection on the accuracy of observations by these investigators, but rather an indication of the problem. We have observed that we needed 6 to 12 live specimens to work out the details of pterylosis for any one species. The various ways these are to be used are given in chapter 10 (p. 638).

Our comparative study is based on three orders with three kinds of galliforms, one anseriform, and one columbiform. The turkey and chicken are closely similar but the Common Coturnix is slightly different in some details. The White Pekin Duck and Common Pigeon are both considerably different from the galliforms and show numerous points in common with each other. Among these are the absence of a lateral cervical apterium, an expansion of pectoral and sternal tracts to form one continuous tract on the breast, a poor separation of the femoral tract from pelvic, crural, and abdominal tracts, and a reduction in apteria generally.

The few kinds of birds used here were inadequate for determining taxonomic relationships among groups, yet we hope that the conspicuous differences we observed among a few kinds of birds will stimulate others to apply the tool of pterylosis to other groups of birds. Heimerdinger (1964) has shown the value of assembling data in depth. We suggest that even more detail be included in compiling comparative data. Until this has been done, information from pterylosis studies will continue to be regarded of limited value when applied to the study of phylogenetic relationships.

Spinal tracts and apteria

The series of spinal tracts extends from the base of the head to the tail. It forms a continuous covering of feathers except for a narrow band along the midline of spinal apteria; all transverse boundaries between subdivisions of the spinal tracts and apteria, therefore, are arbitrary. In figure 95 a dashed line separates capital and dorsal cervical tracts, and a similar line separates the dorsal cervical and interscapular tracts; the latter boundary is placed at the shoulder level. The interscapular tract widens caudally; its two rami diverge on each side of the interscapular apterium (fig. 95). The caudal points of the two rami lie at the level of the metapatagial margin. The follicles within the interscapular tract are more closely placed than those in the adjoining dorsal tract, but the interscapular tract is most easily identified by

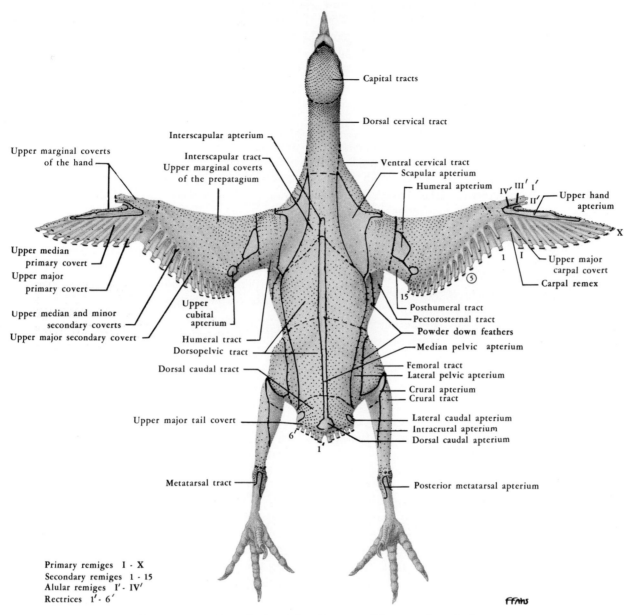

Capital tracts

Dorsal cervical tract

Interscapular apterium

Interscapular tract
Upper marginal coverts
of the hand
Upper marginal coverts
of the prepatagium

Ventral cervical tract
Scapular apterium
Humeral apterium

Upper hand
apterium

IV′ III′ I′
II′

X

Upper median
primary covert
Upper major
primary covert

Upper major
carpal covert
Carpal remex

1 I

Upper median and minor
secondary coverts
Upper major secondary covert

Upper
cubital
apterium
Humeral tract
Dorsopelvic tract

15

Posthumeral tract
Pectorosternal tract
Powder down feathers
Median pelvic apterium

Dorsal caudal tract

Femoral tract
Lateral pelvic apterium
Crural apterium
Crural tract

Upper major tail covert

Lateral caudal apterium
Intracrural apterium
Dorsal caudal apterium

6′

1′

Metatarsal tract

Posterior metatarsal apterium

Primary remiges I - X
Secondary remiges 1 - 15
Alular remiges I′ - IV′
Rectrices 1′ - 6′

FFAHS

FIGURE 95.—Pterylosis of the Common Pigeon—dorsal view.

the underlying V-shaped pad of fat. The spinal apteria are narrow. The anterior part begins in the interscapular region and extends through dorsal, pelvic, and caudal regions. Lateral to the interscapular tract is the scapular apterium, a broad featherless space that follows the course of the cervicoalar groove. The scapular apterium lies above the anterior end of the scapula. It is considerably longer than it is broad, and its anterior tip extends into the neck region, thus separating for a short distance the dorsal and ventral cervical tracts.

The dorsopelvic tract covers the full width of the back in the dorsal region and narrows in the pelvic region. We place the dividing line between the dorsal and pelvic parts at the anterior end of the ilium. The lateral boundaries of the dorsal tract are the elongated powder down feathers placed

in the lateral body and lateral pelvic apteria.[2] A narrow median pelvic apterium extends the full length of the pelvic tract and continues on to the tail where it becomes the dorsal caudal apterium. A lateral pelvic apterium separates the pelvic and femoral tracts and bears the powder downs already mentioned.

The arbitrary anterior boundary line for the pelvic portion of the dorsopelvic tract has already been identified as the cephalic tip of the ilium; the caudal boundary has been

[2] The term "costo-thoracic powder down patches" was given by Murie (1872) (ch. 2, table 5) to powder down feathers in this area, but Murie's terminology was applied to birds in which the powder downs were concentrated into patches and not widely distributed along apteria, as in the pigeon.

placed at the anatomic boundary between the pelvis and tail. The lateral boundary is the lateral pelvic apterium which in the pigeon contains powder down feathers. The pelvic tract is broader than in other domestic birds examined. Perhaps this is related to the more-than-average breadth of the girdle, the broad tail, and the absence of a distinct caudal indentation.

Ventral tracts and apteria

The ventral tracts extend from gonys to tail. The ventral cervical portion of the tracts includes the interramal and submalar tracts. The boundaries of these two small tracts coincide with boundaries for regions having the same names and are not repeated here (fig. 97). The interramal apterium coincides with the ventral edge of each jaw ramus and extends longitudinally from the pigmented keratin of the beak to the beginning of the submalar tract.

The remainder of the ventral cervical tract begins at a line connecting the caudal ends of the mandibles. At the side of the neck there is complete continuity between the dorsal and ventral cervical tracts so that the line we have drawn (fig. 96) to separate them is arbitrary. Placement of the dashed line on each side of the neck follows the same reference points we have already described for the White Pekin Duck.

Along the ventral midline of the neck, beginning a short distance behind the submalar region, is a narrow, ventral cervical apterium that extends caudally across the thoracic inlet and continues on as the sternal apterium.

The pigeon, like the duck, has the breast entirely covered with feathers, thereby merging the feathers of the pectoral and sternal tracts into a combined tract, the pectorosternal. In figure 97, we have arbitrarily separated the ventral cervical and pectorosternal tracts by a dashed line that follows the margin of the thoracic inlet. A sternal apterium extends the full length of the tract and is broader in its cephalic two-thirds than in its caudal third; it is continuous posteriorly with the median abdominal apterium.

Although the feather rows suggest no natural separation between pectoral and sternal tracts, the location of the pectoral tract is indicated by a thick pad of fat. This pad underlies the skin from the thoracic inlet to the knee in approximately the same location that a similar fat pad exists in those birds having a pectoral tract that is well separated from the sternal tract by an apterium. Liebelt and Eastlick (1954) identified this as the lateral thoracic fat organ. Smaller quantities of fat are associated with the follicles on each side of these fat organs.

The breast of the pigeon is broad, and modifies the shape of the lateral border of the pectorosternal tract. The tract covers not only the breast but much of the side of the body (fig. 96). The dorsal margin of the tract curves abruptly downward toward the knee. Between the wing and knee, the dorsal margin lies adjacent to the powder down feathers. The caudal boundary of the pectorosternal tract is shown on figure 97 as a dashed line that follows the caudal contour of the sternum.

The abdominal tract extends from the caudal edge of the sternum, sufficiently far posteriorly to include the vent. Both laterally and caudally these boundaries are marked by a narrow continuous apterium; the longitudinal limb of the apterium lies in the groin groove, and the transverse part overlies the curved ends of the pubic bones. Each longitudinal portion is clearly the lateral abdominal apterium, and, since it is continuous with the transverse part, the transverse part has been named the lateral abdominal apterium (fig. 97). The vent lies in the midline between the right and left transverse limbs of these apteria. The longitudinal portion has continuity with an intracrural apterium.

Lateral body tracts and apteria

Our pterylosis studies failed to reveal a separate lateral body tract, yet such a tract does exist. It consists of the lateral part of the pectorosternal tract. This was discovered when the feather musculature was studied (ch. 8, p. 459).

Powder down patches

The feathers of the costo-thoracic powder down patches are indicated in figures 95 and 96 in the lateral body and lateral pelvic apteria by dots. These powder down feathers occupy much of the lateral body apterium and thereby reduce the featherless area of the lateral body apterium to a small size. Murie (1872), in a table, refers the costo-thoracic patches to the lateral trunk tract, which we assume to be equivalent to that which we have designated as the lateral body tract. Murie listed no "portions" as he had done for many of the other patches. Some subdivisions of this kind would have been useful for the pigeon since the costo-thoracic patches are so extensive. They begin in the axillary region, reach to the vent, and, near its middle, dip ventrally along the front margin of the thigh.

If the powder downs are plucked, the empty follicles often are distinguishable from the follicles of contour feathers; the most distinguishing characteristic between the follicles of the two feather types is the shallow, cone-shaped follicle bounded by an elevated margin of white cornified epithelium of the powder down feather, while the follicles of contour feathers tend to collapse when empty, so that the opening becomes indistinct. Although a cornified rim may locate the opening, the opening is not as distinct as it is in the powder down follicles. The distribution of the powder downs is most clearly delineated when the surrounding contour feathers have been carefully removed. (For details of distribution, see the Archangel Pigeon, fig. 226, p. 336.)

A narrow band of powder feathers, one to two follicles wide, extends from the posterior axillary fossa, along the margin of the pectorosternal tract to the abdomen and lateral tail. A ventrally directed side branch follows the anterior margin of the thigh. The powder follicles are located in the lateral pelvic apterium. Powder feathers are also

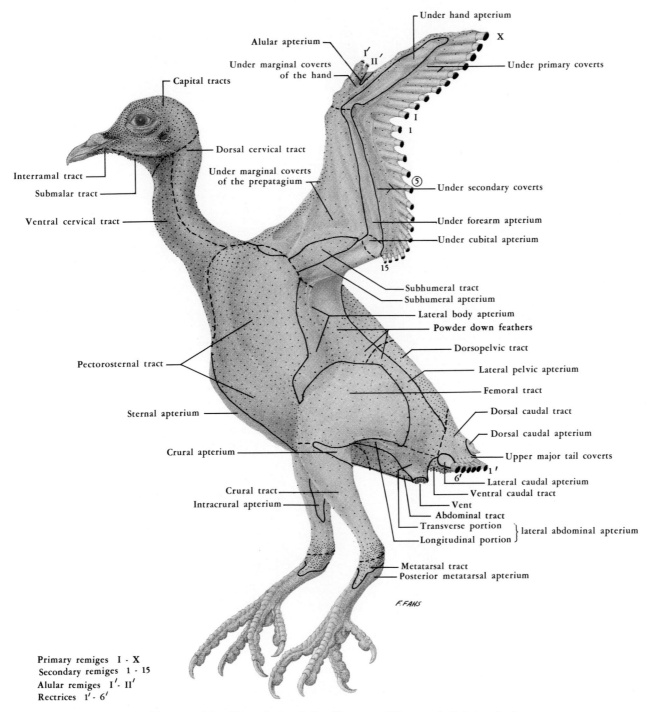

Under hand apterium

Alular apterium

Under marginal coverts
of the hand

Capital tracts

X

Under primary coverts

Interramal tract

Submalar tract

Dorsal cervical tract

Ventral cervical tract

Under marginal coverts
of the prepatagium

Under secondary coverts

Under forearm apterium

Under cubital apterium

Subhumeral tract
Subhumeral apterium

Lateral body apterium

Powder down feathers

Dorsopelvic tract

Lateral pelvic apterium

Femoral tract

Dorsal caudal tract

Dorsal caudal apterium

Upper major tail coverts

Lateral caudal apterium

Ventral caudal tract

Vent

Abdominal tract

Transverse portion   } lateral abdominal apterium

Longitudinal portion

Metatarsal tract
Posterior metatarsal apterium

F. FAHS

Pectorosternal tract

Sternal apterium

Crural apterium

Crural tract
Intracrural apterium

Primary remiges I - X
Secondary remiges 1 - 15
Alular remiges I' - II'
Rectrices 1' - 6'

FIGURE 96.—Pterylosis of the Common Pigeon—left lateral view.

located along the sides of the body, between the thigh and tail, and in the groin region. Those parts of the lateral body apterium devoid of feathers are limited to anterior and posterior axillary fossae.

Caudal tracts and apteria

The caudal tracts of the pigeon are closely similar to those described for the other domestic species. The dorsal caudal tract covers the entire surface of the tail except for a small bare area around the uropygial papilla and adjacent uropygial eminence and a narrow bare area continuous with the median pelvic apterium. These featherless areas on the dorsal tail, as a group, are designated the dorsal caudal apterium (fig. 95).

There are six rectrices on each side, the first rectrix of each row is elevated to a higher level than the others of the

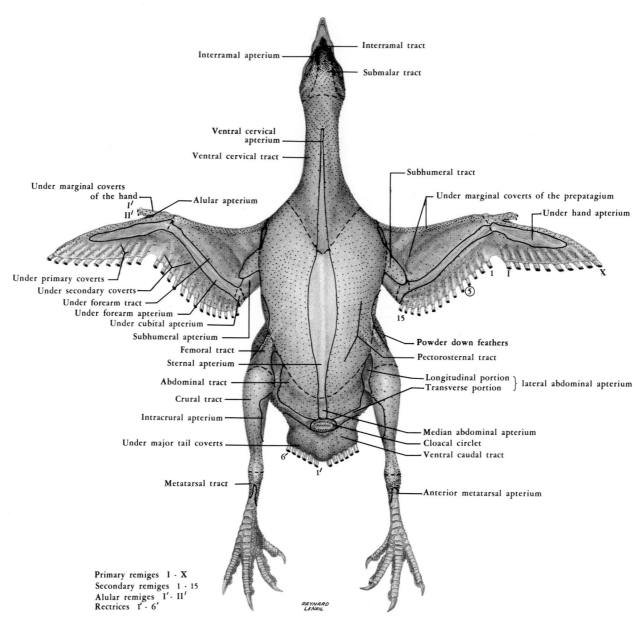

Interramal apterium — — Interramal tract

Submalar tract

Ventral cervical apterium

Ventral cervical tract

Subhumeral tract

Under marginal coverts of the hand
I′
II′   — Alular apterium

Under marginal coverts of the prepatagium

Under hand apterium

Under primary coverts

Under secondary coverts

Under forearm tract

Under forearm apterium

Under cubital apterium

Subhumeral apterium

Femoral tract

Sternal apterium

Abdominal tract

Crural tract

Intracrural apterium

Under major tail coverts

Metatarsal tract

Powder down feathers

Pectorosternal tract

Longitudinal portion
Transverse portion   } lateral abdominal apterium

Median abdominal apterium

Cloacal circlet

Ventral caudal tract

Anterior metatarsal apterium

Primary remiges I - X
Secondary remiges 1 - 15
Alular remiges I′ - II′
Rectrices 1′ - 6′

RAYNARD
LENEIL

FIGURE 97.—Pterylosis of the Common Pigeon—ventral view.

row. The tip of the pygostyle separates the rectrices of the first pair (fig. 95). Six upper major tail coverts form a row above the rectrices but lie so close together that the first is located between rectrices 1 and 2 and the last, between rectrices 5 and 6. The rows anterior to the row of majors merge into the nonspecific pattern of upper tail coverts.

The under surface of the tail is a broad triangular space without apteria (fig. 97). A row of six under major tail coverts parallels the rectrices on each side. A small lateral caudal apterium overlies the follicle of the sixth rectrix (figs. 95 and 96).

Brachial tracts and apteria

The humeral tract of a plucked bird is readily identified by the underlying broad band of fat. The tract is one or two

rows wider at the forward margin than it is in the caudal half of the band (fig. 95). Some follicles close to the humeral tract produce powder down feathers. They lie within the scapular apterium.

A narrow featherless space lies just anterior to the humeral tract and separates it in part from the caudal end of the ventral cervical tract that lies on the dorsal surface of the cervical patagium (fig. 95). This featherless space extends laterally outward from the middle of the lateral edge of the scapular apterium and therefore is considered to be part of the scapular apterium (fig. 95).

Due to the presence of two additional rows on the proximal side of the anterior half of the humeral tract, the boundary on the proximal edge is not straight, as it is on the distal side of the margin. At the anterior end of the lateral border, the humeral tract merges with the upper marginal coverts of the prepatagium. The caudal part of the humeral tract extends to the free edge of the metapatagium, and occupies the distal half of this fold of skin; the proximal half carries the scapular apterium (fig. 95). The humeral apterium is a triangular space between the humeral tract, posthumeral tract, and upper marginal coverts of the prepatagium. The upper cubital apterium is a small area on the dorsal side of the elbow.

The posthumeral tract lies on the dorsal and posterior surfaces of the caudal edge of the upper arm and is composed of three rows of follicles paralleling this margin (figs. 95 and 96). The ends of the rows adjacent to the last secondaries are indefinite, but the ends adjacent to the humeral tract are clearly distinguishable.

The subhumeral tract, on the ventral side of the upper arm, extends from the elbow region to the boundary between breast and wing. The proximal end of the subhumeral tract is continuous with that part of the pectorosternal tract equivalent to the lateral body tract (fig. 96). The posterior row has large follicles. The next row anterior has follicles of intermediate size, and the one beyond that has small follicles.

The narrow subhumeral apterium lies between the subhumeral and posthumeral tracts. It is continuous proximally with the lateral body apterium, and distally with the under cubital apterium.

Alar tracts and apteria

Upper surface of the hand.—The postpatagium of the hand supports 10 primaries, all well developed (figs. 99 and 100). The 10th lies parallel to the phalanges of digit III; the ninth and eighth approach the basal phalanx of digit III; the seventh parallels the phalanx of digit IV; and the sixth to the first cross the metacarpus of digit IV to approach the corresponding bone of digit III. When the wing is extended, the intersecting axes of the first and 10th primaries make an angle of about 45°.

The upper major primary coverts have long follicles that lie in the grooves made by the closely placed follicles of the primaries and are about four-fifths as long. There are 10 upper major primary coverts, each distal to the remex of the same number. The last one of the series lies parallel to the leading edge of the middle finger. The complete set of upper major coverts in the pigeon, like that in the turkey, gives supporting evidence that the large feather proximal to primary I is the carpal remex rather than a first upper major primary covert.

The only other coverts on the dorsal surface of the hand, except marginals, are those forming an incomplete row of upper median primary coverts. In the specimen illustrated (fig. 99), this row is composed of follicles 4 to 10 of the series. In other specimens, a feather was in position 3; this agrees with Steiner's (1917: 341) diagram for *Columba*.

A row of upper marginal coverts of the hand is implanted along the leading edge of the wing. Between these follicles

and the bases of those belonging to the primaries and major coverts, is a narrow under hand apterium.

At the base of the hand is the alula bearing four remiges, I' to IV'; this number agrees with Steiner's (1917) observation that four is the usual number. The four small feathers, each located at the base of an alular remex, are identified as upper alular coverts, presumably the major row. These are covered in turn by the upper marginal coverts of the hand from which the alular coverts are distinguished by their larger size. On the web between digits II and III is the upper alular apterium.

Upper surface of the carpal region.—A distinct carpal remex is present, parallel to primary remex I, but about half as long (figs. 98 and 99). Its size and appearance are closely similar to those of an upper major primary covert. Slightly anterior to the carpal remex is its upper major covert. In the four kinds of domestic birds studied, this covert characteristically crosses dorsally over the remex and points toward the tip of the wing; the turkey presents a different case. Near the base of the upper major carpal covert is a smaller follicle that is similar in size to those of the upper median secondary coverts and clearly lies at the end of the median row of the forearm. It is therefore identified as an upper median carpal covert. Anterior to this is still another feather, located at the end of the row of upper minor secondary coverts, that we designate as the upper minor carpal covert–first row. The placement of upper major, median, and minor coverts is identical with that present in the chicken (compare figs. 68 and 98). This agrees with Steiner's (1917: 341) naming of feathers in the carpal region, but he went beyond the minor carpal covert–first row—to identify and measure upper minor carpal coverts–second and third rows. He did the same for the upper minor secondary coverts, but it is our opinion that these second and third rows should be included with the upper marginal coverts on the basis of follicle placement. A further discussion of this subject is given in chapter 8, page 444.

Upper surface of the forearm.—The forearm bears a total of 15 or 16 secondary remiges, if included in the count is the one missing at the gap (diastema) between secondaries 4 and 6 and shown in figure 98 as 5. Following the 15th feather, the follicles become smaller and merge with those of the posthumeral tract. Since the upper major, median, and minor rows each have 16 feathers, however, we assume that theoretically, at least, there should be a 16th secondary remex.

The upper major secondary coverts have follicles about one-half to two-thirds as long as those of the remiges with which they are associated. Each one has its base on the proximal side of its associated remex and then crosses dorsally over the remex so that all of the major coverts point in a distal direction. The upper major secondary covert for the missing fifth remex is as large as those proximal and distal to it. There are 16 upper major secondary coverts, the last one of the series lying dorsal to the follicle of the 15th secondary remex.

Usually, there are 16 upper median secondary coverts, but this number can vary. Steiner (1917), for species of birds with a diastataxic type of wing, showed an intercalated row between major and median coverts involving five feathers at the beginning of a row. As he diagrammed the shift, all of the rows proximal to the fifth feather in each row have moved posteriorly the width of one row—even to the extent of passing around the trailing edge of the wing and becom-

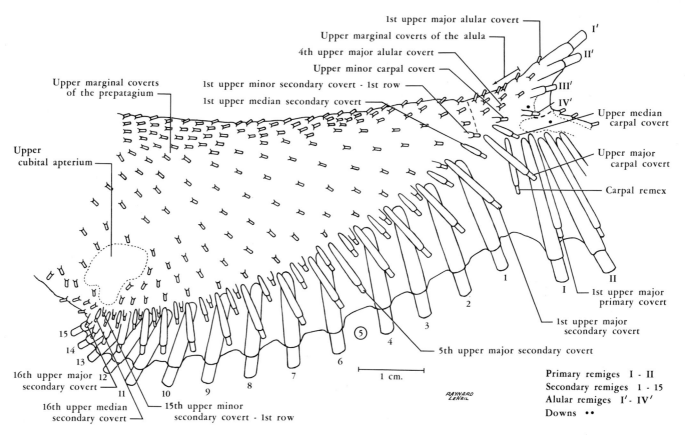

FIGURE 98.—Contour and down feathers on the dorsal surface of the forearm of the Common Pigeon.

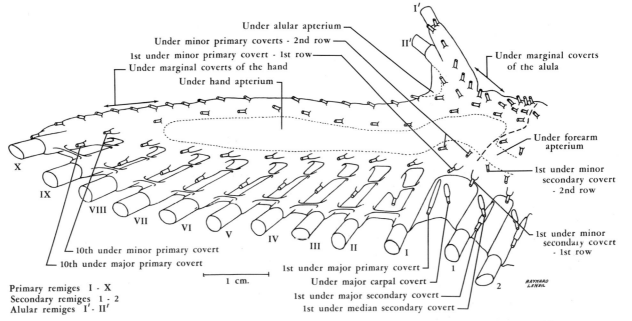

FIGURE 100.—Contour feathers on the ventral surface of the hand of the Common Pigeon.

ing part of the under coverts. Numerous investigators before and after Steiner supported the idea of positional shift of parts of rows, although the direction of the shift may differ according to the investigators' studies. As far as the arrangement of feathers within a row is concerned, there is nothing in the pterylosis of the adult pigeon wing to directly indicate a shift in rows or the existence of an "intercalated" row. This is not intended as refutation of

Steiner and others who have worked on this interesting problem; rather it indicates that in the anatomy of follicle placement of the adult bird, we have not been able to identify an intercalated row.

The first row of upper minor secondary coverts has 15 follicles. In the specimen illustrated (fig. 98), a sixth minor covert was absent. The arrangement of upper coverts in the pigeon clearly bears out the scheme presented in figure

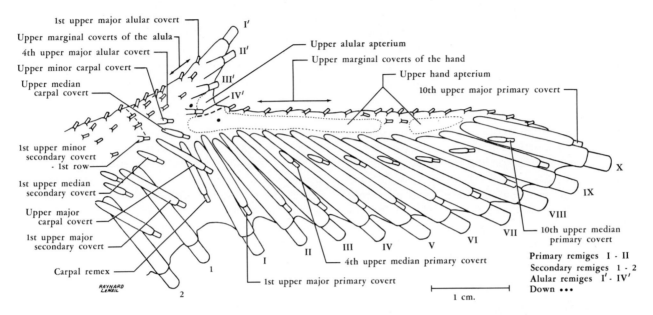

FIGURE 99.—Contour and down feathers on the dorsal surface of the hand of the Common Pigeon.

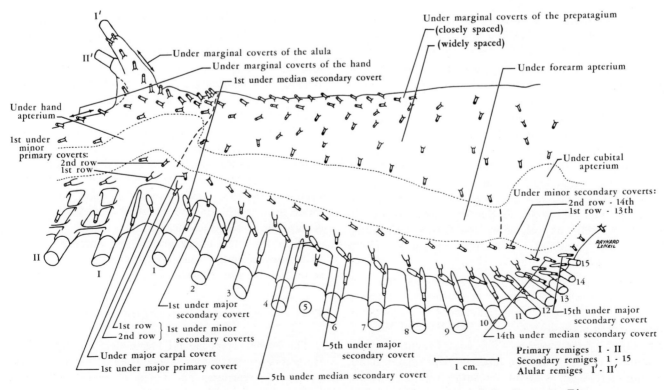

FIGURE 101.—Contour feathers on the ventral surface of the forearm of the Common Pigeon.

72, where the perpendicular rows of feathers incline in a distal direction. Most authors identify a second row of upper minor secondary coverts and some a third, but on the basis of material that we have studied, this appears to be an unrealistic handling of the arrangement of the follicles. We recognized, however, that classification of rows based on plumage can give results at variance with a study based on the arrangement of follicles.

The upper cubital apterium interrupts some of the marginal covert rows. The apterium overlies the elbow.

The pigeon has very few down feathers on the wing. Only two were found on the specimen used for figures 98 and 99; one was near alular remex IV′ and the other at the caudal end of the upper hand apterium.

Under surface of the hand.—The necks of the 10 remex follicles are joined together by ligamentous bands placed close to the free edge of the postpatagium (fig. 100). These have not been studied enough in the pigeon to determine if smooth muscles are included. There are 10 under major primary coverts, each one lying on the proximal side of the follicle with which it is associated. All except the first are broadly attached to the remex follicle wall, and all except the first have a narrow connecting band that joins the follicle of the under major primary covert to the remex follicle proximal to it. Thus, the under major follicle is firmly connected to the follicles proximal and distal to it. Each covert follicle agrees in number with the remex just distal to it.

The pigeon carries but a single row of under minor primary coverts except for two or three feathers at the carpal end of the row, suggestive of a second row (fig. 100). Each under minor primary covert of the first row, like the under major coverts, lies on the proximal side of each remex having the same number. A complete set from 1 to 10 is present. There may be some question whether the first feather in the first row of minor coverts belongs to the hand or to the wrist, and the same is true of the first feather of the two or three feathers belonging to the second row.

A distinct under hand apterium is present that is continuous with the under forearm apterium; the arbitrary separation is indicated by dashed lines (figs. 100 and 101). Anterior to the under hand apterium are two rows of under marginal coverts of the hand. The row adjacent to the apterium carries fewer feathers than the one along the leading edge. One short row of about four follicles is implanted on the ventral surface of the first alular remex. On the ventral (fig. 100), as well as on the dorsal surface (fig. 99) of the alular patagium, small upper and under alular apteria are present.

Under surface of the carpal region.—There is only one unequivocal under carpal covert; it is labeled as belonging to the major row, but in size and placement it is similar to the under median secondary coverts (figs. 100 and 101).

Under surface of the forearm.—The complement of under coverts is more complete on the forearm than on the hand. The spacing of feathers is about the same, but the forearm is larger and therefore can accommodate more feathers. The

15 secondary remiges (counting the missing fifth) are linked together by ligamentous bands, but these bands are not as well developed as they are on the hand. They do not produce abrupt elevations of the skin of the postpatagium. (See Pelissier, 1923, for details of these ligaments.)

Each of the 15 under major secondary coverts lies on the proximal side of the corresponding remex (fig. 101). In most of the row the follicles lie parallel to the remex follicles. At the proximal end, covert and remex follicles are somewhat divergent. The fifth under major secondary covert (the remex of which is absent or displaced) is smaller than those on each side of it.

The under major and minor coverts of the hand form anteroposterior rows across the wing that are inclined proximally away from the remex. This agrees with the diagram (fig. 72), but in the forearm a line that connects the major to the minor under coverts is inclined distally. The under median secondary coverts are placed distal to each under major secondary covert. The feather shafts of the under median secondary coverts are directed proximally and posteriorly at about a 45° angle. The row includes 14 feathers in the series; the 15th is absent in the specimen from which the illustration was made (fig. 101), but not enough specimens were examined to discover if it was present in some individuals. The fifth under median secondary covert is present and has a typical positional relationship with the fifth under major covert.

The under minor secondary coverts are represented by two rows; the first of these rows lies close to the bases of the under median secondary coverts and includes feathers 1 to 13, the last two in the series are absent. We assume that the first feather of the second row is represented by the follicle immediately anterior to the first feather of the first row. There are 14 in the specimen represented in figure 101, but the number varies among specimens. In this row the spacing between follicles is very irregular. As a result, some are close together and well alined with the corresponding follicles of the other posteriorly positioned members of the rows, and some are far apart and poorly alined.

The under forearm apterium is broad and has continuity distally with the under hand apterium and proximally with the under cubital apterium. Between the under forearm apterium and the under prepatagial apterium is a single row of feathers representing the under forearm tract. At each end, the row joins the under marginal coverts; we have made no attempt by the use of dashed lines to indicate a separation of these feather groups.

Anterior to the under prepatagial apterium are three or four rows of under marginal coverts of the prepatagium; some follicles are directed distally and some obliquely.

Posterior appendage tracts and apteria

The femoral tract has follicles widely but regularly spaced. Both its anterior margin and its dorsal margin are bounded by powder feathers. The posterior margin of the femoral tract is established by the longitudinal portion of the lateral abdominal apterium (fig. 96). The crural apterium places the ventral boundary at the knee region. The apterium does not cross the entire surface of the knee; thus, in this area, an arbitrary dashed line is placed at about the level of the knee joint. The follicles in the infracaudal rows are placed closer together than in other parts of the tract. Beebe (1915) designated these as the pelvic flight feathers, pelvic wing tract, and pelvic alar tract in studies primarily of a pigeon and a dove but also of American Jaçana (*Jacana spinosa*) and the Great Horned Owl. In a study of the pterylosis of the Passenger Pigeon (*Ectopistes migratorius*), Clark (1918b) found 19 quills of the "pelvic wing" and 18 in the White-winged Dove (*Zenaida asiatica* = *Melopelia asiatica*). He noted 12 quills arranged transversely across the proximal crus. On the femur, he identified three coverts as part of the group located above the knee.

The crural apterium on the medial surface of the knee is continuous with the transverse and longitudinal portions of the lateral abdominal apterium and with the intracrural apterium. In figure 97 these apteria could be separated by dashed lines, but this would make the general relationships hard to follow in the drawing. The individual apteria are clearly identifiable in an actual specimen.

The crural tract begins at the knee and extends to the hock joint and beyond. The intracrural apterium lies on the medial surface of the lower leg (shank) but extends only about two-thirds of the distance toward the ankle. In the ankle region there is a small bare area on the anterior surface, but it is too small to be named. Likewise, there is a bare area on the posterior surface of the ankle.

The crural tract extends distally on the lateral and medial surfaces of the proximal third of the metatarsus leaving between these extensions of feathers onto the metatarsus the scales of the anterior and posterior surfaces of the metatarsus. Scaly skin is not generally called apteria, but in the pigeon where they are surrounded on three sides by feathers, they may be called, anterior and posterior metatarsal apteria. In the Common Pigeon, a few feathers may be found on the medial side of the metatarsus as far distally as the tarsometatarsophalangeal joints.

PTILOSIS

Feather Coat Excluding Head

We have already emphasized that pterylosis and ptilosis are different and distinct aspects of the bird's feather coat. Pterylosis covers the implantation point for each feather follicle in the skin of the bird; ptilosis deals with the size, shape, and appearance of the feather that comes from each follicle as well as the total plumage coat. When studying the pterylosis of a bird, it is necessary to be mindful of the kind of feather that is involved. Likewise, a critical study of ptilosis is not possible or at least would be difficult if the pterylosis were not known.

Many workers have described the color pattern and appearance of plumage for many wild birds and have given names appropriate for each of the plumage regions; some references on this subject were given in chapter 1. These names have been established over many years in an extensive ornithologic literature and are not reviewed here. Likewise, the poultry husbandrymen have given names to feather groups in domestic fowl. We are concerned here with associating and naming each plumage group in respect to its associated feather tract. We have done this in detail for the chicken and touch only on certain points for the remaining four domestic and laboratory species. In all five species, we have paid particular attention to the plumage of the wing.

Chicken

The terminology for the various parts of the undisturbed feather coat (figs. 104 and 105) suggests associations with the underlying pterylae, but the exact boundaries cannot be determined accurately by examining the feather coat only. The feathers must be lifted to expose the skin, implanted follicles, and also the featherless spaces. To point out the plumage for each tract, a series of eight illustrations was made (figs. 102, *A* to *D*, and 103, *A* to *D*) to show certain groups of feathers. Some of the drawings, used in earlier illustrations on pterylosis studies and carrying an overlay of dots, serve as a base to which additional overlays are added to show the feathers associated with specific pterylae.

Dorsal cervical tract (hackle).—The hackle is a group of feathers from the dorsal cervical tract. As shown in the pterylography (figs. 60 and 61), this group has a broad base adjacent to the head and then narrows to join the interscapular tract. Hackle is a term sometimes limited to the individual slender and tapering neck feathers of the male chicken, but it is equally correct to apply the name to neck feathers of both sexes and to extend it to other orders of birds, although it is generally applied to galliforms. As illustrated in figures 102, *A*, and 104, the feathers in the male droop over the sides of the neck, entirely covering the lateral cervical apterium. These feathers also cover the anterior end of the wing (figs. 104 and 105) and most of the interscapular tract or cape. The feathers of the hackle in the female are not as long as they are in the male and therefore cover slightly less of the neck and trunk. In the male, the tips of the feathers are narrow and pointed, and in the female they are rounded. The individual feathers of the male are shown in the exploded views of the feathers of the dorsal tracts (fig. 181) and are described in detail in chapter 6. We suggest that throughout the reading of material on ptilosis that illustrations in chapter 6 be examined and supplemented by a study of the text material in this chapter.

Interscapular tract (cape).—The feathers of the interscapular tract or cape are largely covered by the hackle, especially in the male, but as a chicken moves its neck, varying amounts of the cape are exposed. The feathers at the anterior end are always covered and characteristically are short (fig. 103, *B*) and plumulaceous. The feathers from the more caudal part of the tract are typical contours. The follicles in the midline are directed backward, but toward the margins they point more and more away from the median axis. As a result, although the interscapular tract is narrow, the plumage attached to it covers the scapular apterium completely and lies on top of the medial half of the feathers of the humeral tract. The feathers of the humeral tract have been named shoulder plumage and wing front (fig. 105) in the "American Standard of Perfection" (1938–40). Caudally, the interscapulars cover the first half of the dorsal tract group of feathers.

Dorsopelvic tract and anterior end of the dorsal caudal tract.—The dorsopelvic tract, as evident from the pterylosis (fig. 60), extends from the interscapular tract to the base of the tail. The portion as far caudal as the anterior end of the ilial bones is the dorsal tract. Its plumage, called the back (figs. 104 and 105), is composed of relatively short feathers in the female (fig. 103, *A*); in the male they are long and taper to a point, as do the hackle feathers. The follicles are largely directed caudally, but again those toward the margins extend laterally. In the female, the feathers being short, cover about one-third of the anterior part of the pelvic tract, whereas in the male, they cover about two-fifths of this tract. The laterally placed feathers of the back are directed outward at about a 45° angle or more, but they are short and do not cover much of the lateral body apterium. Some of them lie upon plumulaceous feathers from the anterior end of the femoral tract.

The feather coat from a male shown in figure 102, *B*, has its feathers implanted in the pelvic tract and in the anterior part of the upper caudal tract. The rectrices and upper tail coverts have been removed from the tail. As shown in the illustration this permits an unnatural drooping of feathers over the end of the tail. When the rectrices are present, as in figures 104 and 105, the pelvic tract feathers are lifted upward to form the saddle in the male and the slope of the back in the female. As may be observed in the exploded view (fig. 181), many of these feathers are long and tapering, especially in the male, and drape down over the side of the body, the end of the wing, and the rear body feathers. In the male they are grouped together under the term "saddle" (fig. 104), and in the female, "cushion" (fig. 105). Only the follicles in the midline point directly caudally; the others point progressively laterally.

The feathers from the caudal end of the saddle and cushion spring from follicles implanted on the dorsal surface of the tail from the caudal indentation to the uropygial eminence. In both sexes these feathers merge with the upper major and median tail coverts; in fact, they are indistinguishable from them. Their identity is marked only by the fact that they lie anterior to the rows of tail coverts. On the dorsal surface of the uropygial eminence, of both sexes, arise a few short feathers that are entirely overlaid by those from the anterior part of the upper caudal tract. An oil gland circlet is present in the chicken (fig. 65 and ch. 9, figs. 388, 389, 394). Beddard (1898: 19) stated: "It has been pointed out that when the oil gland has a tuft of feathers upon its apex the rest of the gland is unfeathered, and that, on the contrary, when the tip is nude the general surface of the gland is feathered." This statement is not applicable to the chicken since both the gland and tip are feathered. On the oil gland eminence there are short feathers with widely spaced barbs; these feathers are arranged around the base of the oil gland duct. The vanes of these feathers are oriented in transverse planes rather than concentric to the duct. Those posterior to the duct are short and form a transition to the upper coverts of the tail, and those lateral and anterior to the duct are longer and are transitional in size and structure to those of the pelvic tract.

The chicken seems to have two oil gland circlets, each consisting of four or five feathers (fig. 65). They are arranged in two semicircles, one around each oil gland duct opening. Circlet feathers are often broken; if broken close to follicles, ends of oil gland papillae may appear bare, like papillae of birds lacking an oil gland circlet.

Posterior part of the dorsal caudal tract (tail feathers and coverts).—The posterior part of the upper caudal tract includes the upper major and median tail coverts and the tail feathers or rectrices. The rectrices arise from the posterolateral margin of the tail (figs. 60 to 62). Vaulted or roof-shaped tails of jungle fowl and domestic chicken (figs. 104 and 105) are not unique; they may be found in some other Phasianidae and in some megapodes. The slope of the sides of the vault may be different in the various kinds of birds. The tail of birds is not folded in most orders but lies in one plane or is slightly arched. The fold of the chicken tail is 30° or less. In the female all the rectrices are shaped like large contour feathers, but in the male the median pair forms the greater sickles. In the female, the median pair, also called the deck feathers, forms the ridge of the vaulted

→

FIGURE 102.—Feather coat associated with individual feather tracts of the male Single Comb White Leghorn Chicken—lateral views. (Feather overlays drawn by R. B. Ewing.)

A, hackle feathers from the dorsal cervical tract (group on dorsal neck). Thigh plumage and rear body feathers from the femoral tract (group on the thigh).

B, saddle feathers from the pelvic tract including some feathers at the anterior end of the dorsal caudal tract.

C, breast feathers from the pectoral tract (group on breast). Lower leg feathers from the crural tract—medial view (group on inner side of shank). Fluff from the lateral abdominal tract (group below the tail).

D, feathers from the lateral body tract (group below wing). Lower leg feathers from the crural tract—lateral view (group on outer surface of shank). Feathers of the cloacal circlet (group of short feathers at rear of body).

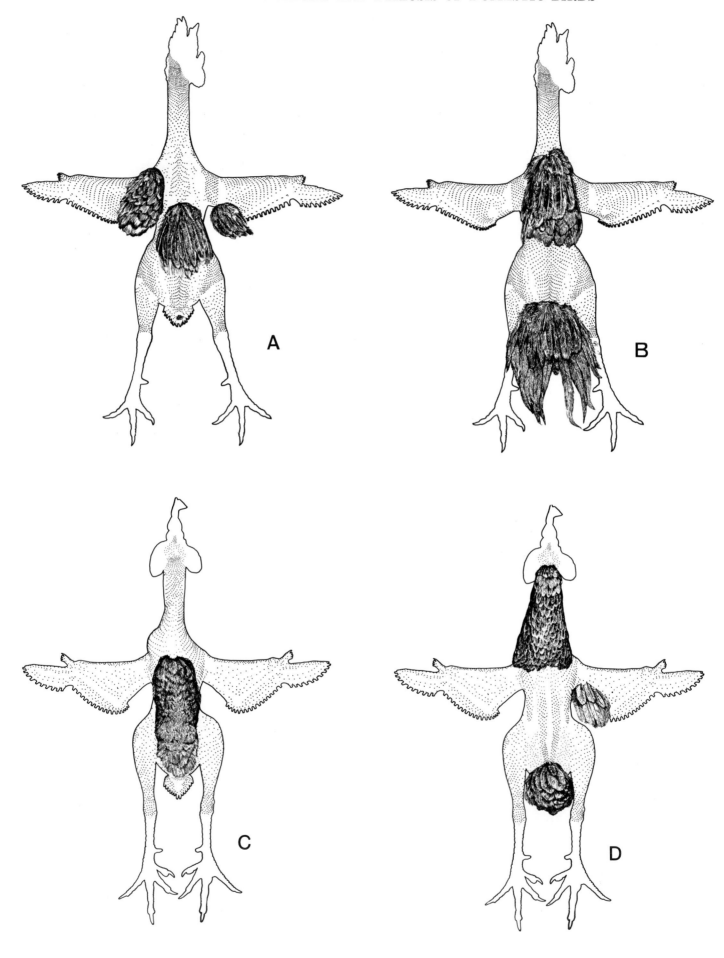

tail; whereas, in the male, the ridge is formed by the second pair of rectrices. The number of rectrices seems to vary as indicated in table 5. In either sex the number of rectrices may be seven or eight; the upper major tail coverts, six to eight; upper median tail coverts, one to six; and under major tail coverts, five to eight.

When the tail is folded, the tips of the rectrices form a slightly curved margin (figs. 104 and 105). When the tail is spread in flight, it is nearly flat and the line established by the tips of the feathers forms about one-third of a circle. The outer vane of each feather overlaps the inner vane of the feather lateral to it, like overlapping shingles, so that water is readily shed. The inner vanes of the two rectrices that form the ridge of the roof tend to overlap—sometimes one way and sometimes the other. In order to facilitate sliding past each other and not to fray the edges, the barbs on these vanes are curved downward. The shafts of all the tail feathers curve medially, the curvature is least in the pair forming the ridge of the vault and most in the peripheral ones of each row. The curvature, especially of the peripheral rectrices, tends to lift the lower edge of the tail.

The placement of the median rectrix dorsal to the other rectrices is common among birds. Berger and Lunk (1954), noted that the central pair of rectrices in the nestling Red-capped Coua (*Coua ruficeps*) was elevated to the extent that the second pair nearly met beneath them. The association of the median rectrices with the lateral surfaces of the pygostyle (fig. 67, *A* and *B*) shows that these two feathers have been lifted by the growth of the pygostyle.

The greater sickle of the male, rectrix 1, is the longest feather of the body. Both vanes are fully developed and of nearly uniform width except near the ends. The rachis curves about 90° (fig. 197, *B*).

The upper major tail coverts for each sex are best described separately. Those in the female are not specialized (fig. 105), whereas in the male they are modified to form the lesser sickles (fig. 104). The shifting in position of rectrices 2 to 7 in respect to the first rectrix has put the first rectrix in approximately the same row as the upper major tail coverts. To compensate, the coverts have been displaced laterally. They may be reduced in number to one pair less than the rectrices (table 5), but this is not always the case. The first covert in the female is implanted between the first and second rectrices; thus, it functions as the covert for both these feathers. The second covert lies above the third rectrix. The remaining ones shift medially so that the

TABLE 5.—*Rectrices and tail coverts of 11 male and 11 female Single Comb White Leghorn Chickens*

Sex	Rectrices (includes greater sickle in males)		Upper major tail coverts		Upper median tail coverts		Under major tail coverts	
	Left	Right	Left	Right	Left	Right	Left	Right
	No.	No.	No.	No.	No.	No.	No.	No.
Males.....	8	8	7	6	4	2	8	7
	8	8	8	8	5	4	6	5
	7	8	7	7	1	2	8	6
	7	8	7	7	4	5	7	8
	7	8	6	7	5	6	6	7
	7	7	6	6	5	5	7	7
	8	8	7	7	4	5	6	7
	8	8	7	7	5	6	8	8
	8	8	7	8	5	5	7	7
	7	8	7	7	4	3	7	7
	8	8	7	7	6	5	8	8
Females...	7	8	7	7	4	3	8	8
	7	7	7	7	3	3	7	7
	7	7	7	7	3	3	8	8
	8	8	7	7	5	5	7	7
	7	8	7	8	6	6	8	8
	7	8	6	7	2	4	7	8
	8	8	7	8	4	3	7	6
	7	7	6	7	4	2	7	8
	7	8	7	7	6	4	8	8
	8	8	7	6	4	4	7	7
	8	8	7	7	6	6	7	7

last in the series lies above the sixth or between the fifth and sixth rectrices.

In the cock there are usually seven upper major tail coverts (lesser sickles). In table 5 the number varies from six to eight. These coverts decrease in length laterally so that the seventh one is often so short that it is questionable whether it should be included in the series. These feathers, like the greater sickle, arch downward across the side of the tail. The shafts are implanted approximately like those in the female except that, due to their larger size, they are spread farther laterally, and the seventh one lies above the shaft of the seventh rectrix instead of the sixth as in the female.

The extremely long tail feathers (greater and lesser sickles)

←

FIGURE 103.—Feather coat associated with individual feather tracts of the Single Comb White Leghorn Chicken. *A* and *B* are dorsal views, *C* and *D*, ventral views. (Feather overlays drawn by R. B. Ewing.)

A, shoulder feathers of the humeral tract (group on the left wing). Back feathers of the dorsal tract—female (group on the dorsal body). Feathers of the posthumeral tract—female (group on the right wing).

B, cape feathers of the interscapular tract (group between wings). Sickle feathers and others of the caudal tract—male (group on tail).

C, feathers of the sternal tract.

D, feathers of the ventral cervical tract (group on front of neck). Feathers of the subhumeral tract (group on the left wing). Fluff of the median abdominal tract (group at the rear of the body).

of the Japanese long-tailed fowls are known to reach a length of 23 feet. These feathers exist partly because of genetic selection and partly because of physical stimulation that is applied to the feather follicles. This treatment delays retraction of the feather pulp and cessation of growth. These feathers do molt, but the replacement grows very rapidly (Cunningham, 1903).

The number of upper medial tail coverts of the female varies from two to six, as shown in table 5. In the "American Standard of Perfection" (1938–40: 13) the coverts are shown

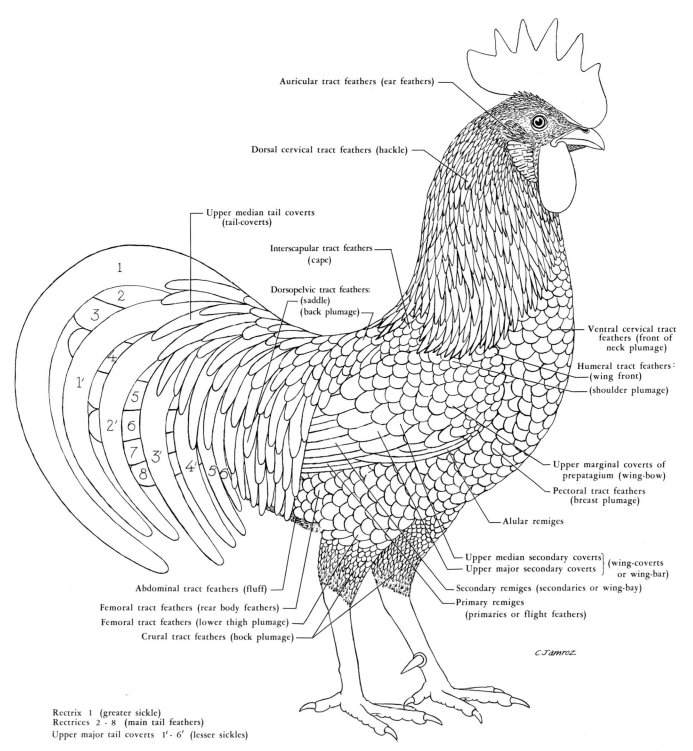

FIGURE 104.—Feather coat of the male Single Comb White Leghorn Chicken—right lateral view. We gave most feather groups two names: first, the feather tract name from the general avian literature; second, in parentheses, a name from general poultry husbandry literature, particularly the "American Standard of Perfection" (1938–40).

projecting definitely beyond the feathers of the cushion that come from the upper caudal tract, but our specimens show them as relatively short and not projecting much beyond the tips of the feathers from the upper caudal tract.

The upper distal downs of the tail lie close to the follicle neck of the rectrices. The afterfeather and the main feather are about equal length.

Ventral cervical tract (*front of neck plumage*).—The density and character of feathers in the interramal and submalar regions (throat) of the chicken are described under the pterylosis of the neck. Ptilosis in the present section begins with the ventral cervical tract at the level of the wattles and extends to the shoulder (fig. 62). The feathers of the

ventral cervical tract are short (fig. 103, *D*) compared to the hackle feathers of the dorsal cervical tract (fig. 102 *A*). The feathers of the ventral neck blend with those from the dorsal neck (figs. 104 and 105), but can be distinguished by their size and arrangement. Most of the lateral cervical apterium is covered by the dorsal cervical feathers; but along the inferior margin of this space, the ventral cervical feathers that are directed dorsocaudally provide some coverage. The ventral cervical apterium in the midline of the neck, is covered entirely by the feathers from the ventral cervical tract curving in a ventrocaudal direction. When these become wet and matted, the underlying semiplumes as well as the skin of the apterium may be exposed.

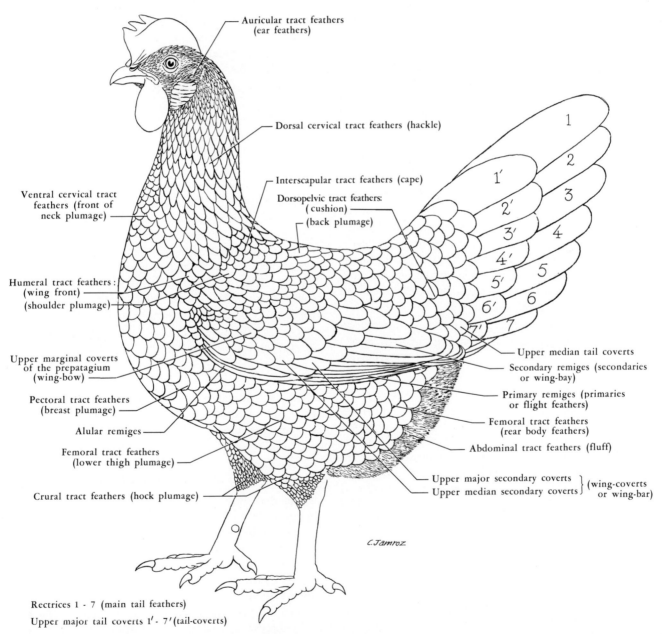

FIGURE 105.—Feather coat of the female Single Comb White Leghorn Chicken—left lateral view. (The naming of feather groups is explained in fig. 104.)

Pectoral tract (breast plumage).—The plumage of the ventral cervical tract continues caudally and has complete continuity with the breast feathers of the pectoral tract (figs. 102, *C*; 103, *D*; 104; and 105). The pectoral tract follicles begin at the shoulder and end in front of the knee (fig. 62). The feathers of this tract cover the pectoral apterium and overlie feathers implanted along the margin of the sternal tract. Those on the upper margin of the pectoral tract cover much of the lateral body apterium and some feathers of the lateral body tract. Those at the caudal end of the tract overlap the anterior margin of the thigh and knee. The pectoral tract feathers on the shoulder are covered by those of the dorsal cervical tract.

Sternal tract.—The sternal tract is weak at the anterior end but becomes strong caudally. All the follicles point in a mediocaudal direction so that they tend to form a ridge of feathers over the sternal apterium (fig. 103, *C*). At the extreme caudal end of the tract there is a transition to the fluff of the abdominal tract. As one views the live, erect bird, the ending of one tract and the beginning of the next is not readily apparent in either sex, especially in an all-white bird. The feathers and their overlap blend into an uninterrupted feather coat, as shown in figures 104 and 105 for the neck, breast, and sternal areas.

Abdominal tract (fluff).—The posterior feathers shown in figure 103, *D*, are from the medial abdominal tract, a strong tract between sternum and cloaca. These are semiplumes in both sexes, but they are a little more plumulaceous in the female where the fluff is more conspicuous, especially in the laying hen. The feathers are implanted in the skin at about a 45° angle posteriorly in relation to skin surface. The feathers on the sides of the tract are directed laterally and merge with the semiplumes of the lateral abdominal tract (fig. 102, *C*). The latter is a weak tract, and the semiplumes are downy, especially in the groin region.

The cloacal circlet (fig. 102, *D*) is formed by one or two rows of very short down feathers that are covered by the fluff of the abdominal region. Often the feathers of the cloacal circlet are broken.

Ventral caudal tract.—The under tail coverts are implanted on the ventral surface of the tail. The major row is definite, and, as seen in table 5, has about the same number of feathers as rectrices. The pterylosis of the ventral caudal tract is shown in figure 62. In the male, the first under major covert lies opposite the space between the first and second rectrices. The second covert lies in the space between the second and third rectrices, the third one lies ventral to the shaft of the fourth rectrix, the fourth lies in the space between the fifth and sixth rectrices, and the fifth lies ventral to the sixth shaft. The remaining two are close together, near the corner of the tail; they are either somewhat separated from the bases of the seventh and eighth rectrices, or they lie on each side of the base of the seventh shaft.

The vanes and shafts of the under major tail coverts are curved so that their upper surfaces are cupped and fitted one below the other like a stack of spoons. The cupped side of the feather is directed toward the tail feathers. The first one is the longest and the seventh the shortest, and they form a pair of rows filling in the **V**-shaped gable formed by the folded tail.

The under major tail coverts in the female have a larger proportion of downy barbs on the bases of the feathers than do those of the male, and rachises extend outward, perpendicular to the margin of the tail. Thus, in the female the shafts of these feathers tend to cross the shafts of the tail feathers, whereas in the male the shafts of the two groups tend to be parallel to each other. As a result there is a wider spread of under major tail coverts in the female than in the male. In the female the outer two or three feathers project beyond the lateral margins of the tail, and their tips meet the tips of the laterally located upper major tail coverts. In the female the first covert is implanted between the bases of the first and second rectrices; the second and third lie directly below the third and fourth tail feathers, and the fourth, fifth, and sixth are lateral to the tail feathers having one higher number.

Between the rectrices and the under major tail coverts is a row of down feathers, identified here as the under distal downs of the tail. They have the same position relative to the follicles of the rectrices that the upper distal down feathers of the tail had on the dorsal side, except that they are placed slightly farther anteriorly.

Cephalic to the under major tail coverts are about three partial rows separated in the midline by a ventral caudal apterium (fig. 62). These may be considered as under median and minor tail coverts or, where grouped together, as the ventral caudal tract proper. These feathers are similar in both sexes except that they spread more laterally in the female than in the male, and in adult males there is a greater bowing of the shafts toward the midline. These rows parallel the row of under major tail coverts, and there are about three to four feathers in each row on a side.

Lateral body tract.—The lateral body tract is a small group of feathers on the side of the body beneath the wing (figs. 61 and 102, *D*). The feathers vary in structure from well-developed semiplumes to typical contour feathers. The shafts are directed backward and slightly upward covering the caudal half of the lateral body apterium and overlapping the anterior margin of the femoral tract.

The anterior part of the lateral body apterium is covered by the feathers of the pectoral tract.

Femoral tract (lower thigh plumage and rear body feathers).

The distribution of the follicles of the femoral tract is shown in figures 60 to 62. The tract extends from the hip to the knee across the full width of the thigh. The anterior surface of the knee is covered by feathers of the femoral tract, but the small amount of exposed medial surface of this part of the leg bears only downs that merge with the down feathers of the groin region.

The feathers from the anterior margin of the tract, adjacent to the lateral body apterium, are large semiplumes that are covered by the contour feathers of the pectoral tract. The semiplumes point directly caudally. Semiplumes are present also along the dorsal margin of the femoral tract adjacent to the lateral pelvic apterium. The feathers of the dorsal margin of the femoral tract are covered by the tip of the wing (figs. 104 and 105) and by the feathers from the lateral margin of the pelvic tract. The feathers of the dorsal part of the femoral tract point directly caudally.

Contour feathers are found on the more exposed parts of the femoral tract; those on the anterior surface of the knee are largely plumulaceous but have a pennaceous tip. The shafts point downward and caudally, completely covering the anterior and lateral surfaces of the knee. These feathers, together with the feathers from the anterior three-fourths of the lateral surface of the thigh, form the group that the "American Standard of Perfection" (1938–40) designated as the lower thigh plumage (figs. 102, *A*; 104; and 105). The feathers of this group, as well as those from the knee, slope downward and backward at about a 45° angle, making them stand apart from the long contour feathers arising from the several closely packed rows at the infracaudal margin of the tract. The feathers from the latter rows are long, contour feathers directed caudally so that they cover the sides of the abdomen and most of the fluff. The "American Standard of Perfection" named this group "the rear body feathers" (figs. 104 and 105). The lower thigh feathers cover all of the crural apterium and approximately the upper two-thirds of the crural tract feathers that lie on the external surface of the leg.

Crural tract (hock plumage).—The crural tract extends from the knee to the hock joint. The feathers are longest on the external surface of the shank and shortest on the medial surface; also, they are longer in the upper part than in the lower. Generally, the feathers point directly toward the ankle, but on the anterior surface of the shank they swing across it toward the medial side and overlap some of the shorter feathers on the inner surface of the leg (figs. 102, *C* and *D*). The upper two-thirds of the lateral surface are covered by the lower feathers of the femoral tract. The feathers of the knee region and those immediately below the knee are covered by feathers from the tip of the pectoral tract.

Humeral tract (wing front and shoulder).—The humeral tract crosses the upper arm from the shoulder to the metapatagium (figs. 60 and 103, *A*). The feathers near the leading edge of the wing are short. They form the wing front (figs. 104 and 105) and may be covered by the hackle feathers. Caudally the humeral feathers become progressively longer. When the wing is extended, the long feathers from the trailing edge fill the gap between the wing and body and form the plumage group called the shoulder. Along the medial margin of the humeral tract, the feathers point directly posteriorly and do not contribute significantly to covering the scapular apterium. Progressively toward the lateral margin, they point toward the axis of the extended wing and cover some of the feathers of the upper marginal coverts of the prepatagium. At the leading edge of the wing, the feathers project upward from the surface of the wing at a rather large angle. Since their shafts are strongly curved,

they produce a rounded leading edge with the adjacent marginals. Some of the follicles are directed forward rather than backward.

Posthumeral tract.—The posthumeral feathers are a small group along the posterior margin of the arm between the humeral tract and elbow (fig. 103, *A*). Usually there are three rows on the dorsal side, and the longest feathers are in the middle row. We have sometimes used the term "quills" for the feathers of the middle row, and the term "coverts" for those above and below. However, all the feathers of the posthumeral tract are relatively short compared to the large overlying humeral feathers and the adjacent secondaries and coverts of the forearm. The vanes of the most posterior row have a "contrary overlap." This term is applied when the overlapping of vanes is contrary to that of the remiges. Actually, the feathers are set almost at right angles to the axis of the humerus. The most posterior row of the posthumeral tract lies on the ventral side of the wing. These feathers are more downy than those of the adjacent dorsal row.

Subhumeral tract.—The subhumeral feathers on the under surface of the upper arm are composed of about two rows. The longest feathers are in the most caudal row; those anterior to these are much shorter and are similar in character to adjacent feathers on the ventral surface of the prepatagium (fig. 103, *D*). The feathers extend posteriorly and toward the elbow and form a thin covering for the under surface of the upper arm and the posthumeral apterium.

Alar tracts.—The feathers of the forearm and hand are illustrated in a series of drawings (figs. 106 to 123) and the accompanying text. It is desirable to associate plumage with the pterylosis. Several points are brought out: (1) Identification of feathers in the intact plumage and their relationship to the named coverts; (2) the types of overlap found in major, median, and minor coverts of domestic species; (3) reversed and nonreversed coverts; (4) comparison of eutaxic and diastataxic wings and evidence for intercalated rows or for shifting of rows; and (5) significance of down feathers when arranged in definite rows.

Feather coat of the folded wing.—The folded wing is an example of neat and efficient packaging (figs. 104 and 105). It lies snugly against the side of the body at right angles to the position taken when extended in flight, the forearm is folded close to the upper arm, the hand is bent to within about 45° of the forearm, and the feathers of digit II overlap the anterior margin of the hand. The folded wing covers the side of the body, the wrist region lies at the level of the shoulder, and the tips of the remiges lie beyond the pygostyle of the tail. The feathers of the folded wing touch the dorsal and pelvic feathers above and the pectoral feathers below. The folded wing removed from the body (fig. 106) shows a little more detail, and the expanded wing (fig. 107 and 108) shows at least the tips of most of the feathers.

The anterior part of the humeral group forms the wing-front. In the fully folded wing, some of the wing-front humerals overlie the wrist: the feathers along the distal margin of the tract of this wing are curved downward and

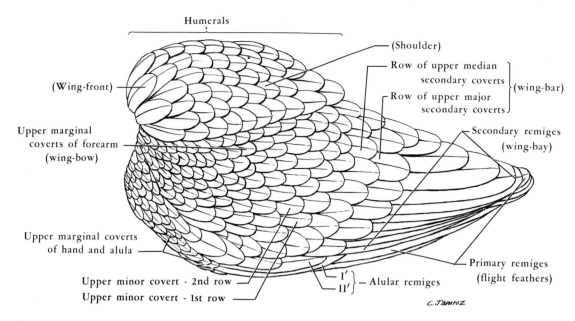

FIGURE 106.—Plumage of the folded left wing of the Single Comb White Leghorn Chicken. (The naming of feather groups is explained in fig. 104.)

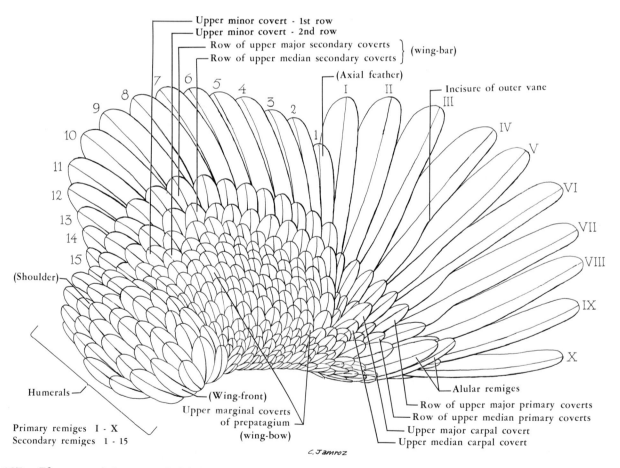

FIGURE 107.—Plumage of the extended left wing of the Single Comb White Leghorn Chicken—dorsal side. (The naming of feather groups is explained in fig. 104.)

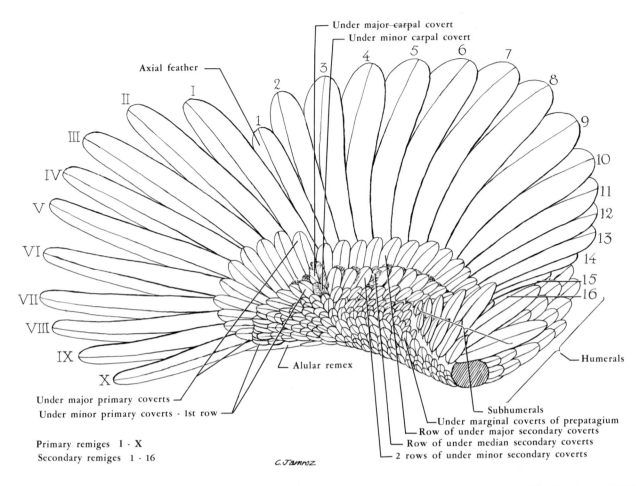

FIGURE 108.—Plumage of the ventral surfaces of the extended left wing for the Single Comb White Leghorn Chicken. (The naming of feather groups is explained in fig. 104.)

backward and cover approximately the anterior half of the upper marginals of the prepatagium. The feathers along the medial margin of the humeral tract parallel the scapula and cover it; these feathers are called the shoulder in poultry husbandry literature. They extend caudally beyond the wing nearly to the hip joint in the male or slightly beyond it in the female.

When the wing is extended, the ligamentous bands attached to the follicles of the secondary remiges pull these feathers to a position at right angles to the axis of the ulna. When the wing is flexed, the release of tension allows the secondaries to fold back against the forearm. The second secondary is the first feather of this series to be visible in the folded wing (fig. 106); the first one of the series, the key or axial feather, is entirely covered by coverts.

Secondaries 8 through 11 extend farthest caudally and their tips practically coincide with the tips of the farthest-reaching primaries, namely, 5 through 7. The exposed ends of the secondaries form a triangle, the wing-bay. Those toward the elbow shorten abruptly, and the small ones at the end of the series are covered by feathers from the hu-

meral tract. The exposed tips of the upper major and median coverts form the wing-bar. The coverts are discussed in more detail in the section on the extended wing.

The primaries are folded medial to the secondaries, and usually only the distal two, the ninth and 10th, are visible. The bases of these are covered by alular remiges. The shape of the joint at the wrist is such that when the hand is extended, the primaries are brought into nearly the same plane as the secondaries but as the hand is flexed, movement at the wrist is enough to rotate the hand away from the axis of the forearm by about 30°, which has the effect of pressing the hand against the side of the body. This, combined with the fact that the overlap of all the remiges is such that, like a spread stack of cards, the outermost feather, corresponding to the bottom card, lies next to the body. This arrangement allows the feathers to slide past each other without being ruffled. The overlap is such that the outer vane lies above the inner vane of the next feather distally positioned.

The alular remiges, combined with the alular coverts, provide strength for the leading edge of the hand. The alular

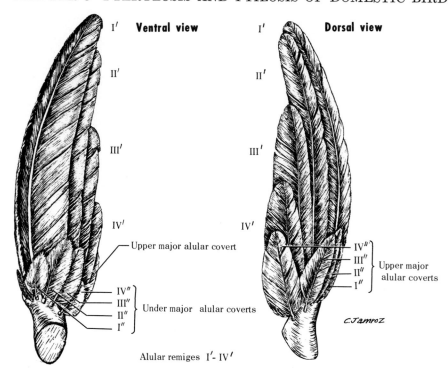

FIGURE 109.—Dorsal and ventral views of the alular remiges and their coverts for the Single Comb White Leghorn Chicken.

feathers maintain about the same position relative to the distal primaries in both the extended and the flexed condition.

Feather coat on the upper side of the extended wing.—Unfolding the wing brings most of the dorsal feathers into view (fig. 107). The outer vane of primary remiges 4 through 7 possesses an incisive notch, that is, the vane is broad at the base and abruptly becomes narrower toward the tip. The same thing occurs in primary 3, but the notch is made by a long gradual transition. In primary 2, the notch is scarcely apparent (fig. 113). For descriptions of feather structures, see chapter 6, page 297.

Upper major primary coverts 2 through 9 uniformly cover the basal third of the primaries. Covert 10 is much shorter and narrower—only about two-thirds as long as the adjacent ninth and the first is shorter than the second. All have a conforming overlap, namely they overlap in the same direction as the primaries. This applies even to the overlap of the ninth on the 10th and the first on the second (fig. 113). In figure 113 the first upper major primary covert is hidden behind the first upper major secondary covert.

In the extended wing, the tips of the upper major primary coverts lie along the same line as do the upper median secondary coverts (fig. 107), but this illusion has no significance in naming the rows. The upper median primary coverts are small and narrow (figs. 107 and 115). The major primary coverts have a conforming overlap, and the median primary coverts have a contrary overlap. This agrees with the types of overlap on the major and median secondary coverts. In pterylosis studies, the upper minor primary coverts of both the first and second rows were distinct from

the upper marginal coverts of the hand (fig. 69); but when the ptilosis is examined, all of the feathers blend together, giving a rounded dorsal surface to the hand, supplemented by the overlapping alular remiges (fig. 107).

The carpal remex on the wrist region is not shown in figure 107 but is illustrated in figure 111. It is a small feather, hidden between the primary and secondary remiges (figs. 68 and 69). It lies close to the follicle of the first primary and is parallel to it. It is crossed by a larger upper major carpal covert (fig. 113), a conspicuous feather that in the extended wing is longer and broader than those adjacent to it (fig. 107). In the male the upper major carpal covert is about as long as the first upper major primary covert; in the female it is shorter. An upper median carpal covert lies directly anterior to the upper major carpal covert. It also is slightly larger than the upper median primary coverts and shorter than the upper median secondary coverts (figs. 107 and 115).

The follicles of the upper major secondary coverts cross the remiges toward the wrist (fig. 68). The shafts are nearly straight, but the movable skin allows the follicles to shift so that the feathers either may be nearly parallel to the remiges (figs. 107 and 115) or may cross them at a considerable angle (fig. 113). These coverts reach more than half the length of the remiges. The overlap is conforming. At the proximal end of the forearm, where the secondaries abruptly begin to shorten, there is a peculiar relationship between remiges and coverts. All are laid one on top of the other to form a column about the width of the largest feather. This is well shown in the Red Junglefowl (*Gallus gallus*), where the iridescent green color of these secondaries and their coverts strongly contrasts with the adjacent brown feathers. Peculiarly, the coverts and remiges do not alternate in this column; instead the three or four longest stacked feathers of the series are remiges, and the next three or four shortest stacked feathers are major coverts.

The follicles of the upper median secondary coverts are much shorter than those of the upper major secondary coverts, but the feathers are only slightly shorter. The overlap is largely contrary (figs. 107 and 115), but the feathers easily shift to a conforming orientation.

The remaining feathers on the upper surface of the wing are the upper marginal coverts of the prepatagium and alula. The largest are adjacent to the upper minor coverts and the smallest are along the leading edge of the wing. The axes of the feathers between the anterior and posterior boundaries of the tract shift about 90° (fig. 107). The first row of minor coverts may well be considered as part of the coverts covering the secondaries, but additional rows beyond the first appear to be part of the upper marginal coverts of the prepatagium, whether judged by the arrangement of the follicles (fig. 68) or by the morphology and arrangcment of the feathers (fig. 107). Moreover, in the Red Junglefowl the upper marginal coverts of the prepatagium adjacent to the wing-bar are a dark reddish brown that is in striking contrast to the iridescent green tips of the median coverts. Among these marginal coverts, color does not prove the existence of upper minor covert rows.

The downs are not visible on the dorsal side of the wing, but a few can be seen on the ventral side. The distribution of downs in rows is discussed after the description of the contour feathers.

Feather coat on the under side of the extended wing.—The feathers on the ventral surface of the wing are smaller than those on the dorsal surface; nonfeathered spaces are larger and more numerous.

The shafts of the 10 under major primary coverts curve proximally across the axes of the remiges (fig. 114). These under coverts cover exactly the same length of remex feathers as is covered by the upper major primary coverts. The under major primary coverts, like the upper ones, have a conforming overlap. The major coverts on the under side have their afterfeathers directed outward rather than toward the skin surface; in other words, these feathers are reversed.

Sometimes a feather or two is present representing the under median primary coverts. One is shown in the pterylosis illustration (fig. 70). In figure 122, reversal of an under median primary covert and an under major carpal covert is demonstrated.

There are 10 under minor primary coverts, as shown in figures 70 and 108. In figure 116 the most distal in the shaded series on the under surface of the hand is a marginal covert, and the 10 proximal ones are under minor primary coverts. The shafts of the under minor primary coverts of the first row are directed distally. The crossing of the remex feather shafts in one direction by the under major primary coverts and in the opposite direction by the under minor coverts gives strength to the under surface of the primaries. The follicles are short and the skin is loose. As a result the shafts of the first row of under minor coverts easily point in various directions. However, when the feathers are pushed into a regular pattern, as shown in figure 116, they have a contrary overlap.

Usually it is possible to find a few feathers that represent the second row of under minor primary coverts. In the

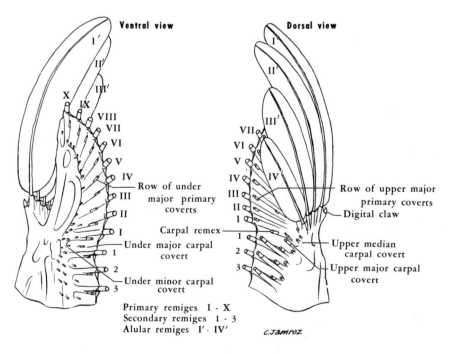

FIGURE 110.—Dorsal and ventral views of the alular remiges showing their relation to the anterior edge of the hand. See figures 69 and 70 for details on pterylosis in relation to adjoining areas of hand, wrist, and forearm.

specimen shown in figure 70, feather 1 was present. In another specimen, feathers 1 through 4 were present. These feathers are more commonly found adjacent to the wrist than elsewhere. When present, the feathers of the second row of under minor primary coverts have a contrary overlap like those of the first row.

The under marginal coverts of the hand are directed obliquely distally, which permits them to cover the under hand apterium (fig. 108). Those adjacent to the apterium are similar in size and morphology to those of the minor coverts; those on and near the leading edge are smaller and are pointed directly toward the tip of the wing.

The alular remiges of the folded wing fit snugly over the basal halves of primary rectrices 8 through 10, and only the edge of the first alular remex is visible from the ventral side of the wing (figs. 108 and 110). This remex is the longest, the second is nearly as long as the first, the third is about two-fifths as long, and the fourth is about one-third as long (figs. 109 and 110).

The short feathers covering the dorsal and ventral bases of the alular remiges, as shown in figure 109, may be regarded as alular coverts; but they have no distinguishing features that differentiate them from the adjacent and overlapping marginal coverts, except on the dorsal side, where they are somewhat longer than the adjacent marginal coverts. Even that feature is lacking on the ventral side.

The feathers of the under surface of the wrist can be identified readily in the extended wing (fig. 108). The under major carpal covert is close to the posterior margin of the joint (fig. 70). It is not as long as the adjacent under major primary and secondary coverts, but like all feathers in the major and median rows the under carpal covert is reversed.

Since there is only one reversed under carpal covert, it might be question whether it is major or median. We have labeled it major. On the ventral side of the wristbones are implanted the under minor carpal coverts, first and second rows. The carpal feather of the first row usually points toward the tip of the wing and is about as long as the feathers of the first row of the under minor primary coverts. The under minor carpal covert, second row, lies directly anterior to the minor carpal covert of the first row but is small like the adjacent under minor coverts on each side of it.

The under forearm is more sparsely feathered than is the hand. The under major secondary coverts are shorter than those of the under major primary coverts (figs. 108 and 114). The follicles and feather shafts of these secondary coverts approximately parallel the axes of the remiges. All have a conforming overlap and are reversed.

The under median secondary coverts in the chicken are feeble contour feathers (see ch. 6, p. 301). They are almost completely hidden by the first row of under minor secondary coverts (fig. 108). Under median secondary coverts 2 through 10 (fig. 71) form only part of a row; in figure 122 the row is slightly longer—1 through 11. In figure 122 is the evidence that they are reversed coverts, the afterfeather being located externally (ventrally). The first row of under minor secondary coverts are short feathers. These point proximally while the feathers of the same row on the hand point distally, the break coming at the carpal region; the gap is filled by the under major and minor carpal coverts. An under median carpal covert appears to be absent.

Figure 71 shows that there is a second row of under minor secondary coverts; in figures 108 and 117 they appear so short that they scarcely cover the bases of feathers forming

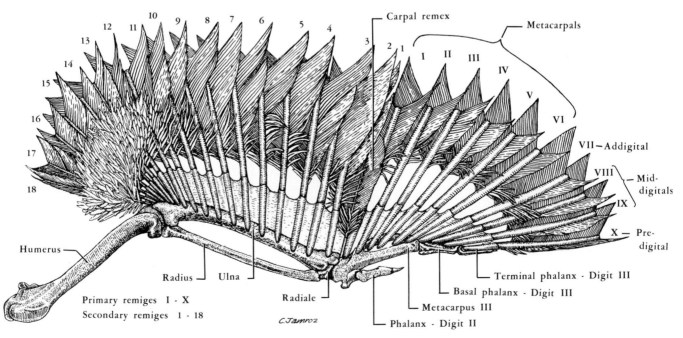

FIGURE 111.—Dorsal view of the remiges of hand, wrist, and forearm showing their relationship to the skeleton of the wing for the Single Comb White Leghorn Chicken.

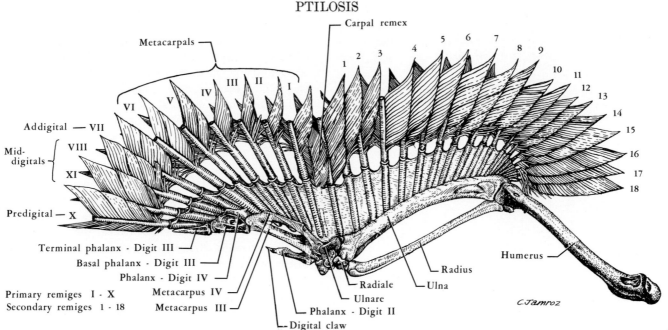

FIGURE 112.—Ventral view of the remiges of hand, wrist, and forearm showing their relationship to the skeleton of the wing for the Single Comb White Leghorn Chicken.

the first row of minor coverts. However, this is true only in the female; in the male the feathers of the second row are as long as those of the first row. In both sexes the feathers are inclined in a proximal direction on the forearm and have a conforming overlap like the first minor row. In both minor rows, the afterfeathers are on the side toward the skin surface.

The several groups of under marginal coverts of the prepatagium are composed of (1) scattered, small contour feathers (fig. 71) that effectively cover the under arm apteria (fig. 108) and (2) short, narrow feathers along the edge, which point distally.

Finally, when all of the plumage has been plucked except the primary and secondary remiges and the muscles and skin covering the bones have been removed, one may then see the relationship of the follicles to the bones of the hand and forearm (figs. 111 and 112). On page 115, names are applied to the primaries according to the bone of the hand with which they are associated, namely, the metacarpal primaries I through VI that overlap metacarpus IV; the addigital primary that lies beneath the phalanx of digit IV; the middigital primaries that touch the basal phalanx of digit III; and the predigital primary that parallels the terminal phalanx of digit III.

The implantation of the remiges in relation to the radiale and ulnare and the bones that articulate with them—the radius, ulna, and carpometacarpals—is important. As delineated in figures 111 and 112, the first primary lies at the extreme proximal end of the carpometacarpus IV, the carpal remex is opposite the ulnare, and the first secondary is near the extreme end of the ulna.

This, however, does not agree with radiographs made of

this area. In the radiographs, the first primary lies at about the point where the second is shown in the drawings, and no feather is implanted on the distal end of the carpometacarpus. This agrees with the relationship shown by Wray (1887a) for a duck. The basal end of the first secondary is aimed directly toward the middle of the posterior surface of the ulnare and is in line with the ulnocarpometacarpal articulation; the carpal remex that one might expect to have this position, is placed well forward on the hand. However, this is understandable because the carpal remex is so closely associated with the follicle of the first primary.

Figures 111 and 112 also bear out the fact that the secondaries are not implanted beyond the anconeal end of the ulna. Wray (1887a) showed that all 19 secondaries in the duck reach the ulnar bone. Also, our numerous examples of partially cleaned, dried wings show all secondaries attached to the ulna. The radiographs, however, make it appear that the proximal four secondaries are directed toward the distal end of the humerus.

Generally, the carpal remex, its upper major and median coverts, and its under major and minor coverts occur with a high degree of constancy. But variations do occur, as illustrated in figure 118. The typical pattern for these feathers is shown in figures 68 through 71 and in figures 118, A and B. The carpal remex is always present; in 118, C, the upper major and median carpal coverts are absent and in D the carpal remex, as in C, lacks upper major and median carpal coverts, but proximally there is a second carpal remex with two upper coverts, indicated in D by an asterisk.

The variation in the carpal remex and its coverts among Single Comb White Leghorns is presented in table 6. The carpal remex and its under major carpal covert and under

TABLE 6.—*Variability in the presence of certain feathers in the carpal region and on digit II of the Single Comb White Leghorn Chicken*

[+, present; −, absent]

Age (post-hatching, in days)	Carpal remex	Upper major carpal covert	Upper median carpal covert	Under major carpal covert	Under minor covert—1st row	No. of upper alular major coverts[1]
35.........	+	−	−	+	+	4
	+	+	+	+	+	4
	+	−	−	+	+	3
	+	−	−	+	+	3
	+	+	+	+	+	3
	+	−	−	+	+	3
	+	+	+	+	+	3
	+	−	−	+	+	4
	+	−	−	+	+	4
	+	−	−	+	+	3
105.........	+	−	−	+	+	4
	+	−	−	+	+	3
	+	−	−	+	+	3
	+	+	+	+	+	3
	+	+	+	+	+	4
	+	+	+	+	+	3
	+	+	+	+	+	3
	+	+	+	+	+	3
	+	+	+	+	+	3
	+	+	+	+	+	4

[1] When only three feathers are present, the first of the series is absent.

minor carpal covert of the first row was found in all of the 20 birds examined. The upper major carpal covert and upper median carpal covert are often absent, and there appears to be no difference between the two ages, 35 and 105 days.

The discussion of contour feathers of the wing is not complete. Down feathers are described next, and then reversed and unreversed feathers and conforming and nonconforming overlap are discussed in relation to the eutaxic and diastataxic wings.

In figures 68 through 71, dots placed among the remiges and coverts locate the downs. In the Great Horned Owl, three rows of downs are present—distal, median, and proximal. In the chicken, there are but two rows; the median row is absent. The number of downs for each row varies for individual birds; therefore, figures 68 to 71 do not show the exact number and placement shown in figures 119 through 123. Figure 122 is included in this series because of the downy character of the under median secondary coverts.

The chicken has two rows of down feathers on the dorsal surface of hand and forearm; one row on the ventral surface of forearm and hand. The upper distal primary down feathers can be seen satisfactorily only by plucking the overlying feathers and leaving the remiges in their normal position (fig. 119). They are downy with a short rachis, and cover only the necks of the follicles; they do not adequately substitute for the absence of a plumulaceous base on the rachis of the primaries. The upper proximal primary down feathers are about the same size as the distal downs and cover the follicle neck of the upper major primary coverts (fig. 120). They have a small rachis and do not resemble the down feathers in the distal row.

The under distal primary down feathers (fig. 121) are implanted close to the trailing border of the wing and lie between each of the remiges and opposite the upper distal primary down feathers. The distal down feathers are not as downy as those of the proximal row and have a main rachis and an after-rachis; their barbs are long and the rachises are not conspicuous. These feathers, together with the ones on the opposite surface, effectively cover the follicle necks of the primaries.

There are two rows of down feathers on the upper surface of the forearm (figs. 119 and 120). The upper distal secondary downs are much larger than those in the same row on the hand (fig. 119). The basal ends of the shaft of the secondaries are much more plumulaceous than the same region of the primaries, and the fluff of the secondary downs merges with the fluff of these remiges. The follicles of these down feathers are implanted on the dorsal surfaces of the secondary remiges close to the follicle necks. The follicles are associated with remiges 1 to about 13, but they are absent from the small secondaries near the elbow. The down feathers have a moderately long but very delicate rachis and a small afterfeather with a rachis that is hardly discernible.

The upper proximal secondary down feathers form a row parallel to the distal downs and are implanted on the carpal side of secondary follicles 1 through 10 (fig. 120) or 1 through 11 (fig. 68). These downs are relatively large; they mingle with plumulaceous portions of the adjacent coverts. There seem to be no rachises on these down feathers except adjacent to the calami. In the absence of a well-defined rachis, the afterfeather is difficult to identify, but it is present.

The under median secondary coverts are downy but actually have the structure of rudimentary semiplumes. As described earlier, they form an incomplete row (figs. 71 and 122). The feathers lie at about a 45° angle to the skin, maintaining a conforming overlap. A small afterfeather is present and, as shown in figure 122, the feather is reversed.

Down feathers vary in relation to the alular remiges. Figures 69 and 70 show a few downs; in figure 123 there are three on the dorsal surface and four may be present. Examined on an anesthetized adult bird, they are entirely hidden by the upper major alular coverts. The down feathers are small and are implanted on the dorsal surface of the alular remex follicles near their necks. The down feather is about as broad as it is long and has a well-developed main rachis and a smaller one in the afterfeather.

General considerations.—The reversal of feathers has important implications in respect to the ancestral wing and how the surface may have been rotated around the caudal edge of the wing. A feather basically has two surfaces: an outer surface away from the body and an inner surface toward the body. All body feathers and most wing feathers

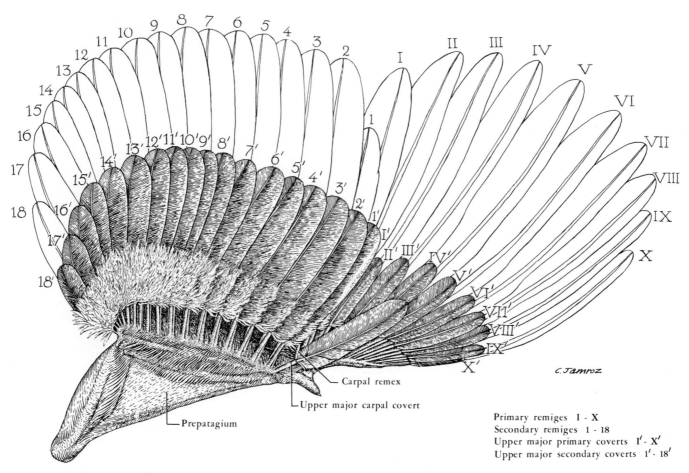

Primary remiges I - X
Secondary remiges 1 - 18
Upper major primary coverts I' - X'
Upper major secondary coverts 1' - 18'

FIGURE 113.—Dorsal view of remiges and upper major coverts of the hand, wrist, and forearm for the Single Comb White Leghorn Chicken. The location of the first upper major primary covert is indicated by I', but the feather is hidden in the drawing.

have this unreversed orientation; however, the major and median coverts on the ventral surface of the wing are seemingly rotated 180° so that the natural "outer" surface is against the wing and the natural "inner" surface is away from the wing. There are several means of determining the natural outer and inner surfaces, and the chicken is particularly favorable for this type of study because—(1) the afterfeather is on the inner side; (2) the inner side of the main rachis usually has a groove; (3) the outer side of the rachis is smooth; and (4) in some birds there may be a difference in color, each color characteristic of an outer or an inner surface.

The last point was described by Bates (1918) and was cited in chapter 2, page 82. Sundevall (Dallas, 1886) noted reversed under major and median coverts in the carinate birds and interpreted it as being due to an elongation of the aftershaft rachis and a corresponding regression of the main shaft rachis; but Bates (1918: 530) noted that Wray (1887a: 353) gave an interpretation that was generally accepted, namely:

... that these feathers or their antetypes were originally on the dorsal surface and have been carried down to the ventral in the formation of the "ala membrana" by the excessive development

of the remiges and tectrices majores. That is, that originally on the dorsal surface of the arm and manus there took place a special modification of the scales or feather foretypes by which rows of these were directed backwards in the "primitive embryonic" position of the limb. Next two or three rows began to be specialized and to become larger and more prominent than the others; then these, by their unequal growth, carried over a fold of skin and formed the wing-membrane, carrying some of the structures to the ventral side, which are now seen as the reversed feathers. . . . In the embryo bird the feather-rudiments first appear on the dorsal surface, pointing to the fact that the modification here is very ancient and deep-seated; the remiges and greater coverts (superior) being the earliest to appear; quickly they begin to assume larger proportions, and at the very earliest stages the remiges are distinguishable. At this stage the wing is quite rounded in section, there being no trace of the "ala membrana;" the next feathers to appear are the t. majores (inferior), closely followed by the other ventral coverts, the other dorsal coverts meanwhile having appeared. At this stage . . . the inferior major and median coverts are distinctly more on the dorsal half of the rounded edge of the wing than its ventral, but very quickly they become quite ventral, owing to the rapid growth of the remiges. This stage is quickly passed over, but sufficient is visible to show that these feathers are carried to the lower surface by inequality of growth. . . .

Wray clearly stated an idea that persists today as the accepted interpretation of reversed under coverts. Identi-

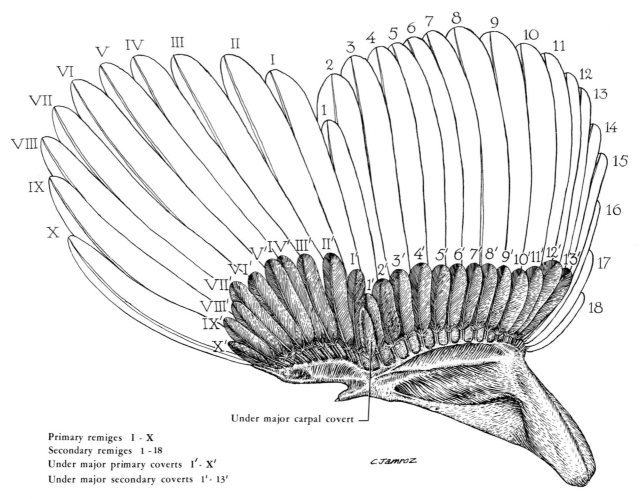

Primary remiges I - X
Secondary remiges 1 - 18
Under major primary coverts I' - X'
Under major secondary coverts 1' - 13'

C. Jamroz

FIGURE 114.—Ventral view of remiges and under major coverts of the hand, wrist, and forearm for the Single Comb White Leghorn Chicken.

fication of reversed under coverts is relatively simple in the chicken and, as summarized, gives a fairly distinct picture of the supposed downward rotation of the caudal edge of the wing. All of the 10 under major primary coverts have reversed feathers, most readily recognized by the distinct ventral grooves in the rachises; the afterfeather is merely a ring of barbs arising from the superior umbilicus. The absence of a well-developed afterfeather suggests a remex, at least in the chicken where nearly every feather has an afterfeather. The alular remiges like the primary and secondary remiges lack distinct afterfeathers. The sharp demarcation between a reversed and an unreversed feather may be noted at the distal end of the row of under major primary coverts. Immediately adjacent to the 10th in the series is an under marginal covert of the hand; its under surface is toward the skin, and it has a distinct afterfeather. All of the under primary marginal coverts have unreversed orientation; the same is true for the under distal primary downs. The alular remiges are unreversed also.

The under major carpal covert has a well-developed afterfeather and rachidial groove, both directed ventrally. All of the feathers anterior to this one have unreversed orientation; therefore, it is questionable to designate one of these above the major as an under median carpal covert.

All of the under major secondary coverts are reversed. An afterfeather is absent, but the groove of the rachis is directed away from the skin. The row ends at about the 14th feather. Beyond that, the coverts adjacent to remiges 15 through 18 are unreversed and are the feathers of the cubital end of an under minor row. The feathers representing the under median secondary coverts have well-developed afterfeathers oriented ventrally. The remaining feathers on the forearm— two rows of under minor secondary coverts and under marginal coverts—are unreversed. The same is true for the subhumerals and for the posthumerals.

We do not want to give the impression that all of the coverts in any one row must have either conforming or contrary overlap. Bates (1918) demonstrated in text and figures that they may be mixed. Sometimes the under major coverts may have conforming overlap except for a few at the proximal end of the hand.

In a great number of the birds examined by Bates, reversal of the under median secondary coverts was similar to that in the chicken, and the under median primary coverts were absent. If under median primary coverts were present, they were limited to a few coverts adjacent to the wrist. In the chicken, there were one or two such feathers. This reduction in the number of rows or complete absence of the row was considered by Bates as due to the crowding of feathers on the hand, derived from the small size of the hand and the large size of the primaries.

Turkey

The feather coat of the Bronze Turkey is described as briefly as possible. We have not provided illustrations other than those for the pterylosis (figs. 73 through 79), but the feather groups shown for the chicken should provide an adequate visual image for discussion and reference. Different parts of the feather coat of the turkey may have the same terminology as that used for the chicken, but certain terms were omitted for the turkey both in the "American Standard of Perfection" (1938–40) and in "Turkey Management" (Marsden and Martin, 1949). Examples of these are: hackle, cape, saddle, cushion, and sickles. Two of these, cape and saddle, are used by Jull (1930).

Dorsal cervical and interscapular tracts.—The dorsal cervical tract in a young poult begins at the base of the head. As the individual grows older, the contour feathers are replaced by bristle feathers, the skin becomes red, and the

so-called naked skin of the head and neck develops. The tract is still present, but less evident. The feathers beginning at the carunculate skin of the neck are small but they increase in size toward the base of the neck up to the junction with the dorsal tract.

Most of the feathers of the dorsal neck are similar to one another in pattern, namely, they have truncate tips and copper brown iridescent banding near their ends. A few at the caudal end are narrower and more rounded on the tips, and have a speckled pattern of brown dots or U-shaped bands alternating with black, but these feathers are covered by adjacent longer feathers. The broad lateral cervical apterium is covered by the laterally directed feathers placed near the margin of the dorsal cervical tract and also by the dorsally directed feathers from the upper margin of the ventral cervical tract. The markings and color pattern for feathers implanted on both of these tracts are similar; therefore, the feather coat of neck and breast blend together. There tends to be a slight linear depression over the lateral cervical apterium between the feathers from the dorsal and ventral cervical tracts.

Dorsopelvic tract.—The beginning of the dorsal tract is most easily located by pushing the feathers aside. This locates the level at which the tract on the base of the neck broadens laterally to become the dorsal tract. The feathers

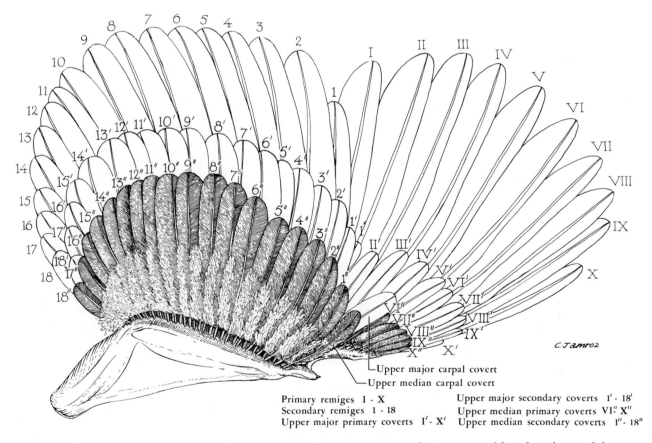

Primary remiges I - X
Secondary remiges 1 - 18
Upper major primary coverts I' - X'

Upper major secondary coverts 1' - 18'
Upper median primary coverts VI" X"
Upper median secondary coverts 1" - 18"

FIGURE 115.—Dorsal view of the remiges and the upper major and upper median coverts of hand, wrist, and forearm for the Single Comb White Leghorn Chicken.

down the middle of the dorsal and pelvic tracts have truncate ends bordered with white. Subterminal to this border is a transverse black band, and proximal to it is a dark, iridescent band, 4 to 10 mm. wide.

The lateral borders of the dorsal pelvic tract are covered by the scapulars of the humeral tract and by the wing. These hidden feathers have practically none of the color markings of those more medially placed. The ends of the covered feathers are slightly more rounded and are bordered by a very narrow margin of white but without black or iridescent bands. These feathers are a flat, dark gray. These feathers are directed laterally and caudally at about a 45° angle and cover the dorsal part of the lateral body apterium.

Caudal tracts.—The feathers of the pelvic region continue to the dorsal surface of the tail. They are long and have white, black and iridescent bands that are wider than those on the anterior part of the pelvic region. Toward the base of the feather are alternating dark-brown and dark-gray transverse bands. These become more conspicuous in the feathers of the dorsal caudal tract, and the iridescent part may be 15 mm. wide. The iridescence is associated with the

ascending barbules of the feather and can occur only when a flat vane is present; the details of the physical basis for this type of color are discussed in chapter 7. When the light strikes the feather from a certain angle, the iridescent band may appear a metallic blue or green.

On the anterior surface of the oil gland, between the large feathers of the upper caudal tract and the uropygial papilla, are several transverse rows of dark-gray down feathers. Some of these show organization into flat vanes like contour feathers.

Distal to the oil gland and parallel to the rectrices is a single row of upper major tail coverts that cover two-thirds the length of the rectrices. In these, the black band is wider than it is in feathers placed more anteriorly. This expansion seems to be at the expense of the iridescent band distal to it. On these upper major coverts, narrow brown transverse bands are more abundant than in those placed more anteriorly, and in the alternating dark bands there is some iridescence.

The bands in the upper major tail coverts expand on the rectrices; each band is now conspicuously wider, and the

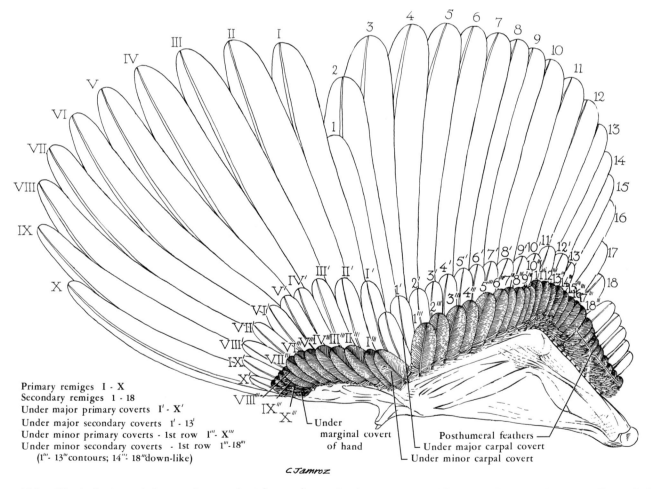

Primary remiges I - X
Secondary remiges 1 - 18
Under major primary coverts I' - X'
Under major secondary coverts 1' - 13'
Under minor primary coverts - 1st row I''' - X'''
Under minor secondary coverts - 1st row 1''' - 18'''
    (1''' - 13''' contours; 14''' - 18''' down-like)

Under marginal covert of hand

Posthumeral feathers
Under major carpal covert
Under minor carpal covert

C. Jamroz

FIGURE 116.—Ventral view of the remiges and under major and minor coverts of hand, wrist, and forearm. Two of the three posthumeral rows are shown. The under median coverts are not shown because on the hand most of them are absent and in the forearm they are hidden by the first row of under minor coverts. Single Comb White Leghorn Chicken.

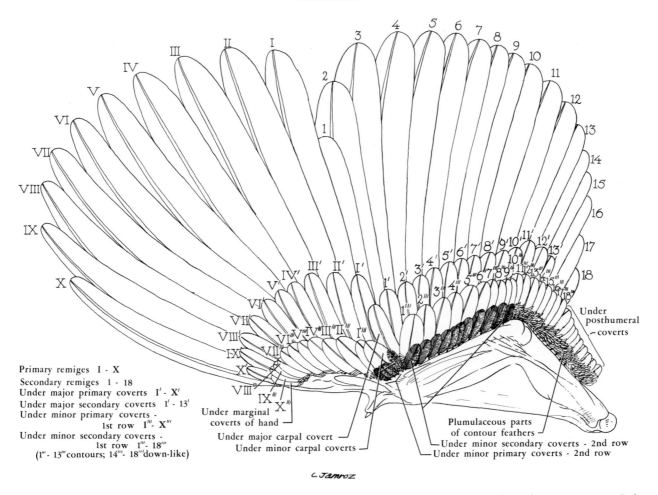

Primary remiges I - X
Secondary remiges 1 - 18
Under major primary coverts I' - X'
Under major secondary coverts 1' - 13'
Under minor primary coverts -
                      1st row I'' - X''
Under minor secondary coverts -
                      1st row 1'' - 18''
      (1''' - 13''' contours; 14''' - 18''' down-like)

Under marginal
coverts of hand

Under major carpal covert
Under minor carpal coverts

Under
posthumeral
coverts

Plumulaceous parts
of contour feathers
Under minor secondary coverts - 2nd row
Under minor primary coverts - 2nd row

L. Jamroz

FIGURE 117.—Ventral view of the remiges, under major coverts, first and second rows of under minor coverts and the ventral
row of posthumerals for the female Single Comb White Leghorn Chicken.

mottled brown on dark gray extends to the plumulaceous part of the feather. When the tail is displayed, the rectrices are elevated vertically and spread in a fan-shape nearly 180°. The upper major tail coverts are carried upward and lie closely against the rectrices. The feathers of the dorsal caudal tract and the caudal end of the pelvic tract are erected also.

A row of upper proximal down feathers of the tail lies dorsal to the bases of the upper coverts close to the necks of the follicles. These downs are short in the center of the row and have relatively few barbs, whereas at the ends of the row they are several times longer and much fluffier. A row of very small upper distal down feathers of the tail is present on the dorsal surfaces of the necks of the rectrix follicles. Ventral to these follicles is a row of under distal down feathers of the tail that vary widely in size.

The under surface of the tail bears approximately nine transverse rows of follicles. The feathers of the most distal row are the largest and are the under major tail coverts. They have a band of white across the truncated tip and proximal to that a slight iridescence. The under surface of the central pair faces the under surface of the median rec-

trices, but all others of this row are set at about a 90° angle facing toward the median plane.

The feathers of the next row, the under median tail coverts, are shorter and have a larger plumulaceous portion, but they carry the white band at the tip. The next two rows can be considered as under minor tail coverts and are almost semiplumes; the vanes are pennaceous only at the tip and carry only a trace of white. These feathers are relatively short, and those in the remaining rows are shorter still. The last two rows form the dorsal half of the cloacal circlet. These feathers are less than a centimeter long and, strictly speaking, belong to the abdominal tract.

Ventral cervical and pectoral tract.—The ventral cervical tract begins at the caudal end of the carunculate skin of the neck and continues to the shoulder, where it continues as the pectoral tract (fig. 75). The plumage pattern on both tracts is the same. The feathers on the upper ventral neck are short and have light-brown borders. Caudally, the feathers increase in length; the brown border changes to white; the black bands adjacent to the white and the iridescent area are wider and more definite than in the anterior part of the neck. The feathers along the lower margin of the lateral cervical apterium cover the lower half of this space. Near the midline, the feathers easily cover the narrow ventral cervical apterium, but at the beard they spread apart. At the base of the neck, and over the thoracic inlet, the apterium is wide; within the space numerous large downs and semiplumes are present. Normally, these are all well covered by medially directed contour feathers from the margins of the right and left ventral cervical tracts.

The feathers from the end of the pectoral tract extend so far caudally that they cover at least half of the thigh. Along the dorsal margin, the shafts of the feathers are directed upward and abut the lower edge of the folded wing. On the inferior margin, the feathers of the pectoral tract are directed medially and cover most of the feather coat of the sternal tract; in so doing, they cover completely the pectoral apterium.

Sternal and abdominal tracts.—The feathers of the sternal tract are plumulaceous contours. Small feathers that lie adjacent to the broad sternal apterium are covered by somewhat larger ones, some of which have a narrow margin of white on the tips. These are directed medially and caudally at about a 45° angle and effectively cover the sternal apterium, especially in its posterior part. If in the anterior part of the keel the skin has thickened and a breast blister has developed from the sternal bursa, then the bare skin of this part of the sternal apterium and the feathers lateral to it cannot cover the bare area.

At the caudal end of the sternal tract, the feathers are transitional to the semiplumes forming the fluff in the median abdominal tract. At the feather tip is a semblance of a pennaceous vane, but the barbs are so far apart that the space cannot be spanned by barbules. Furthermore, the barbules have the characteristics of down barbules and do not bear hooks and flanges typical of the flat vanes of contour feathers. Somewhat lower on the shaft the barbs are closer together, but the barbules are still of the down type. The barbs that form the rounded ends of the fluff feathers are crossed by bands of white, but the barbs are so widely spaced that the effect of the white is largely lost.

On each side of the abdominal tract is the lateral abdominal apterium. The groin groove between the inner surface of the thigh and the side of the abdomen is deep and narrow, and the two skin surfaces are so close together that the plumage is reduced to a few short downs, and much of the skin is bare.

Toward the cloaca, the abdominal tract feathers become shorter, and the row on the anterior lip of the vent is the shortest of all; but these feathers are considerably longer than those on the posterior lip referred to in our description of the feather coat of the tail.

Lateral body tract.—The lateral body apterium is large but not as bare as in some smaller birds; short downy contour feathers are present in the bare area at the anterior end of the shoulder. These have relatively large afterfeathers. Long semiplumes form several vertical rows in front of the thigh. These lie on the lateral body apterium, near its caudal

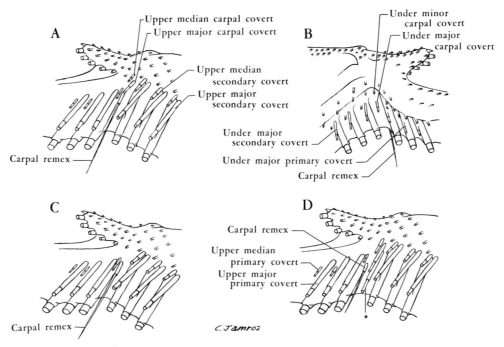

FIGURE 118.—Typical condition and variations observed in the carpal region for the Single Comb White Leghorn Chicken.

A, dorsal view of a typical arrangement of carpal remex and upper major and upper median carpal coverts.
B, ventral view of a typical arrangement of under carpal feathers.
C, dorsal view of a specimen in which the upper major and upper median carpal coverts were absent.

D, dorsal view of a specimen in which the upper major and upper median carpal coverts were absent for the feather labeled "carpal remex," but which has a second carpal remex, indicated by the asterisk. The latter feather had both upper major and upper median carpal coverts.

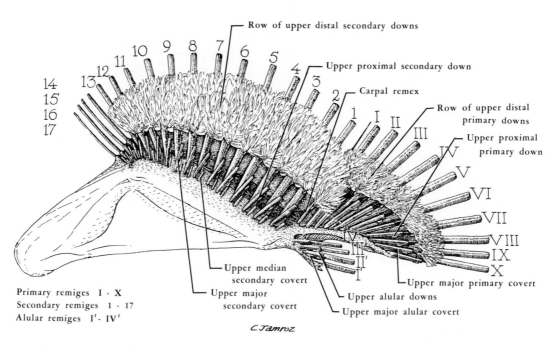

FIGURE 119.—Dorsal view of distal down feathers on the hand and forearm of the Single Comb White Leghorn Chicken.

margin. Across the middle of the apterium extends a band of moderately large contour feathers and semiplumes that have continuity with the small contours transitional to downs that cover the shoulder. These lateral body tract feathers are separated from the semiplumes by a large bare space just anterior to the thigh.

Femoral and crural tracts.—The femoral tract depicted by the boundaries in figure 74 is relatively small, and the pelvic

apterium above it is correspondingly large. These observations are supported by the study of feather musculature (fig. 268). We suggest that large apteria occur around the femoral tract because much of the thigh is covered by feathers from other tracts; those apteria dorsally are separated by feathers from the dorsopelvic tract; those ventrally, by the pectorals; and all of the lateral pelvic apterium by the wing. The feathers in the lateral pelvic apterium are

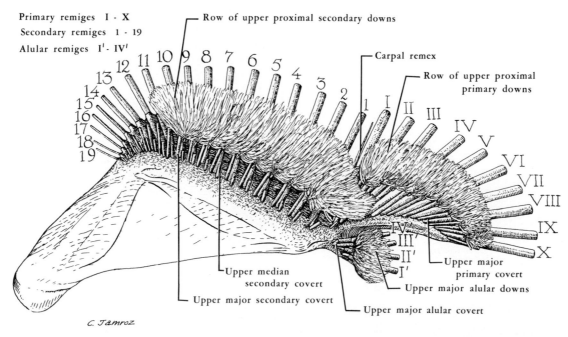

FIGURE 120.—Dorsal view of proximal down feathers on the hand and forearm and of upper alular down feathers of the Single Comb White Leghorn Chicken. See figure 123 for more details on the upper alular downs.

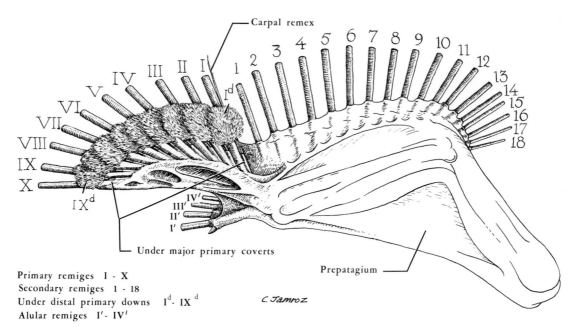

Primary remiges I - X
Secondary remiges 1 - 18
Under distal primary downs I^d - IX^d
Alular remiges I' - IV'

C. Jamroz

FIGURE 121.—Ventral view of the under distal primary down feathers of the Single Comb White Leghorn Chicken.

long, large semiplumes without distinctive markings or color.

Within the femoral tract are implanted contour feathers with white edges, black bands, and iridescence. The tips of these feathers diverge and encompass a sector equal to about an eighth of a circle; those on the dorsal margin and from the infracaudal margin are directed backward. As in the chicken, feathers from the infracaudal margin cover the entire abdominal fluff and hide it from lateral view. Ventral to this the contour feathers on the lower portion of the

femoral tract cover the outside surface of the knee and the outer surface of the upper half of the crus.

A large crural apterium separates the femoral and crural tracts along the caudal margin of the thigh and is continuous with the lateral pelvic apterium. It also is continuous with the bare area on the medial surface of the shank, the intra-crural apterium. The feathers within this apterium vary from small to large semiplumes, and some are like down feathers. They point directly toward the hock joint as do the contours

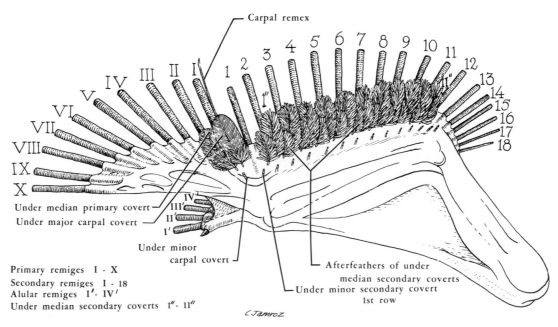

Under median primary covert
Under major carpal covert
Under minor carpal covert

Afterfeathers of under
median secondary coverts
Under minor secondary covert
1st row

Primary remiges I - X
Secondary remiges I - 18
Alular remiges I' - IV'
Under median secondary coverts I" - 11"

C. Jamroz

FIGURE 122.—Ventral view of some under coverts of hand, wrist, and forearm of the Single Comb White Leghorn Chicken. Most of these are plumulaceous, and all are the reversed type like the under major primary and secondary coverts.

on the outside and anterior surfaces of the crus. Approaching the hock they become progressively shorter. These feathers have a margin of white but otherwise are a dull gray.

Brachial tracts.—The interscapular feathers of the turkey, like those of the chicken, cover the scapular apterium, and the humerals spread out to cover the humeral apterium and the adjacent upper marginal coverts of the prepatagium. Therefore, the humerals between the wing-front and the scapulars spread out over about one-quarter of a circle. The colors of the humerals are like those of the back and cape. These contrast with the feathers of the posthumeral tract that are covered by the scapular part of the humerals.

The posthumerals are contour feathers with rounded tips and with vanes crossed by mottled bands of brown. The hue contrast is helpful in determining that there are approximately nine feathers in a posthumeral row. As in the chicken, the row with the longest feathers lies in the middle of the three dorsal rows. In the turkey, no apterium separates these from the adjacent upper marginal coverts of the prepatagium.

The relationship of feathers in the closed wing is the same as in the chicken. One may apply the same terms—"wing-bow" to the marginals, "wing-bar" to the first two rows of upper secondary coverts, and "wing-bay" to the distal ends of the secondary remiges.

The primary, alular, and secondary remiges are crossed by white bands on a black background. Much of the white is lost before the 12th secondary is reached. This secondary and the 13th show iridescence; but from the 14th secondary to the end of the row the feathers are mottled brown on black, which is characteristic of feathers hidden by those lying on top of them.

The arrangement of the upper primary and secondary coverts (figs. 76 and 77) in the turkey is sufficiently similar to that of the chicken (figs. 68 and 69) so that detailed description need not be repeated. As mentioned on page 124, there is a 10th upper major primary covert of the hand as well as an adjacent upper marginal covert, so that by counting backwards it is possible to identify with certainty the first upper major primary covert. Confirmation that the identification is correct comes from the hue patterns of the feathers; the alternating black and white banding of the upper major primary coverts carries through to the 10th, even when the distal upper major coverts are covered by the first alular remex, whereas all of the upper marginal coverts have the flat gray associated with hidden feathers.

The dark brownish gray in the upper median primary coverts merges with a similar color in the upper marginal coverts of the hand. Both the median and marginal coverts have a conforming overlap.

In the chicken the carpal remex resembles an upper major primary covert in size and appearance, but in the turkey the carpal remex is a small contour feather. In the chicken, the upper major carpal covert is conspicuous by its large size (figs. 107 and 113), but in the turkey it is a short, downy semiplume. The carpal remex has a few white spots but the covert is a dull gray.

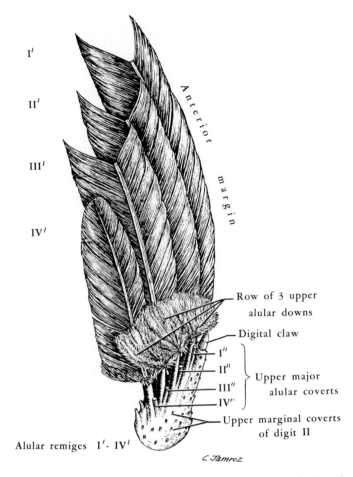

FIGURE 123.—Dorsal surface of digit II from a Single Comb White Leghorn Chicken. A down feather is implanted on the follicle wall of three of the four alular remiges.

Most of the upper major secondary coverts have a conforming overlap, but in a molting hen the fourth is contrary. All of the upper median secondary coverts have contrary overlap except those at the cubital end, where they are stacked. The adjacent lower minor coverts and marginal coverts have a mixed overlap and many of the feathers are too spread apart to have any overlap. The marginal coverts near the edge of the prepatagium generally have a conforming overlap.

Differences in feather color make the study of the under surface of the wing particularly interesting. As in the chicken, the under major primary coverts of the turkey have conforming overlap and the feathers are reversed. Reversal is clearly evident; the upper surface adjacent to the remiges is dark gray and the rachis on this side is a dark brown. On the ventral or exposed surface, the feathers are light gray and the rachis is white. On this surface there is an exceedingly small afterfeather.

When we studied the plumage, the feather labeled first under median primary covert in figure 78 was found to have an unreversed orientation. On the basis that under major and median coverts are always reversed, we assumed that this feather must be a misplaced minor covert, but when we studied the downy under median secondary coverts, we found that they also had an unreversed orientation. This same row in the chicken had reversed orientation. It seems that about the only satisfactory interpretation to be made from these facts is that in the turkey only one row of feathers, originally located on the dorsal side, has been carried to the ventral surface. It seems that Bates, Steiner, and others who have studied this problem on so many species of wild birds might have added valuable material and information if they had also included the domestic chicken and turkey.

The two rows of under minor secondary coverts are sufficiently similar to those of the chicken so that they need not be discussed. The under forearm tract is composed of two or three rows of feathers directed at about a 45° angle toward the posterior edge of the wing and toward the elbow.

Scattered large down feathers may be found in the under prepatagial apterium. Here the afterfeather is as long as the main feather. This feature is often mentioned in the literature as a characteristic of feathers in the Emu (*Dromiceius novaehollandiae*). In this bird the main feather and afterfeather are long, narrow, and tapered to a point; whereas in the down of the turkey, the main feather and afterfeather are broad and rounded. The relative length of the afterfeather to that of the main feather can vary in the same individual (i.e., turkey) from lengths that are equal to a total absence of the afterfeather. Only in some feathers in some birds is it a characteristic of small semiplumes and downs to have long afterfeathers. Those feathers on the under surface of the shoulder of the turkey have afterfeathers as long as the main feather but not as wide. The subject of variable ratios in length between the main and afterfeathers is discussed more fully in chapters 5 and 6.

Common Coturnix

The Common Coturnix is the third galliform whose ptilosis we have studied. The basic principles for the three species are the same; therefore, no attempt is made to cover this subject in detail; instead, only the most significant differences are mentioned.

Dorsal and ventral neck.—The follicles of the dorsal cervical tract are scattered irregularly, but it appears that all the rows are directed laterocaudally from the midline as in the turkey. Therefore, any separation between the dorsal cervical and interscapular tracts is arbitrary. On the side of the neck, the feathers above and below the border of the lateral cervical apterium are directed toward each other across this space. The apterium when fully exposed is relatively broad. Normally, in the living animal the apparent width of the unfeathered area on the side of the neck is merely a narrow band. This is due to the fact that the dorsal portion is folded under the dorsal cervical tract as in the Great Horned Owl. The ventral portion forms a deep groove on the dorsal surface of the cervical patagium, which brings the dorsal and ventral cervical tracts close together. Therefore, the space spanned by these feathers is small. The light

brown plumage of the ventral neck blends with the dark brown plumage of the dorsal neck. The transition is gradual on the side of the neck.

Dorsal and pelvic tracts.—The feathers of the interscapular tract overlap those from the anterior end of the dorsal tract. There is a distinction in the colors of the feathers from these two tracts. The brown in the interscapulars is slightly lighter than that in the feathers of the dorsal tract. The narrow apterium along the middle of the back (dorsal and median pelvic apteria) bear small gray semiplumes, covered by striped feathers directed across the apteria from each side.

From each lateral margin of the pelvic tract, the feathers spread outward and cover a lateral pelvic apterium and the upper part of the femoral tract. The apterium is actually covered by gray contour feathers rather than by the striped feathers externally visible. The striped contour feathers at the caudal end of the pelvic tract are long; they cover all the feathers of the upper caudal tract, the oil gland, the upper major tail coverts, and the basal parts of the rectrices.

Ventral surface of the body.—The tan ventral neck feathers become an even lighter tan in the pectoral feathers. Those at the anterior end of the pectoral tract are short; caudally they are long and are directed upward on the outer margin, where they partially cover the lateral body apterium and the femoral tract. These feathers are as long as the tract itself and cover the lower half of the thigh; the remiges of the wing cover the upper half.

The feathers along the medial margin of a pectoral tract overlie the adjacent pectoral apterium but do not extensively cover the very short feathers of the sternal tract. An exceedingly narrow sternal apterium is present and is fully covered, although the feathers along its border are not directed medially. There is a gradual transition toward longer feathers at the caudal end of the sternal tract that continues on to the abdominal tract. As in the fluff in the turkey, the terminal barbs stand apart, giving a coarse effect to the surface of the fluff.

The groin groove is relatively deep, and the inner surface of the thigh contacts the lateral surface of the abdomen, so that the feathers in the groin are small and plumulaceous. Only as one approaches the lateral margin of the medial abdominal tract do the feathers become densely distributed and slightly larger. Some of these are small contour feathers, but it is probably more realistic to regard all of the area lateral to the strong abdominal tract as lateral abdominal apterium, as labeled in figure 82.

Posterior appendage tracts.—The femoral tract on the quail is relatively large compared to that on the turkey, and the lateral pelvic apterium is correspondingly narrow, yet the same placement of short to long feathers is present in both kinds of birds, irrespective of size. The feathers in the anterior part of the femoral tract are short and are covered by the feathers of the pelvic and pectoral tracts, whereas the uncovered feathers more caudally located are longer, especially those from the infracaudal margin of the femoral tract. Contour feathers from the lower part of the tract cover the knee, the crural apterium, and part of the anterior surface of the shank, as in the chicken and turkey. The feather coat of the shank is similar to that of the chicken and turkey. The rather large intracrural apterium is only partially covered by adjacent contour feathers.

Anterior appendage tracts.—The humeral tract is basically like that of the chicken and turkey; the anterior feathers are short, and the longest feathers project beyond the metapatagium to fill the space between body and secondaries, when the wing is extended. Located beneath the scapular part of the humerals are the posthumerals that contribute to filling the gap between the body and wing. These posthumerals, overlaid by the humerals, are a light grayish brown without pattern. Their appearance easily distinguishes them from the dark-brown banded feathers of the humeral tract. There are three rows of posthumerals—two on the dorsal surface and one at the edge, slightly on the ventral surface. The posthumeral quills arise from the middle of the three rows. These feathers are slightly longer than those of the first row. The under coverts are a row of gray and white downs.

The subhumeral tract is composed of double or triple rows of white feathers, those of the posterior row being much the longer. The feathers of the middle row are about half as long; those of the anterior row are short, but are still typical contour feathers. As in the turkey, the whole group serves as under coverts to the feathers of the posthumerals and humerals that project beyond the edge of the upper arm.

The exposed (distal) vane on primaries and secondaries carries the banded pattern typical of feathers on the coturnix wing. The proximal vane, lying below, shows faint traces of the pattern, but this is not pronounced. The upper major primary coverts are partially covered by the alular remiges, especially by the first and second; these remiges have a mixed pattern of bars and streaks. To the extent that they overlap the upper major primary coverts, they reduce the area of flat grayish-brown characteristic of the coverts. The upper major primary coverts have a conforming overlap. The afterfeather is reduced to a few barbs that arise from the rim of the superior umbilicus.

The upper median primary coverts are small rounded contour feathers that fail to overlap the major coverts and hardly cover the basal ends of the follicles of remiges and major coverts. As shown in figure 84, they do not form a complete row; seven or eight appears to be a typical number. All have a conforming overlap. They have afterfeathers about as rudimentary as were found on the upper major primary coverts.

The carpal remex and its covert are very small. In the chicken and turkey, the remex and its covert lay close to the follicles of the first primary, but in coturnix the carpal remex lies near the middle of the carpal postpatagium. The remex is a light gray contour feather, about 1 cm. long. Its upper major carpal covert is slightly larger than the remex. It lies at the proximal end of the upper median primary covert row.

Conspicuous on the dorsal surface of the wing is the first secondary (axial feather) and its upper major covert. In the flexed wing, the first secondary extends distally above the first primary or the first and second primaries. Its tip lies about midway between the unattached ends of the remiges and of their major coverts. Its upper major covert of the first secondary swings distally beyond the first secondary and along with the alular quills covers some of the upper major primary coverts. All the feathers of this row of secondaries have conforming overlap. This can be readily confirmed even when feathers are displaced because, like the remiges, they carry a strongly patterned distal vane and a less colorful proximal vane. The afterfeather is nearly half the length of the main feather.

The upper median secondary coverts have a contrary overlap, although the 10th feather in the row may maintain a conforming overlap. These have well-developed afterfeathers that are more than half the length of the main feathers. The upper minor secondary coverts and the row above it have an irregular overlap, but the small upper marginal coverts of the prepatagium maintain a conforming overlap. The afterfeather is smaller in the small marginals than it is in the large ones.

The under major primary coverts have reversed orientation, but the under minor primary coverts have unreversed orientation. The former have conforming overlap, the latter, contrary overlap. The exposed (ventral) surface of the under major primary coverts matches the brownish gray of the exposed portions of the vanes of the under surface of the remiges. In contrast to this, the under minor primary coverts that form the next row anterior are a light tan. There are no more than one or two under median primary coverts, as shown in figures 85 and 86.

Based on our study of the dorsal and ventral surfaces of the rachis, the under major carpal covert seems to be unreversed. The under major secondary coverts are reversed and have conforming overlap. The relatively few under median secondary coverts are semiplumes or even downs at the cubital end of the row and semiplumes or small contour feathers at the carpal end. They have reversed orientation but no afterfeather, and the several feathers near the carpus show a contrary overlap. The first row of under minor secondary coverts has a contrary overlap; the second row of the very small feathers apparently has the same; but in many places the feathers are too small to touch or to overlap one another. The under marginal coverts of the prepatagium have a contrary overlap, no doubt because they tend to be oriented in a distal direction.

White Pekin Duck

The domestic duck exhibits many differences from the chicken, turkey, and Common Coturnix. It was noted in the study of pterylosis (figs. 88 through 90) that the duck was more extensively covered with contour feathers than were any of the galliform birds studied; that apteria were absent or small except for the lateral body apterium; and that the down feathers were so abundant that if all of the contour feathers were removed, the skin would still be fully covered except in a few places, chiefly the upper neck and head. The all-white feather coat of this variety of duck limits the description of plumage to such items as the character of the feathers, the direction of their shafts, the feathers that they cover, the feathers that cover them, and the transition among contours, semiplumes, and downs. Many plumage areas for the domestic goose and duck have been named in labeled diagrams (Jull, 1930). The feathers of the duck have afterfeathers that are limited to a tuft of umbilical barbs. The absence of an afterfeather with aftershaft is a distinct handicap in the study of the ptilosis of the anserines. This feature was much used in the ptilosis study of galliforms.

Dorsal and ventral neck.—It was pointed out in the study of the pterylosis of the head of the duck (fig. 58) that very few down feathers are present on the head; nearly all are small contours. This also holds true for the upper neck. The contour feathers are relatively short and are closely packed. The basal halves are narrow and are not plumulaceous; the distal halves are broader, and the barbs here become spread increasingly far apart along the rachises. This type of feather continues to the level of the cervical patagium, where it increases in length and breadth and takes on the characteristics of a typical contour feather. The barbs at the basal end are long, and those forming the vanes are closely packed and are not spread apart. In the interscapular tract, the plumulaceous barbs at the base become very long and the vanes wider.

On the lower side of the head the interramal region has closely packed miniature contour feathers, with a minimum of plumulaceous bases. The feathers of the submalar tract are longer than those of the interramal tract, the basal halves of the feathers are relatively narrow, and the barbs of the distal half are close together. This type of feather continues a short distance down the neck; toward the lower end, the feathers undergo a transition to the contour type and have long plumulaceous barbs on the basal end of the rachis. In the area of the thoracic inlet, the feathers as a whole become much larger than those placed more anteriorly on the neck.

The feathers on the side of the neck near the head are structurally intermediate between those on the dorsal and ventral surfaces of the neck. They retain the narrow bases characteristic of both dorsal and ventral cervical tracts. On the distal halves of these feathers, the barbs are farther apart than are those of feathers on the ventral side of the neck, but not as far apart as are the barbs on the feathers of the dorsal side of the neck. Spreading of the distal barbs becomes greater about half way down the side of the neck. At the lower end of the neck the feathers are large. The barbs are long and plumulaceous on the basal halves, but those on the distal ends of the rachises are placed close together.

The directions of the shafts follow about the same pattern found in birds that have a distinct lateral cervical apterium.

Shafts on the lateral margin of the dorsal cervical tract point downward and backward, and those on the ventral cervical tract point upward and backward. The feathers from the two tracts meet at about the dashed line shown on the side of the neck in figure 89. Here the feathers project directly outward and produce a ridge of feathers, which can be easily eliminated by stroking the feathers. The ridge of feathers continues forward on to the side of the head, above the ear opening, and below the lid opening. Down the side of the neck, this ridge disappears, and the feather shafts generally parallel the axis of the neck, although on the lower end of the ventral neck they are directed somewhat laterally away from the midline.

In the midline, namely, in the area of the ventral cervical apterium, the plumage may curve inward, producing a median groove. The apterium is closely packed with downs, and these are overlaid by contours from the tracts adjacent to the apterium. The longer feathers at the base of the neck are strongly arched, even as much as 135°. On the other hand, the small feathers on the anterior neck are only slightly curved.

Dorsopelvic tract.—The feathers of the back uniformly overlap those caudal to them. They form one continuous cloak, and a grouping of feathers into specific, named areas is absent. Even the lengths of the feathers are about the same throughout the back. The curvature of the shaft toward the skin varies from about 45° to 90°. The feathers point directly caudally, but those near the lateral margins of the tracts tend to curve medially. This direction is opposite that found in the galliforms.

Pectorosternal and abdominal tracts.—An especially dense coat of contour and down feathers is present on the ventral surface of the body. The feathers are so closely spaced that the contour feathers cannot decline against the skin. Instead, they are implanted perpendicular to the skin. When each feather reaches the surface of the plumage layer, it curves backward, flat against the surface, so that the shafts of most of the feathers bend 90° or more. The longest contour feathers arise from the lateral margin of the pectoral tract. They abut the inferior edge of the closed wing, and in their caudal projection they cover the knee and much of the shank plumage. These feathers have some barbs emerging from the edge of the superior umbilicus, but an afterfeather with aftershaft is not present.

The plumage on the ventral surface of the body between the legs is even denser than that on the anterior end of the pectorosternal tract. The feathers in the latter area show a narrowing of the basal half of the feather; the barbs remain long but are directed toward the tip and are folded toward the shaft. The plumage layer of the abdominal region is still denser than that on the more anterior ventral parts of the trunk, the contour feathers are shorter, and the shafts are more delicate. As before, they are implanted perpendicular to the skin and turn caudally at the surface of the plumage feathering pad, but only for a short distance. The curvature of the shaft is about 45° in the anterior part of the abdomen and about 90° in the more caudal part beyond the level of the thighs. The barbs from the basal half of a contour feather are long but curve upward over the shaft, thereby reducing the apparent width of this part of the feather.

The free ends of the feathers have barbs that appear to be bare when viewed with the unaided eye; but under a hand lens tiny barbules can be seen, except at the tip where the barbs are entirely bare. This modification of the feather seems to be present on nearly all the contour feathers of the male. This modification is more prevalent and conspicuous in chicken feathers than in duck feathers. In the female duck, barbules are present, although somewhat less well developed than in the male. The difference between feathers of male and female ducks is not as great as observed in hackle feathers of male and female chickens.

The cloacal circlet is absent in the duck; the cloacal opening is surrounded by down feathers, especially anterior to the opening. Immediately posterior to the dorsal lip of the vent, contour feathers are again present.

Caudal tracts.—The tail is relatively longer in the duck than in the chicken or turkey. Therefore, the dorsal and ventral surfaces are larger. The conical shape of the posterior end of the body of the duck masks the beginning of the tail, but it can be readily palpated. The anatomical boundary is indicated on the pterylosis drawings (figs. 88 through 90). The plumage at the base of the tail is about 10 cm. across in an adult duck. The stiff contour feathers of the anterior end of the dorsal caudal tract overlap the surface of the tail as far posteriorly as the coverts; when the tail feathers are elevated, the oil gland and its duct are exposed. These organs (gland eminence and duct) are covered and surrounded by contour feathers 3.5 to 7.5 cm. long. Their shafts are much narrower than those in a contour feather of the same length from the pelvic tract. On the tail this is probably because the barbs are widely spaced from the tip to the base of the rachis. These feathers surround the oil gland duct symmetrically and give to that area about the same appearance as fluff on the abdomen of the chicken, and if a name were needed, it could be designated the dorsal caudal fluff.

Caudal to the fluff is a row of upper major tail coverts. There are approximately 10 of these on each side. Laterally, it is hard to tell where the row ends because the type of feather forming these coverts continues on to the thigh. The medial pair is longest and is rotated 90° so that the curved shafts face the median plane. All the other coverts are stacked the same way, including those on the part of the thigh adjacent to the tail. This adds to the difficulty of determining the exact number of upper major tail coverts. A row of upper median tail coverts does not exist except as the first row of fluff feathers, and these project upward from the skin surface rather than caudally.

There are 10 pairs of rectrices in the adult male; the tips of the median pair are slender and pointed, and the shafts are curved back on themselves about 180°. Each rectrix in position two also has a pointed, tapering tip, but the shaft is not greatly curved. The tips of the remaining rectrices have blunt points and the shafts curve medially.

A broad expanse of feathers arises from the ventral caudal tract and fills the triangular area between the vent and the rectrices. There are no well-defined rows of under tail coverts. The feathers in the center, for several rows deep, are the longest and stiffest, and they are cupped upward against the under surface of the rectrices. The feathers on the rows near the vent are progressively shorter; they all are typical contour feathers with a plumulaceous basal half and a distal half with flat vanes on each side of curved shafts. The bend of the shaft is about 90°. This curvature aids in keeping the feathers pushed against the upturned tail.

Lateral body tract and apterium.—The wing, when folded, is long, and it covers the side of the body. A great deal of the lateral body apterium lies below the very long feathers of the subhumeral tract. As expected, with this effective covering in a bird that has such an abundant under coat of down feathers, the lateral body apterium is packed with these downs. In this dense sea of downs, a row of several contour feathers, each longer than the surrounding down feathers, extends from the proximal end of the subhumeral tract across the lateral body apterium to the pectoral tract. These feathers are of various lengths but some measure 10 cm. They are somewhat more delicate than the large ones of the subhumeral tract.

Posterior appendage tracts.—The thigh is covered by the folded wing, while the knee and crural tract are covered by feathers from the superior margin of the pectoral tract. As one might expect when the leg is covered so effectively, the leg has plumulaceous contour feathers. The flat vane structure is limited to the tips of the feathers. When the femoral tract feathers are pressed against the leg it is hard to determine the distribution of the types that may be there, but by ruffling the feathers toward the head in an anesthetized bird, the flattened vane tips stand out. A few small contour feathers can be seen anterior to the thigh. Some feathers from the infracaudal margin of the femoral tract are up to 8.0 cm. long, but they are soft and half plumulaceous rather than stiff as were the rear body feathers of the chicken. These soft feathers from the caudal margin of the femoral tract merge with similar feathers from the side of the tail.

Near the knee the feathers are directed downward, but in the middle femoral region they are directed backward. The knee is covered by plumulaceous contour feathers. On the lateral surface of the crus they are somewhat longer—up to about 6.0 cm. Most of them are directed downward toward the hock. Adjacent to the hock the crural tract feathers become very short and end about 8 mm. above the joint. At the transition of feathers to scutes a minute down feather emerges from the lower corner of each scute. On the inner and posterior surfaces of the shank, in the area of the intracrural apterium, the contour feathers disappear and only down feathers are present.

Brachial tracts.—The feathers from the humeral, posthumeral, and subhumeral tracts are large. Those of the humeral tract spread about 90° like a fan. Those at the anterior end are short and are directed distally along the leading edge of the wing. When the wing is strongly flexed, the tips of these feathers lie above the wrist joint. More caudally other feathers cover most of the upper marginal coverts of the prepatagium. The longest feathers are at the posterior end of the humeral tract. In the chicken these form the scapulars, which term could probably be applied to the duck also, although they do not stand apart as distinctly as they do in the chicken. As a group, the humerals cover at least three-fourths of the forearm plumage in the folded wing. All the feathers of the tract have curved shafts, which range from 90° for the short ones at the anterior end to about 45° for the long ones coming from the metapatagium. The shorter feathers have a greater proportional length of naked or nearly naked barbs at the tip than have the longer feathers.

There are about seven posthumeral quills. The longest are in the center of the row; the shortest are adjacent to the elbow. The latter ones overlie the small secondaries at the proximal end of the row. On superficial examination it would appear as if the posthumeral feathers were a continuation of the secondaries, but closer study shows that they are a continuation of some row anterior to the secondaries. The caudal posthumeral coverts are stiff, typical contour feathers in the distal half of the row and are delicate, lacy contour feathers in the proximal half. The anterior posthumeral coverts are short and constitute one full row. Between these and the quills near the cubitus, there may be an intermediate row of a few short, downy feathers.

The subhumeral tract is composed of three rows. The contour feathers at the proximal end of the posterior row are 15 cm. long. At the opposite end of the row they are half as long. The feathers of the intermediate row are approximately 4 cm. long. An average feather of the anterior row is 2.5 cm. long. There may be a few contour feathers in additional anterior rows, but the change to the down feathers of the prepatagium is relatively abrupt.

Alar tracts.—The closed wing may have two tips—one formed by the secondaries and one formed by the primaries; the secondaries extend to the end of the pelvic girdle and the primaries, to the base of the rectrices. The most caudally extended secondary is the 12th and the most caudally extended primaries are the ninth and 10th, the ninth extending backward slightly farther than the 10th.[3] Usually the tips of the most caudally extended primaries overlap the feathers of the upper caudal tract. In a semidomestic Mute Swan, they may project well above the level of the back. The feathers from the lateral margin of the pectoral tract are turned dorsally and form a pocket or slot into which the wrist and leading edge of the hand are snugly deposited.

The duck has 11 primaries, the 11th being the remicle at the distal end of the wing. It is a feather distinctly different in size from the upper major primary coverts. It is about three-fourths as long as the adjacent 10th covert.

---

[3] Humphrey and Butsch (1958) found in the Labrador Duck that the ninth and 10th were the longest primaries, and of the secondaries they depicted the 14th as projecting farthest caudally.

The primaries have narrow distal vanes and wide proximal vanes. There is a slight incisure on the inner vane of the 10th primary. All of the primaries and the first four to six secondaries move together as a group and fold proximal to the remaining secondaries in the closed wing. When the forearm is held strongly flexed against the humerus and the hand is forcibly extended, these secondaries move out with the primaries, seemingly tied in with the same ligaments that spread the primaries. About half of the proximal primaries slide in medial to the first six secondaries so that in the folded wing of the duck there are stacked three sets of remiges, one above the other, the primaries being at the bottom, secondaries 1 to 6 next, and the remaining secondaries on top of the stack.

The upper major primary coverts are slender, and their shafts are parallel to those of the remiges. The shortest feather of the series is at the carpal end and feathers 7 through 10 are the longest. As shown in figure 92, the row of upper median secondary coverts begins with the third. It is not possible, of course, to say why the feathers are absent at the beginning of the row, but since these lie close to the hub of an arc, they would, if present, certainly be crowded in the flexed wing. In the extended wing, the space produced by their absence is covered by the large first feather in each row of upper major, median, and minor secondary coverts. As shown in figure 91, the shafts of these secondary coverts point toward the hand. The upper marginal coverts of the hand are completely covered by the alular remiges and alular coverts. The upper major primary coverts and the upper median primary coverts have conforming overlap. The upper minor primary coverts are too small to determine the type of overlap.

There are at least four alular remiges. There may be a small fifth at the basal end of the row; in figures 91 and 92, this is the feather that lies immediately anterior to the upper median carpal covert. The upper alular coverts lie nearly parallel to the remiges and are short and rather stiff, like the small coverts on the edge of the hand. Some coverts from the carpal region cover in part the short alular remiges at the inner end of the row.

The carpal remex and its upper major covert are hard to identify in the dense aggregation of downs in the carpal region. The remex can most easily be located by first finding the major covert. It is a typical covert about 7 cm. long and, as shown in figures 91 and 92, points almost parallel to the axis of the wing. Only by following it to the base implanted in the carpal region can one be sure of the identification. When the major covert is lifted, there will be found a shorter feather about 5 cm. long that is almost entirely plumulaceous. The downy barbs are curved toward the shaft, making the carpal remex much narrower than its covert. Probably the most distinguishing feature is this: when the major carpal covert is lifted, the remex comes with it and superficially looks like a large afterfeather. The upper median carpal covert has been identified as the feather immediately anterior to the major covert. It covers the basal half of the major carpal covert. These carpal feathers should be identified before a study of secondaries and their upper coverts is begun.

The first secondary remex is as long as the second and is not shortened as in the chicken and turkey. The secondaries gradually increase in length up to the 12th (including the missing fifth in the count). Those proximal to the 12th get shorter abruptly. The last ones in the row are not as long as the posthumeral quills that cover them.

There is a complete row of upper major secondary coverts as shown in figure 91. We made a special effort to find in the extended wing some indication of an intercalated row representing the first four secondaries that Humphrey and Clark (1961: 372) diagramed according to Steiner's ideas. We failed to find any indication of a shift anteriorly in the pterylosis, nor did the ptilosis seem to offer support for the idea. In Humphrey and Clark's diagram of the dorsal surface of the forearm of the Mallard the secondary remiges and major coverts show continuity for the full length of the rows, but the first five feathers of the median row are shifted posteriorly to form an accessory row. Our studies indicate an interruption in the continuity of the upper minor secondary coverts and especially in the upper marginal coverts of the prepatagium. The rows are not straight as diagramed by Humphrey and Clark nor as we have shown them in figure 88, but curve as shown in figure 91, and the curvature of the rows seems to account for the interruption in their continuity. The same curving of marginal rows of the prepatagium is to be found in the pigeon (fig. 98), whereas in the galliforms (figs. 68, 76, and 83) the rows parallel the basal ends of the remex follicles much more closely.

Goodchild (1891) illustrated the upper surface of the wing of a wild duck and stated that this anseriform as well as representatives from other orders are (p. 332): "Usually with five Medians lengthened by the faulting sequence upon the absence of the fifth cubital remex." Degen (1894) referred to the fifth secondary as absent. With this guidance from the literature, we are ready to begin an examination of the forearm plumage of the domestic duck. In the extended wing, the tips of the upper major secondary coverts form a remarkably straight line; although one of these is the covert for the missing fifth remex, there is no indication by its appearance which is the fifth covert, so it must be identified by counting.

All of these coverts, at least up to the 12th, have a contrary overlap. Those toward the proximal end of the row have a conforming overlap. At the cubital end of the row they tend to be stacked as in the chicken, so overlap in this area is without meaning.

There is a complete row of upper median secondary coverts. At the distal end of the forearm the feather rows curve anteriorly. This upward curvature is still more exaggerated in the minor and marginal coverts. The median row covers the basal half of the upper major secondary coverts. Because the skin holding the median coverts is easily moved, these coverts can assume various positions, but generally there is a contrary overlap. When the wing is folded and the first four through six secondaries slide behind those of a higher number, all of the upper coverts—majors, medians, and others—remain at the outside surface of the wing and are not carried inward with the remiges. It is evident, therefore, that the secondaries, as the wing is closing, separate into two groups, the break coming in the general area of the "missing fifth." Theoretically, the possibility exists, therefore, that the flexion of the outer group of secondaries in respect to the inner group may have, in effect, squeezed the fifth feather out of existence. We have been unable to find literature on the clustering of feathers in groups during flexion of the wing. We realize that the implications of what is said here go far beyond domestic birds, but it would certainly seem that a reexamination of the folding of feathers of the wing on living specimens in eutaxic and diastataxic species might bring to light a new facet in the interpretation of the "missing fifth" secondary. This problem is discussed further on page 192.

If lines were drawn to join the tips of those feathers that constitute the upper median and upper minor secondary coverts and the adjacent several rows of upper marginal coverts of the prepatagium at the carpal region, the tips of feathers would not lie exactly on the exact same line. This agrees with the slight irregularities in the placement of the follicles (fig. 91). The feathers in the vertical row adjacent to the heavy dashed line in figure 91 are somewhat longer than the others and they, with the carpal coverts, form an effectual covering for the feathers of digit II. The overlap of marginals and upper minor secondaries is not definite. The small feathers along the edge of the wing appear to have a conforming overlap.

The under surface of the wing presents problems associated with reversed and unreversed feathers. All 11 under major primary coverts are reversed. Since there are no significant afterfeathers, it is necessary to base judgment on the existence of a groove in the ventral surface of the rachis. The overlap is conforming, but it is easy for a feather to be shifted from one type of overlap to the other. The tips of the under major primary coverts lie opposite the tips of the upper major primary coverts.

The under median primary coverts also have a reversed orientation. Adjacent to the carpus these feathers are about half as long as the under major coverts, and near the distal end of the row they are about one-third as long. It was not possible for us to determine the overlap for this row because the overlapping of the feathers was very slight and they were easily shifted from one position to another.

The drawing of the pterylosis (fig. 93) shows only about a half row of under minor primary coverts; four to six such feathers seem to be a typical number. These feathers are unreversed. The under marginal coverts of the hand lie anterior to the underhand apterium, and their shafts point toward the wing tip.

In figures 93 and 94 no under carpal coverts are labeled. One of these, labeled first under median primary covert, lies in the carpal region and probably should be designated as the under major carpal covert. Examination of the feather itself showed a contour exactly like that of the adjacent under median primary coverts, except that it was slightly longer. It has the reversed orientation of the adjacent under median primary coverts. However, none of these facts prove that it is not an under major carpal covert.

The under major secondary coverts are almost as long as the remiges which stand in contrast to the very short major secondary coverts on the upper side of the forearm. All the feathers of this row have reversed orientation and conforming overalp.

If there is any evidence at all that there has been a shifting of rows involving the distal five feathers, it should be found in the under median secondary coverts. The pterylosis shows this as a continuous unbroken row (fig. 94); the fifth under median secondary covert is pointed in a direction slightly different from the others. This is the only irregularity. In the intact plumage, the first five or six feathers tend to clump together as a group and point toward the carpus. They lie on top of each other in a small stack. Beyond these, the under median coverts point backward toward the elbow. The stacking of feathers is an intricate maneuver as the wing is folded. The distal group of five or six under median coverts stays with the secondaries of corresponding number and slides outside the under medians of higher number. In this shifting like an accordion, the seventh under median covert is brought close to the carpal region.

All the under median secondary coverts have reversed orientation. If there had been a migration of rows around the trailing edge of the wing, as has been suggested for species showing diastataxis, it would be expected that the first four reversed under coverts would be affected also and would be represented by either one row or by three rows, depending on the direction which the rotation had taken. It is hard to explain rotation when the same number of rows is present both proximal and distal to the diastema, and there are never more than two rows of reversed under coverts.

Common Pigeon

The pigeon has pigmented feathers, which add greatly to the ease of studying feather groups; but the actual intensities of color that may be present in the various feathers have no significance. In the description of ptilosis that follows, values of gray are mentioned frequently, rather than hues or chroma of colors, because the specimens available had feathers that were white, black, or slate. If others studied pigeons colored differently, their descriptions of the colors would not be the same as ours. They, however, would presumably do as we have done, namely use color dimensions associated with groups of feathers and especially between tracts as an aid in analyzing ptilosis.

Dorsal and ventral neck.—The head is covered with closely placed soft contour feathers that end at about the beginning of the neck. On the ventral side, soft gray plumage covers the interramal and submalar regions. The feathers of the head overlap those of the upper dorsal and ventral neck for a short distance. The neck feathers in some specimens show an iridescent green when light is reflected toward the observer; otherwise they have the same intensity of gray as have the feathers of the head. It is not possible to smooth the ruffled feathers of the neck. This is due to the action of the feather muscles, to the flexibility of the skin of the neck, and to the rigidity of the feathers. Apteria are lacking on all surfaces of the neck. The neck skin is loose but not folded as in the Great Horned Owl and in the Common Coturnix. All the feathers point directly caudally, and there is no tendency to form a ridge of feathers along the side of the neck as was observed in the White Pekin Duck, where feathers from the dorsal and ventral neck piled up because they pushed against one another. Nitzsch (1867:109) described a lateral cervical apterium for *Columba livia* reaching almost to the head. Such a space is shown in his illustration of pigeon pterylosis. The only evidence for such an apterium that we have found is a small area on the dorsal surface of the cervical patagium that has continuity with the scapular apterium.

The separation for the dark plumage of the neck from the light plumage of the interscapular region coincides with the transverse dashed line that arbitrarily separates the dorsal cervical from the interscapular tracts (fig. 95). This anterior boundary of the interscapular tract is placed across the dorsal neck shortly caudal to the beginning of the cervical patagium. This would be about at the level of R'L' in figure 275 (p. 458). The interscapular tract branches at its caudal end as shown in figure 95, a fact that was originally observed by Nitzsch (1867), who showed a deep cleft between these two points. The separation between the caudal end of the interscapular tract and the beginning of the dorsal tract is poorly defined because one tract continues over into the other, but the feather coat shows the separation very clearly in the specimens examined because of a color difference. When the pigeon is at rest, the interscapulars lie as a pointed group of feathers down the axis of the back and overlap slightly some of the humerals on each side of the tract. When the wings are pulled apart and the humerals are separated from the interscapulars, the feathers at the caudal end of the interscapular tract pull apart and form a pair of points corresponding to the points shown in the pterylosis.

Dorsopelvic tract.—At the anterior end of the dorsal tract are short feathers entirely covered by the long caudal interscapulars. Caudal to this the contour feathers overlap in a regular manner, so that the curved tip of each feather projects a short distance beyond the one that covers it. The lateral margins of the dorsopelvic tract merge into the powder downs in the lateral body and pelvic apteria. Some feathers along the lateral margin of the tract cover the adjacent short powder down feathers. The line of separation can be distinguished more readily in a bird that has its feathers clipped because of the fact that the powder down feathers have very shallow follicles compared to the contour feathers, and these are conically shaped rather than tubular. In the pelvic area, the powder down feathers and contour feathers producing powder continue to the base of the tail and are overlapped by the pelvic contour feathers. In the specimens studied, the entire dorsocaudal tract carried white plumage. At the caudal indentation there was an abrupt shift to gray plumage, indicating that, although the separation between pelvic and dorsal caudal tracts seemed artificial when studying the pterylosis, there does exist sometimes a color or a pattern basis for separating two adjacent tracts having continuity. We assume that in some specimens there would be color patterns that failed to agree with tract boundaries as closely as described above.

Pectorosternal tract.—The pectoral and sternal tracts are fused into one, as in the duck and many passerines (Heimerdinger, 1964), so that the broad breast, sternum, and abdomen are covered by an uninterrupted expanse of contour feathers on each side. The only break is in the midline, where there is a broad sternal apterium continuous with the cervical apterium; caudal to this is a narrow median abdominal apterium. On the ventral neck over the thoracic inlet are small contour feathers; in most birds this space is an apterium bearing down feathers. There is no interruption in plumage color or pattern at the transition to the pectorosternals. The follicles of the sternal part of the tract are pointed medially so that the feathers cover the apterium, but the shafts curve caudally so that the exposed tips of the feathers appear to be parallel and point directly toward the rear.

The feathers from the pectoral portion of the pectorosternal tract extend backward outside the leg, entirely covering much of the lower part of the thigh. They merge with thigh plumage that comes chiefly from the infracaudal margin. The pectoral part of the tract extends laterally and dorsally even farther than in the duck and continues to the base of the wing. Feathers of the pectorosternal tract covered by the folded wing are different from those of the central two-thirds of the tract. Those hidden beneath the wing are the equivalent of the lateral body tract of other birds and are light in color. The caudal boundary for this feather type is very sharp, and there is no gradation from these to the powder down feathers that follow. At the forward end, namely on the shoulder of the lateral-body-tract portion of the pectoral tract, the feathers are small and downy as would be expected because they are covered by the cervicals.

Examination of pterylosis and ptilosis for the pigeon indicated that by the presence of certain differences, lateral body, pectoral, and sternal tracts could be partially distinguished from one another. More substantial evidence that the three tracts, although fused, are distinct comes from a study of feather muscles (ch. 8, p. 459).

Abdominal tract.—From the abdominal tract to the sternum the contour feathers undergo a gradual transition to a type with fluffy tips that resemble semiplumes. These feathers become shorter and more plumulaceous toward the vent. The abdominal tract is broad, and there is no division into a medial strong and a lateral weak tract. A small lateral abdominal apterium along the extreme lateral margin is closely packed with downs, some of which are powder downs.

Around the cloaca are small contour feathers in at least two rows; in the central parts of the anterior and posterior lips there may be four rows. The transverse portion of the lateral abdominal apterium is found lateral to the vent; the abdominal tract along its anterior side bears semiplumes and contour feathers, and posterior to the apterium there are down feathers.

Caudal tracts.—We indicated earlier that a sharp color change in the feathers of one of the specimens examined enabled us to separate the pelvic and dorsal caudal tracts. This color difference made it evident that there was considerable overlap of the pelvic tract upon the dorsal caudal tract. As shown in figure 95, there are several rows of follicles up to the oil gland duct. The feathers are imbricated and close together. At each side of the dorsal caudal tract are small contour feathers and semiplumes that are covered by the rear body feathers of the femoral tract. The powder down feathers end abruptly at the base of the tail, namely at the border of the lateral abdominal apterium. There is a sharp distinction in size between the feathers of the dorsal caudal tract and the upper tail coverts, the latter being larger. These are described after the discussion of the rectrices. Six pairs of rectrices are shown in figures 95 and 97, and this agrees with Clark's observations (1918b:118) on *Columba* and three other genera examined by him. He also found that the number of upper major tail coverts was the same as the number of rectrices; this we have shown in figure 95. When the tail is closed, the rectrices and coverts form a column. The upper major tail coverts form two columns of stacked feathers, one on each side. The feathers in a column lie nearly directly one above the other; the shortest in the pile is the most lateral feather, and the longest is the most medial feather. The three short rectrices of the six on each side are entirely covered by feathers from the dorsal caudal tract. These also tend to arrange themselves into columns. The deck feathers are held flat in the folded tail. They are not arranged like a ridge of a roof, as in the chicken.

The feathers at the anterior end of the ventral caudal tract are fluffy like the adjacent abdominals, but in the successive rows posteriorly, they change to contour feathers, whose tips are bordered by a narrow margin of barbs without barbules. The ventral caudal tract and the under major tail coverts tend to arrange themselves in two stacked columns pushed against the under surface of the rectrices.

Alar tracts.—The color pattern of the dorsal surface of the wing sometimes facilitates the study of ptilosis; one Common Pigeon examined had white primaries and alulars and gray secondaries. But this aid is lacking in a pigeon of uniform color such as occurs in some fancy breeds and in most ordinary breeds. There are 10 primary remiges. The tips extend most caudally in primaries 8 through 10; 9 is the longest. These form the tip of the wing; the tip comes within about 3 cm. of the end of the tail, thereby extending beyond the tail coverts. Each primary, proximal to the ninth, is successively shorter, and in the folded wing they are stacked to give a single row of feather tips. This occurs only when the hand is fully flexed against the forearm.

All the primaries except the 10th have an incisure (see fig. 174, *C*, p. 261). The width of the distal vane is less in the outer half of the feather than in the basal half. This difference in width between the proximal and basal halves of feathers carries over to the first several secondaries.

There are four alular remiges; the first is the longest and each, central to this, is successively shorter. The tips, like those of the primaries, are stacked in the fully folded wing and lie on top of the upper marginal coverts of the hand. Some of the upper alular coverts are longer than the fourth alular remex so that this feather is covered by long members of the alular coverts.

The tips of the upper major primary coverts in the extended wing are on a line with the tips of the secondaries. The eighth major covert reaches out farthest over the primaries. All have a conforming overlap.

In figure 99, the row of upper median primary coverts have shafts that point toward the tip of the wing. They cover the upper hand apterium. Their overlap is conforming. In both the folded and extended wing, they are entirely covered by the alular remiges and their coverts.

The upper carpal feathers are well developed in the pigeon. The carpal remex has the general appearance of an upper major primary covert, except that it has a more plumulaceous basal part. It may be covered either by the first upper major secondary covert or by the upper major carpal covert, which is about 1 cm. longer than the carpal remex. The upper major carpal covert is a typical contour feather and points distally across the upper major primary coverts. In pigeons, where the primaries are white, the carpal remex and its coverts are white. The upper median carpal covert lies adjacent to an upper alular covert of nearly the same size. In the flexed wing, all of these are folded under the secondary coverts.

Fifteen secondary remiges are indicated in figures 98 and 101. The missing fifth is included in the count. The last two or three are small and readily merge with the coverts. Clark (1918b:419) found the same number of secondaries in the Passenger Pigeon (*Ectopistes migratorius*). As shown in the illustrations, there are 16 upper major secondary coverts. These coverts have a conforming overlap. When all the feathers are present, their row of tips is reasonably even; there is no evidence that the first four have been shifted or that they come from a different row.

The upper major secondary coverts have gray and black markings so arranged that unless the feathers are actually handled, it appears that the wing-bar is composed of two rows instead of one. The color pattern for the upper median secondary coverts is more apt to match the upper marginal coverts. All the median secondary coverts do not end exactly on the same line, but we failed to observe an intercalary row among the minor coverts such as Pycraft (1904) depicted in the Little Stint (*Calidris minuta* = *Tringa minuta*). Goodchild (1886:195) found the overlap of median secondary

coverts to be contrary at the distal end of the row and conforming at the proximal end. In specimens that we examined, the overlap seemed to be irregular and mixed perhaps because of some missing feathers.

The overlap of the many rows of upper minor and marginal coverts is mixed, probably without significance. The feathers seem to be randomly distributed; some are in parallel rows, and others tend to form columns of feathers. As in the duck, this tendency probably is related to the fact that the rows curve anteriorly toward the leading edge rather than paralleling a line established by the secondaries and their major coverts.

There are 10 under major primary coverts. The first begins on the proximal side of the first primary. These coverts have a mixed overlap and reversed orientation. The inner surface of the shaft is pigmented, and the outer surface is in part a light gray and in part white. There is a shallow groove in the shaft on the outer (ventral) side, hence they are reversed. The under major primary coverts extend the same distance over the bases of remiges as do the upper major coverts. The overlap may be different for the same birds examined on two successive days, and there are differences between the right and left wing. If the complement of feathers in this row is complete, most or all the feathers have a contrary overlap, but if some are missing, the overlap will be mixed. From observations like these we conclude that the direction of overlap may be inconstant in certain locations.

Under median primary coverts are lacking in the pigeon (fig. 100), and examination of the plumage reveals no downs or rudimentary feathers that might represent this row. At the basal ends of the remex follicles is the first row of under minor primary coverts. They form a complete row of 10; their shafts are directed toward the tip of the wing and slightly caudally. Each feather has an unreversed or normal orientation. The overlap seems to be contrary, but the feathers are almost fully stacked, in which case there is no clear cut overlap one way or the other. The under minor primary coverts merge with the under marginal primary coverts of the hand; these, like the minor coverts, have their shafts pointed toward the tip of the wing.

The under carpal covert consists of but a single feather, at least as worked out in the pterylosis (figs. 100 and 101). However, immediately anterior are two feathers, the first feather in each of the two rows of under minor primary coverts. We question whether these are under minor carpal coverts or, as labeled, under minor primary coverts. These two feathers are identical in appearance with the under major carpal covert, a well-formed contour feather about 4 cm. long. These under minor coverts, in turn, resemble under minor primary coverts, so feather appearance gives no clues. The under major carpal covert is strikingly different from the first under major secondary covert, which is described next.

The under major secondary coverts are shorter than the under median secondary coverts. They have reversed orientation and the same conforming overlap as the secondary remiges. The distal vanes of the first 10 to 12 feathers slip between the large overlapping vanes of the remiges. Associated with this is a plumulaceous distal vane and a pennaceous proximal vane. On the distal vane, there is a sharp line of transition from plumulaceous to pennaceous texture. It follows a curve, the pennaceous part is broadest about in the middle of the feather, and at the tip is almost entirely plumulaceous (fig. 224, p. 333). Near the cubital end of the row of under major secondary coverts, the feathers change to typical contours with both vanes similar. This change occurs in the area where the remiges become small and the coverts and remiges become stacked. Another point that makes these feathers different is the fact that they have a tuft of barbs arising from the border of the superior umbilicus. A more extensive description of these feathers is given on page 333.

The under median secondary coverts are far longer feathers than the under majors, the longest of which may be 7 cm. These secondary coverts have a reversed orientation, as judged by the presence of a groove in the outer (ventral) side of the shaft and darker pigmentation on the inner side. The overlap is contrary.

There are two full rows of relatively large under minor secondary coverts (fig. 101). All these, as well as the marginals, have unreversed orientation. The longest feather of the first row is about 4 cm. The predominant direction for the shaft is toward the trailing edge of the wing, and, although there are irregularities of overlap, generally it is conforming. The feathers of the second row of under minor secondary coverts are shorter. The shafts are directed toward the cubital end at about a 45° angle, and they also mostly have a conforming overlap.

The feathers of the under forearm tract are about the same size as those of the second row of under minor secondary coverts and cover the under forearm apterium. In the area of the under prepatagial apterium are several rows of densely packed downs. Toward the ends of the apterium, transition types lead to the contours of the under marginal coverts of the prepatagium. Of this transition group, those adjacent to the apterium are long, typical contours, some 3 cm. long, which overlap and entirely cover the downs. The under marginal coverts near the base of the wing point caudally and cover the anterior axillary fossa. More distally, there is a transition in direction, so that near the wrist all the feathers are directed toward the tip of the wing.

A discussion of feather placement associated with folding of the wing has been left until after the description of the individual feather groups. The pigeon has a long, pointed wing like the duck, and the tips of the distal primaries are carried well above the tail. All the primaries are folded under the secondaries, and in the folding process the secondaries adjacent to the wrist are moved close together, so that the first through sixth (counting the missing fifth) are almost on top of each other. The secondaries cover the alular remiges. Each under major secondary covert slides in between adjacent remiges. This interdigitation is not uniform; there may be two or three coverts between two secondaries, or there may be only one or none at all.

On the ventral surface, the under major and median primary coverts move with the remiges. Several long feathers next to the wrist belong to the first row of under minor secondary coverts and cross the under coverts of the hand. The primaries slide in between the secondaries and the long under median secondary coverts, while the under major secondary coverts remain close to these remiges as described earlier. When the wing is closed, the long feathers from various rows line up together and form an under layer for the wing. Another layer beneath these and parallel to them is that of the long subhumerals.

When the compactness and efficiency of feather arrangement are examined in the folded wing, the impression is gained that the length, placement, and direction of feathers are adapted to the needs of the species rather than that an ancient rearrangement of rows or parts of rows is slavishly followed. The reversal of the under major and median coverts is real enough, but we failed to find on the dorsal surface convincing evidence of an intercalated row associated with diastataxy. The conforming and contrary overlaps of the feathers likewise have a function; when the feathers have the same overlap as those in the adjacent underlying row, it is possible for one edge of the overlying feather to slip between two feathers of the row beneath. For example: (1) in the folding of the wing some of the upper major primary coverts slide to varying degrees between the remiges, and (2) the under major secondaries slip between their remiges, and part of the vanes involved are modified structurally to fit the process. The feathers of one row do not always slip between those of the next row. For example, the upper major secondary coverts conform in overlap with the remiges, but in the folding of the wing there is no interdigitation; they remain as a separate unit, moving together independent of the remiges.

When the overlap is opposite that of the row underneath, the two groups of feathers move independently of each other. This is illustrated by (1) the under major primary coverts which, when the wing is folding, slide together as a group independent of the remiges, and (2) the under median secondary coverts, which move entirely independently of the under major secondaries. The separation of these two rows provides a slot into which the primaries may be placed. The complexities of these adaptations make it appear that the direction of overlap is more related to function than to phylogeny. The direction of overlap for wing covert rows in the Common Pigeon is summarized as follows:

Coverts	Overlap[1]
Upper major primary	Conforming.
Upper median primary	Stacked—potentially conforming.
Upper minor primary	No overlap.
Upper major secondary	Conforming.
Upper median secondary	Mixed.
Upper minor secondary	Do.
Under major primary	Mixed to contrary.
Under minor primary	Stacked—potentially contrary.
Under major secondary	Conforming.
Under median secondary	Contrary.
Under minor secondary (row 1)	Mixed to conforming.
Under minor secondary (row 2)	Conforming.

[1] Overlap is defined as follows: Conforming, the direction of overlap is the same as that of the remiges; contrary, the direction of overlap is opposite that of the remiges; mixed, conforming and contrary in the same row; stacked, feathers piled on top of each other. When stacked, one of the edges of the feathers may project beyond the pile and indicate a potential conforming or contrary overlap.

A comparison of feather shifting in the closure of the wings of the duck and pigeon should offer some clues concerning the significance of the diastema because of its presence in one and its absence in the other. In the duck, the space between the fourth and sixth secondaries is large enough to carry the missing feather, whereas in the pigeon, as noted by Pycraft (1904:324), the space has closed secondarily so that it is no greater than other spaces in the row. In the duck the first four to six secondaries are folded as a separate group beneath the remaining secondaries, the break coming about at the diastema, whereas in the pigeon the entire group of secondaries remains as an intact row moving as a unit, exactly the same as in the eutaxic secondaries of the chicken. This fact seems to indicate a functional relationship between the presence or absence of a diastema and the shifting of feathers in the folding of the wing.

Gerbe (1877) observed that the fifth secondary was absent from the pigeon as did Gadow (1888), who classified families of birds according to the presence or absence of the fifth secondary. He used the terminology common at that time, aquintocubitalism, which later became diastataxy; quintocubitalism, later becoming eutaxy. Pycraft (1904) also placed the pigeon among the diastataxic birds. He also called attention to the fact that the space between the fourth and sixth remiges was reduced to the average space between feathers on each side of the diastema. Therefore, superficially it resembles a eutaxic wing. Steiner (1917) investigated two genera of pigeons, one of which was *Columba*, and gave measurements of length for many of the feathers, especially the upper and under secondary coverts. In chapter 2 we indicated that the Columbidae had a diastataxic wing (Miller, 1924b). Steiner (1956) noted at least five families of the Columbiformes that had this type of wing. In one of these families both diastataxy and eutaxy were represented and, there are numerous families among birds of various orders where both types exist.

Many ornithologists have tried to determine which condition is more ancient, diastataxy or eutaxy. Steiner (1917 and 1956) suggested that *Archaeopteryx* had a diastataxic

wing. Our data are much too meager to offer more than a suggestion as to the functional significance of a diastema; the few species with which we have worked indicate that the diastema can be a point of breaking of the secondary row in the process of folding the wing. We hope that others will determine the validity of our suggestion, but to do so they will need to use live birds anesthetized with some compound such as Equi-thesin (see ch. 10). When given intramuscularly, Equi-thesin keeps a bird in a flaccid, fully relaxed condition but permits the bird to refold its feathers in a normal manner. The bird will rouse from its stupor when the wing is handled, especially if a growing feather is manipulated. It seems to us that this problem could offer a fruitful line of research.

We have not found any references on the shifting of feathers in the folding of the wing; therefore, comparisons with the work of others cannot be made. Since Degen (1894) set forth his theory on the origin of diastataxy, it has generally been discarded, perhaps in part because Pycraft (1899) stated (p. 246):

> Though none will grudge this writer the credit of having evolved a very ingenious hypothesis, few probably will be found willing to adopt it. [Pycraft went on to summarize the theory concisely and accurately.] Degen carries us back to an imaginary quadri-dactyle manus in which each digit supported a set of remiges and major coverts. In course of time the 4th digit became suppressed and its remiges, 3 in number, migrated inwards on to the ulna—ousting the cubital remiges 1—3. Next, the remiges of Digit II. moved inward on the ulna. Originally there were five of these, but the 5th, lying in the carpal angle between the bases of Metacarpals III. and IV., became suppressed,—just as occasionally happens in the case of the 'carpal remex.' The coverts of this suppressed 5th remex were retained. Feathers 1–4 only remained to migrate on to the ulna. The 5th is now only indicated by its coverts,— hence the diastataxic wing. The carpal covert and remex of existing birds represents the short 1st remex and covert of Digit III., which has travelled inwards along Mc. III. to rest finally on the carpal joint at the base of Mc. II.

Degen's numbering is based on the assumption that the ancestral bird had digits I to III rather than II to IV. Degen conceived of each phalanx of each digit as well as the ulna and the radiale carrying remiges. This theory has a relationship to the wing imprint of *Archaeopteryx*. Some authors, including de Beer (1954), consider that the imprint of a second set of feathers overlaid on the first as "double-struck," but these include only the rachises and not the vanes. On the basis of Degen's concept of the ancestral form, the double-struck rachises could have belonged to metacarpus III in the partially separated fingers of the ancestral four-fingered hand. This theory was revived by Bohlin (1947) but was refuted by de Beer (1954:34).

Posterior appendage tracts.—Much of the femoral tract is covered by the feathers of the pectoral tract, not only the gray ones of the pectoral tract proper but also the long feathers of the lateral body tract. The down feathers of the lateral body apterium merge into the small semiplumes and contour feathers at the anterior margin of the thigh. These become increasingly long toward the infracaudal margin of the tract. All these point directly caudally and do not spread out like a fan as in the other species studied. We mentioned (p. 157) that the long feathers from the infracaudal margin of the tract were called a pelvic wing by Beebe (1915), but neither from a study of the pterylosis or ptilosis does it seem desirable to retain this name.

The feathers of the knee and upper anterior crural tract are covered by feathers from the pectoral tract. The crural

feathers are truly loose contour feathers and strongly resemble semiplumes. Only adjacent to the rachis are there narrow flat vanes typical of the contour feather. The crural fluffy contour feathers on the lateral surface of the leg are long and project backward beyond the shank and curl around the posterior surface. Those near the anterior margin of the shank are also fluffy; they are long and curl across the front surface of the shank.

FEATHER WEIGHT AND NUMBER

The size (weight and area) and number of feathers are physiologically and statistically related to temperature, rate of metabolism, body weight, and surface area of birds. No mathematical equation has yet been derived that will express exactly the relationship of all these variables for all birds. Progress has been made in this direction, though based on rather limited numerical data in comparison with studies of mammals. The text that follows is derived from literature rather than from our personal investigations. We have made no attempt to cover any topic fully but merely to mention some of the significant findings of quantitative studies for feathers.

Feather counts

Chickens.—Data on the number of feathers in chickens are limited indeed. Wetmore (1936) mentioned that a dairy employee counted 8,325 feathers in a Plymouth Rock. Greenwood and Burns (1940) counted 6,356 and 7,250 on two Brown Leghorn capons. A 5.6 pound (2,540 gm.) White Wyandotte female carried a total of 9,515 feathers, excluding filoplumes (Jaap and Turner, 1943). This amounted to 1,699 feathers per pound of chicken or 267 feathers per gram. In another White Wyandotte, Jaap and Turner listed 888 feathers per pound, excluding those of head and neck. If

these two specimens of White Wyandottes were equivalent, than the values in column 2 of table 7 need to be increased by 52.3 percent to attain an estimate of the total number of feathers. Column 3, table 7 presents the results when this correction factor was applied.

When the feathers of the head and upper neck were excluded in compiling data on total feather weight, Jaap and Turner estimated that the error introduced was no more than 10 percent. On the other hand, exclusion of feathers from head or from head and neck introduces a large error in the number of total feathers counted. This was shown in the White Wyandottes studied by Jaap and Turner, and in the review of literature presented in the text that follows. Greenwood and Burns (1940) sorted the molted feathers according to the parts of the body from which they come. On this basis, 1,633 (24 percent) of 6,803 feathers had come from the neck. It was not stated how many were present on the head.

Wild birds.—Some investigators have given data on the number of feathers in species of wild birds. Dwight (1900:119) made a total count of contour feathers on a Bobolink (*Dolichonyx oryzivorus*); downs, semiplumes and filoplumes were omitted. Feathers were grouped by tracts as follows:

TABLE 7.—*Some interrelations between body weight and feather number for several breeds of chickens*

Breed[1]	Average live weight[2]	Feather number		Feather weight as a percentage of body weight[1]	Feathers per gram of body weight	
		Less feathers on head and upper neck[3]	Calculated total per bird		Observed[2]	Calculated[4]
	Grams	Number	Number	Percent	Number	Number
Dark Cornish Bantam	1,533	4,881	7,434	3.70	3.18	2.32
Dark Cornish	2,971	5,725	8,719	3.50	1.92	1.38
Cornish × Red cross	3,048	5,685	8,658	4.40	1.87	1.32
Rhode Island Red	3,688	5,870	8,940	4.60	1.59	1.12
Barred Plymouth Rock	3,470	5,500	8,377	4.69	1.58	1.18
White Plymouth Rock	3,719	5,576	8,492	5.01	1.50	1.12
White Wyandotte	3,057	5,985	9,115	6.05	1.96	1.34

[1] Data taken directly from Jaap and Turner (1943).

[2] Values derived from Jaap and Turner.

[3] Weight of feathers excluding those of head and upper third of neck.

[4] The calculated values are those obtained when the formula derived by Hutt and Ball (1938) was applied to data of Jaap and Turner.

Tracts	No. of contour feathers	Percent
Alar	492	15.2
Humeral	96	3.0
Capital	1,385	42.8
Dorsal	506	15.6
Ventral	465	14.4
Caudal	55	1.7
Lumbar	70	2.2
Crural	166	5.1
Total	3,215	100.0

More feathers were concentrated on the head than on any other part of the body (42.8 percent). Others have contributed data on number of feathers present on the head or on head and neck. McGregor (1902) made a total count of 6,544 feathers on a Glaucous-winged Gull (*Larus glaucescens*), of which 2,620 were on the head and 803 on the neck, a total of 3,423 on head and neck (52 percent). In the Whistling Swan (*Cygnus columbianus*), Ammann (1937) found that 20,177 of the 25,216 feathers of this species (80 percent) were located on the head and neck. Korelus (1947, table 11) listed the number of feathers on the head and the number on the whole bird for 15 species of wild birds. Wing (1952) counted a total of 4,297 feathers on a Brown-headed Cowbird (*Molothrus ater*), of which 1,246 (29 percent) were on the head. Brodkorb (1949) made counts of feathers from birds representative of 12 families and recorded subtotals for various regions of the body including the head and neck as follows: Pied-billed Grebe (*Podilymbus podiceps podiceps*), total contour feathers 15,016, head and neck 7,912 (53 percent); Green-winged Teal (*Anas crecca carolinensis*), total contour feathers 11,450, head 4,832, neck 2,226, head and neck together 7,058 (62 percent); Pintail (*Anas acuta*), total contour feathers 14,914, head and neck 10,492 (70 percent); Southern Screech Owl (*Otus asio asio*), total contour feathers 6,458, head 2,345, neck 340, head and neck together 2,685 (42 percent). The following counts were made by Markus (1963a) for a female specimen of a Laughing Dove (*Streptopelia senegalensis*):

Tracts	Contour and semiplume feathers	Percent
Capital	922	21.9
Caudal	143	3.4
Legs, crural and femoral	353	8.4
Spinal	535	12.7
Ventral	1,145	27.2
Wings, alar and humeral	1,112	26.4
Total	4,210	100.0

In three species of barbets, Markus (1963b) noted that the capital tract carried 30.5, 31.6, and 32.8 percent of 2,210, 3,014, 2,904, respectively, of the total number of feathers.

Some have recorded feather counts for the whole bird without tabulating the number of feathers that came from each part of the body. The first recorded count was made in 1882 on Brewer's Blackbird (*Euphagus cyanocephalus*) (Markus, 1963a). Wetmore (1936) reported counts of contour feathers for 152 birds, most of which were passerines. Some of his data, arranged in a descending sequence of body weights, are as follows:

Bird	Weight in grams	Feathers
Mourning Dove (*Zenaidura macroura*)	152.7	2,635
Common Grackle (*Quiscalus quiscula*)	117.7	2,730
Blue Jay (*Cyanocitta cristata*)	97.2	1,898
Common Nighthawk (*Chordeiles minor*)	69.3	2,265
Loggerhead Shrike (*Lanius ludovicianus*)	50.9	2,170
Brown-headed Cowbird (*Molothrus ater*)	41.4	1,622
Great Crested Flycatcher (*Myiarchus crinitus*)	33.8	1,570
House Sparrow (*Passer domesticus*)	28.1	1,359
Orchard Oriole (*Icterus spurius*)	24.0	1,601
Louisiana Waterthrush (*Seiurus motacilla*)	19.6	1,525
Kentucky Warbler (*Geothlypis formosa*)	14.4	1,511
Magnolia Warbler (*Dendroica magnolia*)	9.4	1,414
Golden-crowned Kinglet (*Regulus satrapa*)	5.8	1,268
Ruby-throated Hummingbird (*Archilochus colubris*)	2.8	940

From this sample of Wetmore's data, it is clearly evident that feather number is some exponential function of body weight. For example, the weight of the Mourning Dove is 26.3 times that of the Golden-crowned Kinglet, yet the Mourning Dove has only 2.1 times as many feathers as has the Golden-crowned Kinglet. One obvious accompaniment to reduction of bird size is reduction of feather size. Jaap and Turner (1943) tabulated lengths and widths for the first primary, second primary, and fourth tail feathers from the Dark Cornish Bantam and for the six layer breeds listed in table 7. We found from their data that the ratio of the average areas was 1:1.73, respectively.

In summarizing the body weights and feather counts of wild birds we stated that a ratio of 1:26.3 for body weights accompanied a feather-count ratio of 1:2.1. The body weight ratio of small and large chickens was 1:2.2, the feather count ratio was 1:1.17, and the feather area ratio was 1:1.73. All three variables decrease, with decrease in size of the bird but at different rates. Hutt and Ball (1938) arrived at formulas equating variables of feather number, body weight, and body area, but in their calculations they did not include the variable of feather size for birds of different weights.

Effect of season on feather counts.—Season may have an effect on feather counts for some birds. Wetmore (1936, p. 164) summarized his extensive data on this subject as follows:

It is evident from this that in the species studied from a maximum number of feathers found in the winter plumage there is a steady decline through early spring to a final low at the entrance of summer. The loss in feathers seemingly progresses steadily as cold weather passes and warmer weather advances. In other words, birds have a natural adjustment in dress to the needs of the season, a sensible arrangement that while apparently hitherto unknown is one that might be expected. As the lessening number of feathers is accompanied by considerable wear in those that remain, the amount of body covering is very appreciably lessened. The final

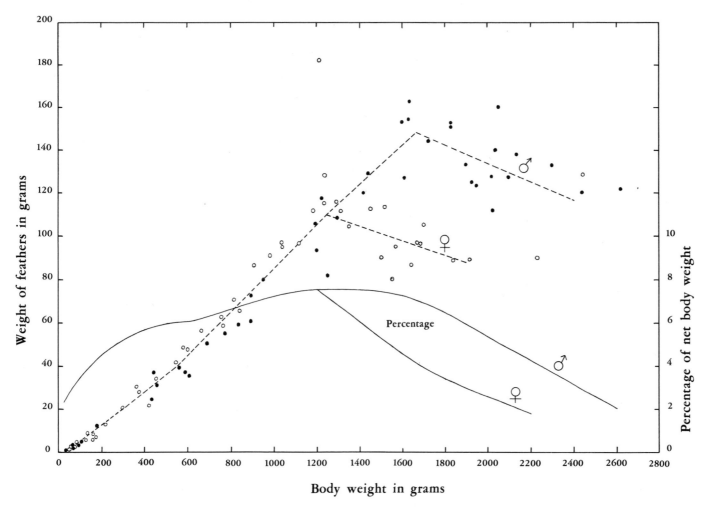

FIGURE 124.—Change in weight of feathers with age. The dashed line plots the absolute weight and the solid line plots the percentage of feather weight to body weight. Based on studies of the Single Comb White Leghorn Chicken. (Redrawn from Latimer, 1924.)

low ebb of summer culminates in the post-nuptial molt by which the plumage is renewed for another season.

Staebler (1941) used a single species, the House Sparrow, and found 3,138 and 3,179 contour feathers in July for two specimens and an average of 3,519 for six specimens taken in Michigan in colder months.

Similar studies were undertaken more recently (Markus, 1963a) on a relatively small sample of wild birds. It was concluded that there was no great difference in the number of feathers with season, when the seasonal temperature changes were small.

Feather weights

Chicken.—Figure 124, reproduced from Latimer (1924: fig. 9), shows two sets of curves—a dashed line where the weight of the feathers was plotted against the body weight and a solid line where the percentage weight of feathers to body weight has been plotted against the body weight. At about 1,270 gm. body weight, the curves (dashed lines) diverge for males and females. In females, feather weight

decreases as body weight increases. In the male, feather weight continues to increase until body weight reaches about 1,640 gm. Then feather weight begins to decrease and establishes a curve parallel to that shown for the female. The curves (solid lines) based on feather weight as a percentage of body weight against body weight show a striking initial rise for both sexes up to about 600 gm., after which there is a slight leveling off up to the point when the hens establish a declining curve. This is paralleled by the curve for males at about 400 gm. greater body weight.

Latimer (1924:375) concluded:

This rise and fall in both relative and absolute weights, plotted against both the gross body weight and against time, are correlated with changes in the structure of the feathers. Until the feather is completely developed, the shaft contains a large amount of vascular tissue, but later the vascular tissue in the shaft atrophies and dries out. This results in a marked decrease in the weight of the plumage.

The weight of the feather pulp is discussed in chapter 7, page 366. Pulp weight may be several times the weight of the feather. In a study of 12 chickens, Weiske (1889:table

A), reported a slight decrease in feather weight after body weight attained 1,094 gm. When feather weight was converted to percentages of body weight, the same decrease was observed. This takes place at about the time that the growing feathers have established a constant length.

Latimer (1924, 1925) noted similarity in the curves of feather to body weight and thymus to body weight but attached no significance to this similarity.

In a later paper, Latimer (1932) observed that the feathers of a male Single Comb White Leghorn Chicken formed 3.7 percent of the body weight at hatching. This ratio rose to a maximum of 9.8 percent at 1,100 gm. body weight and declined to 5.5 percent in the adult. The ratios for the females were similar except that the maximum percentage was reached at 1,300 gm., and in the adult it decreased to 4 percent of the body weight. These values for adult birds are of the same order of magnitude as those given by Jaap and Turner (1943) (fourth column of table 7). They do not differ widely from results in earlier studies by Zaitschek (1908) in which calculations of feather to body weight ratios on 131 chickens of various breeds and ages gave an average value of 7.7 percent with a range of 2.7 to 11.4 percent. The actual weight of feathers varied from 21 to 143 grams with an average of 85 grams. The data were based on birds of different breeds and ages. Turček (1966) determined feather weight as a percentage of body weight for 91 species representing 34 families of birds. The values varied from 4 to 11, however, plus or minus 3 standard errors fell within the narrower range of 5.97 to 6.63 percent. Turček obtained a highly significant negative correlation between plumage weight and the logarithm of body weight.

Hammond (1944) found that in the Beltsville Small White Turkey the feathers formed 6.93 percent of the live weight and that the quill feathers formed 26.23 percent of the total feather weight.

Hutt and Ball (1938) plotted the curve shown in figure 125 and utilized the data on passerine birds presented by Wetmore (1936). From these data, Hutt and Ball arrived at the regression equation of—

$$Y = 910.17 \, X^{-.815}$$

where

$$Y = \frac{\text{number of feathers}}{\text{body weight in grams}} \text{ and } X = \text{body weight in grams.}$$

The fit of the curve to the points is shown by the solid line. When this equation for passerines is applied to chickens (Jaap and Turner, 1943), the feathers per gram of body weight are consistently higher than the calculated values. This may be due to the difference in body weight of passerines and chickens.

The study of Hutt and Ball (1938) was concerned with feather number, body weight, and surface area; the last of these is represented by the dashed line in figure 125 and demonstrates that a decrease in surface area takes place with an increase in weight. This curve accounts only in part for the associated decrease in feather number with increase

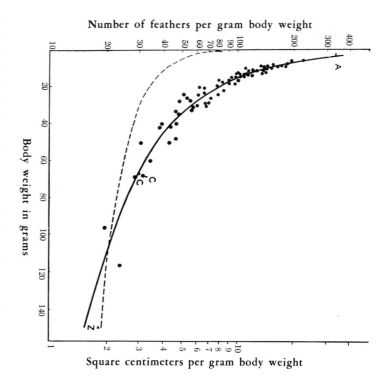

FIGURE 125.—Relationships of feather weight to body weight for various species of passerine birds. The solid line plots the relationship of the number of feathers per gram of body weight to the total body weight. The relationships of four species of nonpasserine birds are indicated by dots A, C, C, and Z. The dashed line plots the relationship of the square centimeters per gram of body weight to the total body weight. (From Hutt and Ball, 1936.)

in weight. It is necessary also to take into account the increase in feather area with increase in body weight. Some estimates of the importance of feather size, weight, and area to body area could be attained as follows: The number of feathers could be considered to be constant in a chicken from hatching to maturity. The areas of contour feathers could be determined for representative areas of the body, multiplied by the number of feathers in the area, and set forth as a ratio with surface area. From the curve (dashed line of fig. 125) presented by Hutt and Ball (1938), it is assumed that with increasing age the ratio of surface area to body weight would become less. One should plan to use an all-white chicken such as a Single Comb White Leghorn in view of conclusions by Giaja (1931) and by Korelus (1947:231) that pigment significantly adds to the weight of feathers.

The problem of determining surface areas accurately for birds has been difficult. Hutt and Ball discussed the problems involved, and for the dashed line reproduced in figure 125 they used the formula derived by Mitchell (1930) for the chicken, namely, $S = 8.19 \, W^{.705}$ where S = surface area and W = body weight. Wetmore (1936) tried several physical methods for determining surface area of a bird and was unable to obtain less than 2 percent error; however, this error is undoubtedly less than that obtained by the use of generalized formulas.

CHAPTER 4

Molts and Plumages of Domestic Chickens

INTRODUCTION

Phenomenon of Molting

The feathering of fully grown birds was described in chapter 3. However, from the time the bird is hatched until it becomes an adult, feathering passes through several changes of appearance. These changes are due largely to replacement of the feathers. In most birds, the shape of each feather is established during its growth and does not change thereafter except through wear. All feathers of fully grown birds are replaced by molting, usually at regular intervals.

The outermost layer of the skin and some other integumentary derivatives besides feathers also molt. This is not true of structures composed of so-called hard keratin (e.g., rhamphotheca and metatarsal spurs) that normally wears down. Structures of so-called soft keratin (e.g., skin, comb, and wattles), however, characteristically slough off the outer cornified layer. This sloughing off is thought to occur in adult chickens during the annual complete molt of the feathers (Spearman, 1966:73). In puffins the corneous plates of the rhamphotheca and fleshy growths at the rictus and above the eyes are shed after the breeding season (Bureau, 1879). The claws and horny fringes on the toes of many grouse and ptarmigan are shed in the spring. In certain nestling birds, special structures of functional significance are lost about the time of fledging. These include the claws on the first two digits of the hand in the Hoatzins (*Opisthocomus hoazin*) and the thick, horny heel pads on the back of the tarsal joints in woodpeckers, toucans, and barbets (Harrison, 1964:489).

Molting is a process that involves two phenomena—the shedding of an old part (ecdysis) and the growth of a new one (endysis). It is commonly thought that these steps occur in this order, and even that the old part must be lost in order to make way for its replacement. Watson (1963b: 493) has shown, on the contrary, that—

> In the repeated molt cycle of many, if not all birds, the dropping of the old generation of feathers is brought about by the initiation of growth in the new generation which pushes the old feathers passively out of the follicles. Molt in birds is consequently a single growth process actively concerned only with the production of the new generation of feathers.

Our observations confirm the pushing out of one feather by another as the normal situation in all five species we studied. This is described and illustrated in this chapter.

Terminology

The single generation of feathers that is brought in by each molt is known as a plumage. This restricted meaning of the term was proposed by Humphrey and Parkes (1959) in their important analysis of the concepts and terminology of molts and plumages. A bird may wear feathers of more than one generation at the same time. As will be shown, this is because some molts are complete—affecting all the tracts—while others are partial—affecting only certain tracts or specific feathers. Hence, on certain tracts the feathers of a given plumage may be retained, whereas on other tracts they are replaced by those of a new plumage. The aggregate of feathers worn by a bird at a given time, regardless of the relative time that they were acquired, is called the feather coat (Humphrey and Parkes, 1959) or the feathering (Palmer, 1962). In summary, the feathering is composed of one or more plumages.

Molts and plumages can be identified most easily with numbers. Accordingly, the natal down is the first plumage and the molt that brings in the next plumage is the first molt. This plan is adequate for a study of plumage succession during the first year of life, and it is followed in this chapter. It is less useful for studies of older birds, however, where the number of a plumage or molt is less important than its place in the cycle. As used here, a cycle in an adult bird is the period that "runs from a given plumage or molt to the next occurrence of the same plumage or molt" (Humphrey and Parkes, 1959: 3). The cycle of molt for most birds is 1 year. Some species or populations of species (e.g., Sooty Tern, *Sterna fuscata*) have a reproductive cycle that is shorter or longer than a year, and their cycles of plumage succession may be adjusted in a like manner. We have not found any reliable data on the adult plumage cycle of modern varieties of chickens. It seems to be annual in chickens under natural photoperiod but is commonly suppressed or altered in those under artificial photoperiod.

The most widely used terminologies for molts and plumages have been derived from Dwight (1900a, 1902). In these systems, the names of plumages are related either to seasons or to events in the reproductive cycle. The molts of adults are named in reference to the nuptial plumage, that is, prenuptial molt and postnuptial molt. Humphrey and Parkes (1959) pointed out several flaws in this scheme and proposed a new approach to replace it. Neither the traditional (Dwight-based) system nor the new (Humphrey-Parkes) system is strictly necessary for a study of the early molts and plumages of chickens. Certain features of the new system appear to be more appropriate than the traditional one for birds in general and domestic species in particular.

First, Humphrey and Parkes (1959:10) recognized that "the energy expenditure and other physiological changes connected with growth are significant in relation to the *incoming* feathers and have nothing to do with the feathers that have been shed." Accordingly, they named molts in reference to the plumages that they introduce, that is, pre- instead of post-.

Second, the names they chose are not related to the seasons or events in the annual cycle. This is an obvious advantage in domestic birds, which commonly live indoors under controlled conditions and may lay eggs during most of the year. Both the Dwight and the Humphrey-Parkes terminologies are based on the assumption that most normal adult birds in nature have at least one complete molt per cycle. This molt is considered homologous in most species. In the Humphrey-Parkes system, the term "basic" is used for the plumage that is completely renewed every cycle. This plumage is introduced by a prebasic molt. Many species have two plumages per cycle; the second one is known as the alternate plumage. It is introduced by a prealternate molt that is usually partial, but is complete in certain species. A few species have still another change of feathers per cycle, known as the partial presupplemental molt and the supplemental plumage. Many examples of different plumage sequences are given by Humphrey and Parkes (1959).

A third advantage of their system is that it clearly distinguishes between the feather coat and its age components (plumages). As will be seen, the feather coat of young chickens consists of two or more plumages in a constantly changing proportion. It is much easier to deal with this situation with the Humphrey-Parkes approach than with the traditional one.

The new system has been severely criticized (Stresemann, 1963), and its authors acknowledge that there will be difficulties in applying it to certain groups of birds (Humphrey and Parkes, 1963). Nevertheless, it works well for chickens and, within the limits of available information, can be used for comparing the plumage succession of these birds with those of wild galliform species.

Table 8 shows the numerical designations for plumages and molts, the equivalent terms used by poultrymen, and those proposed by Humphrey and Parkes. Explanations of three of these terms and a related one (not shown) are in order here. The term "prejuvenal molt," shown as a synonym for the first molt, was not actually used by Humphrey and Parkes. We have coined it here, in accordance with their system. We use "juvenal" to designate the first generation of contour feathers after the natal down. This follows the distinction made by Dwight (1900) and discussed critically by Eisenmann (1965). "Juvenile" is a less specific term that refers to immaturity in general. It can be applied to either plumages or developmental stages before the adult condition. In poultry terminology, juvenile has been restricted to a specific plumage, that which precedes the adult, but we do not use it in this sense.

The term "definitive" refers to "plumages which do not change further with age" (Humphrey and Parkes, 1959:16). Such plumages are molted, of course, but they reoccur at the same stage in successive cycles, and the feathers are identical in appearance each time.

One may wonder why, if molts are named according to the plumages they introduce (in the Humphrey-Parkes system), they are numbered corresponding to the plumages they follow. If the prejuvenal molt, for example, leads to

TABLE 8.—*Terminology of molts and plumages*

Numerical terms used		Terms proposed by Humphrey and Parkes (1959)		Terms used by poultrymen (Chu, 1938)
Molt No.	Generation No.			
	1st		Natal plumage[1]	Down plumage
1st		Prejuvenal molt[1]		
	2d		Juvenal plumage	Chick plumage
2d		First prebasic molt		
	3d		First basic plumage	Juvenile plumage
3d		Second prebasic molt or prealternate molt[2]		
	4th		Second basic plumage or alternate plumage[2]	Adult plumage

[1] Terms not actually used by Humphrey and Parkes but consistent with their system.

[2] The homology of these molts and plumages in chickens is not known. See text, page 233.

the juvenal or second plumage, why is it not numbered the second molt? The reason is simply that it is the first molt, the natal or first plumage having been grown in the embryo.

Methods of Study

The onset of a molt can be dated most accurately by examining histological sections of follicles, in search of growing feathers. This method, however, is hardly practical for following the course of molting through the feather tracts. Castoff feathers are a good sign that a molt has begun, and if found promptly they may reveal the date of onset within a few days. A drawback to the use of shed feathers is that they must be examined closely in order to identify accurately the site of molting. Remiges and rectrices can often be located within three follicles, but other feathers cannot be identified so precisely. The descriptions of the feathers of domestic birds in chapter 6 can be helpful in identifying castoff feathers.

The course of a molt can best be followed by repeated, periodic examinations of the same birds. At each examination, the developmental stage of every feather, or at least portion of a tract, is recorded. The original data in this chapter were obtained by this method. They include records of the onset of molts, based on the first observations of the ensheathed tips of new feathers above the surface of the skin. These emerge several days or a week later than the

actual onset of regeneration, but the delay in establishing the dates affects all the feathers in approximately the same way. The time lag between the actual and the apparent onset of molt is greater in the remiges and rectrices, where the follicles are deep, than in the body feathers.

The birds used were 35 Single Comb White Leghorn Chickens from a highly inbred line (coefficient of inbreeding more than 90 percent) at the Regional Poultry Research Laboratory, East Lansing, Mich. They were obtained in February when newly hatched and were raised to an age of 6 months. They were kept in an indoor cage, exposed to normal daylight. Ten chicks were painted with an alcohol solution of eosin when they were a few days old so that the new feathers could be more easily spotted as they replaced the natal down. These birds were identified with numbered aluminum wing bands, and the feathers of each were examined approximately once a week during the first 21 weeks, and every other week for the next 4 weeks. The observations on these chicks gave some indication of the range of individual variation in the timing and progress of molts. The remaining birds were killed and examined at the rate of one per week for the first 13 weeks and then one every other week for the next 6 weeks. For each specimen, the developmental stages of all feathers were marked on diagrams of the pterylosis, as explained in chapter 10. The centers and gradients of molting could be determined from these records.

GROSS APPEARANCE OF GROWING FEATHERS

Virtually all the feather follicles are formed during embryonic life. Throughout the life of a bird after it hatches, each follicle produces a series of feathers. A history of molts and plumages is a composite of the histories of all these series. In order better to understand molting on a broad scale, we will first review the growth of an individual feather. We will describe here only the appearance of the portion of the feather above the skin. Although these conditions described are superficial, they generally cannot be seen through the feathering. It is necessary to push aside some feathers so that others can be seen at their level of emergence from their follicles. The histology of a developing feather, and particularly of the portion inside the follicle, is treated in chapter 7.

The early history of a series of feathers on a chicken is summarized diagrammatically in figure 126. The first-generation (natal) feather (*gens prima pennarum*), or natal down (*protoptilus*), is produced during embryonic life, and is already above the skin at the time of hatching. After it fluffs out, it can be seen to have the structure of a down feather (described on p. 264). A second-generation (juvenal) feather (*gens secunda pennarum*) begins to form in the follicle late in embryonic life. As it grows, it pushes the natal down out of the follicle on its tip. Elevation of the down is the first gross sign that replacement of the feathers is already underway. This occurs in certain remiges and

rectrices by the time of hatching, but not until several days later in most other feathers.

The new feather is tightly furled inside a sheath while it forms. As it appears above the skin, it has a long conical shape with a blunt tip (figs. 127, 131) and a slightly moist surface. A feather at this stage in any generation is often called a pin feather, but we designate it as representing the early immature stage of development.

Starting at the tip the sheath dries and flakes off. This allows the feather to begin to emerge (figs. 128, 131, 132). The ensheathed portion is marked into three zones by color. At the distal end it is opaque white, owing to the presence of air within and around the fully developed, soon-to-emerge barbs and rachis. Approximately in the middle is a narrow, medium-pink zone that marks the richly vascularized top of the pulp. At this level a pulp cap is formed, and the parts of the feather are completing their keratinization. Feathers at this stage in any generation are known as blood quills, but we designate them as representing the midimmature stage of development. The natal down is usually knocked off the juvenal feather by the time the latter reaches this stage. (Compare figs. 127 and 128.) Presence of the natal down is no criterion for the stage of development of the juvenal feather.

The new feather continues to lengthen and emerge from its sheath; the pulp appears to recede as it is resorbed at the

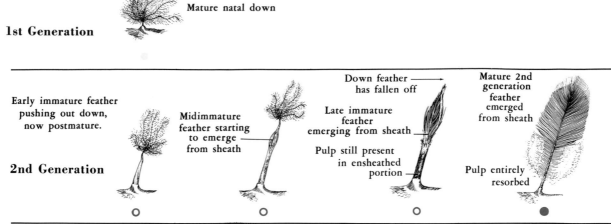

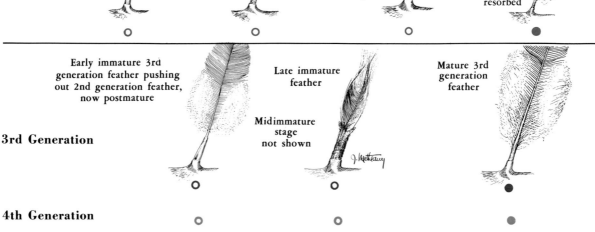

FIGURE 126.—Development of feathers above the skin, during the first four generations. This chart not only summarizes the events, but it also serves as a key to the colored symbols in figures 143 through 156. Colors denote different feather generations; a circle indicates a feather that is still growing; a dot, a feather that is fully grown.

tip (figs. 129 to 133). The process of pulp resorption is discussed on pages 381–383 and illustrated in figure 240. We designate the late immature stage of development as that which lasts from the time a feather has emerged at least halfway from its sheath until it is fully grown. A feather is considered fully grown (mature) when its vanes are entirely free of sheath and when pulp is no longer visible (figs. 129, 130, 133). To see these signs, the portion of a feather just above the surface of the skin must be examined. Development is not quite completed when the pulp disappears below the surface. It takes up to about 10 days for the pulp still in the calamus to be completely resorbed, depending on the length of the calamus.

Another molt begins after the mature juvenal feather has been held for a period of 1 week to a few months. This event is signaled by the loss of such a feather or by the emergence of its calamus from the follicle. These are evidence that a new feather has started to grow and to displace its predecessor. The juvenal feather may be pushed entirely out of its follicle and above the skin before it is lost from the tip of the third-generation feather (fig. 134). As long as an old feather remains on the tip of its successor, we refer to it as being in the postmature stage of development.

The sequence of events in the development of the third-generation feather (*gens tertia pennarum*) is the same as before although the midimmature stage is not shown in figure 126. This molt is less conspicuous than the preceding one because the new feathers are at first similar to those they replace. By the time they are fully grown, of course, differences of size, texture, and pattern can be seen (for example, see fig. 186).

Successive stages of molting can be clearly seen in the row of remiges (figs. 135, 136). The direction of the wave of molting can easily be told after replacement has begun because it goes from the newer generation of feathers to the older (e.g., third generation to second). In the primary remiges of chickens, molting proceeds from the innermost to the outermost. When a third-generation primary near the wrist is late immature, the next few remiges distal to it are less and less advanced (fig. 135). These are followed, closer to the wing tip, by mature and finally immature second-generation primaries. An empty follicle is sometimes found between the youngest third-generation feather and the oldest second-generation feather. The wave of molting can be seen to have reached the mature second-generation primaries when they start to be pushed out of their follicles.

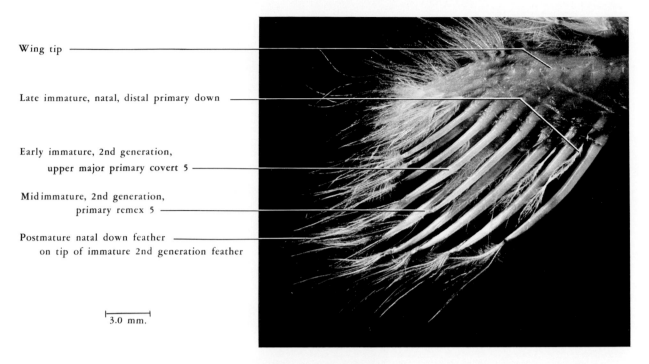

Wing tip

Late immature, natal, distal primary down

Early immature, 2nd generation,
upper major primary covert 5

Midimmature, 2nd generation,
primary remex 5

Postmature natal down feather
on tip of immature 2nd generation feather

3.0 mm.

FIGURE 127.—Feathers on the dorsal side of the left hand of a 1-day-old Single Comb White Leghorn Chicken. The upper major primary coverts 1 to 4, carpal remex, marginal coverts, and upper distal primary downs have been removed.

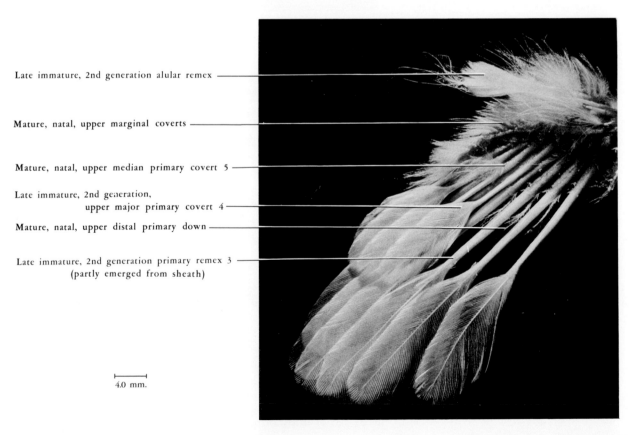

Late immature, 2nd generation alular remex

Mature, natal, upper marginal coverts

Mature, natal, upper median primary covert 5

Late immature, 2nd generation,
upper major primary covert 4

Mature, natal, upper distal primary down

Late immature, 2nd generation primary remex 3
(partly emerged from sheath)

4.0 mm.

FIGURE 128.—Feathers on the dorsal side of the left hand of an 8-day-old Single Comb White Leghorn Chicken. The upper major primary coverts 1 to 3, carpal remex, marginal coverts, and many down feathers have been removed.

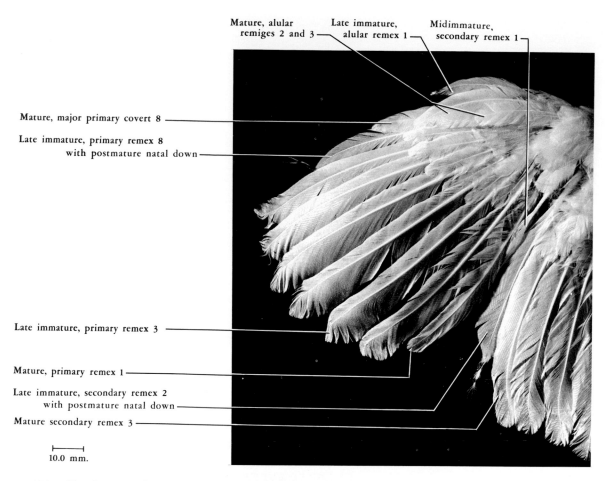

Mature, alular
remiges 2 and 3

Late immature,
alular remex 1

Midimmature,
secondary remex 1

Mature, major primary covert 8

Late immature, primary remex 8
with postmature natal down

Late immature, primary remex 3

Mature, primary remex 1

Late immature, secondary remex 2
with postmature natal down

Mature secondary remex 3

10.0 mm.

FIGURE 129.—Feathers on the dorsal side of the left wing of a 25-day-old Single Comb White Leghorn Chicken.

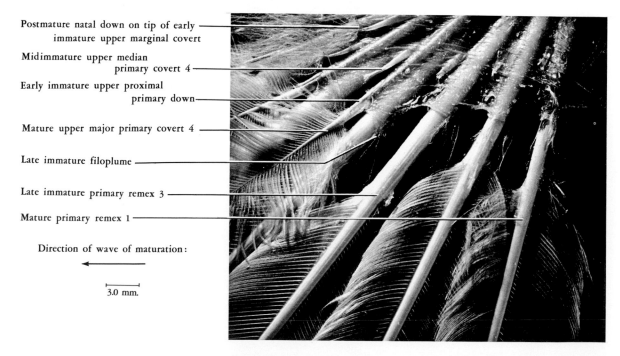

Postmature natal down on tip of early
immature upper marginal covert

Midimmature upper median
primary covert 4

Early immature upper proximal
primary down

Mature upper major primary covert 4

Late immature filoplume

Late immature primary remex 3

Mature primary remex 1

Direction of wave of maturation:

3.0 mm.

FIGURE 130.—Closer dorsal view than shown in figure 129 of inner primary remiges on the left wing of a 24-day-old Single Comb White Leghorn Chicken. The upper major primary coverts 1 to 3, upper marginal coverts, and upper proximal primary downs have been removed.

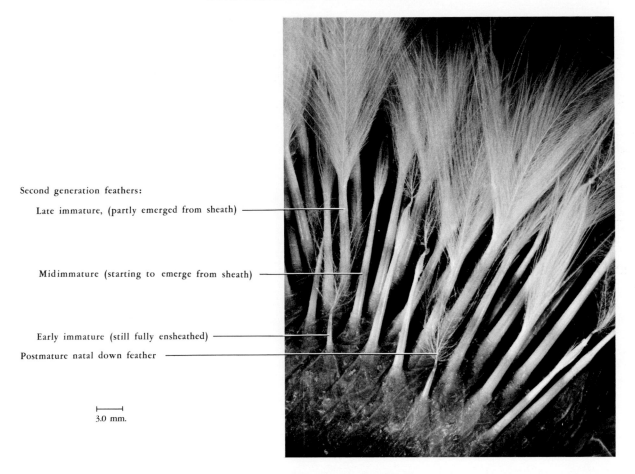

Second generation feathers:

Late immature, (partly emerged from sheath)

Midimmature (starting to emerge from sheath)

Early immature (still fully ensheathed)
Postmature natal down feather

3.0 mm.

FIGURE 131.—Anterior view of feathers on the left thigh of a 20-day-old Single Comb White Leghorn Chicken. Knee region is below middle of bottom edge of picture. Second-generation feathers are shown at various stages of growth. The most advanced are in the background.

DEVELOPMENT OF PLUMAGES

Histories of Separate Tracts

The ages at which plumages are acquired and lost in each tract are shown in a series of bar charts (figs. 138 to 142). Each generation of feathers is distinguished by a color, whereas immature and mature stages of a generation are shown as shaded and solidly colored areas, respectively (fig. 137). The ages at which molts begin or feathers complete their growth vary among individual birds. The transitions between generations or developmental stages are therefore represented by sloping lines that span the range of ages for these changes as seen in our experimental chickens. The more variable the age at which a transition occurs, the more gradual the slope of the line. In the charts for the remiges (figs. 138, 139) and rectrices (fig. 140), each bar represents the history of the feathers from one follicle. In the charts for the body (fig. 141) and limb (fig. 142) tracts, each bar represents the history of an entire tract. The sloping lines in these latter bars actually cover two kinds of variation—the time span needed for a molt or attainment of feather maturity to pass entirely through a tract and the variation in these times among individual birds.

Primary remiges (fig. 138)

The six inner primaries of a newly hatched chicken belong to the second generation of feathers, having attained early to midimmature stages of development (fig. 127). The four outer primaries are represented by mature natal downs. The innermost primary (primary 1) becomes mature on the 22d to 28th day after hatching (figs. 129, 130), and it molts at 44 to 51 days. The third-generation feather reaches maturity at 77 to 90 days, and the molt into a fourth-generation feather may begin by the 175th day.

The nine remaining primaries have similar histories, but each develops later than its proximal neighbor. As a result, the center of development is at the follicle for the first primary and the wave of molting proceeds distally to the wing tip. The first molt is complete but subsequent ones are either complete or partial, depending on the fate of the second-generation 10th primary. This feather is replaced in some chickens by the 145th day, whereas it is held for much longer in others, even until a bird is more than 1 year old.

Three generations of feathers may be present simultane-

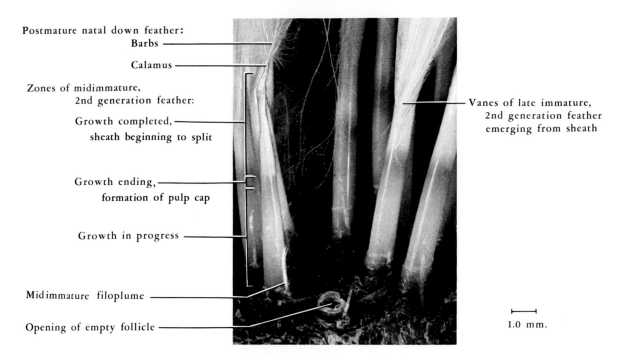

Postmature natal down feather:
Barbs

Calamus

Zones of midimmature,
2nd generation feather:

Growth completed,
sheath beginning to split

Growth ending,
formation of pulp cap

Growth in progress

Midimmature filoplume

Opening of empty follicle

Vanes of late immature,
2nd generation feather
emerging from sheath

1.0 mm.

FIGURE 132.—Feathers on the back of the neck of a 26-day-old Single Comb White Leghorn Chicken. The pulp inside the ensheathed portion of a feather (zone of growth in progress) imparts to it a pinkish tinge in life, shown here as light gray. Blood is released during the formation of a pulp cap, giving this zone (where growth is ending) a stronger pink color, shown here as medium gray.

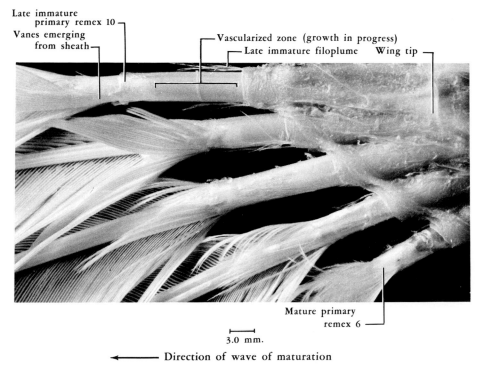

Late immature
primary remex 10

Vanes emerging
from sheath

Vascularized zone (growth in progress)

Late immature filoplume   Wing tip

Mature primary
remex 6

3.0 mm.

← Direction of wave of maturation

FIGURE 133.—Ventral view of second-generation primary remiges 10 to 6 (upper left to lower right) on the right wing of a 47-day-old Single Comb White Leghorn Chicken. The under primary coverts and downs have been removed.

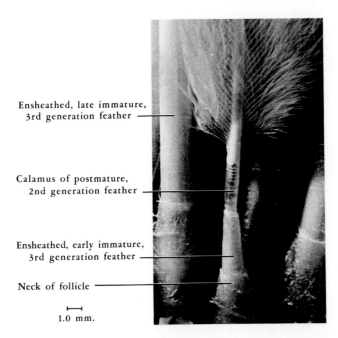

Ensheathed, late immature, 3rd generation feather

Calamus of postmature, 2nd generation feather

Ensheathed, early immature, 3rd generation feather

Neck of follicle

1.0 mm.

FIGURE 134.—Feathers on the back of a 62-day-old Single Comb White Leghorn Chicken.

ously for a while, because in some chickens the third molt begins before the second molt has ended. At the 175th day, primaries 1 and 2 may be in the fourth generation, 3 through 9 in the third generation, and 10, still in the second generation.

Secondary remiges (*fig. 139*)

In a newly hatched chicken, secondaries 1 and 2 are natal downs, 3 through 11 are early immature second-generation feathers, and 12 through 18 are again natal downs. Secondaries 3 and 4 lead the way in the subsequent history of this tract, for their schedule is close to that of primaries 1 and 2. The juvenal secondary 3 reaches maturity within 30 to 40 days and molts by the 62d day. Its successor matures at 98 to 112 days and is held for at least 6 months.

The sequence of growth and molting in the other secondaries proceeds first toward the elbow and then toward the wrist. Second-generation feathers 1 and 2 and 12 through 18 appear at 12 to 23 days after hatching. During the first 5 months, secondaries 2, 12, and 13 all develop on much the same schedule, but later 2 becomes slower than the others. Secondary 1 is the slowest of all, for at 6 months of

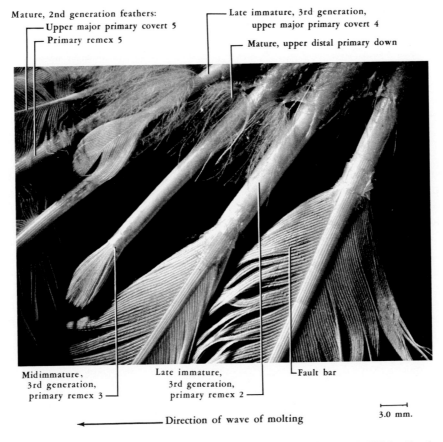

Mature, 2nd generation feathers:
Upper major primary covert 5
Primary remex 5

Late immature, 3rd generation, upper major primary covert 4

Mature, upper distal primary down

Midimmature, 3rd generation, primary remex 3

Late immature, 3rd generation, primary remex 2

Fault bar

Direction of wave of molting

3.0 mm.

FIGURE 135.—Feathers on the dorsal side of the left hand of a 57-day-old Single Comb White Leghorn Chicken. Upper major primary coverts 1 to 3 and upper proximal primary downs 1 to 3 have been removed.

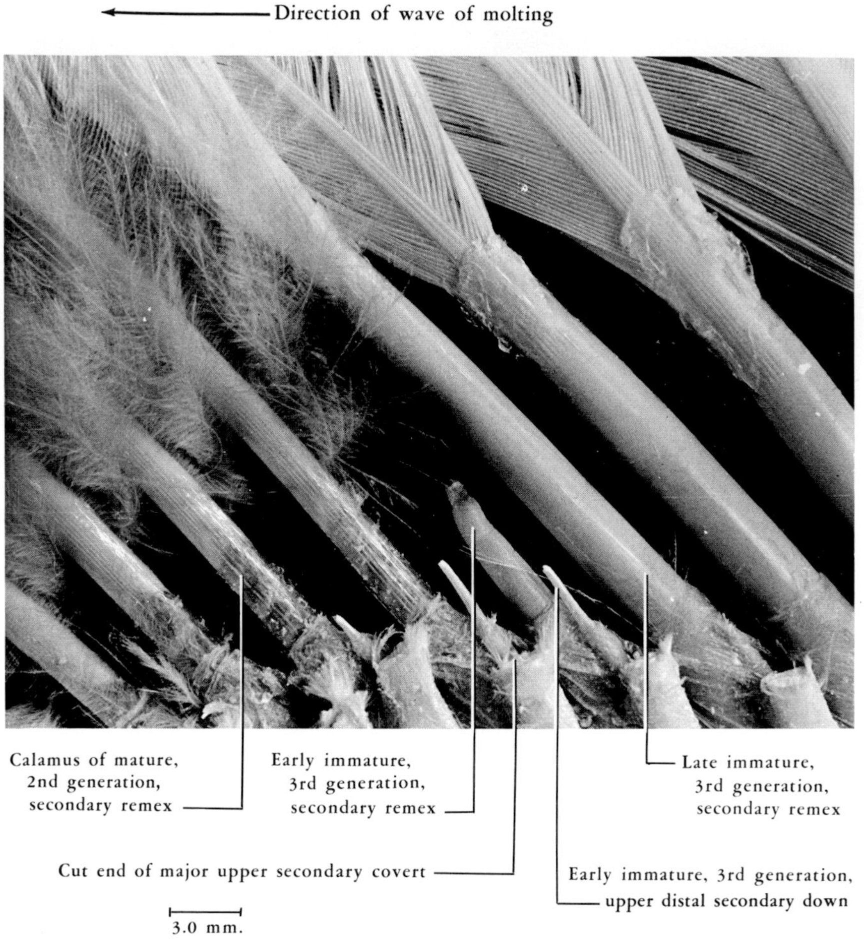

←———————— Direction of wave of molting

Calamus of mature,
2nd generation,
secondary remex

Early immature,
3rd generation,
secondary remex

Late immature,
3rd generation,
secondary remex

Cut end of major upper secondary covert

Early immature, 3rd generation,
upper distal secondary down

3.0 mm.

FIGURE 136.—Dorsal view of secondary remiges on the left wing of a 91-day-old Single Comb White Leghorn Chicken. All upper major secondary coverts and some distal secondary downs and filoplumes have been removed.

age it is the only second-generation feather still present in the series. As with the primary remiges, the later the secondaries pass through the first molt, the more the time of molt onset varies among individuals.

Rectrices (*fig. 140*)

At the time of hatching, the rectrices are present as down feathers, but within 2 days the central pair of these is pushed out of the follicles. Waves of molting proceed outward, and pairs 2 through 6 (numbered by pairs outward from the central pair) are replaced by the end of the first week. Pairs

1 through 6 become fully grown by the 32d day in some birds; pairs 1 through 3 are then held for only about 1 week before they are molted. Although these last feathers do not reach maturity until after certain remiges and humeral feathers, they are the first to be replaced by third-generation feathers. A difference between the sexes appears in the rate at which this (second) molt progresses through the tract. The two outermost pairs of rectrices are replaced at 76 to 90 days in most females and 90 to 105 days in most males. The acceleration of the rate of tail development in females is more noticeable at the next molt. Fourth-generation

Key

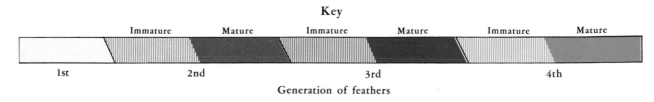

Generation of feathers

FIGURE 137.—Key to charts shown in figures 138 through 142. The feather generations are represented by the same colors as shown in figure 126. Shading indicates that a feather or group of feathers is growing; solid color indicates that it is fully grown. See text for further explanation.

Primary Remiges

Primary
number

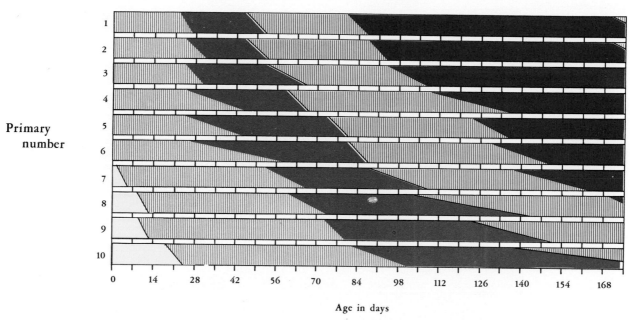

Age in days

FIGURE 138.—History of the primary remiges in Single Comb White Leghorn Chickens. Each bar represents the series of feathers from one follicle. See text and figure 137 for further explanation.

central rectrices appear within 124 to 138 days in females but not until after 175 days in males.

Capital tracts (fig. 141)

The head is one of the last and slowest regions to develop new feathers. The tips of second-generation feathers emerge from their follicles here at about 18 days, 1 week after they have appeared elsewhere on the body. The first molt in this region begins on the occipital and auricular tracts, and spreads, forward and downward across the sides of the head. It starts 1 week later in the submalar and interramal tracts and proceeds upward. Development and molting thus converge toward the eye. Natal downs finally disappear from this area at 62 to 69 days, just as third-generation feathers are being introduced on the top of the head. The course of the second molt is the same as before. The tips of fourth-generation feathers (*gens quarta pennarum*) begin to appear at about 175 days in females but not until a later age in males.

Spinal tracts (fig. 141)

The dorsal cervical, interscapular, dorsal, and pelvic tracts form a continuous series in their history of plumages. The first molt begins along the midline of the interscapular tract, and early immature juvenal feathers appear there at 13 days. Three days later, such feathers are present on all the spinal tracts. At 16 days, in some chickens, a few feathers on the interscapular and pelvic tracts have started to emerge from their sheaths. By the 23d day, all the natal downs have been replaced except for a few at the upper end of the neck and along the margins of the tracts. These last

may be retained until about the 40th day. At this age, some of the second-generation feathers on the interscapular, dorsal, and pelvic tracts have become mature. Third-generation feathers appear near the middle of these tracts by the 55th day. Molting proceeds outward, and reaches the dorsal cervical tract within a week. Most of the third-generation feathers make their appearance by the 91st day, but the last of them, on the borders of the tracts, do not show up until about the 138th day. These feathers begin to reach maturity by the 84th day, starting with those in the dorsal tract.

The molt into a fourth plumage begins at about 138 days of age. Some of these feathers become fully grown on the dorsal tract by the 161st day.

There does not seem to be any difference between the sexes in the history of the spinal tract plumages up to this time.

At least the first three molts start along the midline, chiefly in the interscapular and dorsal tracts. Gradients in development and molting radiate from here—anteriorly into the cervical tract, posteriorly into the pelvic tract, and laterally through all these tracts.

Pectoral and ventral cervical tracts (fig. 141)

The tips of the juvenal feathers on the tracts appear between about 11 and 23 days after hatching. They are introduced later and more slowly—until about the 47th day—on the ventral and cervical apterium and the pectoral apterium. A few natal downs may persist on these apteria up to about 124 days. Some of the new feathers on the tracts become fully grown by the 35th day, but it is not until about

Secondary Remiges

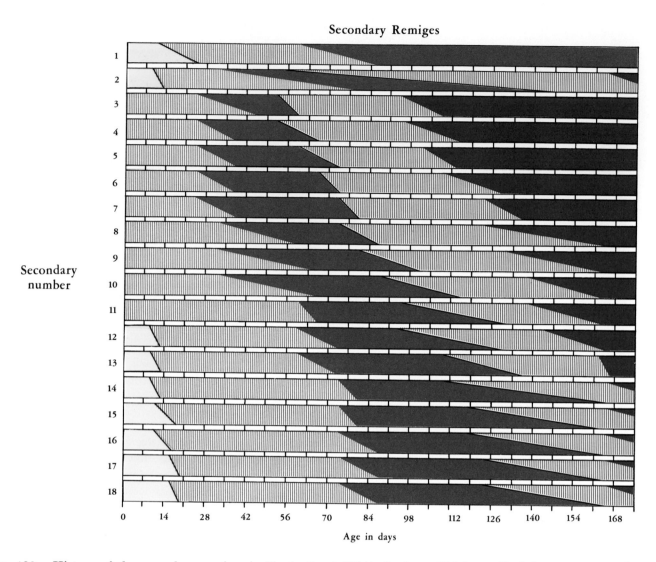

FIGURE 139.—History of the secondary remiges in Single Comb White Leghorn Chickens. Each bar represents the series of feathers from one follicle. See text and figure 137 for further explanation.

Rectrices

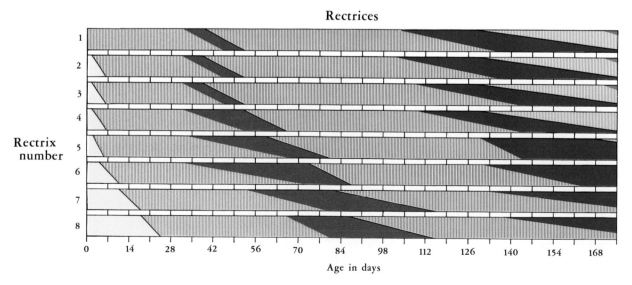

FIGURE 140.—History of the rectrices in Single Comb White Leghorn Chickens. Each bar represents the series of feathers from one follicle. See text and figure 137 for further explanation.

Body Tracts

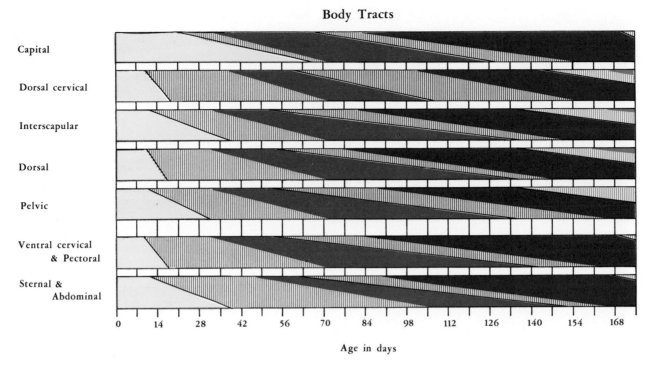

FIGURE 141.—History of the feathers on the body tracts in Single Comb White Leghorn Chickens. Each bar represents all the feathers in one or two tracts. See text and figure 137 for further explanation.

the 77th day that all of them reach this stage. Third-generation feathers begin to appear about the 56th day. The molt that brings them in is much slower than the molt into second-generation feathers. In many chickens, the molt that brings in the third-generation feathers is not finished until about the 105th day. The new (third-generation) feathers reach maturity at 84 to 168 days of age. By the end of this time the molt into the fourth plumage has begun.

In all this history, the most advanced feathers are those in a pair of narrow zones along the axes of the tracts. These areas run from the posterior half of the ventral cervical tract through the anterior half of the pectoral tract. Waves of development and molting radiate from here, first anteriorly, then medially and laterally, and finally posteriorly. The last feathers to be replaced are those on the cervical and pectoral apteria and on the posterior end of the pectoral tract.

Sternal and abdominal tracts (fig. 141)

During the first 6 months, the feathers of the sternal and abdominal tracts develop later and more slowly than those of the pectoral and the ventral cervical tracts. The tips of the second-generation feathers first appear above the surface at the 16th day after hatching and continue to appear until about the 40th day. Even the earliest feathers do not reach maturity until almost the 55th day, about 3 weeks later than on the pectoral and ventral cervical tracts. Replacement by third-generation feathers begins about the 62d day but is not completed until about the 161st day. These feath-

ers start to reach maturity at about the 105th day, still 3 weeks behind the pectoral and ventral cervical tracts. Fourth-generation feathers begin to appear at 161 to 175 days in all the ventral tracts.

Molting and development start along the midline of the abdominal tract. They proceed anteriorly along the middle of each sternal tract, laterally in both tracts, and medially in the sternal tracts. The last feathers to develop and molt are those in the lateral abdominal tract. The history of plumages on all ventral body tracts is the same in both sexes during the first 6 months.

Humeral tracts (fig. 142)

The emergence of feathers from the right and left humeral tracts is among the most advanced during the first few molts. The tips of the second-generation feathers appear between the 6th and the 26th days after hatching. Some of these feathers become mature by the 33d day. The molt into the third-generation feathers begins about the 50th day, and lasts until about the 138th day in some chickens. This plumage reaches maturity from about the 76th day until about the 175th day, a longer span of time than found generally in other tracts. This situation is apparently due to the wide range in the size of the feathers from the cranial to the caudal ends of the tract (fig. 195, p. 294). All the feathers seem to grow at about the same rate but some require much longer to reach their final size than others.

The initial precedence of the humeral tracts gradually lessens, and fourth-generation feathers appear concurrently

Limb Tracts

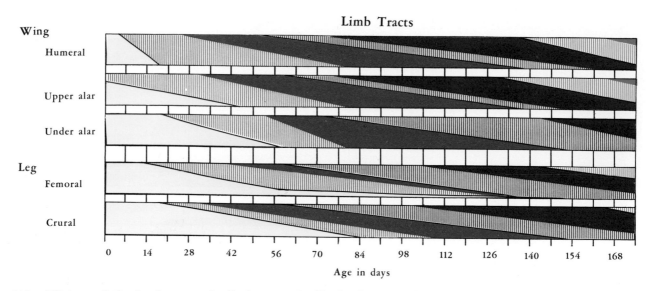

FIGURE 142.—History of the feathers on the limb tracts in Single Comb White Leghorn Chickens. Each bar represents all the feathers in one tract, except that the remiges are not included in the alar tracts. See text and figure 137 for further explanation.

in the spinal, femoral, and humeral tracts about the 138th day.

The first molt begins at the posterolateral region of each humeral tract and proceeds anteriorly and medially. The feathers do not reach maturity in this sequence, however, but in a more or less random fashion within the entire tract. Subsequent molting and feather development start in a longitudinal area through the middle of each tract and proceed toward the margins.

Upper alar tracts (fig. 142)

The upper coverts of the remiges are among the most advanced feathers of a young chicken. Upper major coverts develop and molt at about the same times as their underlying remiges; they are sometimes even ahead of the secondary remiges. In a newly hatched chicken, all the upper major primary coverts and upper major secondary coverts 3 to 12 are already early immature second-generation feathers. The three outer alular remiges reach this stage by the fifth day after hatching. Molting proceeds anteriorly through the coverts into the marginals. Within each row, it goes from the wrist outward on the hand, and from the middle of the forearm toward the ends. New feathers appear along the margin of the anterior patagium, the posthumeral region, and on the alula by the 13th day, and along the anterior margin of the hand by the 19th day. Molting proceeds from these areas, and finally the marginal coverts of the hand and the alula appear about the 44th day. The first feathers to complete their growth are the upper major primary coverts, at about the 26th day. Other feathers reach maturity in the same sequence as that of the molt. It is not until the 84th day that all the second-generation feathers of this tract are mature.

The tips of third-generation feathers begin to appear about the 62d day, and the last of them appear about the 113th day. The feathers reach maturity from about the 90th to the 160th day. About the 131st day, fourth-generation feathers first appear as alular remiges and a few upper major secondary coverts. The secondary remiges are less advanced than their upper major coverts at this time because they are still third-generation feathers. It is not the upper major coverts, however, but the anterior marginal coverts of the prepatagium which, by 175 days, are the first fourth-generation feathers on the tract to reach maturity.

Molting proceeds from five areas in the tract as follows:
1. Anteriorly from the upper major secondary coverts.
2. Anteriorly from the upper major primary coverts.
3. Posteriorly and medially on the alula.
4. Posteriorly from the anterior margin of the prepatagium.
5. Anterolaterally from the posthumeral tract.

The last feathers to change are usually the marginal coverts on the hand and on the center of the prepatagium. The course and schedule of molts on this tract appear the same in both sexes during the first 6 months.

Under alar tracts (fig. 142)

The under alar tract is among the last and the slowest to develop its feathers. The tips of juvenal feathers do not start to appear here until about the 18th day, and they continue to appear almost until the 63d day. Even the earliest of these new feathers do not reach maturity until at least the 55th day. Their subsequent history is not certain because feathers of the second and third generations resemble each other closely. The molt into third-generation feathers seems to begin about the 77th day, and many of these feathers are fully grown by the 131st day. At 175 days, there is not yet a sign of the fourth plumage.

The first molt starts in the distal two-thirds of the rows of under major and median secondary coverts. Next to change are the marginal coverts on the anterior border of the wing and the more proximal of the under major primary coverts.

Femoral tracts (fig. 142)

The femoral tracts (right and left) are among the earliest to start molting but the last to finish. The tips of juvenal feathers appear here on the 9th or 10th day, just after they have emerged on the humeral tracts. It is not until about the 90th day, however, that most of the natal plumage has been replaced. A few natal downs persist at the knee until almost 161 days. The second-generation feathers are slow to grow, and the first of them are not fully grown until the 44th day. Third-generation feathers appear above the skin about the 62d day, and first reach maturity about the 105th day. In some chickens, the second-generation feathers over most of these tracts are replaced by third-generation feathers more rapidly than they, themselves, replace natal downs at the knee. The thighs of these birds are consequently furnished with only first- and third-generation feathers from about the 124th day until the natal downs are lost. The fourth generation of feathers is introduced about the 138th day.

The first molt begins along the posterior border of the tract and proceeds forward. It progresses most rapidly across the dorsal border of the tract. A second wave of molting soon starts along the dorsal border and passes downward, last affecting the feathers on the knee and the area just in front of it. The feathers do not complete their growth in the same order that they were molted. The posterior feathers appear before the anterior ones but, being larger, take more time to complete their development. Subsequent molts also start at the posterior side of the tract, but their progress is no longer regular.

Crural tracts (fig. 142)

The legs rank with the face, the knee region, and the underside of the wings as one of the last regions to lose the natal down. The tips of second-generation feathers first appear above the skin about the 18th day. It is not until about the 90th day that all the downs have been replaced. The second-generation feathers complete their growth from about the 37th until the 113th day. Third-generation feathers begin to appear about the 84th day, and the molt is almost completed by the 175th day.

The foci of molting and feather development in these tracts are around the ankles. Waves of molting and maturation proceed upward, faster on the posterior side than on the anterior. They also spread around the legs, faster on the medial surface than on the lateral. Accordingly, the last feathers to molt and to finish their growth are those on the anterolateral surfaces, below the knees.

Dorsal caudal tract (no chart)

The tips of second-generation feathers emerge above the skin on the upper side of the tail from about the 13th to the 36th days. The earliest of these feathers complete their growth by the 35th day. The upper major tail coverts above the outer rectrices develop before the rectrices themselves, just as happens with the outer primary remiges. Third-generation upper major and minor coverts begin to appear by the 55th day, but in some birds it may take until at least the 103d day before all the juvenal feathers have been replaced. There are no signs of the fourth-generation feathers even by the 175th day.

Molting and growth proceed from the upper major coverts to the minor coverts and other feathers. They progress laterally from the midline in each row. These sequences break down during the maturation of the third-generation feathers, which develop somewhat at random.

Ventral caudal tract (no chart)

The first molt takes place about 5 days later on the under side of the tail than on the upper side. Second-generation feathers appear from about the 18th day to the 40th. The first of the new feathers complete their growth by the 35th day, and the rest reach maturity during the next 4 weeks. The subsequent history of the plumages on this tract is obscure because of the similarity between second and third generation feathers. It appears that the latter are introduced during a long period of time, but that some second-generation feathers may still be present at 131 days.

Molting and development generally start with the under major coverts near the midventral line and progress anteriorly and laterally through the tract.

Changing Composition of Feathering

The history of any tract shows that the age-composition of its feathers changes constantly, starting at hatching or soon afterward. This state of flux lasts until the chicken is at least 6 months old, the duration of our study. It can best be seen by surveying the entire feathering of a chicken at each of several ages. This approach shows not only the changing mixture of plumages but also the foci and gradients of molting and feather development. The descriptions that follow are illustrated by a series of diagrams of the pterylosis of a fully grown chicken (figs. 143–156). Although the shape of the body, and hence that of the tracts, changes as the bird grows, the numbers and relative placement of the feather follicles remain constant from hatching onward. In each diagram, all the feathers of a particular generation are shown in a certain color. The colors used for the different generations are the same as those already used in figure 126 and in the bar charts. In all generations, feathers that are still growing are designated by circles, whereas those that are fully grown are designated by dots. These symbols correspond to the striped and the solidly colored areas, respectively, in the bar charts. The combination of colors and symbols thus tells the plumage and developmental stage of every feather shown in the pterylosis diagram.

0 days (no figure)

A newly hatched chicken is clothed in natal down except for certain remiges and rectrices, which are very early immature second-generation feathers.

8 days (figs. 143, 144)

At 8 days, most of the rectrices, remiges, and upper major remex coverts are early to midimmature second-generation feathers. There are a few very early immature second-generation feathers at the posterolateral corners of the humeral tracts. The rest of the feathers are natal down.

19 days (figs. 145, 146)

At 19 days, all remiges, rectrices, and their upper major coverts are second-generation feathers. Most of them are midimmature to late immature, but those at the outer ends of the rows have not started to break from their sheaths. Midimmature to late immature second-generation feathers are present throughout the spinal, humeral, ventral cervical, pectoral, and caudal tracts. These are surrounded by early immature second-generation feathers and natal down. Early to midimmature new feathers also occur at the upper end of the neck and around the base of the comb, on the upper and under alar tracts, the sternal and abdominal tracts, the posterior and dorsal portions of the femoral tracts, and the crural tracts.

Three weeks after hatching, all the tracts have entered the first molt. The sequence by which second-generation feathers began to appear on the tracts of our birds is summarized as follows:

Feathers present—

At hatching................	Primary remiges 1 to 6, secondary remiges 3 to 11.
By the 3d day...............	Central pair of rectrices.
By the 7th day..............	Upper alar, humeral tracts.
By the 11th day.............	Femoral, pectoral tracts.
By the 14th day.............	Interscapular, dorsal caudal tracts.
By the 17th day.............	Dorsal and ventral cervical, dorsal, pelvic, sternal, and abdominal tracts.
By the 21st day.............	Capital, crural, lateral body, ventral alar, and ventral caudal tracts.

35 days (figs. 147, 148)

At 35 days, many remiges, rectrices, and their upper major coverts are fully grown second-generation feathers. This stage has also been reached in the middle of the ventral cervical and pectoral tracts, among most of the upper secondary coverts and upper marginal coverts of the forearm, and around the ankles. Immature second-generation feathers prevail elsewhere, but natal downs persist in patches on the face, dorsal side of the wing tip, knee region, and the underside of the wing. Natal downs are also present on the lateral pelvic, ventral cervical, pectoral, and abdominal apteria.

55 days (figs. 149, 150)

By the 55th day the second molt has begun, and numerous third-generation feathers have appeared. A few primary remiges, rectrices, and humeral feathers of this plumage are already midimmature. Early immature third-generation feathers are present on the interscapular, dorsal, pelvic, dorsal caudal, upper alar, and pectoral tracts, and around the ankles. The feathering is composed chiefly of fully grown second-generation feathers; it also includes many immature feathers of this plumage around the borders of the tracts and over much of the femoral and crural tracts. Some natal downs still remain on these two tracts, on the lateral body tracts, around the eyes, on the dorsal portions of the abdominal tract, and on the ventral cervical apterium.

77 days (figs. 151, 152)

At 77 days, a few third-generation feathers are already fully grown in the humeral, upper alar, and ventral cervical tracts and in the alular remiges, the first two primary remiges, and the upper major coverts of these remiges. The second molt has spread, with the result that immature third-generation feathers prevail on the spinal, humeral, upper alar, ventral cervical, and pectoral tracts. Fully grown second-generation feathers are common within and around these tracts; they are the prevailing category on the head, the under alar, femoral, crural, sternal, and abdominal tracts. A few second-generation feathers are still growing on all of these tracts except on the capital tracts. Natal downs now occur only on the lateral body tracts, the knee regions, and the lateral body apteria.

103 days (figs. 153, 154)

At 103 days, third-generation feathers prevail on most tracts, though it is only on the dorsal, humeral, and upper alar tracts that most of these feathers have completed their growth. Mature second-generation feathers are still the most numerous type on the capital, under alar, and lateral abdominal tracts. A few second-generation feathers are still growing on the crural tracts and the pectoral apteria. Natal downs persist on the knee regions and the lateral body apteria.

131 days (figs. 155, 156)

At 131 days, the third molt has already begun, and a few upper secondary coverts, alular remiges, and inner pairs of rectrices are young, fourth-generation feathers. The feathering consists chiefly of mature or nearly mature third-generation feathers. Fully grown second-generation feathers occur along the borders of the spinal, humeral, pectoral, and sternal tracts, over most of the under alar tract, and on the crural tract. Primary remiges 8 to 10 and secondary remiges 1 and 13 to 18 may also be mature second-generation feathers. There may not be any immature feathers of this plumage. Only a few natal downs, if any, remain at the knees.

171 days (no figure)

At 171 days, fully grown fourth-generation feathers are common on the interscapular, dorsal, humeral, and upper alar tracts. The three inner pairs of rectrices have reached this stage in females, though not in males. The feathering is mostly composed of immature fourth-generation feathers and mature third-generation feathers. It is possible that the latest molt is not as extensive as it seems, and that some of the immature body feathers actually represent the third plumage. Immature third-generation feathers, as well as feathers of more advanced stages, are definitely still present on the femoral, crural, and under alar tracts. The under alar tract is the only one that did not show evidence of fourth-generation feathers in any of our birds. The second generation is represented only by a pair of secondary remiges 1, and in some birds by a pair of primary remiges 10 as well. Natal downs have been entirely lost.

The foregoing accounts have shown that Single Comb White Leghorn Chickens produce four plumages during their first 6 months of life. The molt into the second plumage is complete and that into the third plumage is virtually complete, but the molt that introduces the fourth plumage is only partial. Since molting does not take place simul-taneously in all the tracts, a young chicken always wears feathers of various ages. Indeed, at least two plumages are always represented in the feathering.

The relative amounts of the plumages change continu-ously during the first 6 months, as shown in figure 157. To prepare this chart we first noted the categories of feathers (generation and degree of maturity) present at each of 22 ages. For every age, we then estimated the percentage of the feathering in each category. These values were then plotted in relation to four horizontal lines, each of which was the axis for a single generation. The percentage of feathers in a given generation that are still growing was placed below the line, while the percentage of fully grown feathers was placed above it. Hence, the height of the shaded areas above or below the lines indicates the percentage of that category in the feathering. Separating the generations in this way shows the fluctuations more clearly than if they were combined as parts of a single block. The spacing be-tween the horizontal axes is arbitrary, and has no significance for the meaning of the chart.

It is clear from this chart that the molts overlap in time. Feathers of the third and even the fourth plumages begin to appear before the last of the natal downs have been re-placed by feathers of the second plumage. As a result, a chicken is molting or growing feathers somewhere on its body at all times during at least the first 6 months.

TIMING AND ORDER OF MOLTING

Establishment in the Embryo

Feathers and their follicles develop from masses of cells that are first discernible when an embryo is 5 days old. These feather primordia form in regular sequences within each tract and among tracts. This process has been investi-gated by Holmes (1935), Gerber (1939), and Broman (1941), and we describe it in chapter 7. During the first molt, feathers in each tract are replaced in much the same order as that in which their primordia were formed. This sequence is repeated in at least the next three molts, though with less similarity.

The sequences of primordium development and of molting differ most noticeably in the humeral and crural tracts. The first follicles of the humeral tract arise in a longitudinal row near the lateral margin; subsequent rows arise laterally and medially. At the first molt, however, feather replacement begins at the posterolateral corner of the tract and proceeds anteromedially. The original sequence reappears at the second molt, when new feathers first emerge in a longi-tudinal zone in the middle of the tract.

The first primordia of the crural tract are reported (Holmes, 1935) to originate in a line down the front of the leg, with more rows added laterally and medially. Feather replacement at the first molt begins on both anterior and posterior surfaces of the leg and spreads, first medially and then laterally. At the second molt, the process starts on the anterior and posterior surfaces of the ankle, but subsequent new feathers appear at random around the leg.

The sequence in which feathers complete their growth may or may not repeat the sequence of primordium develop-ment and molting. On the femoral tract, for example, during the first molt the wave of feather replacement reaches the anterodorsal corner of the tract about 3 weeks after it has started along the posterior border. The new feathers in both areas become fully grown, however, at the same age. This appears to be due in part to the fact that the antero-dorsal feathers are shorter than the posterior ones (fig. 191) and hence do not require as much time to complete their growth. In addition, the posterior feathers may grow at a faster rate than the anterior ones. Streich and Swetosarov (1937) demonstrated in pigeons that the longer a feather will be when fully mature, the faster it grows. If differences in the size and growth rate are superimposed on the sequence of molting, it is likely that feathers will complete their growth in a different order from that in which they began.

Comparison of Sexes

Poultrymen have long known that the plumages of female chickens tend to appear sooner and develop faster than those of males. There have been many studies of the rate

(Text continued on page 228.)

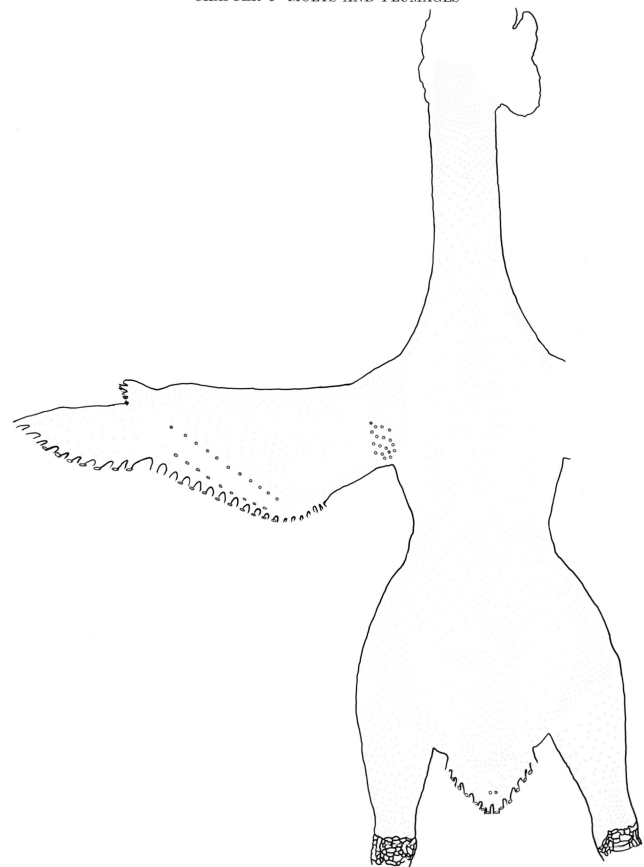

FIGURE 143.—Composition of the feathering on the dorsal side of an 8-day-old Single Comb White Leghorn Chicken. Open circles represent feathers that are still growing; closed circles, feathers that are fully grown. Colors have the following meaning: yellow, first generation feather; green, second generation; red, third generation; and blue, fourth generation. See also figures 126 and 144 to 156.

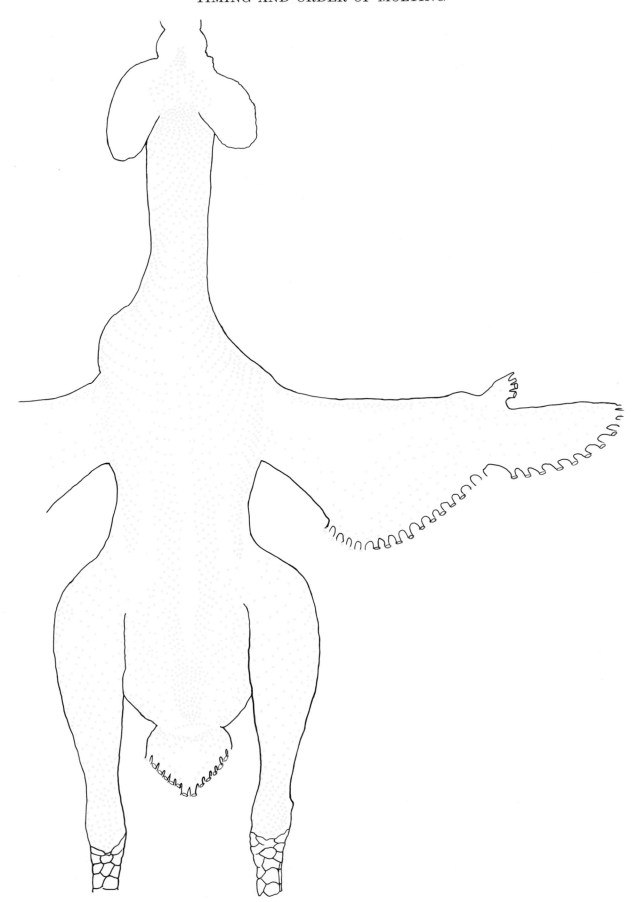

FIGURE 144.—Composition of the feathering on the ventral side of an 8-day-old Single Comb White Leghorn Chicken. See text and figures 126 and 143 for explanation.

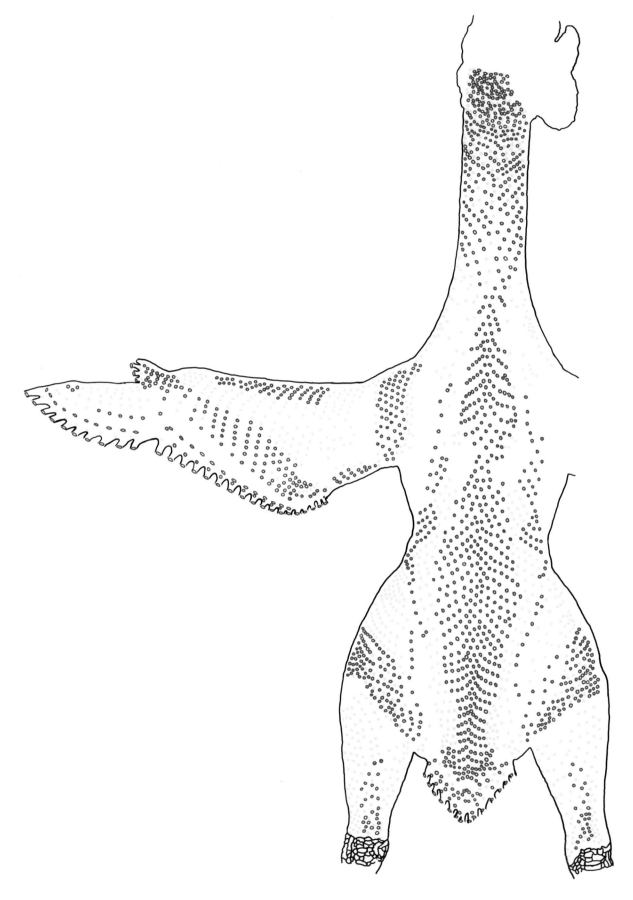

FIGURE 145.—Composition of the feathering on the dorsal side of a 19-day-old Single Comb White Leghorn Chicken. See text and figures 126 and 143 for explanation.

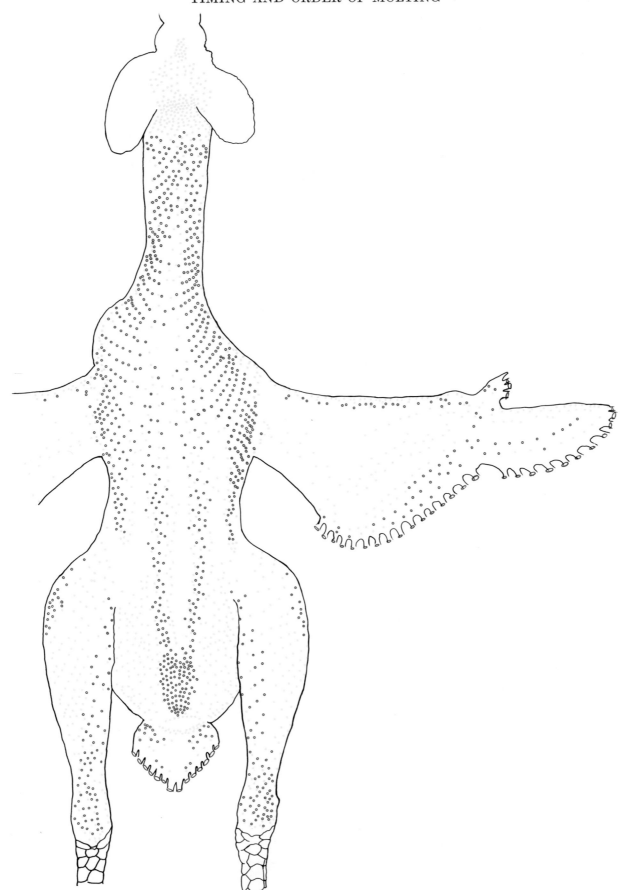

FIGURE 146.—Composition of the feathering on the ventral side of a 19-day-old Single Comb White Leghorn Chicken. See text and figures 126 and 143 for explanation.

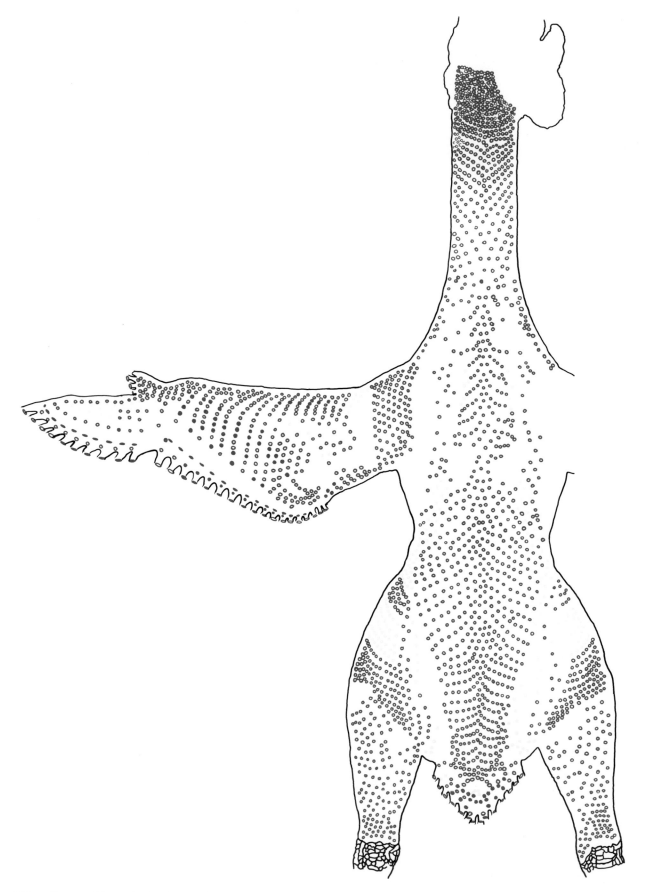

FIGURE 147.—Composition of the feathering on the dorsal side of a 35-day-old Single Comb White Leghorn Chicken. See text and figures 126 and 143 for explanation.

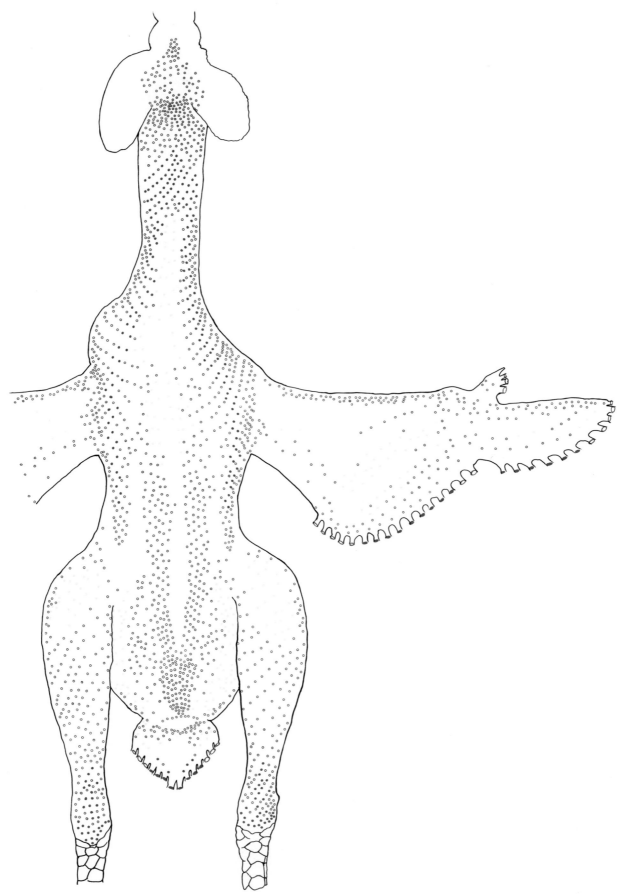

FIGURE 148.—Composition of the feathering on the ventral side of a 35-day-old Single Comb White Leghorn Chicken. See text and figures 126 and 143 for explanation.

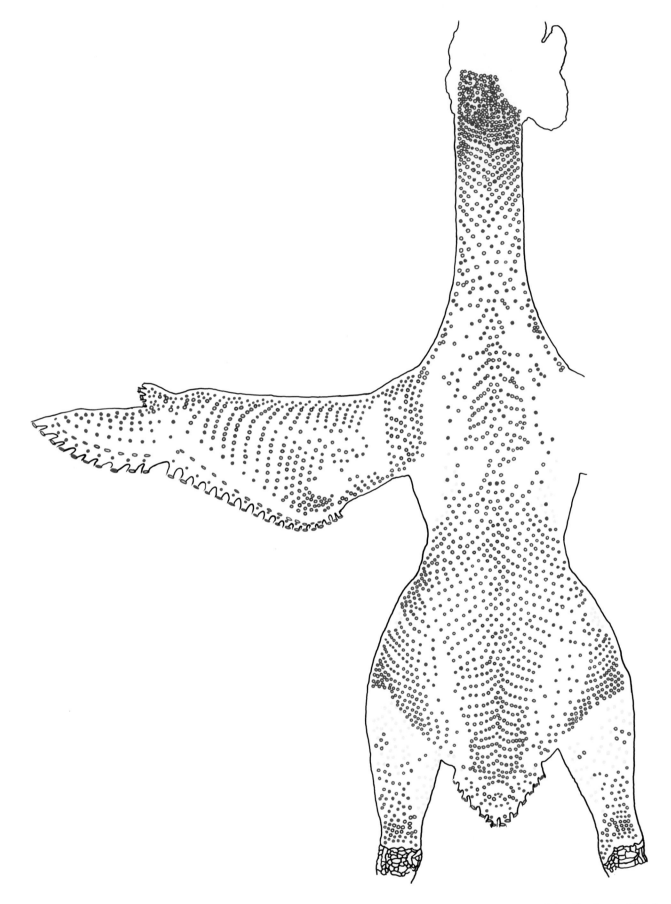

FIGURE 149.—Composition of the feathering on the dorsal side of a 55-day-old Single Comb White Leghorn Chicken. See text and figures 126 and 143 for explanation.

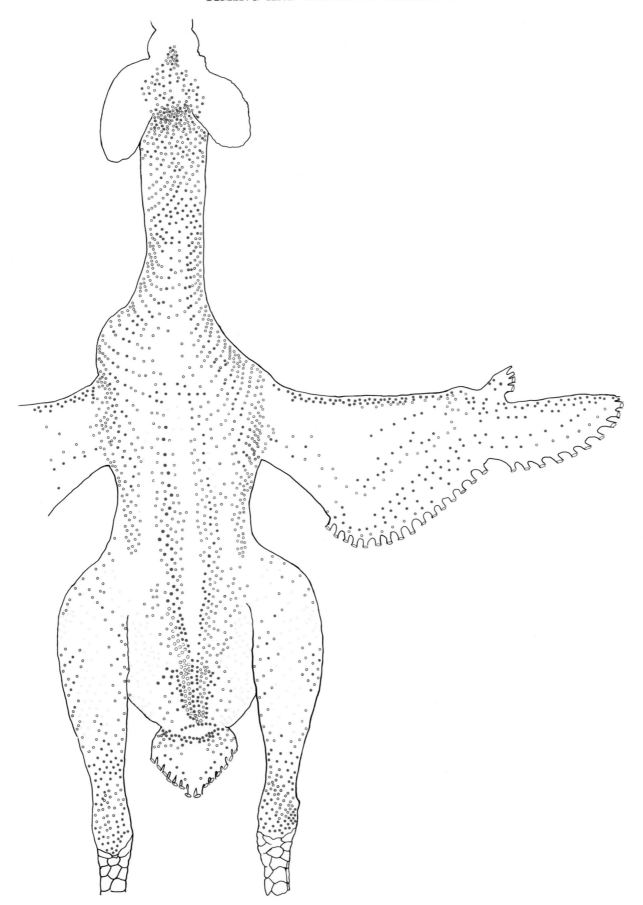

FIGURE 150.—Composition of the feathering on the ventral side of a 55-day-old Single Comb White Leghorn Chicken. See text and figures 126 and 143 for explanation.

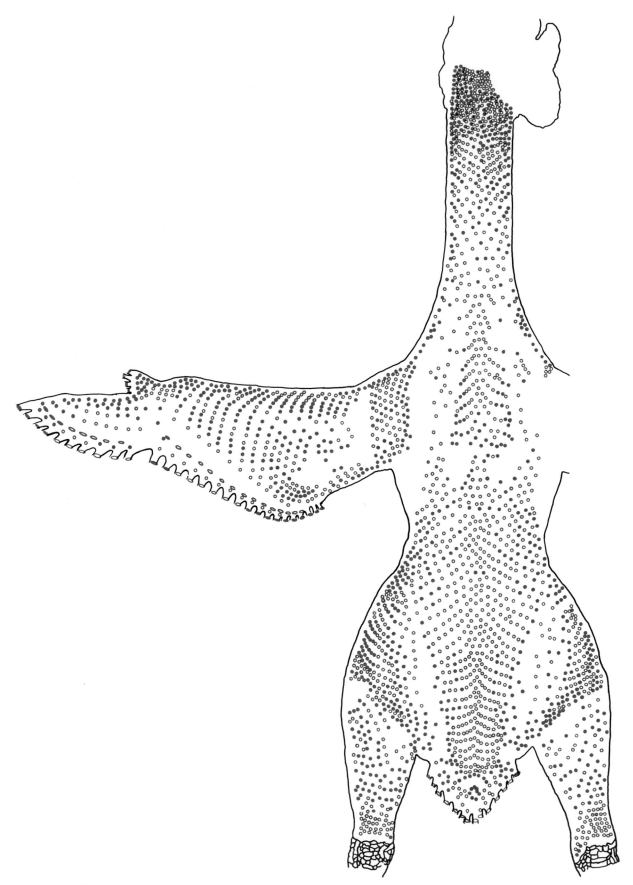

FIGURE 151.—Composition of the feathering on the dorsal side of a 77-day-old Single Comb White Leghorn Chicken. See text and figures 126 and 143 for explanation.

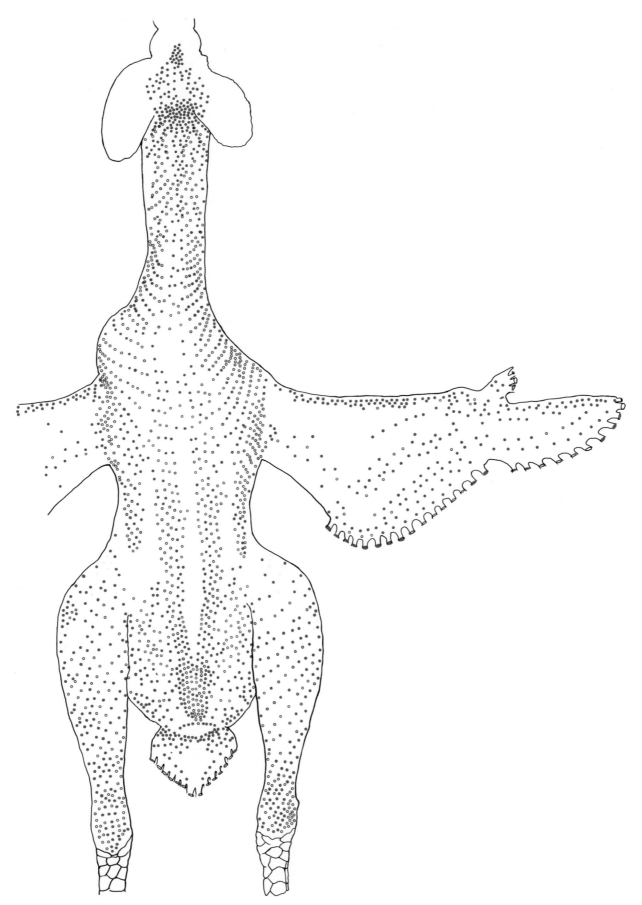

FIGURE 152.—Composition of the feathering on the ventral side of a 77-day-old Single Comb White Leghorn Chicken. See text and figures 126 and 143 for explanation.

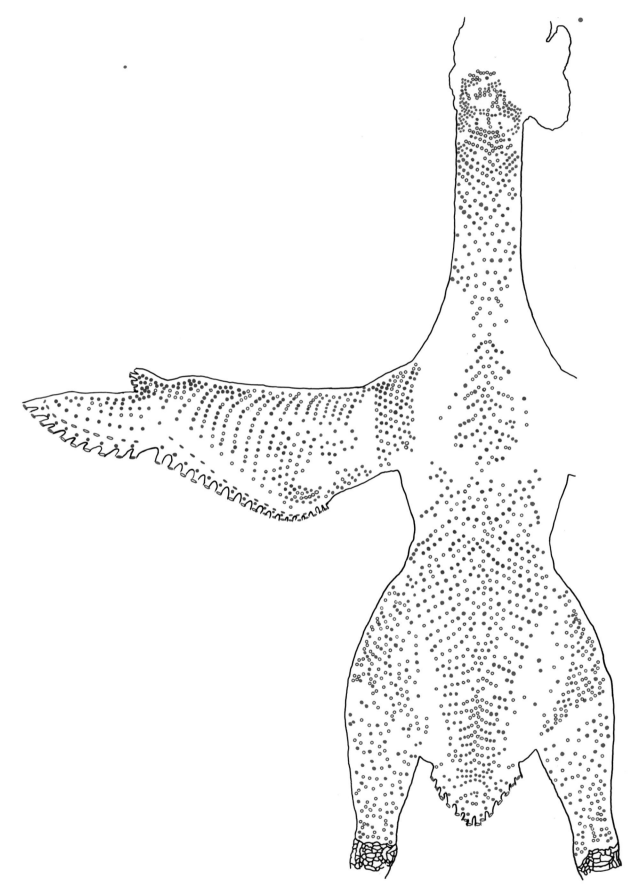

FIGURE 153.—Composition of the feathering on the dorsal side of a 103-day-old Single Comb White Leghorn Chicken. See text and figures 126 and 143 for explanation.

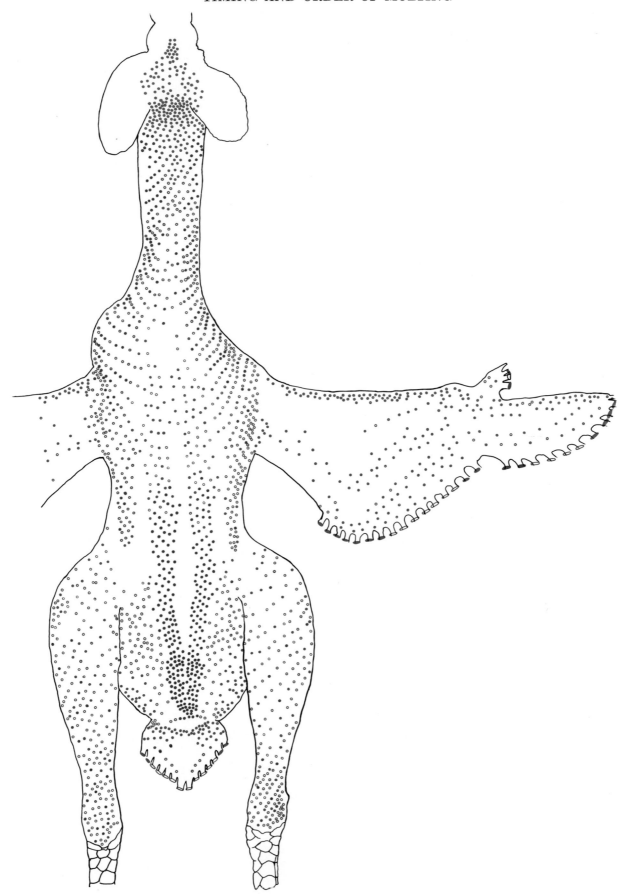

FIGURE 154.—Composition of the feathering on the ventral side of a 103-day-old Single Comb White Leghorn Chicken. See text and figures 126 and 143 for explanation.

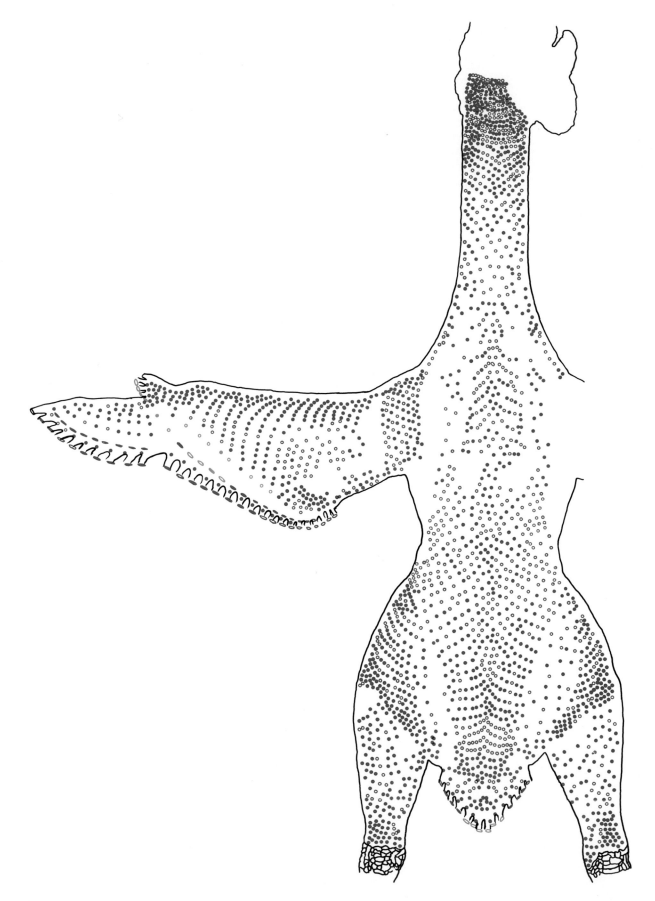

FIGURE 155.—Composition of the feathering on the dorsal side of a 131-day-old Single Comb White Leghorn Chicken. See text and figures 126 and 143 for explanation.

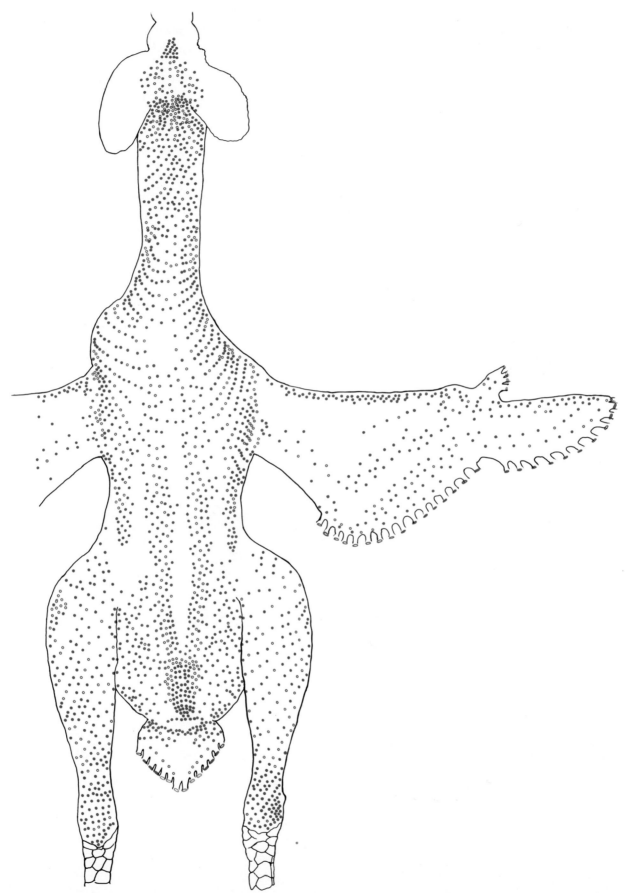

FIGURE 156.—Composition of the feathering on the ventral side of a 131-day-old Single Comb White Leghorn Chicken. See text and figures 126 and 143 for explanation.

of plumage growth in chickens, a few of which are those by Radi and Warren (1938), Martin (1929), and Onishi et al. (1954). The sexual difference in the onset of the first molt and the rate of juvenal plumage development, particularly as seen in the primary remiges, has long been used for sexing baby chicks (Warren, 1942). It can be applied to certain strains of broiler chickens but not to modern strains that have been bred for egg production. The latter are rapid feathering; in both sexes, numerous juvenal feathers have appeared above the skin by the time of hatching, and they subsequently grow rapidly. In practice, the primary remiges are simply compared with their upper major coverts in a day old chicken. If the primaries are no longer than the coverts, a chicken is male, but if they are longer than the coverts, it is female.

The chickens we studied showed very few sexual differences in the timing of their molts. The second- and third-generation rectrices and the fourth-generation capital feathers began to appear above the skin sooner in females than in males (p. 206). A similar discrepancy in the introduction of third-generation rectrices has been observed in Silver Spangled Hamburgs (Dunn and Landauer, 1930).

The order of feather replacement appears to be the same in both sexes of chickens. We found no evidence of sexual dimorphism in this regard in our birds, and none has been mentioned in references to other studies.

Comparison of Breeds of Chickens

Breeds of chickens vary in the timing and rate of development of second-generation feathers. The age at which these feathers are said to appear on a particular tract varies as much as 6 weeks among reports on several breeds of chickens (table 9). The feathers tend to appear later and to develop more slowly in most of the American and other heavy breeds than in Leghorns, Minorcas, and Anconas. The rate of growth in the wing and tail feathers is controlled by a single pair of sex-linked genes, that for slow growth being dominant over that for rapid growth. The condition of the wing and tail feathers at 10 days of age is a good indicator of whether a chicken will develop the rest of its juvenal feathering slowly or rapidly. Procedures for identifying so-called rapid feathering and for distinguishing sexes of baby chicks are described in textbooks of poultry science (Card, 1961:71–74; Hutt, 1949:134–142).

Inherent differences in the rate of juvenal feather development among breeds are less today than formerly, owing to

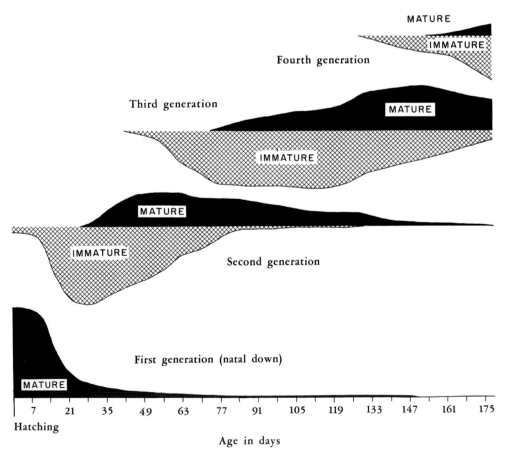

FIGURE 157.—Composition of the feathering in Single Comb White Leghorn Chickens, from hatching to 6 months of age. The percentage of the feathering comprised by each generation and growth stage is indicated by the height of the areas above and below the horizontal base lines. See text for further explanation.

TABLE 9.—*Age at which second-generation feathers appear in five breeds of chickens*

Tracts	Single Comb White Leghorn (present study)	White Leghorn (early feathering) (Radi and Warren, 1938)	Brown Leghorn (Chu, 1938)	Rhode Island Red (early feathering) (Radi and Warren, 1938)	Barred Plymouth Rock (Gericke and Platt, 1932)	Silver Spangled Hamburg (Dunn and Landauer, 1930)
	Days	*Days*	*Days*	*Days*	*Days*	*Days*
Capital (head)	19	21–28	[1]	21	42–49	[1]
Cervical (hackles)	16	14–21	15	14	28–35	30–40
Interscapular (cape)	13	[2] 14–21	[2] 17	[2] 14	[2] 35–42	30–35
Dorsal (back)	16	14–21	17	14	35–42	25–35
Pelvic (saddle)	16	[2] 14–21	[2] 17	[2] 14	[2] 35–42	50–60
Pectoral (breast)	13	7–14	13	7	21–28	20–30
Sternal and abdominal (ventral)	16	21–28	21	21	28–35	35–45
Humeral (shoulder)	6	7	3	7	14–21	15–20
Upper alar (coverts, wing bow, web)	1	14–21	2	14	42–49	18–22
Femoral (thigh, pelvic wing)	12	7–14	13	7	14–21	15–20
Crural (leg)	19	21	[1]	14	28–35	[1]

[1] Not recorded.

[2] Not recorded separately. We assigned this tract the same age as the dorsal tract, in which it was probably included.

improved nutrition, management, and breeding. Chickens of some breeds, such as Barred Plymouth Rocks, produce second-generation feathers at an earlier age (and perhaps more quickly) now than when this breed was studied by Gericke and Platt (1932).

Some of the differences in data published on various breeds are probably due to differences in the experiments themselves. The chickens reported on were kept under different conditions, particularly the regimes of lighting. The observers themselves undoubtedly differed in the care and frequency with which they examined their birds, or in the criteria they used for determining the ages when feathers appear.

Molting has been followed in greater detail in the remiges and rectrices than in other feathers. In comparing our results with those from studies of other breeds and strains of chickens, it seems convenient to discuss these categories of feathers separately.

Primary remiges

Newly hatched chickens have been reported as showing seven second-generation primaries in Silver Spangled Hamburgs (Dunn and Landauer, 1930), Brown Leghorns (Chu, 1938), Single Comb White Leghorns (Warren and Gordon, 1935), and several rapid-feathering breeds (Onishi et al., 1954). Only six such feathers were found in Rhode Island Reds (Warren and Gordon, 1935), as in the Single Comb White Leghorns of our study. In slow-feathering breeds, however, second-generation primaries could not be seen until about 10 days after hatching, when the first to sixth primaries emerged almost simultaneously (Onishi et al., 1954).

Third-generation primaries start to appear above the skin 40 to 50 days after hatching in rapid-feathering breeds,

as in the chickens of our study. Their appearance may be delayed until 70 to 80 days in slow-feathering breeds such as Rhode Island Reds (Warren and Gordon, 1935: Onishi et al., 1954).

All reports agree that molting of the primaries starts at the wrist and proceeds outward. There are few variations in the pattern, and feathers are rarely shed more than one ahead of the normal order in the series (Marble, 1930). Individual variation in the retention of the juvenal 10th primary, observed in our birds, was previously noted in White Leghorns by Warren and Gordon (1935).

The rate of growth has been shown to vary among second-generation primaries (Juhn, 1938), and our observations support this. As shown in figure 138, the duration of each feather's growth and retention until it is molted increases from primary 1 to 10. This period is not simply proportional to the length of the feather because primary 10 is nearly the same size as primary 5. Furthermore, since primary 8 is the largest of the second-generation primaries but does not have the longest period of growth and retention, it must grow more quickly than some of the others.

Secondary remiges

The number of second-generation secondaries present at hatching has been reported as seven in Brown Leghorn and Silver Spangled Hamburg chicks (Chu, 1938; Dunn and Landauer, 1930); all the White Leghorn Chickens in our study had at least nine such feathers. Rhode Island Red Chickens have been reported to show three juvenal secondaries when hatched (Warren and Gordon, 1935). The sequence in which the second-generation secondaries appear above the skin is the same in other breeds as that observed in our birds.

Third-generation secondaries are introduced in the same

order as the preceding ones. The order and timing of the molt as observed in our birds are similar in most respects to those noted in other White Leghorns (Warren and Gordon, 1935), Brown Leghorns (Juhn, 1938), and Silver Spangled Hamburgs (Dunn and Landauer, 1930). Molting was found to continue at least 2 weeks longer in our study than in others because we included the axial feather and the secondaries on the elbow as well as those on the forearm. The only notable difference in timing concerned the juvenal secondary 1, which was lost at 18 to 20 weeks in other studies but not until after 25 weeks in our chickens. This feather was found to be retained for an equally long period in Rhode Island Reds (Warren and Gordon, 1935). Many variations in the order of molting among secondaries were reported by Marble (1930) but we saw none in our birds.

Rectrices

Second- and third-generation rectrices appear at about the same times in Brown Leghorns (Chu, 1938; Juhn, 1938) as we noted in our White Leghorns. Rhode Island Reds, however, do not start to show second-generation feathers until the second week in females and even later in males (Hosker, 1936). Silver Spangled Hamburgs, on the other hand, develop rectrices rapidly, for they already have five or six pairs of ensheathed juvenal feathers when hatched (Dunn and Landauer, 1930). These feathers complete their growth about 1 week sooner than their counterparts in the White Leghorns of our study. Third-generation feathers start to appear above the skin during the sixth week in Silver Spangled Hamburgs as in both varieties of Leghorns. Fourth-generation feathers, however, are introduced about the 13th week in Hamburg females but not until the 18th week in White Leghorn females. In both these breeds, the fourth-generation rectrices start to appear at least 7 weeks later in males than in females.

The direction of molting varies among breeds of chickens. In Brown Leghorns and White Leghorns, molting is centrifugal because it starts with the central pair of rectrices and proceeds laterally. In Silver Spangled Hamburgs, however, the molting that brings in the third-generation rectrices is centripetal; it starts with the outermost pair of feathers and goes toward the center. Curiously, the direction reverses at the next molt in this breed (Dunn and Landauer, 1930).

The extent to which rectrices are replaced varies among breeds, and from one molt to the next. The second molt affects all the feathers in Brown Leghorns and White Leghorns but only the inner six pairs in Silver Spangled Hamburgs. The third molt affects only a few inner pairs in Brown Leghorns (Juhn, 1938). Its full extent could not be learned in our White Leghorns because only the first four or five rectrices in hens had been replaced at the time the study ended.

Body and limb tracts

Second-generation feathers generally appeared at approximately the same ages in our White Leghorns as in the early-feathering White Leghorns observed by Radi and Warren (1938) and the Brown Leghorns observed by Chu (1938). The order of molting among tracts is therefore similar, except for the later appearance of the wing coverts as noted by Radi and Warren (1938). Early-feathering Rhode Island Reds also started to produce most of their juvenal feathers during the first 3 weeks, but in a somewhat different sequence (Radi and Warren, 1938).

Late-feathering Rhode Island Reds and White Leghorns started showing new feathers about 1 to 2 weeks later than the early-feathering strains (data from Radi and Warren, 1938). Barred Plymouth Rocks and Silver Spangled Hamburgs tended to be even slower in starting and carrying out the first molt (Gericke and Platt, 1932; Dunn and Landauer, 1930). Feathers appeared at approximately the same ages on most tracts in these breeds, differing chiefly in the pelvic and upper alar tracts. It was not until the birds were at least 7 weeks old that second-generation feathers had begun to appear on all the tracts of these heavy-bodied chickens.

The sequence in the onset of molting from one tract to another shows some measure of constancy among breeds, in spite of the variation in actual ages. The earliest feathers or tracts tend to be the remiges, rectrices, upper wing coverts, humeral, femoral, and pectoral tracts. Next come the cervical, interscapular, and dorsal tracts. The last to show juvenal feathers are the pelvic, sternal, abdominal, capital, and crural tracts.

COMPARISON OF MOLTS AND PLUMAGES IN CHICKENS AND OTHER GALLINACEOUS BIRDS

Studies of molts and plumages have proceeded in quite different directions in domestic and laboratory birds as compared with those in nature. Intensive research on domestic chickens, turkeys, ducks, and pigeons has dealt with the physiology of molting. Extensive studies of species in nature have dealt with gross changes in the feathering as caused by plumage replacement, and with the relationship between molting and other events in the annual cycle. Plumages have been analyzed primarily so that they can serve in identifying birds as to species (or subspecies), age,

and sex. Unfortunately, poultry scientists and laboratory zoologists, on the one hand, and ornithologists and wildlife biologists, on the other hand, seem to have paid little attention to each other's work. This has been detrimental for all, since each has methods and information that would be useful to the rest. The former bring detailed knowledge of how molting operates, while the latter bring an understanding of it as a natural process that is part of the whole biology of a bird.

To conclude this chapter, we will briefly survey the early

molts and plumages of gallinaceous birds in nature, and compare them with those in chickens. This will give some idea as to how far the conditions found in the domestic birds typify those of the galliform order as a whole. Such an appraisal may be useful when observations on chickens are applied to other species, and vice versa.

A comparison of molts and plumages between domestic chickens and true, wild junglefowls would be extremely interesting. It is not possible at present, however, because of the apparent lack of detailed information on junglefowls. Many captive junglefowls in the United States are not reliable for a study of the molts and plumages of wild birds (Kimball, 1958).

Information on the molts and plumages of many gallinaceous birds can be found in the works by Bent (1932), Dwight (1900b), Stresemann and Stresemann (1966), and Witherby et al. (v. 5, 1944). References for particular species are cited in conjunction with the discussion of those species in the following account. In all these books and articles, the concept of plumage is more nearly equivalent to a stage of feathering than to a generation of feathers, as used here. Date on the timing and order of molting in most tracts are scarce. Attention has been focused on the history of the primary remiges because these have proved to be very useful for estimating age in many species.

General Sequence

First molt and second plumage

All gallinaceous chickens are covered with a dense coat of down when they hatch. The first (prejuvenal) molt is already under way, for a few second-generation feathers appear above the skin within a few days, if indeed they are not already apparent. These earliest juvenal feathers are invariably some of the remiges. New feathers generally emerge next on the upper alar, pectoral, humeral, interscapular, femoral, and caudal tracts. They appear later on the spinal, abdominal, and crural tracts, and last of all on the capital tracts. This molt is eventually completed though it may take a long time—more than is generally recognized. As we have seen in Single Comb White Leghorn Chickens, natal down feathers may persist and be concealed by juvenal feathers long after they have disappeared from the face.

The sequences of molting among and within tracts vary somewhat among species. Variation in the order of tracts is illustrated by the relative timing in the appearance of second-generation rectrices and pectoral feathers. These start concurrently in the California Quail (*Lophortyx californicus*) (Raitt, 1961), whereas the rectrices come first in turkeys (Leopold, 1943) and the pectorals come first in the Ruffed Grouse (*Bonasa umbellus*) (Bump et al., 1947), Bobwhite (*Colinus virginianus*) (Lyon, 1962), and Common Coturnix (Lyon, 1962). Tracts themselves differ in the uniformity of their foci and gradients of molting. On the head, for example, the process invariably seems to start along the middorsal line of the crown and to finish around the eyes. In the humeral tract, on the other hand, molting

begins at the anterior end of the Ruffed Grouse, at the center in the Gray Partridge (*Perdix perdix*) (McCabe and Hawkins, 1946), and anywhere in the tract in the Bobwhite or the Common Coturnix. The sequence of feather replacement during the first molt, as seen in Single Comb White Leghorn Chickens, is similar to that in galliform birds in nature.

Second molt and third plumage

The second (first prebasic) molt usually begins within 4 to 6 weeks after hatching. In many species, including chickens, natal down is still present on the head and the sides of the body. This contradicts the statement by Chu (1938:536) that "only after the feather tracts are completely developed does moulting and replacement of chick [second-generation] feathers take place."

The earliest third-generation feathers to appear in most galliform species are the primary remiges, but in chickens and turkeys, both domestic and in nature, they are the rectrices. The subsequent order of molting is fairly similar among the species, so far as is known. The head and throat are usually the last regions to show new feathers, but in the California Quail, Ring-necked Pheasant (*Phasianus colchicus*) (Westerskov, 1957), and Scaled Quail (*Callipepla squamata*) (Wallmo, 1956), they are said to molt before most of the body tracts. This discrepancy may result from a confusion of two molts. As we have mentioned, the first molt takes several weeks, and often has not finished before the second molt begins. The two molts, proceeding concurrently on different parts of the body, are especially liable to be confused with each other if the last second-generation feathers to appear resemble the third-generation feathers.

It takes 2 to 3 months for the third plumage to replace the second plumage all over the body. This is the same time in gallinaceous birds in nature as that in chickens.

Typically in galliform birds, the two or three outermost primary remiges in the second plumage are not molted directly after the inner primaries. They are kept for nearly a year, that is, until they are replaced during the complete molt after the first breeding season. The same phenomenon also occurs with the upper major primary coverts and affects the outermost feathers in some species and all of these feathers (usually) in the New World quail (subfamily Odontophorinae) (Thompson and Kabat, 1950). On the other hand, there are groups such as curassows, megapodes, francolins, and certain silver pheasants (*Gennaeus* spp.) in which all the second-generation primaries and their coverts are molted as usual (Stresemann, 1965). The fact that Ring-necked Pheasants and chickens may also molt all these feathers before they are fully grown is thus unusual but not unique for gallinaceous birds. We have found that some chickens are very slow to finish molting, for they still have their 10th second-generation primaries when they are 6 months old. Wild turkeys retain both outer primaries whereas domestic turkeys replace the ninth second-generation primary during their first winter (Leopold, 1943).

The third plumage in gallinaceous birds is almost invariably repeated through complete molts in subsequent years. Under these criteria, it represents the "first basic plumage" in the Humphrey-Parkes system. According to Lyon (1962), the early plumages of Common Coturnix may be an exception to this pattern.

Third molt and fourth plumage

Differences in the sequence of plumages within the order Galliformes show up after the third plumage has been established. In some species, this entire plumage is worn until after the first breeding season. Then in the fall, when the birds are about 1¼ years old, they undergo a complete molt into a fresh plumage. The fourth and subsequent plumages are repetitions of the third; hence they can all be termed basic, whereas the molts are prebasic. In summary, these birds have only a complete (prebasic) molt and one (basic) plumage per cycle. This pattern is shown by the Chachalaca (*Ortalis vetula*), Blue Grouse (*Dendragapus obscurus*), Ruffed Grouse, California Quail, Ring-necked Pheasant, Red-legged Partridge (*Alectoris rufa*), and Chukar (*Alectoris chukar*) (Bureau, 1911, 1913; Watson, 1962).

Many species pass through a third molt during their first year, and replace some of their third plumage. The new feathers usually differ in color brightness from those preceding them. They constitute an alternate plumage and the molt that introduces them is prealternate. This fourth plumage and the remainder of the third plumage are both molted in the fall, when the birds are about 1¼ years old. Thereafter, the birds have a complete (prebasic) molt and a partial (prealternate) molt per cycle. Their feathering is composed at first of a single (basic) plumage, but later of two plumages (a basic and an alternate). The partial molt usually occurs before the breeding season, starting in winter or spring.

The plumage brought in by this molt is restricted in some species to the head and neck; it often consists of only a few feathers. Such a limited plumage can be found in the Capercaillie (*Tetrao urogallus*) (known from males only according to Witherby et al., 1944), Black Grouse (*Lyrurus tetrix*) (known from males only according to Witherby et al., 1944), Greater Prairie Chicken (*Tympanuchus cupido*), Sharp-tailed Grouse (*Pedioecetes phasianellus*), Bobwhite, Mountain Quail (*Oreortyx pictus*), Harlequin Quail (*Cyrtonyx montezumae*), Scaled Quail, and Gray Partridge. An extensive (alternate) plumage that covers much of the body can be seen in ptarmigans and their close relative, the Red Grouse (*Lagopus scoticus*).

A most unusual partial molt occurs in three of the four species of junglefowls (*Gallus gallus*, *G. sonneratii*, and *G. lafayettii*) in summer, during or after the breeding season. It has been reported (Baker, 1930; Delacour, 1951) to take place only in males but Morejohn (1968:62) found it in both sexes of *sonneratii*. The long, lanceolate, brightly marked hackles are replaced by short, spatulate feathers colored black, dark gray or brown. Delacour stated that the

rectrices are also replaced, but he gave no details about any change of color. This situation is the reverse of that usually found among gallinaceous birds in which the alternate plumage is brighter or bolder than the basic plumage. Junglecocks are said to be in eclipse plumage while wearing these somber feathers. This term has been used by some (e.g., Delacour, 1951; Kimball, 1958) in reference to the appearance of the entire feathering, but by Morejohn (1968) in reference to the new generation of feathers alone. The partial molt is accompanied in males by a diminution of masculinity as seen in the secondary sexual characters and behavior (Kimball, 1958; Morejohn, 1968:62). In summary, the partial molt is unusual in its time of occurrence, the character of the plumage it introduces, and in the concurrent changes elsewhere in the body.

The homology of plumages in junglefowls is uncertain, but at least the bright plumage appears to be equivalent in all four species. Several pieces of evidence indicate that the bright plumage is basic and the eclipse plumage is alternate. The former is introduced by a complete molt and the latter by a partial molt. Only a bright plumage is worn by the Green Junglefowl (*Gallus varius*). The hackle feathers of the first basic plumage in *G. gallus* are the bright, lanceolate type although shorter and duller than those of adults.[1] Studies by Morejohn (1968) support the above interpretation of the plumages of junglefowls.

Additional molts and plumages

Ptarmigans have three plumages per annual cycle after their first year. The third (supplemental) plumage is acquired by a partial (presupplemental) molt that replaces most of the preceding plumage on the body tracts. This molt occurs in the spring, but its timing varies among local populations, as shown by Salomonsen (1939).

Molting of Rectrices

The sequence of molting on the tail differs among gallinaceous birds, even within the family of quail, pheasants, and peafowl—the Phasianidae. The partridges, francolins, and their allies have a centrifugal tail molt, whereas the true pheasants, including the junglefowls, are characterized by a centripetal tail molt (Beebe, 1918). In the argus pheasants and peafowl, molting starts at the third pair of rectrices from the center and proceeds both outward and inward. Certain pheasants and partridges replace their juvenal rectrices by a centrifugal molt but later generations replace them in the opposite direction (Mueller and Seibert, 1966: 494). Silver Spangled Hamburg chickens replace feathers centripetally at the first molt but centrifugally thereafter. Junglefowls regularly molt their rectrices in centripetal order, whereas both Brown and White Leghorns follow centrifugal order.

The number of rectrices in gallinaceous chicks of many

---

[1] Kenneth C. Parkes. Written communication.

species gradually increases until the final number is reached (Stresemann, 1965:62). As an example, Stresemann stated that in *Gallus* (whether junglefowl or domestic chicken not specified) the original five pairs increase to six during the first molt, and a seventh pair is added in the second molt. This process was accelerated in our Single Comb White Leghorn Chickens, for the seventh pair was introduced during the first molt. In some individuals, even an eighth pair was added at this molt. Variability in the number of tail feathers of these birds is shown in table 5 (p. 161).

Discussion

We have uncovered four unusual aspects of the early molts and plumages of chickens, as follows: (1) The second molt begins with the rectrices in chickens and turkeys, but with the primaries in other species. (2) Second-generation primaries 9 and 10 may be replaced rather than held during the first year. (3) The fourth plumage during the first year includes several remiges and rectrices as well as body feathers, whereas in most other species it is confined to the body feathers. (4) Rectrices are molted in centrifugal order (at least after the first molt), in contrast to the centripetal order in junglefowls and closely related pheasants.

The first three plumages of chickens are clearly equivalent to those in junglefowls and other gallinaceous birds. The homology of the fourth plumage, however, is uncertain. The fact that it follows a basic plumage suggests that it is an alternate plumage. As such, however, it is different from the eclipse plumage (feather generation) of junglefowls in timing and extent. If chickens after the first year were known to have a partial as well as a complete molt every cycle, this would be evidence for regarding the fourth plumage as an alternate. Data on chickens more than 1 year old are very scanty, but they suggest that normally there is only a complete molt every fall (Card, 1961: 100). It is possible that a partial molt does take place but has been overlooked owing to the unchanging color of the feathers, like the molt into eclipse plumage of female Gray Junglefowls.

Some chickens may replace a few neck feathers in the spring if their molting has not been inhibited through management and feeding. This is reminiscent of the partial (prealternate) molt in many galliform species, but it is far from a repetition of the first-year molt into a fourth plumage.

It does not seem plausible to interpret the fourth plumage as an alternate, derived from a plumage of very limited extent in junglefowls. Parkes[2] suggested that this plumage may better be regarded as a second basic. Its occurrence soon after the first basic plumage suggests that the cycle of molts during the first year has been compressed and accelerated. This may have been a consequence of selective breeding for rapid growth or earlier onset of egg production. These hypotheses on the sequence and homology of plumages in domestic chickens cannot be tested further until more is known about the molts and plumages of young junglefowl and of chickens more than 1 year old.

In general, the order of feather replacement differs no more between chickens and galliform species in nature than these species differ among themselves. The sequence of plumages, however, differs to a greater degree, because chickens have a fourth or extra plumage during the first year. This phenomenon may indicate the extent to which chickens have become modified from their ancestral stock. Still, they are similar enough so that knowledge of the physiology and mechanism of feather replacement in chickens can be applied to other gallinaceous birds. Conversely, the concepts of molts and plumages as gained from the study of species in nature can be applied to domestic birds.

---

[2] Kenneth C. Parkes. Written communication.

CHAPTER 5

Structure of Feathers

INTRODUCTION

Feathers are probably the most complex derivatives of the integument to be found in any vertebrate animal. Their many parts display an enormous variety of modifications. Size, alone, often has a very wide range. The longest tail feathers of a rooster, for example, may be more than 1,000 times as long as the feathers on its eyelids. Even a single bird bears such diverse feathers as (1) large, stiff remiges and rectrices; (2) moderate-size, partly firm feathers that cover the body; (3) small, fluffy down feathers; (4) hairlike filoplumes; and (5) tiny bristles on the face. These five categories represent the five main structural types of feathers. Subordinate types can be distinguished under some of these main types. Our classification of feather types is based on that of Chandler (1916). Other workers have classified feathers along slightly different lines, but this is not surprising in view of the fact that the categories are not always clear cut. Examination of a bird reveals intergrading feathers between most categories. Sometimes it is necessary to establish criteria for classification rather arbitrarily, but it seems more convenient to do this than to have to cope with large, ill-defined polymorphic groups.

The terms of orientation for a feather are determined by intrinsic features and are independent of the feather's location on the body. The outer surface can always be told by the smooth side of the shaft; it faces away from the body except in certain coverts on the underside of the wing. The terms, proximal (or basal) and distal (or terminal), can be used to indicate location along the shaft. They have a special meaning, however, when applied to the branches of the shaft, as discussed on page 247. Other terms of orientation are introduced as they are needed.

CONTOUR FEATHERS

The predominant feathers on a bird's body are known as contour feathers. They have also been called pennae (singular: penna); but in spite of its conciseness, this synonym is not commonly used. In describing the structure of feathers, we will start with this type because it is the most familiar and because it incorporates nearly all the parts to be found on other types of feathers.

Typical Body Feathers

Preview of major parts

The major parts of a body contour feather are the shaft, the plates or vanes on either side of it, and, in most birds, an afterfeather on the undersurface (fig. 158). The shaft (quill) is the longitudinal axis and is composed of two segments, the calamus and the rachis. The calamus (barrel) is the short, tubular base, largely implanted in the feather follicle. It is approximately circular in cross section and often slightly tapered toward the ends. At its lower end is a hole, the inferior umbilicus, through which the pulp entered the feather during its growth. The hole is closed by a horny plate in a fully grown feather.

The rachis is the long, essentially solid portion of the shaft above the skin. On each side of this shaft is a row of closely set, fine branches that are known individually as barbs and collectively as a vane (web, *vexillum*). Proximally, each vane is fluffy, while distally it is firm and flat. The division between the calamus and the rachis is marked by the lowermost barbs and by a small opening to the calamus, the superior umbilicus (*umbilicus superior*, umbiliciform pit) on the ventral surface of the shaft (fig. 159). The rim of the umbilicus (*ora umbilici superioris*) often carries an afterfeather in the form of a cluster of barbs or even a small, featherlike appendage. The term "afterfeather" is a translation of the German word, "Afterfeder," introduced by Studer (1878), but it does not seem to have been previously used in English. The featherlike form of an afterfeather consists of an axis, the aftershaft (hyporachis), with its own vanes. We have not found any name for the latter, and therefore suggest that they be called aftervanes (*hypovexillum, -a*). An afterfeather is not an accessory to a feather but an integral part of it. The barbs of the afterfeather, whether they arise from an aftershaft or the rim of the superior umbilicus, form a row around the shaft that is continuous with the lower end of the vanes (fig. 159). Discussion of afterfeathers is resumed on page 252.

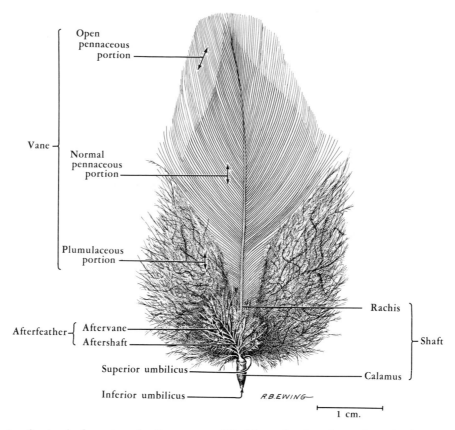

FIGURE 158.—Main parts of a typical contour feather, exemplified by a feather from the middle of the dorsal tract of a Single Comb White Leghorn Chicken.

Calamus

The calamus is a tubular structure composed of stratified, squamous epithelium and is never pigmented. The wall is solid for most of the length of the calamus (fig. 160, *A*), but the intermediate and sheath layers separate (fig. 160, just above the cross section taken at *B*). The former layer is thick, the latter is thin. The intermediate layer continues distally into the circle of the rachis, the hyporachis if any, and their barbs. The outer layer continues into the long, tapering sheath that encloses the feather during its early growth. Later, the sheath disintegrates, and its only remnant in a fully grown feather is a collar around the calamus, just below the superior umbilicus (fig. 161). Freed from the sheath, the barbs unroll, and the originally tubular form of the intermediate layer is lost (fig. 160, *D*).

Inside the calamus is a thin-walled tube that contains a number of transverse partitions (fig. 159). It is formed from the innermost or basilar layer of the epidermis of the feather germ. Vascularized pulp fills the tube during the early phase of feather growth but this is later resorbed, starting at the tip (for details see ch. 7, pp. 381–383). As this happens, the epidermal membrane around the pulp becomes cornified at periodic intervals and forms a series of downward-opening cups known as pulp caps (*galerus pulposus*) (Lillie, 1940). This name seems better than the more commonly used name, feather caps, because it refers to the location of the

structures during their formation. These pulp caps can be seen inside the calamus because the wall is unpigmented and somewhat transparent. If a piece of the calamus is cut away, one can clearly see that each pulp cap consists of a plate and the segment of the tube proximal to it. The plates may be concave, convex, or curved in a more complex manner, and the wall is often compressed and folded lengthwise. These variations appear to result from the partial collapse of the tube after it has dried. A cornified strand, the remains of the axial artery in the pulp, runs through the centers of the caps.

The stalk of caps originally extends through the superior umbilicus to the tip of a feather. The portion next to the rachis is fragile, however, and breaks off when it is exposed by the unfolding of the barbs. A few external pulp caps on the underside of a remex are shown in figure 161. Inside the calamus, the pulp caps go from one umbilicus to the other; they may adhere to the inner surface of the calamus wall or they may be freely suspended. The caps beside the rachis and in the distal two-thirds of the calamus are spaced fairly evenly, but those in the basal third are progressively closer together. The lowermost plate closes the inferior umbilicus.

The caps inside the calamus differ from those beside the rachis in cross-sectional shape and in the contour of the wall. Figure 159 shows that the internal caps are circular and have a smooth wall, whereas the external caps are variously ridged (as in fig. 159), flattened, or concave on the upper surface; the wall of the external caps bears many fine, parallel grooves that run longitudinally or slightly diagonally. The contour of the upper surface is produced by the impression of the rachis, and the fine grooves are produced by the impression of the barbs into the basal layer of epithelium before it becomes cornified. The roof of

an external cap was never in contact with the barbs and therefore is not grooved.

Rachis

The rachis has already been characterized as the long segment of the shaft that bears the barbs. A second feature distinguishing the rachis from the calamus is that it is essentially solid instead of tubular. It is a thickened continuation

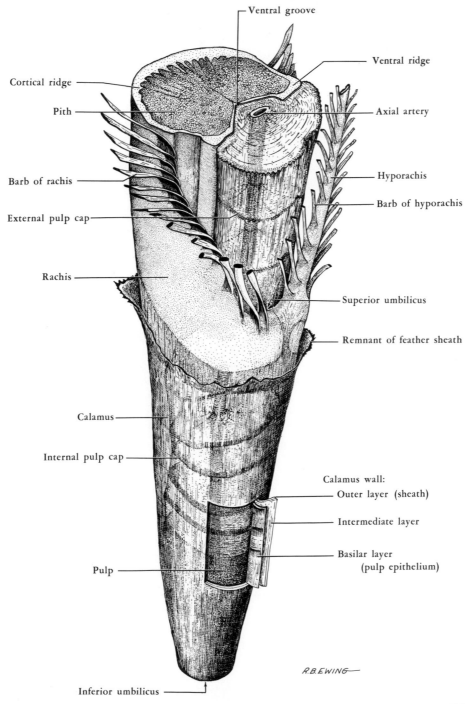

FIGURE 159.—Calamus and proximal end of rachis in a typical contour feather of a Single Comb White Leghorn Chicken. The pulp caps start beside the rachis and extend into the calamus. The wall of the calamus has been cut and is turned back to show its layers.

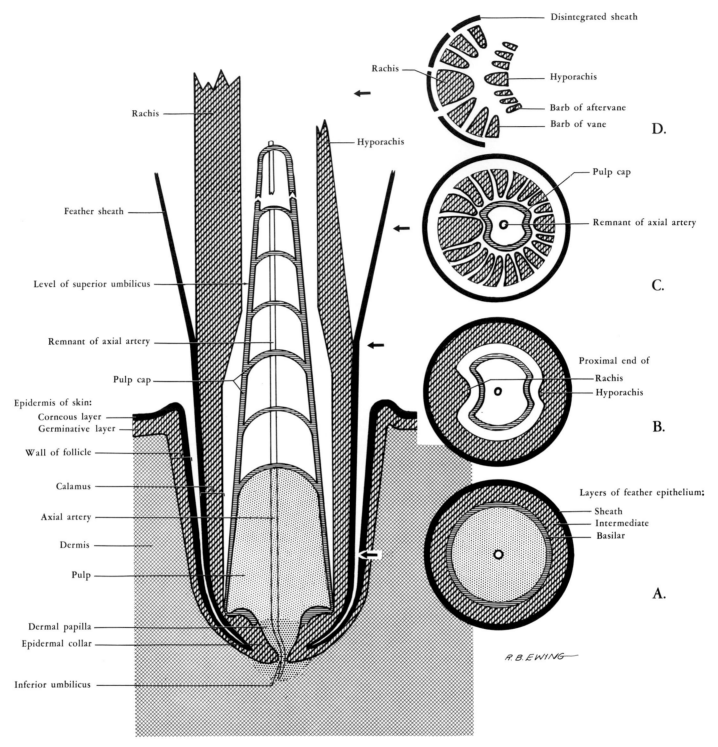

FIGURE 160.—Layers of the epidermis and the dermis in a growing contour feather. Inserts A through D are cross sections through the feather at the levels shown by the heavy arrows. Compare D with figure 165, A, and C with 165, B.

of the middorsal portion of the original feather tube, beyond the basal remnant of that tube, which later becomes the calamus (fig. 160, B, C, D).

In a fully grown feather, the lower end of the rachis arises as a pair of thickenings in the sides of the calamus, at or close below the superior umbilicus. Here the intermediate layer of the wall contains pith—a firm, spongy tissue formed from the keratinized walls of large, polygonal, epithelial cells. Because of the air inside these cells, the rachis is opaque, in contrast to the transparent wall of the calamus. The bars of pith swell and fuse; therefore, the rachis is as wide and very nearly as thick as the calamus at the level where the rachis emerges from the superior umbilicus. The lumen of the calamus is almost obliterated, and the pulp and subsequent pulp caps are constricted as they pass through the superior umbilicus. The rachis extends nearly to the tip of a feather, ending at the last symmetrical branching of barbs in the midline. This point is easily located if the last barbs are simple but requires a close look if either or both of them are divided.

Cross sections (figs. 159, 162, and 165, *A*) show that the rachis is generally four-sided and slightly wider than thick. The upper surface is slightly convex and the sides, that hold the barbs, are flat or convex. The under surface is marked in the proximal portion by a pair of ridges that correspond to the bars of pith described previously. The depression between them—the ventral groove—varies in width and depth. Two layers can be seen in the rachis—a thick, inner medulla composed of pith, and a thin, outer cortex, the same compact tissue as the wall of the calamus. One or more ridges of cortex (cortical ridges) often project downward into the medulla along the upper side of the rachis. From the outside the ridges appear as fine dark lines against the paler pith. As the rachis tapers, the ridges do not converge but simply disappear along the sides.

Vanes and the measurements of barbs

The shaft serves as the scaffold of a feather while the vanes provide the surface for an airfoil or for covering and insulating the body. Texture is the most important characteristic of the vanes. Variation in texture is related to the structure of the barbs and the function(s) of the feather. The proximal portion of the vanes has a soft, loose, fluffy texture designated as plumulaceous or downy (fig. 158). This portion, concealed by other feathers, gives a feather its property of insulation. The remaining portion of the vanes has a firm, compact, closely knit texture designated as pennaceous. It is a thin sheet of barbs that covers the body. The proportion of downy and pennaceous texture varies and is one of the criteria for defining certain types of feathers. A body contour feather has some of each, though the downy part may range from very short (as in upper major coverts of the remiges) to nearly the full length of the vanes (as in some sternal tract feathers). Remiges and rectrices have entirely pennaceous vanes, whereas semiplumes are entirely plumulaceous.

The vanes of most contour feathers are 1.2 to 4 times longer than their combined greatest width. Some feathers, such as the lesser sickles and the lateral pelvic feathers of

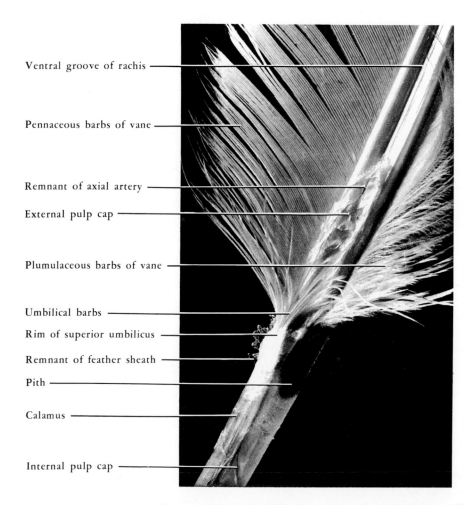

Ventral groove of rachis

Pennaceous barbs of vane

Remnant of axial artery

External pulp cap

Plumulaceous barbs of vane

Umbilical barbs

Rim of superior umbilicus

Remnant of feather sheath

Pith

Calamus

Internal pulp cap

FIGURE 161.—Region of the superior umbilicus on the under side of a primary remex from a Single Comb White Leghorn Chicken.

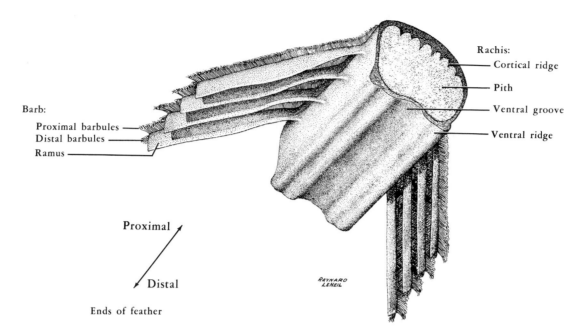

FIGURE 162.—Oblique ventral view of a segment of a contour feather showing the orientation of the barbs, the attachment of rami to the rachis, and the internal structure of the rachis. Single Comb White Leghorn Chicken.

adult male chickens, are relatively much longer. Vanes can be designated medial or lateral, dorsal or ventral in relation to the long axis of the body.

Except for color, there is probably no property of feathers as diverse as shape. It is understandable that no general review of this subject seems to have been published. The more common shapes were classified by Coues (1903: 121), but his scheme confuses the shape of the whole feather with that of the tip. These feathers are better treated separately, as botanists do in their description of leaves. In one of the most common shapes, ovate, the feather is broadest near the basal end; it is exemplified by many body feathers on a chicken. The opposite shapes, obovate and spatulate, are illustrated by semiplumes and contour feathers with short, broad, loosely pennaceous tips such as occur on the sternal and abdominal tracts of a chicken. Lanceolate (attenuate) feathers are narrow in relation to their length; they attain their maximum width a short distance above the base and taper from here to the tip. Feathers of the dorsal cervical tract of adult male chickens illustrate this shape. The tip of a contour feather is most often rounded or bluntly pointed. Sharply pointed tips are exemplified by feathers along the borders of the pelvic tract in a male chicken, and truncate tips are common on the body feathers of turkeys.

Feathers with pennaceous vanes are usually curved to some degree. They may curve downward toward the under surface, as seen clearly in the small feathers near the margin of the anterior alar patagium (prepatagium). In the feathers at the anterior end of the pectoral tract, the plumulaceous part is nearly perpendicular to the skin, whereas the pennaceous part is curved posteriorly. Feathers may also curve sideways along the rachis, as exemplified by the major

upper tail coverts of a junglecock or rooster. To a lesser degree, lateral curvature is shown by the upper coverts of the remiges in many birds. Finally, the vanes may be curved from the rachis laterally. In body contour feathers there may be a slight ventral curvature in this (frontal) plane, but in the outermost primary remiges of such birds as swans, the inner vanes slope downward and then sharply upward. This shape is clearly related to the aerodynamic function of these feathers.

The number of barbs in a vane ranges from a couple of dozen to several hundred, depending on the size of the feather, its location on the body, and the species of bird. The vane of a pectoral feather from a Ruby-throated Hummingbird (*Archilochus colubris*) may be 9 mm. long and have 28 barbs; the vane of a comparable feather from a Single Comb White Leghorn Chicken may be 88 mm. long and have 266 barbs. Barbs do not attach to opposite sides of the shaft at exactly the same level, yet the total number of barbs is very nearly equal in both vanes.

The spacing of barbs varies among feathers and also along the rachis of a single feather. In body contour feathers, the barbs are generally very close together at the base. Their spacing increases abruptly in the next higher barbs, and then more gradually; the barbs are farthest apart near the tip. Barbs at the midpoint may be as far apart as those at the tip, but usually this distance has been cut by as much as one-half. The spacing of barbs in a few feathers is presented in table 10.

The width of a vane depends on two variables—the length of the barbs and their angle from the rachis. The shortest barbs are at the ends of the vane, but the longest ones may be anywhere in between. Commonly, the length of the barbs

TABLE 10.—*Spacing of barbs in body contour feathers*

Species	Tract source of feather	Average distance between barb centers at three locations on vane[1]		
		Base	Middle	Tip
		Microns	*Microns*	*Microns*
Mallard (*Anas platyrhynchos*)	Interscapular	119	333	625
Red-tailed Hawk (*Buteo jamaicensis*).	Interscapular	217	555	714
Common Coturnix (*Coturnix coturnix*).	Pectoral	217	454	833
Single Comb White Leghorn Chicken.	Interscapular	156	357	625
	Pectoral	156	417	417
Mourning Dove (*Zenaidura macroura*).	Sternal	132	294	625
Ruby-throated Hummingbird (*Archilochus colubris*).	Pectoral	182	333	400
Common Crow (*Corvus brachyrhynchos*).	Pectoral	250	556	625
	Interscapular	333	625	833

[1] Calculated from the number of barbs in a 5-mm. span, except in the hummingbird, where a 2-mm. span was used.

increases markedly from the superior umbilicus to a point one-fourth to one-third the distance along the rachis. It then remains constant for a short distance and gradually decreases to the tip. The angle of the barbs tends to change in a simpler manner, being greatest at the base of the vane and becoming more acute toward the tip. This change is very subtle because adjacent barbs appear to be parallel. Since the spacing and the angle of the barbs vary in the same way, barbs generally become farther apart on the rachis as their angle becomes more acute. This applies not only to the proximal and distal portions of a vane but also to the vanes of asymmetrical feathers. We return to this point in describing remiges and rectrices (p. 255).

Ramus

Before examining the structure of barbs, we must clarify terminology. Some authors have applied the term "barb" (*barba*) to a primary branch of the rachis with its secondary branches, the barbules; others have applied the term to the primary branch alone. Ramus has been used as a synonym of barb in both senses. We restrict ramus (plural: rami) to the bare primary branch and employ barb as the inclusive term for a ramus and its vanules. Vanule (*vexilla barbae*) is the collective term for all the barbules on one side of a barb (fig. 163), just as vane refers to the barbs on one side of the rachis. These and other names for the parts of barbs and barbules are taken from Chandler (1916) unless otherwise noted.

A ramus has the shape of a somewhat compressed filament that tapers in height from base to tip, as shown in figure 163. The base of a ramus may be called the petiole (*petiolus*) if it is indented by a notch in the ventral border just before it merges into the rachis. Structures that appear to brace the ramus are found at this junction in the primary remiges of certain birds. Cross sections of rami show that shape is highly variable and may be more or less deltoid (fig. 166), ovate (fig. 164, *A, C, D*), lanceolate (fig. 164, *B*), or linear (fig. 165, *A*).

The layers of a ramus are the same as those already described for the rachis—a cortex of solidly compacted squamous cells and a medulla of empty, polyhedral pith cells (fig. 164). A very thin layer covering the cortex was mentioned by Haecker (1890), but this has not been described by other workers and may be an optical effect (Strong, 1902: 160). The superficial cells of the cortex form a pattern of polygons, with their long axes parallel to that of the barb. The deeper cells are longer, less flattened, and similar in shape to the cortical cells in mammalian hair (Auber and Appleyard, 1951: 736).

The medulla of a ramus starts just beyond the petiole and is not continuous with that of the rachis (fig. 165, *A*). Since it is confined to the body of a ramus, there is a contrast between the medulla and the ridges of transparent but solid cortex above and below it. In most birds the medulla is composed of many irregularly packed cells, but in the remiges of owls and goatsuckers there is but a single vertical layer of cells (Mascha, 1905: 5). Typical medullary cells fuse together so completely that no boundary can be seen between them. There are two forms of such cells—(1) apparently thin-walled cells that enclose a single cavity (fig. 164) and (2) spongy cells, that is, cells pervaded by small spheroidal vacuoles of various sizes, except for a thin, external zone of solid appearance (fig. 254, *A*). In the second type, a

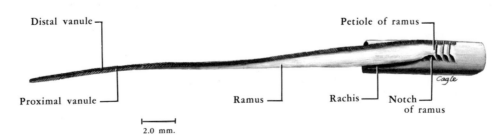

Distal vanule — ⌐   Petiole of ramus — ⌐

Proximal vanule —   Ramus —   Rachis —   Notch of ramus

2.0 mm.

FIGURE 163.—Side view of a pennaceous barb from a Red-tailed Hawk (*Buteo jamaicensis*).

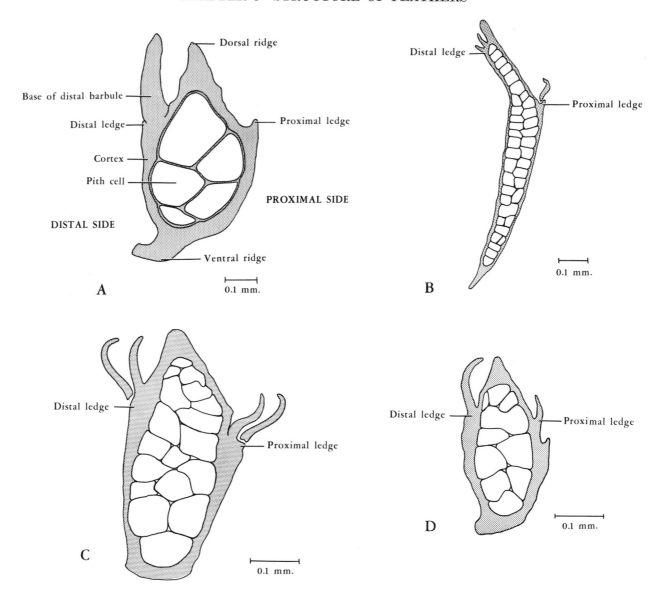

FIGURE 164.—Cross sections of barbs from the inner vanes of remiges. In each section, everything except the barbules constitutes the ramus.

A, secondary of a Single Comb White Leghorn Chicken.
B, primary of a Yellow-shafted Flicker (*Colaptes auratus*).

C, proximal end of barb from primary remex of a Common Crow (*Corvus brachyrhynchos*).
D, distal end of same barb as *C*.

larger vacuole remains amidst the small vacuoles after the nucleus has been obliterated; it may be situated either at or away from the center of the cell (Auber, 1957b: 458). Special medullary cells cause the blue or violet color seen in the feathers of many birds. These are known as cloudy cells owing to their microscopic vacuoles; distinct boundaries are visible between them (fig. 254). These cells and their role in color production are discussed further in chapter 7, pages 403–406.

Plumulaceous barbules

The branches of a barb are the barbules, also known as radii (singular: radius), tertiary fibers (Mascha, 1905), and,

in German, Strahlen (Nitzsch, 1867). Other synonyms are listed by Chandler (1916). A barbule is essentially a stalk of single cells that are serially differentiated to some degree. It is divisible into a laterally compressed base of fused cells and a slender pennulum (*pennula*) of jointed cells.

These parts are seen in a simple condition in the barbules of down feathers or the downy part of contour feathers. A plumulaceous or downy barbule (German: Knöpfchenradius. Hempel, 1931; German: Dunenradius. Sick, 1937) is characterized by a relatively short, straplike base and a long, slender pennulum (fig. 167). Figure 166 shows cross sections of several barbules that have been cut progressively farther from the ramus. The base of a downy barbule usually consists of three or four cells that are discernible because of differential refractility, pigmentation, or reaction to stains in the remnants of their boundaries or nuclei. There are no signs of the cells in the base of downy barbules in certain herons and plovers. The base is commonly 1½ to 3 times as wide as the proximal cells of the pennulum. It is very much wider in the downy barbules of turkeys, but scarcely wider than

the pennulum in albatrosses, cormorants, gulls, and parrots. The flexibility of these barbules is made possible in part by the simple, flat shape of the base. Certain downy barbules are modified by a flat process at the proximal end of the base. It projects almost perpendicularly from the base on the side toward the ramus and acts like an angle iron to stiffen the barbule. This structure was called the ventral

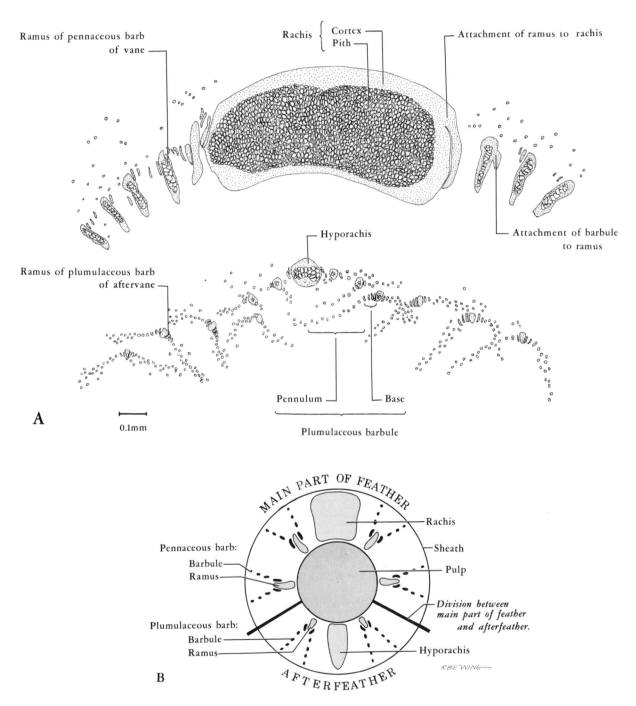

FIGURE 165.—Cross sections of contour feathers.

A, fully grown feather of a Single Comb White Leghorn Chicken. As the feather has unfurled from its sheath, its after-vanes have reversed their curvature and have come to lie spoon-wise beneath the vanes. Only a few barbs close to the rachis and the hyporachis are shown on each side. Compare with figures 160, D and 165, B. B, diagrammatic cross section of a growing feather to show arrangement of barbs. Only a few barbs are shown in the main feather and the afterfeather. Compare with figures 160, C, 165, A, and 236.

Sections through barbules:

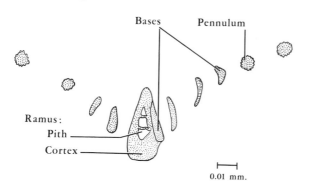

FIGURE 166.—Cross section of a downy barb of a Single Comb White Leghorn Chicken. For orientation see figure 165, *B*.

lamella (German: ventral Lamelle. Hempel, 1931: 663), but we suggest ventral flange (*arcus ventralis*) as a more descriptive term.

The pennulum of a downy barbule resembles a stalk of bamboo, except that each segment is a single long cell (fig. 167). The cells are either uniformly thick or are swollen at their distal end. Since each is slightly narrower than the one proximal to it, the pennulum as a whole is tapered. This is most evident in barbules that have not lost the pointed terminal cell and a few cells before it; such damaged barbules are often seen. The junction of cells has been called the node (*nodus*) (Chandler, 1916: 254), but it is more accurate to restrict this term to the distal portion of a cell, particularly if it is swollen. The main portion of a cell is the internode (*internodus*). A shallow socket in the end of one node holds the proximal end of the next internode.

The nodes of downy barbules vary considerably among birds. Their simplest condition, exemplified by the barbules of cormorants, storks, and herons, is that in which the nodes are but faintly enlarged. The cells may swell gradually toward the distal end, as in rails, plovers, and sandpipers, or they may be of uniform thickness with the nodes marked by rings, as in turacos. Similar barbules occur in tinamous and gallinaceous birds, but in these birds the rings (singular: *anulus*) sometimes break loose and slide along the pennulum (fig. 214, p. 319). Nodes often have two to four (rarely one) outgrowths, the nodal prongs (singular: *dens nodosus*). These may be no more than the accentuated distal corners of the cells, as seen in rails, plovers, sandpipers, and goatsuckers. They may be short, pointed cilia, as in storks and cranes. Cilia that are nearly as long as the cells occur in penguins, albatrosses, petrels, and loons; long cilia that are sometimes forked occur in albatrosses and petrels. The prongs may take the form of knobs or triangular plates that project like fins from the nodes. These can be seen on several cells in the proximal portion of the pennulum in pigeons and owls (fig. 167) and in the distal portion in ducks and their allies (fig. 221, p. 329). They have been called trows (Loconti, 1956: 42), but this term seems inappropriate as well as unnecessary.

In spite of their simplicity, plumulaceous barbules have distinctive characters in many orders and sometimes in lower taxonomic groups of birds. According to Chandler (1916: 270), these features are "always best displayed by barbules on the inner portion of the distal vanule of the basal barbs. Farther distal on either feather or barb, and on the proximal vanules, the structure is often less specialized, and lacks some of the characteristic features of the group." Plumulaceous barbules are less variable than those on the pennaceous portion of a vane. For this reason they are easier to use than the latter for identifying isolated feathers. Chandler's monograph is indispensable for such a task

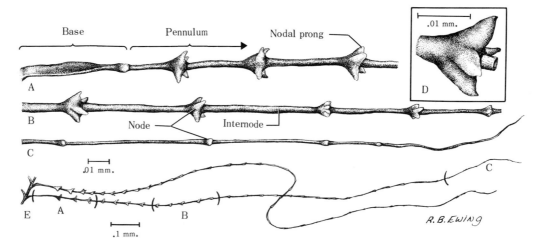

FIGURE 167.—Plumulaceous barbules of a Common Pigeon.

A, base and proximal portion of pennulum with large nodes.
B, intermediate portion with moderately large nodes.
C, distal portion with very small nodes.

D, enlarged view of nodal prongs.
E, two barbules showing location of portions *A* to *C*, enlarged above.

because it describes and illustrates the barbules from a great many birds. The distinctive features of plumulaceous barbules from a number of British birds have been described and arranged in a key as far as the ordinal level (Day, 1966). The key was constructed as a tool for the identification of feather fragments in the gut and feces contents of stoats and weasels, but it has wider application. Similar techniques for identifying barbules have been developed by archeologists concerned with remains of feathers found in their excavations (Hargrave, 1965; Messinger, 1965).

The morphology of downy barbs can now be reviewed to show how their soft, fluffy texture is achieved. The rami bend easily, owing to their fineness and lack of any projections. Many barbules are also flexible, because of the straplike base and the joints along the pennulum. Barbs with these features may become loosely entangled, but there are no structures that hold them together. The function of the nodal prongs is not known, though they appear to limit bending and to catch other barbules. Some barbules project from the ramus at a nearly constant angle, owing to the presence of a ventral flange that stiffens the base. Their pennulums do not become entangled but form a fine fringe along the ramus. Successive barbules may point alternately upward or downward, an arrangement found in some of the downy barbs of gallinaceous birds, jaegers, skimmers, and alcids. This creates two planes of vanules on each side of a ramus, and increases the thickness of the barb as a whole. In the downy barbs at the base of contour feathers of passerine birds, the vanules on the proximal side meet at a smaller angle than those on the distal side. The proximal vanules of one barb accordingly lie between the distal vanules of an adjacent barb (Sick, 1937: 350).

The downy portions of contour feathers are concealed beneath the pennaceous portion of overlapping feathers, and they contribute little to the appearance of a bird. They play an important role, however, in controlling body temperature by the insulating effect of the air they entrap (King and Farner, 1961, 2: 252). According to Nye (1964: 196), "it . . . appears that the main thermo-regulatory adaptation of ducks to their aquatic habits is their thick, dense, waterproof plumage." Man has taken advantage of the insulating property of downy feathers by using them in quilts, sleeping bags, and parkas. The results of basic and applied research on this topic have been reported by Kennedy et al. (1956).

Pennaceous barbules

The pennaceous barbules are those that make up the flat, closely knit portions of the vanes. They are differentiated on both sides of a barb; even the ramus is asymmetrical. The side of a ramus facing the distal end (tip) of a feather is flatter than the side facing the proximal end (base), and may even be concave (fig. 164, B). As in a downy barb, the top of the ramus is formed into a rounded or acute dorsal ridge that is nearly symmetrical (figs. 165, A, and 166). A low, stout ventral ridge projects from the bottom of the ramus; since it is always on the distal side it can be used for orienting cross sections of barbs (Strong, 1902:157). The pennaceous barbules may attach directly to the sides of the ramus, as in downy barbs. In strong vanes, such as those on the flight feathers, the bases of the barbules fit into grooves in ledges on each side (fig. 168).

The distal ledge (i.e., on the distal side of the ramus) is higher than the proximal ledge, as shown in figure 164. It has a straight border, whereas the proximal ledge has an undulating border and tends to be narrower. The dorsomedial surface of each ledge has a series of overlapping grooves that run upward and outward. These features are

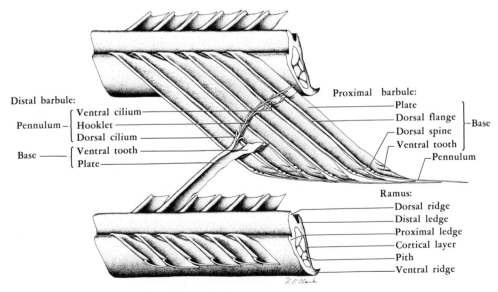

FIGURE 168.—Segments of two pennaceous barbs in dorsal oblique view to show interlocking of parts. Compare with figure 170. The overlapping grooves in the ledges of the rami are not shown.

not shown in figure 168, but were shown by Sick (1937) in his figures 81 and 82. His paper and that by Mascha (1905) discuss in detail the structure and function of the ledges.

Barbules of the main part of a contour feather slope upward as they angle away from a ramus, whereas those on the afterfeather slope downward. This can be seen in a cross section of a contour feather (fig. 165, A), where sections through rows of barbules are in clusters or V's. This arrangement is an outcome of that in a growing feather, diagramed with just a few barbs in figure 165, B. A cross section of a feather germ shows a circle of barbs, interrupted by the rachis middorsally and sometimes by a hyporachis midventrally. The barbules are located peripherally to the rami, the latter being close to the pulp. In each barb, barbule cells are arranged in a narrow U-shape with the ramus at their base. These details are shown in figures 237 and 307. When the feather emerges from its sheath, the main vanes and aftervanes separate and flatten out, but the barbules retain some degree of slope.

The barbules and rami are not joined early in the growth of a feather. They develop in place from separate primordia and later unite. Hence, barbules do not grow out from a ramus as twigs do from a branch.

The horizontal angle between a ramus and the base of a barbule is the radial angle, and the ratio between angles on opposite sides of a ramus is called the angular ratio (Carlisle, 1925:908). The radial angle generally ranges between 20° and 60° (mode about 45°); it tends to be greater on the distal side of the ramus.

Pennaceous barbules have a long, narrow base and a pennulum that is no more than half again as long as the base. The pennulum is shorter than that of a downy barbule from the same bird, and may be even shorter than the base. These barbules are mainly characterized, however, by the differentiation of their cells and their diverse outgrowths, known collectively as barbicels (singular: *processus barbulae*).

All parts of these barbules hold the barbs together, and thereby keep the vane intact. The structure of the barbules varies considerably within and among feathers, in accordance with the functional demands imposed on different parts of the vane. Such variation was discussed in the general analysis by Sick (1937) and by Chandler (1914), Hempel (1931), Brinckmann (1958), and Rutschke (1960) on the feathers of particular birds. The barbicels and other parts are most pronounced on the remiges and rectrices. Pennaceous barbules on the upper coverts of the wing and tail are nearly as well developed as these, but those on the contour feathers of the body tend to have a simpler structure. The cells may show less differentiation and the barbicels may be reduced. These trends are carried farther on the ventral feather tracts than the dorsal ones.

Base.—The base of a pennaceous barbule is a narrow plate, generally 6 to 10 times longer than wide (fig. 169).

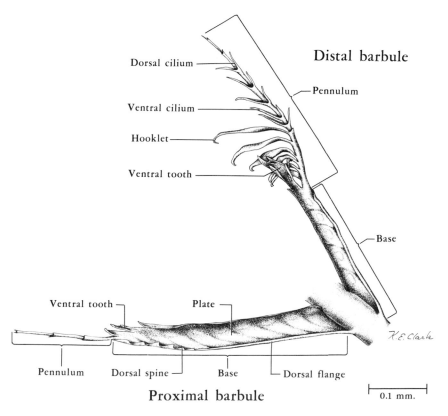

FIGURE 169.—Pennaceous barbules from the middle of a secondary remex of a Single Comb White Leghorn Chicken. Both have been turned on their long axes so that they can be shown in side view.

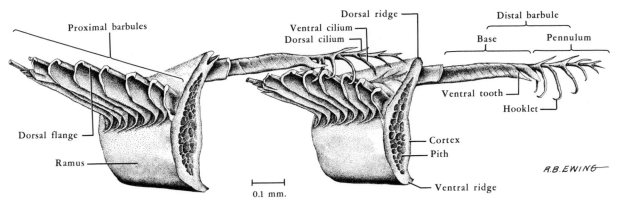

FIGURE 170.—Segments of two pennaceous barbs from a contour feather of a Single Comb White Leghorn Chicken. The barbs are seen obliquely from the distal end to show interlocking of parts.

The synonym basal lamella was applied to it by Sick (1937) and Brinckmann (1958). It is either rectangular or tapered distally, and diminishes in thickness from dorsal edge to ventral. The plate is always composed of several fused cells in which the remnants of the nuclei may appear as oval spots and the boundaries may show as oblique, unpigmented stripes. The ventral edge of the base may be straight, gently curved, or wavy, with protrusions at the cell boundaries. Many pictures of the microscopic structure of feathers show the base of a pennaceous barbule as standing on edge, but this is not correct. The plate is curved around its long axis, with the result that a dorsal portion is oriented vertically and a ventral portion slopes downward toward the ramus (figs. 168, 170). Adjacent barbules may touch or overlap, the ventral edge of one base lying beneath the dorsal edge of the base distal to it.

The base is sometimes a very narrow strip with a triangular or rounded ventral flange at its proximal end. The strip corresponds to the dorsal portion of a fully developed base, and the flange is all that remains of the ventral portion. The flange has received little attention, probably because it is absent from remiges, the feathers that have been studied in most detail. As in plumulaceous barbules, it stiffens the base against flexion, with the result that the barbules remain parallel even if they lack interlocking barbicels.

Proximal barbules.—Pennaceous barbules are so different on opposite sides of a barb that they must be considered subtypes, and described separately in more detail. The distal barbules are those on the distal side of a ramus, where they lie approximately parallel to the shaft. Synonyms for them, based on certain barbicels, are hook-fibers (Mascha, 1905) and the German equivalents, Hakenradii and Hakenfasern. The proximal barbules lie on the proximal side of a ramus, where they point away from the shaft. Synonyms based on the shape of the base are curved fibers (Mascha, 1905) and the German equivalents Bogenradii and Bogenfasern.

As applied to pennaceous barbs, proximal and distal refer to the sides instead of the ends, as is usual elsewhere. When it is necessary to designate barbules at certain places along

a barb, wording must be chosen carefully to make this clear. Barbules close to the ramus can be referred to as basal or at the proximal end. The terms "apical" and "terminal" can be used for barbules at the distal end of a barb.

Proximal barbules are usually longer as a whole and longer in the base than the distal barbules on the opposite side of the ramus. The proportion of base to pennulum is so variable among proximal barbules, even from different parts of the same feather, that it is impossible to generalize about it.

The dorsal border of the base is recurved on the side facing the ramus and forms a dorsal flange (*arcus dorsalis*). At the distal end of the flange are three to five low, pointed processes known as dorsal spines (singular: *stylus dorsalis*) (fig. 169). Synonyms for them are dog-tooth (Wray, 1887b: 421), tooth-like projections (Mascha, 1905:21), little teeth (German: Zähnchen. Hempel, 1931:679), and abutments or little arresting teeth (translated from German: Widerlagern oder Arretierungszähnchen. Sick, 1937:212). The spines are each outgrowths of basal cells, yet Chandler (1916) did not consider them barbicels, as they appear to be. The short, or abutting, side of a spine faces the proximal end of the barbule; the long side slopes upward to the base of the next spine. The spines in the middle of the series are usually the largest.

Below the dorsal spines, the ventral margin of the base is incised between several cells. The distal corners of the cells are drawn out into pointed barbicels called ventral teeth (*dens ventralis*). They were first described adequately by Mascha (1905:21), who referred to them as both lobes and processes of the ventral membrane. As these processes occur only on the ventral margin, they can be called simply teeth, just as their counterparts on the dorsal margin can be called simply spines. It is helpful, however, to use the adjectives dorsal and ventral as reminders of their location. The ventral teeth point toward the tip of the barbule and they overlap on the side of the barbule facing the shaft. They are much larger than the dorsal spines, but like them, the biggest ones are in the middle of the series. The teeth tend to be long, slender, and even slightly recurved in gallinaceous birds, hawks, and kingfishers (Chandler, 1916:

267). In this form, they are analogous to the hooklets of the distal barbules (p. 249), as pointed out by Sick (1937:286).

The waterproof property of the feathering of aquatic birds is due to modifications in the structure and positioning of the barbules. Taken together they make a so-called porous surface through which water cannot enter, owing to its surface tension (Rutschke, 1960). Among the modifications are special barbicels on the bases of both proximal and distal barbules in the body contour feathers of many water birds. In such birds, distally curved fibers arise from the dorsal border in place of the dorsal spines. They have been given a special name "flexules" (singular: *flexura*) (Chandler, 1916: 271) because they are not homologous with any other types of barbicels and are always of the same curved form. Flexules occur in grebes, albatrosses, petrels, pelicans, cranes, limpkins, rails, jaçanas, sandpipers, phalaropes, and alcids.

The division between the base and the pennulum is usually set at the distal border of the outermost cell that bears a ventral tooth (fig. 169). This landmark is based on the belief that the teeth are parts of the base, as expressed by Chandler (1916:252, 254) and Sick (1937:212). According to Brinckmann (1958:490), however, the tooth-bearing cells belong to the pennulum in proximal barbules. On this basis, she set the division between base and pennulum at the proximal margin of the innermost cell with a ventral tooth. This standard may be practical for studies of proximal barbules in which the base tapers into the pennulum, but it leads to certain difficulties. Brinckmann agreed that in distal barbules the teeth belong to the base. A double standard for the landmark between segments of a barbule raises problems of homology and terminology.

The pennulum of a well-characterized proximal barbule (e.g., that on a flight feather) usually has very small nodes or a few ventral barbicels. Rarely, it also has a few dorsal barbicels, and commonly, in less well-characterized barbules (e.g., those on body contour feathers), it is simply a bare filament. The barbicels are simple, pointed processes known as cilia (fig. 169). Synonyms for them are spines (Mascha, 1905:15) and, in German, Wimpern (Nitzsch, 1867) and Fortsätze (Sick, 1937:213). Ventral cilia (singular: *cilium ventralis*) are typically straight or gently recurved, but they may be hooked, as in hawks, falcons, and galliform birds (Chandler, 1916:335). They are in series with the ventral teeth but tend to be longer, finer, and more flexible. It is sometimes difficult, if not impossible, to distinguish the two types of barbicels. The cilia usually dwindle and vanish midway along the pennulum, but they may continue to the tip. Very small cilia resemble the nodal prongs of plumulaceous barbules, but differ in being single rather than multiple on each cell. Cilia are generally absent from the dorsal border of proximal barbules. Birds that have flexules on the base often have very similar processes on the pennulum. These might be called dorsal cilia (singular: *cilium dorsalis*) because of their location, even though they cannot be distinguished structurally from the flexules.

The plane of the pennulum, as defined by the barbicels,

is vertical whereas that of the base, it will be recalled, is vertical oblique. At the level of the last teeth, the pennulum also turns so that it points toward the tip of the barb, more or less parallel to the ramus (fig. 168). The pennula of adjacent barbules thus overlap closely, except in tinamous, where they are fused into a solid bar. This peculiarity was discovered and described by Chandler (1916:346, pl. 25), and its function was discussed by Sick (1937:291).

Distal barbules.—Distal barbules are the more complex subtype of pennaceous barbules. These tend to be shorter overall and to have a relatively shorter base than the proximal barbules opposite them. As compared with the proximal barbules on the same barb, the distal barbules are slightly more numerous and more closely spaced, but they project at virtually the same angle from the ramus. The dorsal portion of the base is again thickened and vertically oriented, but the flange is less pronounced or even absent. There are no dorsal spines. Flexules may be developed with the same form as before, yet more extensively. According to Chandler (1916:272), "They first develop at the proximal end of the base and progress toward the pennulum, ultimately forming a continuous series with a similar series of pennular dorsal barbicels."

The ventral teeth attain a more elaborate structure in the distal barbules than in the proximal barbules, especially on the flight feathers. They vary considerably in form, even within a barb—a reflection of their precise adjustment to meet the requirements of the feather. The structure and function of the teeth have been studied in great detail by Sick (1937); the following account is based on his work. Based on their number, position, and relative size, four main types of ventral teeth can be recognized in different birds. The simplest type is that of a single tooth, formed as an outgrowth of the ventral distal corner of the last cell in the basal lamella. It is oriented horizontally, the same as the ventral portion of the lamella. Hence, although the tooth is called ventral, it actually lies on the side of the barbule toward the tip of the ramus. The tooth may be broad or narrow, rounded or pointed, and entire or notched at the tip. A constant feature is a hump on the dorsal margin known as the tooth nodule (German: Zahnhügel). Proximal to the nodule, the margin is flattened and appears like a ramp up to the main part of the base. Distal to the nodule, and extending to the tip of the tooth, the margin takes a steeper angle and is stiffened. One or two additional teeth may be present, each derived from one cell proximal to the last and largest tooth. These teeth lie in the same plane as the main tooth, without overlapping. The number of teeth in such barbules diminishes toward the tip of the barb. Simple ventral teeth are found in the feathers of falcons, gallinaceous birds, alcids, goatsuckers, owls, swifts, and passerines.

Ventral teeth of the second type are paired, and the lower tooth is larger and lies in a different plane. The upper, distal tooth is horizontal and corresponds to the main tooth of the preceding type. The lower tooth is vertical and split into overlapping lobes, the tips of which may be broadened and notched. Unlike simple teeth, which each come from one cell, these complex teeth are based on two or three cells. Teeth of this type occur in the feathers of such birds as pigeons and hummingbirds. In successive barbules, toward the tip of a barb they become reduced and hence similar to the simple type of teeth.

The third category includes diverse forms of two or more teeth, which have in common an uppermost tooth as large as the rest or larger. A ramp is present but often reduced on this tooth. The teeth overlap and project at an angle from each other, as in the second type. There is relatively little modification of their structure along a barb. Teeth with these characteristics are found in the feathers of Old World vultures, bustards, swans, and crows.

The ventral teeth in the feathers of albatrosses and petrels are so distinctive as to be considered a fourth type by Sick (1937). Both teeth are narrow at the base and very broad at the tip; the tips have one or two rounded notches.

The most distinctive parts of a distal barbule are barbicels with hooked tips that occur on the ventral side of the proximal portion of the pennulum. These are known as hooklets or *hamuli* (singular: *hamulus*), and in German, Häkchen (Nitzsch, 1867) and Haken (Sick, 1937). Distal barbules commonly have two to four hooklets in body contour feathers and three to seven hooklets in flight feathers. The latter have as many as eight hooklets in ducks and hawks and nine in tinamous. The hooklets are outgrowths of the very next cells beyond those that bear ventral teeth. There is no gap or even transition between these two types of barbicels. The contrast between them accentuates the difference between the base and the pennulum, a characteristic of distal barbules. Hooklets hang either from the ventral surface of the pennular cells, as shown in figure 170, or from the medial surface (that which faces the rachis). They always pass on the medial side of the ventral teeth (fig. 169).

A typical hooklet has three sections—(1) a short base that leaves the pennulum at a low angle; (2) a long, gently recurved part that hangs more steeply or even vertically; and (3) a short, thickened, hooked tip. In progressively more distal hooklets along a barbule, their length usually increases while their angle from the pennulum decreases. Since the hooklets project at different angles (in the vertical plane), their tips span a greater distance than their basal cells. The pull they exert on the proximal barbules is thus focused on a relatively short segment of the pennulum (Sick, 1937:324). A hooklet is not bandlike as stated by Mascha (1905), but roughly triangular or circular in cross section (Hempel, 1931:676). The middle portion is stiffened by diagonal ridges along the sides, and may bear one to three tiny pointed bumps on the dorsal (distal) surface. These structures are designated here as prickles, a synonym for Abstemmhöcker (stemming protuberances), the term used by Sick (1937:330). They occur on the feathers of such birds as albatrosses and petrels, ducks, swans, pigeons, turacos, and cuckoos.

TABLE 11.—*Comparison of proximal and distal subtypes of pennaceous barbules*

Characteristic	Proximal barbule	Distal barbule
Present on	Shaft as well as ramus	Ramus only.
Total length	Greater	Less.
Base length	Longer	Shorter.
Dorsal flange	Pronounced	Weak or absent.
Dorsal spines	Present	Absent.
Ventral teeth	Simple, uniform	Complex, different.
Direction of pennulum	Turns toward tip of barb	Continues in direction of base.
Hooklets	Absent	Present.
Ventral cilia	Short or absent	Long or short.
Dorsal cilia	Rarely present	Usually present.

Beyond the hooklets are ventral cilia that are longer and more numerous than those on the proximal barbules. The transition between hooklets and cilia may be abrupt or gradual, depending on the length, angle, and curvature of the first few cilia.

Dorsal cilia, rarely present in proximal barbules, are often present on the cells that bear ventral cilia, though never on the cells with hooklets. They tend to be shorter and less numerous than the ventral cilia. The first two or three dorsal cilia are sometimes specially enlarged in remiges (see p. 260).

Comparison and functional analysis.—The characteristics of proximal and distal barbules are summarized in table 11.

Functional analysis of the barbules explains the structures of the two subtypes. The relation between morphology and function in barbs has been studied by numerous scientists, starting with Robert Hooke, the father of microscopy in England. Important papers on this subject are those by Mascha (1905), Chandler (1914, 1916), Hempel (1931), Sick (1937), Brinckmann (1958), and Oehme (1963).

Pennaceous barbs are held together by a flexible, self-adjusting mechanism that is complex in details yet simple in essence. The distal barbules of one barb cross over the proximal barbules of the next barb on the distal side (toward the tip of the feather). The hooklets of the former grasp the dorsal flanges of the latter, thereby interlocking them (figs. 168, 170). Since the barbules are flexible at several points, they can hold the rami together even when the vane is stretched by air pressure. In this situation, distal and proximal barbules pull against each other, and there is an increase in the radial angles and the angles between the bases of opposing barbules.

The arrangement of the barbules is reflected in the ledges that support them on the sides of a ramus. The proximal ledge is lower and thicker than the distal ledge, a feature that enables it to support not only proximal barbules but also the distal barbules that rest on them (Sick, 1937:338).

Most parts of pennaceous barbules assist in the cohesion of barbs. The first few hooklets of a distal barbule point backward toward the ramus and curve around at the tip into the groove on the underside of dorsal flanges. The remaining hooklets hang downward or point forward toward the tip of the pennulum; they reach over the dorsal flanges, but not into the groove. As long as there is no stress on the vane, the hooklets hold the flanges loosely. When pressure is applied, the barbs swing away from the shaft and the distance between rami is increased. The hooklets then pull on the flanges and also slide distally along them. The dorsal spines stop the proximal hooklets from sliding off the flanges. The remaining hooklets cross over the flanges closer to the ramus and thus do not encounter dorsal spines. As they pull more strongly, they are lifted by the proximal barbules on which they ride. This automatically increases the traction between the hooklets and the flanges. Close study of a hooklet reveals that the flattened basal end permits flexion, while the reinforcements along the middle take up the strain of pulling. The flattened posterior surface and the sharp edges of the hooked tip enable it to get a good grip on the flange (Hempel, 1931:677). The prickles appear to fend off the proximal barbule beyond the one grasped by their own hooklet. If these barbules were too close together, the hooklets would be unable to slide along them.

The bases of the barbules supplement the interlocking mechanism of hooklets and dorsal flanges. When stress on the vane causes barbules to turn, they are soon stopped by the overlapping and crowding together of their bases and ventral teeth. These actions stiffen the barbs and promote cohesion between them, thereby resisting the stress. The degree of stiffening depends on the teeth, which vary in size, structure, and stiffness in different parts of a feather.

Barbules with a narrow base and small teeth, as found in body contour feathers, cannot overlap in the manner just described. They usually possess a ventral flange, however, which keeps them at a constant angle to the ramus and hence parallel to each other. In this way the interlocking mechanism is maintained. The width of the base affects not only the action of the barbule but also the density of the vane. Flight feathers are denser than the pennaceous portions of body feathers, more because of the wider bases of the barbules than the closer spacing between barbs or barbules.

The first few ventral cilia on the distal barbules may act like hooklets though with less force. If the pennulum of such a barbule is so long as to span more than one ramus, only the cilia proximal to that ramus can have any hooking action. The recurved ventral cilia and teeth on the proximal barbules of certain birds (p. 248) appear to exert a similar effect on the dorsal flange of the distal barbules.

Some of the cilia and teeth serve to keep the rami or barbules apart (German: Abstemmen). The outermost teeth of a proximal barbule may be so built as to push against the opposing face of the adjacent ramus, that is, the distal surface of the next lower ramus on the shaft. This action appears to support the proximal barbules when the vane is stressed so that their pennula can stay at the proper height. Both dorsal and ventral cilia of distal barbules may prop

the proximal barbules apart, as do the prickles, but Sick (1937:329) stated that this is not their chief function. The ventral cilia supplement the hooklets as described above, and in pushing against the next ramus they also support their pennulum. The pennulum of a distal barbule may be gently S-curved if it is short; a downward turn at the proximal end better enables the hooklets to grasp the proximal barbules, whereas an upward, lateral turn at the distal end enables the ventral cilia to fend off the proximal barbule. If the pennulum is so long as to span more than one ramus, its distal portion is relatively straight. The ventral cilia beyond the first ramus may assume a horizontal position and enlarge the gliding surface of the pennulum. Alternately, they may turn downward and occupy the spaces between the bases of the distal barbules on the next higher barb. Both conditions render the vane more dense, and accordingly they occur more in remiges and rectrices than in body contour feathers.

The dorsal cilia play an important role in creating friction between overlapping feathers. They will be discussed in conjunction with the flight feathers (pp. 260–261), where they are most highly developed.

Not until recent decades have some of the finer details of structure and operation in pennaceous barbs been worked out. The essential features, however, were seen by Robert Hooke. Let us digress to view our subject in the perspective of time, and see what he reported in 1665.

> For examining a middle ciz'd Goose-quill, I easily enough found with my naked eye, that the main stem of it contain'd about 300. longer and more Downy branchings upon one side, and as many on the other of more stiff but somewhat shorter branchings. Many of these long and downy branchings, examining with an ordinary *Microscope*, I found divers of them to contain neer 1200. small leaves . . . and as many stalks; on the other side, . . . each of the leaves or branchings, . . . seemed to be divided into about sixteen or eighteen small joints, . . . out of most of which there seem to grow small *fibres*, . . . each of them very proportionably shap'd according to its position, or plac'd on the stalk . . .; those on the under side of it, . . . being much longer than those directly opposite to them on the upper; and divers of them, . . . were terminated with small crooks, . . . The stalks . . . on the other side, seem'd divided into neer as many small knotted joints, but without any appearance of strings or crooks, each of them about the middle . . ., seem'd divided into two parts by a kind of fork, one side of which, . . . was extended . . ., the other, . . . was very short.
>
> The stems of the Downy branches . . ., being rang'd in the order visible enough to the naked eye, . . . the *collateral* stalks and leaves . . . are so rang'd, that the leaves or hairy stalks of the one side lie at top, or are incumbent on the stalks of the other, and cross each other, . . . by which means every of those little hooked *fibres* of the leaved stalk get between the naked stalks, and the stalks being full of knots, and a pretty way disjoined so as that the *fibres* can easily get between them, the two parts are so closely and admirably woven together, that it is able to impede, for the greatest part, the transcursion of the Air; and though they are so exceeding small, as that the thickness of one of these stalks amounts not to a 500. part of an Inch, yet do they compose so strong a texture, as, notwithstanding the exceeding quick and violent beating of them against the Air, by the strength of the Birds wing, they firmly hold together. (Hooke, 1665: 166).

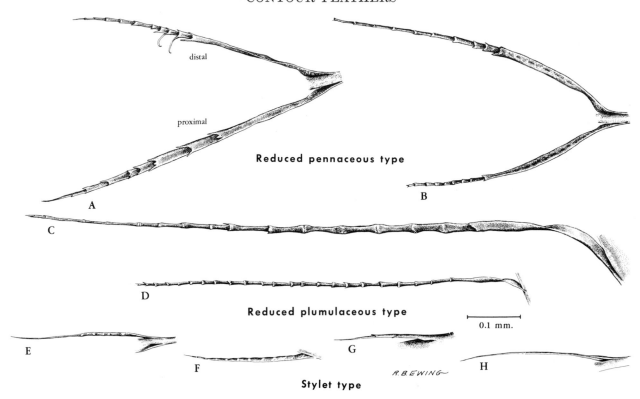

distal

proximal

Reduced pennaceous type

A

B

C

D

Reduced plumulaceous type

0.1 mm.

E

F

G

H

R.B.EWING

Stylet type

FIGURE 171.—Examples of three types of simplified barbules.

A, Single Comb White Leghorn Chicken—crural tract, contour feather.
B, Common Pigeon—pectoral tract, contour feather.
C, White Pekin Duck—oil gland circlet, down feather.
D, Bronze Turkey—occipital tract feather.

E, Green Heron (*Butorides virescens*)—anterior ear covert.
F, Common Pigeon—occipital tract feather.
G, Single Comb White Leghorn Chicken—malar tract feather.
H, Mallard (*Anas platyrhynchos*)—posterior ear covert.

Simplified barbules

Contour feathers sometimes have barbules that are smaller or structurally simpler than typical pennaceous or plumulaceous barbules. Although they grade into these types and into each other, it is worthwhile to designate them separately because they possess certain distinctive features and they create a distinctive appearance in the vanes. At least four types of simplified (reduced) barbules can be recognized, all of which show but slight differentiation among the cells and few or no outgrowths. The first kind of simplified barbules are reduced pennaceous. They have fewer and less pronounced barbicels than typical pennaceous barbules (fig. 171 *A*, *B*). Second are reduced plumulaceous barbules, which lack the characteristic nodal swellings of typical plumulaceous barbules (fig. 171 *C*, *D*). A third kind of simplified barbules are those on the sides of the rachis between the attachments of the rami. We suggest that they be called rachidial barbules (singular: *barbula rachidialis*), as we have not found any published names for them. The sole or chief component of such a barbule is a short base, broad at the proximal end (where there is a ventral flange) and tapered distally (fig. 180, *B*, p. 279). This may be followed by one to three pennular cells, though in many cases these appear to have formed but have broken off. Rachidial barbules form a continuous row with those on the proximal side of each ramus. In the axil between the rachis and the distal side of a ramus, they become very small and closely set. These overlapping, triangular plates hinder air from passing through the axil. Seen grossly, they make the rachis seem thicker than it is.

The fourth category of simple barbules may be called the stylet barbule (*barbula styla*) because of its stiffness and slender, pointed shape. The name is offered as a translation of Spiessradius, the term proposed by Hempel (1931:665) in his extensive discussion of this structure. Stylet barbules display little or no differentiation, and the boundaries of the cells are marked by small nodes, tiny single prongs, paler pigmentation, or affinity for stain (fig. 171, *E*—*H*). In some barbules, the base stands straight, owing to the presence of a low ventral flange. In others, there is no flange and the base is twisted lengthwise through 180°. Straight and twisted stylet barbules may occur either by themselves or alternately along a barb (Sick, 1937:346).

Stylet barbules are present along the margins of the vanes in many body contour feathers. They are the sole or predominant type of barbule in ear coverts (p. 308) and the small feathers on the face of a chicken. Wherever they occur, the vanes have an open—even coarse—texture (fig. 180, *G*). The rami are as stiff and parallel as those in pennaceous barbs, but the barbules do not interlock. Stylet barbules are sometimes very short and pressed closely to the ramus. This gives the ramus a thicker appearance, as rachidial barbules do to the rachis.

Microstructure of vanes in relation to texture

We can now review the appearance of the vanes in a body contour feather in terms of the different types of barbules. Rachidial barbules may be present along the entire rachis. At the base of the vanes these barbules become transformed into plumulaceous barbules on the rami, by acquisition of a long pennulum. This portion of the feather is soft and fluffy because the barbs are entirely fringed with plumulaceous barbules, possibly projecting at different angles.

Further from the base, this texture becomes restricted to the borders of the vanes while the inner portion becomes a firm, flat, closely knit sheet. The latter, of course, is produced by the interlocking pennaceous barbules. At the proximal end of a barb at this level, the proximal barbules become shortened and simplified, as they merge into the rachidial barbules. Proceeding distally, the pennaceous barbules become longer and their barbicels become uniformly simple. They are transformed into structures that are intermediate between the pennaceous and plumulaceous types. Though resembling stylet barbules in their stiffness and slender shape, they differ in retaining nodal swellings or outgrowths. Within a short span along the same barb, the intermediate barbules change to the plumulaceous type as they become longer, the base becomes flexible, and the nodes are enlarged.

The downy texture disappears from the vanes distally along the rachis as more and more of the barbules are pennaceous. The remainder of the vanes may either be uniformly pennaceous or may have a zone of open texture outside a zone of normal, closely knit texture, as shown in figure 158. The open zone may occupy most of the area, as in dorsal cervical feathers of an adult male Single Comb White Leghorn Chicken, or it may be confined to a narrow band at the tip, as in certain pectoral feathers on the same bird. It results from the reduction, even disappearance, of interlocking barbules while the rami remain unchanged. The pennaceous barbules are either transformed to the stylet type or they vanish entirely. The sharpness of the boundary between the pennaceous zones depends on the length of the span on each barb in which the change of barbules occurs.

Afterfeather

An afterfeather is a structure attached to the underside of a feather at the superior umbilicus. This concept readily includes featherlike structures composed of an axis with barbs on each side (fig. 158). Opinions differ, however, as to whether it also includes barbs that directly join the rim of the umbilicus. These views were compiled by Hempel (1931:713) in his introduction. The two conditions are not distinct categories, for intergrades between them can be found among feathers from the same bird. In hawks and most galliform birds, for example, the body contour feathers have conspicuous auxiliary shafts with vanes. These shafts are progressively shorter from the marginal feathers to the major coverts on the dorsal side of the wing. Finally, on the remiges, there is no auxiliary shaft but a V-shaped

fringe of separate barbs (fig. 159). Like Hempel (1931) and Ziswiler (1962), we believe that these separate barbs should be considered a form of afterfeather. An afterfeather can thus be defined as any group of outgrowths on the rim of the superior umbilicus. Such a structure has been variously called an accessory plume, a hypoptile (hypoptilum), and, most commonly, an aftershaft. This last term has been a cause of confusion for it has been used ambiguously for the entire afterfeather and for its auxiliary shaft alone. It certainly is not appropriate for an afterfeather that does not have an auxiliary shaft (i.e., that consists of separate barbs). The term "aftershaft" and its synonym "hyporachis" should be restricted to the auxiliary shaft. An afterfeather with this structure belongs to the aftershaft type.

The aftershaft is a median projection from the rim of the superior umbilicus (fig. 158). At its smallest, it is hardly more than the fused proximal portions of two barbs (Hempel, 1931:718). Unlike the rachis, it does not start inside the calamus but is simply a continuation of the wall, as shown in figure 159. The sides taper from the basal end, forming a flat triangular piece that may constitute the entire aftershaft. In some afterfeathers, however, the apex is drawn out into a portion that is much longer and finer than the basal part. A strand of pith cells may be present inside the aftershaft, but it is relatively thinner than that within the rachis.

The foregoing concept of an afterfeather includes the barbs that arise directly from the rim of the superior umbilicus (fig. 161). These were named pericalamial barbs by Hempel (1931:717), but we suggest as a simpler term, "umbilical barbs" (singular: barba umbilicata). Feathers that lack an aftershaft may have a fringe of such barbs encircling as much as one-third of the circumference of the calamus. The barbs collectively constitute a second type of afterfeather known as an aftertuft (German: Afterbüschel. Hempel, 1931:717) or afterbundle (German: Afterbündel. Ziswiler, 1962:250). We follow Hempel and differ from Ziswiler in two small matters of terminology here. First, we regard the aftertuft as totally lacking an aftershaft, whereas Ziswiler applied the name "Afterbüschel" to a group of ventral barbs inserting on a very short aftershaft (fig. 172, type 5). Second, the median umbilical barbs need not be the longest in the row, according to Ziswiler's definition of afterbundle. They may be arranged either in a straight line, as in certain body feathers, or in a V pointing toward the proximal end of the shaft, as in the flight feathers.

At the sides of the superior umbilicus, the row of umbilical barbs is continuous with the lowermost barbs of the vanes. This is a vestige of the circlet of barb columns that arose in the developing feather. If an aftershaft is present, there are usually a few umbilical barbs on each side of it, and these link the barbs of the vanes with those of the aftervanes.

Regardless of structure, the texture of an afterfeather is entirely plumulaceous except in cassowaries and emus, where it is coarse and lax like the main feather. The barbs vary in length and may be longer than their counterparts in the main vanes. They are usually spaced farther apart on the hyporachis than on the rachis.

If the proximal end of a barb lies close beside the aftershaft before joining it, this may be designated the decurrent portion (German: herablaufendes Stück. Hempel, 1931:720, fig. 35). The barbules of an afterfeather tend to be shorter and simpler than the downy barbules on the main feather. Their bases are somewhat narrower, and special structures such as the detachable nodal rings of turkeys or the basal prongs of passerine birds are absent (Chandler, 1916:270).

Opinions differ as to the extent of variation in afterfeathers from different parts of the body. Miller (1924:1) stated that "it usually varies comparatively little in size" but other investigators have found more diversity. Ziswiler (1962) has found regular gradients in the relative size of afterfeathers on all tracts of the Budgerigar (*Melopsittacus undulatus*). The afterfeather is generally largest, in relation to the main vanes, in down feathers, semiplumes, and body contour feathers with a large plumulaceous portion. It is smallest on the remiges and rectrices and may even be absent from them. An afterfeather of the aftertuft type, as in ducks, varies in relative length and the number of barbs, though not in basic structure. In a Mallard, for example, the aftertuft equals nearly 50 percent of the length of the vanes in anterior lateral body feathers, 30 percent in certain dorsal and pectoral feathers, and 8 to 10 percent in the secondary remiges and their upper coverts. The number of umbilical barbs is more than 30 in the dorsal feathers, about 10 in femoral feathers, and one or two in occipital feathers.

Afterfeathers of the aftershaft type vary among locations on a bird in structure as well as size. A series of transitional stages, from the aftershaft type on the contour feathers to the aftertuft type on the flight feathers, has been described and illustrated for a barbet (*Megalaima rubricapilla = Xantholaema rubricapilla*) (Hempel, 1931:715). The range of variation is especially wide in galliform birds (except curassows and the hoatzin) because the afterfeather may attain a relatively large size. In the Single Comb White Leghorn Chicken, for instance, the aftershaft type of afterfeather is 70 percent as long as the vanes of sternal or abdominal feathers, and the aftertuft type is about 8 percent as long as the vanes of the secondaries. These values are close to those for the relative length of the plumulaceous portion of the vane. They support the observation by Lillie and Juhn (1938:443) that in galliform birds the afterfeather is only as long as the plumulaceous portion, and does not extend to the pennaceous portion of the main feather.

Peculiar variation in the afterfeathers of a thrush (*Cochoa* sp.) was discovered by Ormsby Annan. In a letter, he stated as follows: "Not only are afterfeathers present in some tracts and absent in others, they are also present on others that are adjacent. They are mixed together with no apparent order."

Seasonal variation in the size of the afterfeather was pointed out by Lönnberg (1927) in several grouse (*Tetrao urogallus, Lyrurus tetrix, Tetrastes bonasia*) and ptarmigans (*Lagopus* spp.) that inhabit subarctic regions. There is a large afterfeather on the feathers of the winter plumage, but it is small or absent in feathers of the summer plumage, particularly on the head and upper neck. In pelvic and dorsal cervical feathers of the Rock Ptarmigan (*Lagopus mutus*), the hyporachis equals 70 to 80 percent of the length of the rachis in winter plumage, 50 to 70 percent in autumn plumage, and 0 to 65 percent in summer plumage (Salomonsen, 1939:58).

Many forms of afterfeathers can be found within the entire class of birds. They have been characterized for each order by Ziswiler (1962:285). It is further possible to recognize several major structural categories, although they cannot be sharply delimited because there are intergrades between most of them. The following classification, based on Miller's classification (1924), refers to the most fully developed afterfeathers on the body.

Type 1.—The afterfeather closely resembles the main feather in the length of its hyporachis, its long, narrow shape, and its loosely knit pennaceous vanes (not illustrated). This is the only type of afterfeather that is not plumulaceous. Occurrence: emus, cassowaries.

Type 2.—The afterfeather is long and narrow, though shorter than the main vanes (fig. 172). The hyporachis extends nearly to the tip of the afterfeather. Most of the barbs are relatively short, but those at the tip are almost as long as barbs of the main feather. This type grades into the next as the barbs increase in length. Occurrence: tinamous (*Crypturellus* spp., *Tinamus* spp.), grouse, quail, pheasants, domestic chicken, trogons.

Type 3.—The afterfeather is about one-third to two-thirds as long as the main vanes (fig. 172). The hyporachis is likewise no more than two-thirds the length of the afterfeather and is often less than this. The hyporachis is finer than the rachis but always distinct. The barbs are longer than those of type 2 with the result that these afterfeathers are oval or elliptical. This is one of the commoner and more variable types of afterfeather. It grades into type 4 as the hyporachis becomes shorter. Occurrence: shearwaters (*Puffinus* spp.), herons (*Ardea* spp.), hawks (*Buteo* spp.), falcons, domestic chickens, turkeys, rails (*Porzana* spp.), sandpipers (*Tringa* spp.), parrots, turacos, hummingbirds (*Archilochus* spp.), trogons.

Type 4.—The length of the afterfeather varies and may equal that of the main vanes (fig. 172). The hyporachis is very short and fine and is sometimes broadly flattened at the proximal end. There are a few, long, widely spaced barbs, which are commonly devoid of barbules at their free ends. Although the afterfeather has the appearance of a tuft, the presence of a hyporachis shows that it is structurally not an aftertuft. It is sometimes flanked by a few umbilical barbs. This type of afterfeather grades into type 6 as the hyporachis is reduced and the number of umbilical barbs is increased. Occurrence: grebes (*Podiceps* spp.), hummingbirds, barbets, toucans, woodpeckers, a New Zealand wren (*Acanthisitta chloris*), songbirds.

Type 5.—The afterfeather is less than half as long as the main vanes (fig. 172). Although the hyporachis is very

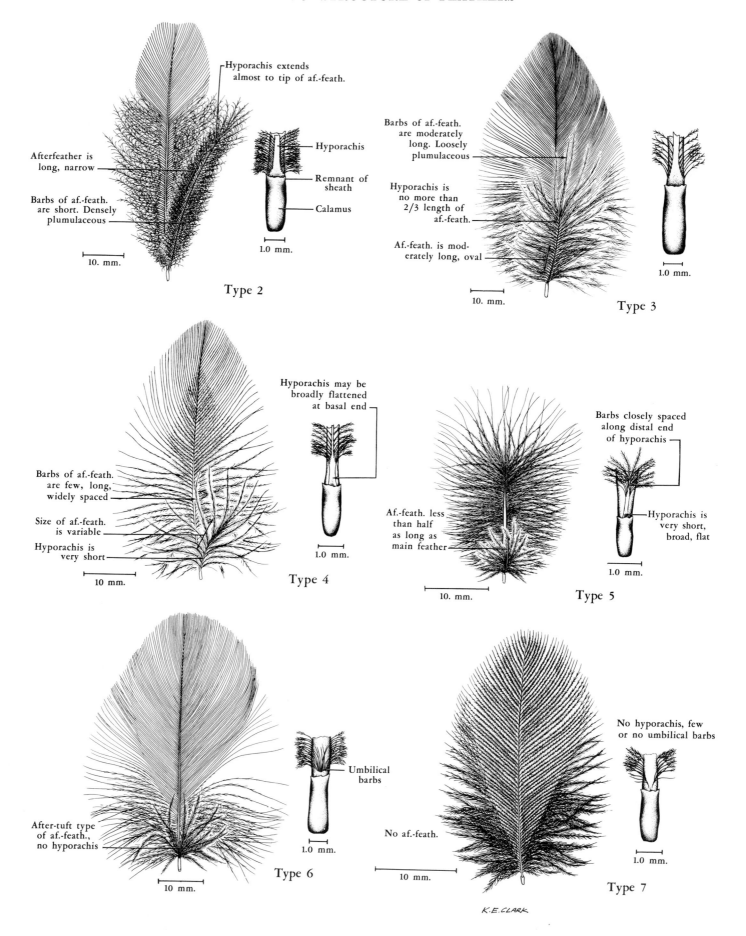

Hyporachis extends
almost to tip of af.-feath.

Hyporachis

Remnant of
sheath

Calamus

Afterfeather is
long, narrow

Barbs of af.-feath.
are short. Densely
plumulaceous

10. mm.

1.0 mm.

Type 2

Barbs of af.-feath.
are moderately
long. Loosely
plumulaceous

Hyporachis is
no more than
2/3 length of
af.-feath.

Af.-feath. is mod-
erately long, oval

10. mm.

1.0 mm.

Type 3

Hyporachis may be
broadly flattened
at basal end

Barbs of af.-feath.
are few, long,
widely spaced

Size of af.-feath.
is variable

Hyporachis is
very short

10 mm.

1.0 mm.

Type 4

Barbs closely spaced
along distal end
of hyporachis

Hyporachis is
very short,
broad, flat

Af.-feath. less
than half
as long as
main feather

10. mm.

1.0 mm.

Type 5

After-tuft type
of af.-feath.,
no hyporachis

Umbilical
barbs

10 mm.

1.0 mm.

Type 6

No hyporachis, few
or no umbilical barbs

No af.-feath.

10 mm.

1.0 mm.

Type 7

K.E.CLARK

short, it differs from type 4 in being broad, flat, and tapering at the tip. The barbs are closely spaced and are present only along the distal half or third of the hyporachis. They split off the hyporachis into a decurrent portion, instead of jutting out like the barbs on other types of afterfeathers. Occurrence: hoatzin, chachalacas (*Ortalis* spp.).

Type 6.—The afterfeather is less than one-third as long as the main vanes and indeed is often very short (fig. 172). There is no hyporachis, but the margin of the superior umbilicus may be slightly pointed at the middle. This is the aftertuft type of afterfeather, consisting entirely of umbilical barbs. Occurrence: ducks, New World vultures, owls, oilbird, goatsuckers.

Type 7.—There is no afterfeather whatever (fig. 172). Occurrence: ostrich, kiwis, rheas, pelecaniform birds, screamers, pigeons, cuckoos, hoopoe, hornbills, broadbills, lyrebirds, most tyrannoid perching birds, swallows.

The prevalence of afterfeathers among birds suggests that they have a function, but it is not certain what this may be. Some ornithologists (e.g., Van Tyne and Berger, 1959:78) have concluded that afterfeathers generally seem not to have any adaptive value. Miller (1924:6) and Stresemann (1927), on the contrary, suggested that afterfeathers increase the thermal insulating property of feathers; Ziswiler (1962:282) stated that this was indeed their principal function. This theory is supported by the downy structure of afterfeathers and the seasonal variation in their size in ptarmigans. Ziswiler also gave evidence that afterfeathers secondarily serve as padding material for filling out a bird's contour, thereby giving it a satisfactory aerodynamic shape. This idea may be what Steiner (1917:242) had in mind when he stated that afterfeathers must have a function for flight, but he did not explain his reasoning.

Afterfeathers have been regarded by some workers (Chandler, 1916; Van Tyne and Berger, 1959:78) as having taxonomic value. Their usefulness in this way is lessened by the fact that afterfeathers of more than one type may be present in the feathering of a single bird. Comparisons of afterfeathers from different birds must be based on specimens from the same part of the body. We support Ziswiler (1962: 305) in the opinion that afterfeathers have little taxonomic value in their structure or in their presence. While it is true that they may occur in birds that are closely related on the basis of other evidence, they may also occur in unrelated groups. Afterfeathers of type 2, for example, are not only characteristic of galliform birds but also they are present in the distant orders of tinamous and trogons.

Developmental studies by Ewart (1921) led Miller (1924:1) to the view that "the presence of the aftershaft [= afterfeather] is unquestionably a primitive character, and its reduction or loss is therefore a sign of specialization." Although this theory may prove true, it cannot be demonstrated by the condition of the afterfeather in several primitive and advanced orders of birds. Recall that the structure is absent in the ostrich, kiwis, and rheas but present in most songbirds. The very large afterfeathers of emus and cassowaries were once thought to represent the prototype condition. Since the afterfeathers in the natal plumage of emus are short, their large size in the adult is now considered a secondary acquisition (Newton and Gadow, 1893–96: 3,245). Variation in the presence and the structure of the afterfeather among orders of birds suggests that it has been independently redeveloped several times.

Under the assumption that feathers evolved from ancestral reptilian scales, Steiner (1917: 242) suggested that the main part of a feather represents the dorsal half of a scale and its afterfeather, the ventral half. The underside of the vanes would thus correspond not to the ventral surface of the scale but to the innermost layer. Studies by Ziswiler (1962) led him to confirm this theory, adding that, in development, the afterfeather part of a feather germ is reduced in favor of the main part.

Remiges and Rectrices

Remiges and rectrices—the large feathers along the posterior edges of the wings and tail—share several features that distinguish them from typical contour feathers. They are characterized by large size, stiffness, asymmetry, vanes that are almost entirely pennaceous, and absence of an aftershaft. The remiges and rectrices comprise most of the airfoil necessary for flying, and are hence referred to collectively as the flight feathers. Nearly all details of their structure, especially in the primary remiges, are adapted to aerodynamic functions.

There is no consistent structural difference between the remiges and the rectrices because the latter are so diverse. The primary remiges (primaries) differ from the secondaries in being stiffer, more pointed, and usually more asymmetrical. The carpal remex resembles the first upper major secondary covert; the alular remiges are small versions of the outermost primary remex.

The remiges and rectrices usually include the largest feathers of a flying bird. They are especially long in many

---

←

FIGURE 172.—Examples of types of afterfeathers, in ventral view. For each pair of drawings, that on the left shows the size of the afterfeather in relation to the main feather, the relative length of the hyporachis, if any, and the arrangement of the barbs. In each pair, the drawing on the right shows the connection of the afterfeather to the rim of the superior umbilicus.

Type 1.—Occurs only in emus and cassowaries. (Not illustrated.)
Type 2.—Dorsal feather. Ring-necked Pheasant (*Phasianus colchicus*).
Type 3.—Interscapular feather. Red-tailed Hawk (*Buteo jamaicensis*).
Type 4.—Dorsal feather. Yellow-shafted Flicker (*Colaptes auratus*).

Type 5.—Dorsal feather. Chachalaca (*Ortalis vetula*).
Type 6.—Dorsal feather. Mallard (*Anas platyrhynchos*).
Type 7.—Dorsal feather. Yellow-billed Cuckoo (*Coccyzus americanus*). Abbreviation: Af.-feath., afterfeather.

species of pheasants; in fact, the largest feathers to be found in any wild birds are the median rectrices of the male Crested Argus (*Rheinardia ocellata*), which are 6 inches (153 mm.) wide and nearly 6 feet (1.83 m.) long. In the Great Argus (*Argusianus argus*) the rectrices are 50 inches (1.27 m.) long and the inner secondary remiges are 34 inches (0.86 m.). The prominent tail feathers of some birds are not the rectrices but the major upper tail coverts. These feathers attain a length of almost 5 feet (1.52 m.) in the Blue Peacock (*Pavo cristatus*).

Calamus

The calamus is relatively longer in flight feathers than in ordinary contour feathers. It accounts for more than 30 percent of the total length of the outer primaries, for example, in large flying birds such as swans. The remiges in cassowaries have become reduced to long spines; their tubular structure suggests that they are solely a calamus and not an entire shaft, as often thought (Boas, 1931:580). They should be re-examined with the possibility in mind that they are shafts that have secondarily become hollow.

The calamus of flight feathers is slightly thicker than wide, with the result that it is elliptical, subelliptical, or oval in cross section. This feature is most pronounced in the primary remiges and has been depicted by Oehme (1963: fig. 33) for the Common Starling (*Sturnus vulgaris*) and the Blackbird (*Turdus merula*). Seen from the side, the calamus is straight except at the inferior umbilicus, where it curves slightly upward.

Rachis

The rachis is usually filled with pith, but it has secondarily become hollow in the primaries of a few large birds. The lumen of the calamus of these feathers opens at the superior umbilicus and also continues into the rachis. A lumen in the rachis extends for several centimeters in the remiges of swans, large hawks, and the Secretary Bird (*Sagittarius serpentarius*). According to Webb (1914:427), it continues for the whole length of the rachis in the Anhinga (*Anhinga anhinga*) and the Ground Hornbills (*Bucorvus* spp.). In the primaries of swans and large hawks, the pith starts at some distance proximal to the upper umbilicus and thickens very gradually as a pair of lateral plates. The ventral borders of the plates project into the lumen and meet each other distally, forming a partition in the frontal plane, the floor of the rachis. This partition divides the pulp of the growing feather into a slender, ventral portion that passes through the superior umbilicus and a thick, dorsal portion that continues distally inside the rachis. In the remiges of swans, the two portions communicate through a long fissure between the halves of the floor of the rachis (Boas, 1931:571). Hawk feathers do not appear to have such a connection because the fissure divides the pith but not the cortex of the rachis. Pulp caps form inside the hollow rachis of these feathers just as they do outside it and in the calamus.

The rachis and vanes of flight feathers usually curve downward and toward the body. The latter curvature is most consistent in the primary remiges. In male junglefowls and domestic chickens, the central rectrices and their upper coverts have an intrinsic curvature away from the midline; owing to their placement, they appear to hang downward.

Other examples of elaborately curved flight feathers of male birds are the 13th secondary remiges of the Mandarin Duck (*Aix galericulata*), the outermost rectrices of the Superb Lyrebird (*Menura novaehollandiae*), and the rectrices of certain birds of paradise (e.g., *Diphyllodes* spp., *Cicinnurus regius*).

The sides of the rachis are generally higher and flatter, and the edges bounding them are more distinct in flight feathers than in body contour feathers. The rachis, particularly of a primary remex, is thus trapezoidal or rectangular in cross section for most of its length. Sections of rachis also show that the dorsal and ventral walls are thicker than the sides (Oehme, 1963: fig. 33). The groove in the ventral wall is often conspicuous at the proximal end for it fades out before the tip. Internally, septa and cortical ridges are often well developed, which serves to give a feather the proper stiffness or flexibility to meet the demands of flight (Rutschke, 1966).

Vanes and measurements of barbs

Flight feathers and their coverts are usually asymmetrical in the shape of their vanes as well as in the curvature of the shaft. The outer vane is always narrower than the inner, a feature that identifies an isolated feather as being from either the right side or the left. The outer vane overlies the inner vane of the feather lateral to it. Thus when the wings and tail are folded, the uppermost feathers are the inner secondaries and the central rectrices. Owing to the disparity in width, the vanes meet unequal air pressure from below, which causes the feather to twist. The degree of difference between the vanes is adapted to each feather's aerodynamic function. It is greatest in the outer primaries and rectrices and least in the inner secondaries and rectrices. The outer feathers form the leading edge of the airfoil, and they twist to slip through the air as they propel or steer and brake a bird in flight. Propulsion is a function of the primary remiges, while steering and braking are functions of the outer rectrices. The secondaries and inner rectrices do not twist as much as the other flight feathers, their function being chiefly the maintenance of an airfoil to create lift.

Secondary remiges 13 through 16 are unusually asymmetrical in male Mandarin Ducks, where they have become modified for display instead of flight (analyzed by Brinckmann, 1958).

The vanes are usually curved gently downward lengthwise and crosswise, though they may be perfectly flat. In addition, the inner vanes of primaries are often curved upward along a proximal section of the margin, as far as the notch, if this is present.

Examples of flight feathers with unusual modifications of the feather plane are the corrugated proximal secondaries and central rectrices of anhingas (*Anhinga* spp.) and the twisted central rectrices of the Pomarine Jaeger (*Stercorarius pomarinus*).

The shapes of flight feathers are diverse, especially among rectrices, probably because they have a less important aerodynamic role than the remiges. The primaries tend to be asymmetrically oval or ovate, whereas the secondaries and rectrices are commonly oval or oblong.

Lanceolate (attenuate) rectrices are present on macaws (*Ara* spp.) and the Ring-necked Pheasant (*Phasianus colchicus*). Linear feathers, long and narrow with parallel edges, occur as rectrices of tropic-birds (*Phaëthon* spp.) and of male Long-tailed Yokohama Chickens and Greater Birds of Paradise (*Paradisaea apoda*).

The tips of the remiges generally range from obtuse to truncate, the outermost primaries being the most pointed. The apex is most often in line with the rachis, but it may be at the end of either vane. In the secondary remiges of pigeons, for example, the barbs of the outer vane become progressively shorter until they vanish at the end of the rachis. Those of the inner vane diminish to a lesser degree, with the result that they project beyond the rachis and form the apex of the feather. The 15th and 16th secondaries of the male Mandarin Duck are more exaggerated examples of this situation (Brinckmann, 1958). While the rectrices may have similar tips, they also display a variety of other conditions among birds.

Truncate tips can be seen on the rectrices of some trogons (*Trogon* spp.). Acuminate tips, in which the vanes taper to a sharp point, occur on the rectrices of woodpeckers (Family Picidae) and woodcreepers (Family Dendrocolaptidae), which use them for support when clinging to a tree trunk (Richardson, 1943). The rectrices of certain swifts (*Chaetura* spp.) have the same role, but their tips are spinose—the sharply pointed tip of the rachis projects beyond the vanes. Racket-tipped feathers have conspicuous vanes at the tip of a partly bare shaft; examples are the second primary remiges of a male Standard-winged Nightjar (*Macrodipteryx longipennis*), the median rectrices of most motmots (*Momotus* spp.), and the outer rectrices of a Greater Racket-tailed Drongo (*Dicrurus paradiseus*). The secondary remiges and occasionally the rectrices of waxwings (*Bombycilla* spp.) are unique in having spangles on their tips. These are red or yellow, with a waxy sheen, and are formed by the widened, flattened end of the rachis, fused with the outer barbs (Chandler, 1916:382; Brush and Allen, 1963).

One or both vanes are abruptly narrowed at some point in certain primary remiges and rectrices of many birds. Such feathers are said to be notched (synonyms: emarginate, incised), and the cut-out space is the notch (synonyms: emargination, incisure). Some of the outer primaries have a shallow notch as in the Single Comb White Leghorn Chicken and the Common Pigeon (fig. 174). More deeply notched primaries can be seen on some ducks and swans (fig. 173, *A*), and still more markedly in vultures, eagles, and buzzard hawks (*Buteo* spp.). The outer vane of the most distal functional primary and the inner vane of the most proximal primary to be notched are never affected. The tips of emarginate feathers do not overlap when the wings are spread but are separated by gaps or slots. Subdividing the wing tip in this way reduces the induced drag of the wing (Graham, 1930; Cone, 1962).

Most modifications of flight feathers serve for locomotion or display, but a few are adaptations for sound production. The outermost primary remiges of certain male ducks cause a whistling sound in flight, whether they are attenuated as in the Common Goldeneye (*Bucephala clangula*), emarginate as in the Common Scoter (*Melanitta nigra*), or lobed on the inner vane as in the Indian Whistling Duck (*Dendrocygna javanica*). A quavering sound is produced by the linear outer rectrices of the Common Snipe (*Gallinago gallinago*) and the Siberian Pintail Snipe (*G. megala*) when the birds dive in flight (Heinroth and Heinroth, 1958:127). The tail feathers of a male Anna's Hummingbird (*Calypte anna*) cause a sharp report at the bottom of a display dive (W. J. Hamilton, 1965:38).

All the barbs of a typical flight feather bear pennaceous barbules except those at the base of the vanes and around the superior umbilicus, which have short plumulaceous barbules. The transition from pennaceous to plumulaceous structure in these basal barbs is often abrupt; barbs more distally placed become entirely pennaceous as the transition shifts toward the margin. The length of the barbs in a typical remex or rectrix increases markedly in the first few barbs at the base, remains fairly constant through most of the vane, and decreases markedly at the tip. The pattern of variation is so diverse among all birds as to defy further generalization. Brinckmann's (1958) analysis of the 13th secondary remex on the male Mandarin Duck shows how this variation can be studied.

The angle between the barbs and the shaft is equal in both vanes of the secondary remiges and vanes of the inner rectrices. On the primary remiges, however, the barbs of the outer vane are set more acutely than those of the inner vane, especially on the farthest feathers on the wing tip. There is a similar but lesser difference between the vanes of the outer rectrices. The angle of the barbs is fairly constant from the base of the rachis to the tip in secondaries and inner rectrices, but it diminishes in the primaries and outer rectrices. Voluminous measurements of the barb angle in many birds have been recorded by Janda (1929). The flexibility and width of a vane are partly dependent on the angle of its barbs. The smaller the angle, the more the barbs restrain each other and the more they supplement the rachis. Unless the barb angles of a flight feather are symmetrical, the outer vane is always stiffer than the inner vane. This difference is most pronounced in the outermost primaries.

The spacing of the barbs on a given feather tends to vary inversely with the angle from the shaft. Hence, the smaller the angle, the wider the spacing (or the fewer barbs per unit of shaft length). In asymmetrical feathers, the barbs of the outer vane are accordingly fewer and farther apart than those of the inner vane. Janda's (1929) measurements show that the barbs of flight feathers are generally closest at the

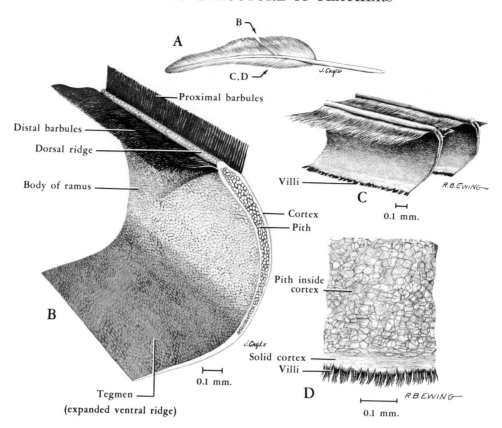

FIGURE 173.—Tegmen (expanded ventral ridge) on the pennaceous barbs of a primary remex from a Mute Swan (*Cygnus olor*).

A, whole feather, indicating location of barbs.
B, section of barb from inner vane with plain tegmen, in oblique view of distal side.

C, sections of two barbs from outer vane with fringed tegmen, in oblique view of distal side.
D, section of tegmen from outer vane barb at higher magnification.

tip of the vane, farthest apart in the middle, and at some intermediate spacing elsewhere. Our measurements (table 12), however, show that the barbs are often closest together at the base although distally their spacing varies in a different manner along both sides of the rachis. The pattern of spacing itself differs among birds (table 12), undoubtedly in relation to properties that are adaptive for different kinds of flight. Porosity of the feathers, determined partly by the spacing of the barbs, may affect boundary layer airflow (Raspet, 1960:197).

Ramus

The attachments of the rami to the rachis are generally the same in flight feathers as in body contour feathers. On the primary remiges of some birds, however, fine ridges run proximally and ventrally across the side of the rachis from the ventral margin of the junctions of the rami. These ridges are present up to the point where the rachis is only as high as the base of a ramus. The ridges are longer and more pronounced on the outer vane than on the inner. The outer side of the rachis may also bear a series of longitudinal ridges, each of which comes from an oblique ridge and runs proximally toward the next ramus, not quite reaching it. Oblique ridges occur on the primaries of hawks, and they

are supplemented with longitudinal ridges in Old World vultures. Another modification at the junction of ramus and rachis can be seen on the inner vanes of the outer primaries of hummingbirds. The proximal surface of the bases of the rami is greatly swollen toward the dorsal side, nearly filling the space between barbs. The ridges and swellings appear to reinforce the rami against upward or downward air pressure while allowing them to flex as though hinged (Sick, 1937:341).

The thickness of a ramus decreases from base to tip, as in the barbs of contour feathers (fig. 163). It decreases from proximal to distal in a vane but varies among flight feathers, with the result that the thickest rami are usually those at the base of the vane in primary remiges and rectrices. Finally, the rami of the inner vane are always slightly thinner than those of the outer vane. This difference is especially noticeable in an emarginate feather, distal to the notch (Chandler, 1916:265). A ramus usually tapers gradually, but in those primaries and rectrices where it bears an expanded ventral ridge (see p. 259), the thickness and the ventral ridge are reduced at the same place, about one-third to one-half the distance along the ramus (Mascha, 1905:7). All these variations are probably related to the demands for flexibility or stiffness in different parts of the airfoil.

The ventral ridges on the rami of flight feathers are narrow or absent in most birds. They are moderately wide on some rami in the primary remiges of pelicans, cormorants, herons, storks, vultures, hawks, sandpipers, plovers, and sandgrouse. The underlapping of these ridges gives a velvety appearance to the underside of the feathers.

Wide ventral ridges occur on certain remiges, rectrices, and coverts of loons, albatrosses, ducks, geese, swans, eagles, some owls, and many galliform birds. Within the last group, wide ventral ridges have been found in the Capercaillie (*Tetrao urogallus*), Black Grouse (*Lyrurus tetrix*), Red Grouse (*Lagopus scoticus*), a few pheasants (*Pucrasia macrolopha, Phasianus* spp., *Chrysolophus* spp.), Common Partridge (*Perdix perdix*), and turkeys. They are absent in quails, guineafowl, Red-legged Partridge (*Alectoris rufa*), most pheasants, and chickens. The presence of wide ventral ridges can easily be detected because they create a glazed sheen along a medial portion of the underside of a feather.

A ventral ridge of the widened type is known as a tegmen (Gladstone, 1918:244). It is a thin shelf that projects almost horizontally from the body of a ramus (fig. 173). A tegmen may touch or underlap the next ramus on the distal side and thus cover the space between the barbs. The margin of the ridge is typically smooth, but it is rough or frayed into extremely fine irregular villi on the outer vanes of the remiges of anseriform, falconiform, and some galliform and ciconiiform birds (fig. 173, *C, D*). The tegmen is flat in cer-

tain species (e.g., Black Grouse, Red Grouse, Grey Partridge, ducks, geese, and swans) and curved outward in others (e.g., Capercaillie, Ring-necked Pheasant, turkeys, and owls). It extends along one-third to two-thirds the length of the ramus and tapers distally. The tip of the tegmen sometimes detaches from the ramus, forming a pennant.

The width of ventral ridges differs between the vanes and varies among birds. For example, it is wide on the inner vane and moderately wide on the outer vane of the remiges of the Grey Partridge, whereas it is wide on the outer vane in Red Grouse and Ring-necked Pheasant. Wide ventral ridges are present on the rectrices of Red Grouse and Capercaillie but absent from these feathers in the Ring-necked Pheasant and Grey Partridge. Gladstone (1918:246), who made these observations, suggested that the presence or absence of these structures might be of taxonomic value. While this may be true for closely related forms, the character must be used cautiously in view of its functional significance. The expanded ventral ridges act as flap valves that prevent air from passing upward between the barbs. They appear to be adaptations for modes of flight in which the feathers are subjected to strong air pressure from below (Richardson, 1943).

Barbules

We have frequently pointed out variation of feather parts in size, proportion, or structure, both within feathers and among birds. In contrast, the pennaceous barbules of flight feathers are fairly constant in size and spacing. These dimensions hardly vary with the size of a bird or even its feathers. The length of a distal barbule from the middle of the inner vane of a primary remex is only 3.5 times larger in a Griffon Vulture (*Gyps fulvus*) than in a Sword-billed Hummingbird (*Ensifera ensifera*), although the vulture is many times larger than the hummingbird (data from Carlisle, 1925). The distance between barbules in all birds ranges only from 20 to 30 microns for distal barbules and 30 to 40 microns for proximal barbules (Mascha, 1905:18, 23). The radial angles, as measured on the inner vanes of primary remiges of various birds, range at least from 29° to 58° on the distal side and 10° to 41° on the proximal side (Carlisle, 1925). Even on a given barb, the distal angle is usually larger than the proximal, though in some passerines the angles may be equal or the proximal angle may be slightly larger.

The barbules on the flight feathers are larger and more highly developed than those on the body contour feathers. Their bases are relatively shorter and do not have flexules or a basal flange. In a row of barbules on a single barb, the base becomes shorter, in relation to the pennulum, from the proximal end to the distal end. The ratio of base length to pennulum length varies considerably among birds, even among the distal barbules of primaries. In his preliminary article on the dimensions of barbules, Carlisle (1925) pointed out that they tended to vary according to the affinities of

TABLE 12.—*Spacing of barbs in primary remiges*

Species	Average distance between centers of rami on vane at three locations on vane[1]		
	Base	Middle	Tip
	Microns	*Microns*	*Microns*
Whistling Swan (*Cygnus columbianus*).	454	833	500
	238	555	714
Mallard (*Anas platyrhynchos*)	385	625	500
	217	454	417
Common Coturnix (*Coturnix coturnix*).	385	500	625
	167	417	417
Single Comb White Leghorn Chicken (*Gallus gallus* var. domesticus).	385	1250	417
	172	454	263
Mourning Dove (*Zenaidura macroura*).	227	555	555
	167	357	454
Yellow-shafted Flicker (*Colaptes auratus*).	312	714	625
	178	417	454
Robin (*Turdus migratorius*).	333	500	555
	250	385	454
Common Crow (*Corvus brachyrhynchos*).	385	714	555
	217	454	555

[1] Calculated from the number of barbs in a 5-mm. span. In each pair of numbers at a vane location for a given bird, the upper value refers to the outer vane, the lower value to the inner vane.

birds. The barbules of the remiges are adapted so closely to the operation of the feathers, however, that their measurements and ratios are best considered in respect to a bird's manner of flight. Actually, very little can be concluded from measurements at a single locus because of the variability throughout vanules and between vanes.

Barbules of the distal type on the inner vane generally differ from those on the outer vane as follows:

1. Base is shorter and relatively wider.
2. Pennulum is longer.
3. Hooklets are fewer.
4. Cilia are more numerous.
5. Proximal dorsal cilia are developed as special lobate processes; homologous cilia are absent on the outer vane. These structures are discussed further on pages 293 and 294.

The barbules of the proximal type are generally very similar in the medial zones of both vanes (i.e., along the basal portion of a barb) but differ in the marginal zones (i.e., terminal portion of a barb). Their base is longer and narrower than that of the distal barbules, and they are also characterized by three to six ventral teeth and a filamentous pennulum. The proximal barbules in the marginal zones differ in their barbicels. On the inner vane, these are weakly developed or absent, whereas on the outer vane there are usually several large, recurved ventral barbicels that resemble the hooklets of distal barbules. It is often impossible to classify them as either teeth or cilia because they grade between these forms, and because the base of such barbules tapers gradually into the pennulum.

Special barbules of the distal type that bear lobes on the dorsal side occur in the inner vanes of flight feathers and their upper coverts, and in the outer vanes of their under coverts. The principles underlying their distribution and function were first explained by Graham (1930), but the barbules themselves were not accurately described until the work of Sick (1937:213). Oehme (1963:576) provided further details on their morphology and action. The German workers referred to the barbules as Reibungsradien, and since we have not found an English equivalent, we propose to translate their term as friction barbules.

Let us consider the arrangement of the remiges when the wing is outspread in order to understand the distribution of the friction barbules before we examine their structure. The rachis, the outer vane, and a medial portion of the inner vane of every remex (except the outermost primary) overlap a lateral portion of the inner vane of the remex distal to it. These zones of overlap between the primaries on the right wing of a Common Pigeon are marked by stippling in figure 174, A. Under normal conditions, shown in figure 174, B, the upcurved (recurved) lateral portion of an inner vane touches the rachis and the downcurved (decurved) outer vane and medial portion of an inner vane on an overlying feather. If the feathers slip apart, the lateral portion of the inner vane on the lower feather remains in contact with only the outer vane of the upper feather. Friction in the areas of overlap between feathers supplements

the action of muscles and ligaments in keeping the feathers in place. A certain amount of friction is created even between ordinary contour feathers because of roughness of the vanes, and it is heightened in the flight feathers and coverts by the modified distal barbules.

The distribution of these barbules on a feather can be mapped by examining, under a microscope, barbs from several levels along the vanes. The distances are measured on each barb from the proximal end to the first and the last barbules that bear lobes. When these measurements are plotted on an outline drawing of the feather and the points are connected, the result is a diagram such as figure 174, C, which shows primary remex 8 of a Common Pigeon.

Two zones of friction barbules can be distinguished on the basis of the morphology of the barbules, as will be explained shortly. They start near the base of the inner vane and extend nearly to the tip or to a notch if this is present. Comparison of figures 174, A and C, reveals that the combined zones of friction barbules correspond closely to the zone of overlap. The absence of friction barbules and a recurved margin beside the notch permits the tip of the feathers to separate for aerodynamic reasons (Graham, 1930). Variation in the zones of friction barbules among the primary remiges, and relationship to the notch were shown by Oehme (1963: fig. 39) for the Common Starling (*Sturnus vulgaris*) and the Blackbird (*Turdus merula*).

If a barb from the inner vane of a pigeon primary is examined from base to tip, it will be seen that the distal barbules near the rachis are normal in shape and have a short pennulum and a single, small dorsal cilium (fig. 174, D). Farther out, the pennulum lengthens, dorsal cilia increase in number, and the first one or two cilia become lobate (fig. 174, E, F, G). According to Oehme (1963:577), all barbules that bear a lobe should be considered long friction barbules (German: langen Reibungsradien), regardless of the length of the pennulum. Near the tip of the ramus there is an abrupt transition to barbules with a short pennulum and a single, slightly enlarged dorsal cilium (fig. 174, H); these are the short friction barbules (German: kurzen Reibungsradien).

Friction is created when the lobes of the friction barbules on one feather rub against the rami of the proximal barbules on the overlying feather, especially along the decurved leading edge (Graham, 1930:18). Sick (1937) believed that the lobes of all the friction barbules opposed the shaft and the normal cilia opposed the vanes. Oehme (1963), however, stated that there is no friction against the shaft, but rather coarse and fine friction against the vanes caused by the long and the short friction barbules, respectively.

As mentioned previously the two forms of friction barbules are the basis for distinguishing two zones on the vane. The short friction barbules lie in a narrow band along the margin and the long friction barbules (graded in length) lie in a much wider band medial to it. In a Common Pigeon, the outer zone is up to 5 mm. wide, and the inner zone is about twice as wide. The inner zone always extends slightly beyond the outer at both ends. In the pigeon, it runs for 60 to 75 percent of the length of the vanes, a proportion that varies among the primaries.

The friction zones are conspicuous on the remiges of hawks and falcons because the dorsal cilia are long and numerous, creating a "forest of spines" (German: Dornenwald. Sick, 1937:227). The remiges of most owls and caprimulgiform birds (i.e., goatsuckers, nightjars, potoos, and their allies) have a distinct velvety nap, but the texture here is created chiefly by long upward-pointing pennula on the distal barbules (for details, see Mascha, 1905:17; and Sick, 1937:242). Although both the dorsal and the ventral cilia are well developed on the remiges of owls, they serve only indirectly to create the nap. They stabilize the vanule by crossing over or under pennula, from one to the next. The long, bare tips of the pennula do not have this function, as in other feathers, but stick up at a large angle. The velvety surface not only magnifies the friction between the feathers

but also quiets the sound of the feathers rubbing against each other. In certain owls (*Scotopelia* spp., *Ketupa* spp., *Lophostrix cristata*), however, the dorsal cilia and raised pennula are reduced, with the result that the feathers have a smoother, harder surface (Sick, 1937:246). The remiges of some birds, on the contrary, are so modified as to cause more noise by friction. The Wattled Bird of Paradise (*Paradigalla carunculata*), for example, makes a distinct rustling noise when flying because of the modified tips of the terminal barbs and their proximal barbules in the outer vanes of the primary remiges (Stein, 1936:23; Sick, 1937:260).

Afterfeather

Remiges and rectrices commonly have an afterfeather, though not an aftershaft, in the restricted sense of that term. Their fringe of umbilical barbs constitutes an aftertuft that is essentially the same as the type 6 afterfeather of

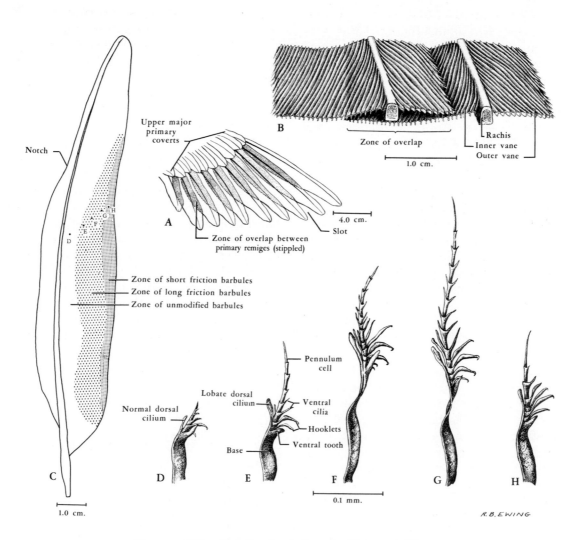

FIGURE 174.—Friction barbules of a Common Pigeon.

A, dorsal view of wing tip, showing slots and zones of overlap between primary remiges.
B, sections of two primaries as seen from distal end, showing overlap of vanes.

C, primary remex 8, showing friction zones and notch.
D to H, series of distal barbules from inner vane of primary remex 8. D, unmodified. E, F, G, long friction barbules. H, short friction barbule.

body contour feathers (p. 255). It differs only in following a deep curve or V-shape instead of a shallow curve or straight line. The aftertuft of a flight feather may easily grade into an aftershaft type of afterfeather, as was pointed out and illustrated by Hempel (1931:713).

Ear Coverts

The outer openings of the ears are covered in most birds by small, distinctive feathers that arise around the rim. These have been collectively called the ear covert (Boulton, 1927:391), but this term is usually applied to the feathers individually. Synonyms for the ear coverts are auricular feathers and opercular feathers. Following Chandler (1916), we classify them as modified contour feathers. There are one to four rows of coverts, though the number is sometimes indefinite because these feathers may grade peripherally into those on the face and neck. There tend to be more rows on the anterior side of the opening than on the posterior. The feathers are closer together than those on the face and neck, but the spacing also varies around the ear. The coverts are usually largest on the anterior or anteroventral side of the opening; they diminish toward the opposite side (fig. 56, p. 100). In spite of their circular arrangement, all the feathers point in the same direction—posterodorsally or posteroventrally. Accordingly, the large anterior coverts project across the ear opening, whereas the small posterior ones project away from it. The tips of the anterior coverts are propped up in most birds by the posterior coverts. They remain unsupported if the feathers are too short to reach across the opening, as in vultures.

Ear coverts agree with typical contour feathers in having a well-developed shaft with moderately stiff, parallel barbs. In such birds as chickens and passerines, their vanes are flat and relatively broad, and hence resemble the pennaceous portion of body contour feathers (fig. 203, D, p. 306). If the coverts are very small and compact, as in coturnix, they may be mistaken for bristles, but such feathers do not have barbs all along the rachis (see p. 323). The ear coverts of herons and grebes resemble semiplumes because of their flexible barbs, but they are not actually downy.

The distinctive features of all these coverts are their location and the open texture of their vanes. Though superficially pennaceous, the vanes are not closely knit, and there is no plumulaceous portion at the base, as in typical contour feathers. The barbs are more widely spaced than in true pennaceous vanes. They appear slightly thicker than usual because the barbules are small and often lie close beside the ramus. Simple barbules are present in any of three forms—reduced pennaceous, reduced plumulaceous, and stylet. The first of these is characterized by tapered thickness along the full length. The proximal cells may bear small dorsal and ventral flanges, in which case a base and a pennulum can be distinguished. If the feather is colored, the nodes of the cells are but lightly pigmented if

at all. There are usually no nodal prongs. Barbules of this type occur on the ear coverts of passerines, for example. Reduced plumulaceous barbules have a straplike base and a fairly long pennulum, but they are stiff and have faint nodes. They are present on the ear coverts of owls. Stylet barbules are the shortest and simplest of the three types. There are no more than faint superficial indications of cell boundaries and only a slight narrowing, at most, to suggest a division between base and pennulum. Stylet barbules occur on the ear coverts of such birds as grebes, herons, ducks, hawks, chickens, and other gallinaceous species (fig. 171, E and H).

An afterfeather is commonly present, and it may resemble that on a body contour feather, as in herons, hawks, and sandpipers. These afterfeathers represent type 3 (p. 253). In chickens and some hawks they are more than half as long as the main vanes (Chandler, 1914:358). Usually, however, the afterfeather is smaller on the ear coverts than on typical contour feathers. Grouse, for example, have only a tiny aftertuft on the ear coverts in contrast with the type 2 afterfeathers on the body feathers (Chandler, 1916: 273). Owls and passerine birds lack an afterfeather on the ear coverts, whereas they have type 6 and type 4 afterfeathers, respectively, on the body contour feathers. On the other hand, the afterfeather is relatively larger on the ear coverts than on the typical contour feathers in grebes and ducks. In ducks, the ear coverts have a long aftershaft with barbs, whereas the body feathers have only an aftertuft.

Ear coverts perform two functions in most birds—they screen the external opening of the ear and they improve hearing ability. The anterior coverts form a lattice that allows the passage of air but not foreign bodies. In diving birds, they may well trap air underneath and thereby keep water out of the ear. The auditory role of the feathers and their analogy with the auricle of the ear in mammals were recognized at least 150 years ago (Tiedemann, 1810:92). Measurement of pressure on the tympanic membrane confirms the theory that the feathers collect acoustic energy and direct it into the ear (Il'ichev and Izvekova, 1961). The structure of coverts diminishes the noise caused by wind in the external auditory meatus but allows significant sounds to penetrate (Pumphrey, 1961: 80). As in mammals, the most efficient external ears occur on birds with the most acute hearing. Owls, of course, are preeminent in this regard, followed by goatsuckers and certain parrots, shorebirds, herons, and hawks (not in order of rank). Within these groups, the ear coverts are most modified for sound catching in species with nocturnal habits (Il'ichev, 1961a, b).

The morphology of the external ear is highly developed in nocturnal owls. Anterior and posterior to the auditory meatus, the skin forms membranous flaps, the preaural and postaural folds (Pycraft, 1898:229. German: Ohrfalte = aural fold). In birds such as the Tawny Owl (*Strix aluco*), where the preaural fold is very large, it is known as the operculum (German: Ohrklappe). The folds are extremely variable among owls, and in species of *Asio* (e.g., Long-eared Owl, *A. otus*), the postaural fold encircles three-quarters of the auricular region. The folds can be erected, and the shape of the ear opening can be altered by the action of three muscles from the skull that insert on the folds (Stellbogen, 1930).

Development of these flaps is complemented by modification of the ear coverts. On the preaural fold are a few, closely spaced rows of feathers that point upward and outward. These coverts are long and narrow, with a stiff, slightly decurved shaft, firm open-textured vanes, and no after-feather. The barbs bear stylet barbules that are extremely short and closely appressed to the ramus. Simplified plumulaceous barbules arise from the bases of the more distal barbs. The feathers anterior to these have a thinner, more curved rachis, and they grade into the feathers on the face. In turn, the postaural fold bears short, upright feathers with a stout calamus. They may be so numerous and closely packed that their embedded bases thicken the rim of the fold. These coverts may resemble bristles because of their stiffness and narrow, inconspicuous vanes. They form a fan that projects forward and outward, opposite the preaural fold. The feathers behind them are progressively larger and graded into those on the back of the head.

The feathers on the orbital region of most owls form a roughly circular, flat or concave surface termed the "facial disk." The posterolateral border of the disk is made up of the ear coverts, and is known as the *limbus facialis* (Il'ichev, 1961a). To a lesser degree this landmark for the ear occurs in other birds with well-developed ears, for example, owlet-frogmouths (Family Aegothelidae) and certain parrots and hawks. The *limbus facialis* in these species appears as a line or low crest of feathers that curves vertically around the side of the head. As in owls, it is formed by the tips of the preaural and postaural coverts. These contrast with the adjacent feathers in the texture, color, or angle of the vanes.

The ear flaps are normally closed, and the feathers cover the auditory meatus. When keener hearing is called for, the flaps open and create with the coverts a funnel that amplifies the signal by gathering sound energy from a larger area (Stellbogen, 1930; Frey, 1952–53). They also improve an owl's ability to determine the direction of the source of sound, particularly in species that have asymmetrical ears or ear flaps. Experiments have shown that a Barn Owl (*Tyto alba*) can catch live mice in total darkness, guided by their rustling or squeaking. The owl can gauge direction but not distance if one of its ears is plugged with cotton (Payne and Drury, 1958).

Various birds have tufts or crests of feathers above the ears, known as ear tufts. These occur in such diverse species as the Macaroni Penguin (*Eudyptes chrysolophus*), Tufted Puffin (*Lunda cirrhata*), Great Horned Owl (*Bubo virginianus*), and Horned Lark (*Eremophila alpestris*). The tufts are composed of elongate feathers from the temporal tract and do not include the ear coverts.

The auricular region is sparsely feathered or entirely bare in such birds as the ostrich, cassowaries, some storks and ibises, New World vultures, Old World vultures, and rockfowls (*Picathartes* spp.).

SEMIPLUMES

While it is convenient to classify feathers into several structural types, they actually intergrade from large, stiff primary remiges to small, fluffy down feathers. Semiplumes are sometimes combined with the downs, but they are considered here as a category between the contour feathers and the downs. It is a combination of features from both these types rather than any unique features that characterizes semiplumes. These feathers were first discussed by Nitzsch (1867:14), and subsequent accounts have been based on his description. Other names for these feathers are half-downs (Newton and Gadow, 1893–96:241) and Halbdunen (Gadow and Selenka, 1891:530). Confusingly, semiplumes are known as fluff, not half fluff, in poultry terminology (Hardy and Hardy, 1949:3). Half fluff refers to contour feathers that are half pennaceous and half downy.

Semiplumes are feathers with a long rachis and entirely plumulaceous vanes (fig. 204, p. 310). The presence of even a small pennaceous portion at the tip of an otherwise fluffy feather distinguishes it as a contour feather. On the other hand, semiplumes can be separated from down feathers by the relative lengths of the rachis and the longest barbs. According to this arbitrary but workable criterion, semiplumes have a rachis that exceeds the longest barbs, and down feathers have a rachis shorter than the longest barbs. The barbs are like those in the plumulaceous, basal portion of the vanes of contour feathers. They consist of long, fine, flexible rami and noded, plumulaceous barbules. After-feathers are present on the semiplumes if they are also present on the contour feathers.

Semiplumes are distributed along the margins of tracts of contour feathers and in tracts by themselves. Pycraft (1898:231) pointed out that they are lined up with the contour feathers, and hence different from down feathers that occur between the contour feathers. This distinction does not necessarily apply to down feathers situated beyond the semiplumes in an apterium, as in chickens. Pycraft observed that the location and structure of semiplumes suggest, first, that they are simplified contour feathers and, second, that they indicate a restriction of once wider tracts. They are concealed by the contour feathers which they supplement in insulating the body. They are often abundant in the abdominal region and reach their greatest size beneath the under tail coverts of certain storks (*Leptoptilos crumeniferus*). These are the "Marabou feathers" once used in millinery (Nitzsch, 1867:14).

DOWN FEATHERS

The term "down" is applied both to plumage composed of small fluffy or lax feathers and to individual feathers. There are two major categories of down feathers—the natal downs, which are present on a bird when it hatches or shortly afterward, and the definitive downs, which occur in later generations of feathers. All downs are wholly plumulaceous. Their rachis is usually either absent or relatively short. Downs can be distinguished from semiplumes by the criterion of a rachis that is shorter than the longest barbs. Their texture results primarily from their slender flexible rami that bear long, segmented, filamentous barbules without hooklets (p. 265). Secondary factors that affect downy texture are discussed on page 311.

Natal Downs

Natal downs (synonyms include nestling downs, neossoptiles, and neoptiles) can be seen on newly hatched birds such as petrels, ducks, chickens and other galliform species, shorebirds, gulls, pigeons, and perching birds (passerines). Other young birds are naked when hatched, but they start to show these feathers within a few days. This is seen in loons, pelicans, cormorants, and frigate-birds. A nestling is said to be ptilopaedic if the natal plumage forms a dense covering over the entire body, as in ducks, chickens and other galliform species, rails, and pelicans. It is psilopaedic (gymnopaedic) if there are only a few feathers on the tracts for the contour feathers, as in herons, pigeons, and passerines. This latter condition has been described for many species by Wetherbee (1957).

A few variations in the sequence of nestling plumages may be mentioned here. Young penguins and Barn Owls (*Tyto alba*) produce two downy plumages before a pennaceous one; the second downs of the owls are distinct feathers

(Witherby et al., 1943, 2: pl. 60, fig. 2; p. 345), whereas those of penguins are actually the plumulaceous tips of the first pennaceous feathers.[1] Nestling hawks also grow two sets of downs, but the second set is composed of feathers of the adult type that emerge from follicles between those for the natal downs; they persist with the contour feathers that follow the natal downs. On the other hand, certain birds never develop any nestling down; kingfishers, rollers, most woodpeckers, and a few passerines are naked when hatched, and then grow a plumage of contour feathers like those of adults.

A nestling bird may show from one to three kinds of down feathers, corresponding to certain kinds of definitive feathers. Two of these were pointed out and named by Pycraft (1898: 253) but were criticized by Schaub (1912:166) on the ground that in hawks, the feathers that precede the definitive downs on the tracts are not a component of the natal feathering. While this is true, as explained above, it does not invalidate the general concept. These categories plus a third, as seen in ducks, were subsequently described by Ewart (1921) and Lamont (1922). By far the most conspicuous are the prepennae (singular: *prepenna*), natal feathers that precede contour feathers (including flight feathers), semiplumes, and definitive down feathers in the apteria. Preplumules are natal feathers that precede downs situated among the contour feathers. They are present in ducks and owls but absent in pigeons, gallinaceous birds (except Blue Peafowl, Sager, 1955:36), and others that do not have definitive downs on the tracts. As seen in White Pekin ducklings (fig. 230, p. 356), they are about one-fourth as large as the prepennae; they consist of a calamus, a very short rachis

---

[1] Clark, G. A., Jr. Written communication.

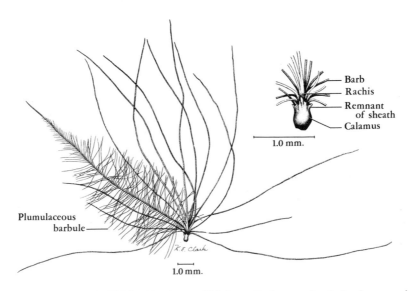

Figure 175.—Natal down of a Single Comb White Leghorn Chicken. Only one barb is shown with barbules. The inset shows the junction of barbs with the rachis and the calamus at a higher magnification.

with a few barbs, and several umbilical barbs (see ch. 7 for details). Prefiloplumes are natal downs that precede the hair-like feathers known as filoplumes. They have been reported in ducklings (Ewart, 1921), but we have not found them in baby chicks. The fact that they have not been reported in other birds may be due to their inconspicuousness. In White Pekin ducklings (fig. 231, p. 356), the prefiloplumes are approximately one-twenty-fourth as large as the prepennae; they consist of a basal tube resembling a calamus, a rachis, and barbs (see p. 354ff. for details). Nestling owls bear filoplumes, but these have the definitive structure and are not prefiloplumes (Pycraft, 1898:258).

Accounts of natal feathers usually refer to prepennae. These appear sooner and are larger and more common than preplumules or prefiloplumes. They consist of at least a calamus and a cluster of barbs, and sometimes a short rachis as well (fig. 175). A hyporachis may be present in the prepennae of birds such as galliforms, which have it in the definitive feathers. Even in chickens, however, it is extremely short, being composed of hardly more than the fused basal ends of a few barbs. No hyporachis is shown in figure 175. Although prepennae are grossly similar in many species of birds, close examination reveals wide differences in the structure of the calamus and its relationship with the barbs. These features reflect, in turn, the relationship between a natal down and the feather that succeeds it.

Natal feathers with a well-developed calamus and a moderately long rachis are exemplified by the prepennae of baby ducklings (fig. 229, p. 355). The structure of these feathers, particularly the condition of the rachis, was regarded by Schaub (1912:168) as representing an early stage in the phylogeny of feathers. He considered it to be a primitive characteristic of ducks, geese, and swans.

Natal feathers with a short calamus and a rachis that ranges from moderately long to extremely short can be seen on the body tracts of chickens, turkeys, and pheasants. The calamus is sometimes weak and shows faint longitudinal streaks inside the wall. These streaks indicate some continuity between the barbs of the natal and the juvenal feathers. These down feathers are discussed further in chapter 7.

The third and most common form of natal down is that in which there is no rachis whatever. Feathers of this sort occur on loons, grebes, petrels, boobies, herons, quails, shorebirds, gulls, pigeons, and passerines (Jones, 1907). In some cases, the barbs attach to the upper end of a calamus that can split into longitudinal segments. Jones regarded this tube as not being a true calamus because of its mode of formation. Becker (1959:519), however, maintained that it is homologous with the calamus of later feathers. The strips represent abortive barbs that provide an indirect connection between the natal and the juvenal barbs. In other birds, the barbs are continuous from one feather to the next as they pass through a short ring of sheath. This ring appears to be a calamus but actually is not, as explained in chapter 7. The barbs undergo a rapid transition as the long, plumulaceous barbules on the natal segment give way to shorter, pennaceous barbules in the juvenal segment. The ramus may or may not change.

Jones (1907), Schaub (1912), and others believed that natal downs of this third category were merely the tips of the juvenal feathers, not separate feathers. Boas (1931:359), however, pointed out that successive feathers of later generations are connected also. His finding has recently been confirmed and amplified by Watson (1963a, b). Boas observed that if a nestling feather is considered as a terminal part of the juvenal feather, then all the following generations of feathers from the same follicle must be considered as together forming one feather. Since this is unreasonable, one is forced to consider the nestling downs as representing a separate generation of feathers. Broman (1941:202) concurred with this opinion. Additional support came from Watterson's (1942:248) finding that in the chick embryo "there is a definite cessation in growth between the completion of the down feather and the onset of juvenile feather formation."

Regardless of the arrangement of the major parts of a natal down, the barbules are always of a plumulaceous type. They are shorter and less distinctively shaped than the downy barbules from definitive feathers of the same species. For example, the sliding nodal ring of turkey feathers and the large triangular nodes of ducks are absent from the barbules of nestling downs on these birds. The segments of the pennulum may taper from the base in nestling barbules instead of being uniformly slender, as in definitive barbules. Schaub (1912:169, 171) observed that in the natal downs of anseriform and galliform birds, the tips of the terminal barbs are free of barbules. Parkes[2] stated that this condition occurs in diversely built natal feathers of many birds. He pointed out that it appears to be a reliable criterion for distinguishing between natal downs and the down feathers of later plumages, as long as unworn specimens are used. At the tips of terminal barbs, barbules are absent in natal downs but present at nearly full length in subsequent down feathers. This difference can be seen by comparing the natal and the adult downs of a chicken (figs. 175, 176).

Usually the natal downs are followed directly by the juvenal contour feathers, except in penguins, rheas, barn owls, and ducks. In these birds, the natal downs are followed by semiplumes, a second set of downs, or abortive feather structures, which in turn are succeeded by the juvenal feathers. These intermediate feathers were first called mesoptyles (Pycraft, 1907:11) and later deuteroneoptiles (Schaub, 1912:137). Both terms, particularly the first, have been restricted to intermediate feathers of downy structure. Thomson (1964:455), for example, defined mesoptile as the "term applied to the second of two nestling down plumages, in cases where there is such a sequence, the first then being called 'protoptile.'" We use the term in a wider sense, designating as a mesoptile (*mesoptilus*) any feather, whether complete or abortive, that succeeds a nestling down yet does not resemble the definitive feather. Parkes and Clark,

---

[2] Parkes, K. C. Oral communication.

Jr.,[3] have suggested that the terms "protoptile" and "mesoptile" be dropped because so many conflicting meanings have been attached to them. They propose instead to use the terms, natal down (stage) A and (stage) B. This is a simpler, less ambiguous terminology, and it is starting to be followed (Palmer, 1962). One drawback, however, is that some feathers following the first downs are so peculiar that it seems unreasonable to call them downs. An example of such a structure can be seen on the remiges of a duckling (fig. 229, C, p. 355; labeled mesoptile). A lesser flaw is that stages A and B may be thought of as referring to parts of the same feather; natal down B, where it occurs, is usually a plumulaceous tip of the following, first pennaceous feather.

Interconnections between parts of a natal down (stage A), a mesoptile (stage B), if any, and the following feather vary at different locations on the feather tracts and among birds (Ewart, 1921:614). Workers studying these feathers should explain in each case the relationships between the stages, regardless of the terminology used.

Definitive Downs

The second category of downy feathers is that of the definitive downs (adult downs or plumules), which occur at various places on the body as part of the immature and the adult feather coats of most birds. The distribution of these feathers appears to be related to the need for insulation in each species and probably does not have as much phylogenetic significance as thought by Chandler (1916:255).

The patterns of distribution of definitive down feathers found among birds are as follows:

1. Evenly distributed over the entire body: penguins, loons, grebes, petrels, cormorants, pelicans, storks, flamingos, ducks, hawks, rails, alcids, and parrots; most abundant on water birds.

2. Sparsely or unevenly distributed: shorebirds, gulls, owls (see Pycraft, 1898:233 for distribution of plumules in owls; cf. Chandler, 1916:386), and kingfishers (dense in apteria, sparse in tracts).

3. Confined to feather tracts: tinamous.

4. Confined to apteria: herons, bustards, most gallinaceous birds, goatsuckers and their allies, and swifts.

5. Sparsely distributed in apteria or entirely absent: ostrich, rheas, cassowaries, kiwis, sandgrouse, pigeons, cuckoos, hummingbirds, colies, trogons, coraciiform birds except kingfishers, piciform birds, and passerine birds.

Some workers have attempted to distinguish the downs on the feather tracts as true, in contrast to those on the apteria, which are presumably false. There does not seem to be any inherent structural feature, however, that will separate the two classes. Downs in both locations are supplied with feather muscles, though these are fewer and more randomly arranged than those of the contour feathers. Granting that the plumules differ in location, there is no evidence to show which type is true. If names

for them are needed, it seems best to base them on location, and hence to speak of tract down feathers and apterium down feathers.

Tract downs are usually situated with a regular relationship to the contour feathers in spite of their apparent randomness. Their number and location vary in different parts of the body and certainly differ among birds (Gerber, 1939: figs. 21, 22, 37). There may be one to four downs near each contour feather. These may be situated close beside the contour feathers, in line with and between them, or in the middle of the space enclosed by four feathers, forming a quincunx. If there are only one or two downs with each contour feather and they are not in line with it, they are usually posterior to it. Some of these variations in owls were described by Pycraft (1898:233). Observing the basic regularity in the arrangement of feathers, Gerber (1939) formulated the concept of the feather complex as the basic unit of pterylosis growth. Each complex is a portion of skin that contains anlagen (primordia) for one contour feather, one or more filoplumes, and a variable number of plumules. Gerber (p. 318) stated that the plumules were largely independent of the pattern set by the contour feathers, but firsthand observations and his own drawings refute this, at least in some birds.

The basic structure of plumulaceous barbules and plumules has already been described (pp. 242 and 264). The following discussion deals with certain details. Definitive down feathers always have a true calamus (fig. 176), and in this respect they are less diverse than natal downs. The rachis, on the other hand, varies among species, though not according to any discernible phylogenetic or functional plan. In some birds the rachis is exceedingly short and sharply tapered, hardly more than a fusion of the basal ends of barbs. In many birds the rachis is somewhat longer and more gradually tapered. In other birds it approaches the length of the longest barb, with the result that these down feathers grade into semiplumes. Examples of all these conditions of the rachis can be found in both tract downs and apterium downs.

Afterfeathers are common on plumules in those birds where they are present on the contour feathers (Chandler, 1916:257). Both plumules and contour feathers possess a distinct hyporachis in such birds as herons, skimmers, sandpipers, and grouse and some other gallinaceous species. Similarly, they both have an afterfeather of umbilical barbs in ducks and owls. In numerous birds, however, the contour feathers and the downs differ in the nature of their afterfeathers, as shown in table 13. These examples show that the growth of the afterfeather is at least sometimes controlled by different factors in the follicles for the two kinds of feathers. This capability for independent development within an individual supports the idea that afterfeathers have independently evolved several times among the orders of birds (p. 255). The character of the afterfeather does not seem to clarify the difference between tract downs and apterium downs. Examples of both can be found either with or without an afterfeather. The presence of a hyporachis on

---

[3] Parkes, K. C. and Clark, G. A., Jr. Personal communication.

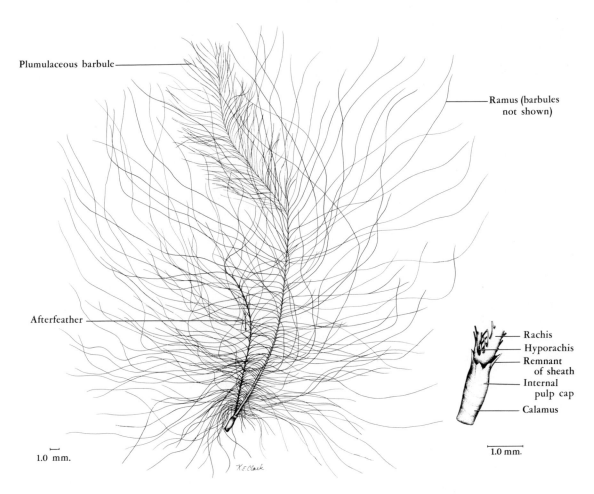

Plumulaceous barbule

Ramus (barbules not shown)

Afterfeather

Rachis
Hyporachis
Remnant of sheath
Internal pulp cap
Calamus

1.0 mm.

1.0 mm.

FIGURE 176.—Adult down of a Single Comb White Leghorn Chicken. Only one barb is shown with barbules. The inset shows the junction of barbs with the rachis and hyporachis at a higher magnification.

apterium downs and contour feathers, as in a chicken, may be interpreted as showing that the down is simply a degenerate contour feather. The same reasoning applied to the tract downs of a duck, however, argues against their being a distinct category of feather with its own phylogeny.

The barbs of a definitive plumule resemble those at the base of a contour feather, but they tend to be longer. The rami are flexible, laterally compressed filaments, much narrower than those of pennaceous barbs, and without a ventral ridge on the distal side. In most birds they appear

to be solidly composed of cortex, but in goatsuckers they have a medulla of pith. The barbules of a plumule are structurally like those in the downy portion of a contour feather from the same species, though they tend to be longer and more closely spaced. Where the plumulaceous barbules on a contour feather differ between the main vanes and the aftervanes, as in gallinaceous birds, the barbules of the down feathers match those on the aftervanes. Variation among barbules from different parts of a feather is much less in down feathers than in contour feathers. The width of the base tends to diminish among barbules from the shaft to the tip of a plumulaceous barb, as exemplified by the plumules of ducks, phalaropes, skimmers, and goatsuckers. The median zone of such feathers hence is not as fluffy as the rest.

Oil Gland Feathers

Most birds possess a bilobed sebaceous organ, the oil gland, on the dorsal surface of the external tail. The walls of each lobe secrete an oily substance into a lumen, from which one or more ducts carry it to the outside. The part of the gland containing the ducts is the papilla (nipple), a protuberance that is cylindrical, conical, or low and rounded

TABLE 13.—*Examples of disparity in afterfeather between contour feather and plumule*

Birds	Contour feather	Plumule
Murres, jaegers........	Hyporachis........	Umbilical barbs.
Shearwaters, albatrosses, turacos.	.....do............	No afterfeather.
Cormorants..........	No afterfeather.....	Umbilical barbs.
Goatsuckers..........	Umbilical barbs.....	Hyporachis and umbilical barbs.

in various birds. The anatomy and histology of the oil gland are described in detail in chapter 9. We are interested here in special feathers associated with it.

The skin covering the lobes of the gland may be either bare, as in pigeons, or feathered to some degree, as in ducks and chickens. These feathers are plumules, semiplumes, or contour feathers in various species, but they are generally ordinary in structure. Their presence or absence in many birds was reported by Nitzsch (1867).

Although the papilla also may be bare, again as in pigeons, it more commonly has a cluster of feathers at or near its tip (fig. 388, p. 614). This was named the oil gland circlet by Nitzsch (1867) but oil gland tuft (Chandler, 1914) is preferred. In some birds, such as chickens and ducks, the feathers are not arranged in a circle. They are usually soaked with oil and hence stuck together so that the tuft resembles a small paint brush. Referring to its appearance and function, Schumacher (1919:293) called it the Bürzeldocht (translation: uropygial wick).

The feathers that comprise the tuft have been spoken of individually as tufts, but while this is understandable, it is likely to create confusion. They can be called oil gland feathers, following Chandler (1914, 1916). The nature and arrangement of these feathers in many birds were reported by Paris (1913) in his monograph on the oil gland. There are commonly 8 to 30 feathers, though there are many more in certain ducks and other aquatic birds. The feathers are often arranged in a single circle or oval around the orifices of the ducts. They may be confined to a pair of semicircular rows at the sides of the tip of the nipple, as in herons. On the other hand, there may be additional feathers inside the circle, between the orifices, as in some pheasants and grouse. This tendency is carried further in ducks and flamingos, where there is a circlet of feathers around each opening. The degree of contact between the clusters and the number of feathers between them differ among species. In addition, the number of feathers per circlet has been reported as varying from 34 to 27 in three specimens of Mallard (Humphrey and Clark, 1961: 384). The orifices are close together in chickens, so that the clusters around them meet (fig. 389, B, p. 615).

Oil gland feathers, more than others, must be cleaned before their structure can be studied. A brief soaking in a solvent such as ether is usually all that is needed to remove the oil. The feathers are then revealed to be modified plumules (down feathers). They differ in various ways from typical plumules, but do not seem to show any distinctive feature of structure that is general among birds. Most of their differences represent reduction of the condition in typical plumules. The oil gland feathers are shorter than body downs, as shown by the following examples of single, representative feathers (table 14). This difference in size is entirely due to the length of the barbs. The calamus of oil gland feathers is longer than that of body downs of the same or even greater size (table 14). It is completely embedded in the skin, however, with the result that the barbs appear to emerge right from the surface.

TABLE 14.—*Length of body down feathers and oil gland feathers of three domestic birds*

Bird	Body down		Oil gland feather	
	Total length	Length of calamus	Total length	Length of calamus
	Millimeters	*Millimeters*	*Millimeters*	*Millimeters*
Single Comb White Leghorn Chicken.	35	1.9	10	2.8
White Pekin Duck....	35	1.0	24	2.1
Common Coturnix....	9	.4	3.5	.5

The rachis is the most difficult part of an oil gland feather to characterize. In some species it varies even among feathers from the same individual. Some of the supposed interspecific differences in feather structure (not the feathering of the gland) may be nothing more than individual variations. A distinct rachis has been found in oil gland feathers of Single Comb White Leghorn Chickens and White Pekin Ducks, though it is variable in both. It is moderately well developed in auks but is extremely short in the Gannet (*Morus bassanus*) and at least certain herons, hawks, grouse, sandpipers, and kingfishers. A rachis has not been found in the oil gland feathers of petrels, Mallards and certain other ducks, coturnix, or certain parrots. Examination of more feathers from these birds might reveal it, at least as a tiny projection from the rim of the superior umbilicus.

A hyporachis is present on some oil gland feathers of chickens and kingfishers, but it has not been found in any of the other birds mentioned. The plumules of grouse and sandpipers have a distinct aftershaft.

Barbs arise from the rachis and hyporachis in oil gland feathers where these are present. In many of these feathers, however, most or all the barbs arise directly from the upper rim of the calamus. They may be either separate or fused in small clusters at the base. The rachis is sometimes hardly more than a fusion of barbs. It is the attachment of the barbs to the calamus instead of to a distinct rachis that is partly responsible for the tufted appearance of these feathers. This situation exists in many natal downs, but in fully grown birds it seems to be common only on the oil gland feathers. A related characteristic of the barbs is that those which attach to the rim of the calamus or to a very small rachis are equal in length. For this reason, they radiate from the base in a dry feather and bunch together, producing a truncate tip, when they bear oil.

The barbules are generally plumulaceous, but are shorter and simpler than those on typical downs (fig. 171, *C*). Even when dry, oil gland feathers are not as fluffy as other down feathers. The nodes are less prominent, being marked by smaller prongs or none, or by difference in pigmentation from the internode. The barbules show little or no variation along the pennulum, and they lack the distinctive features of typical plumulaceous barbules. In some birds the barbules are so reduced as to be of the stylet type.

A bird when preening frequently anoints its bill with oil by rubbing or stroking it on the papilla. It may nibble the gland, apparently to squeeze out the secretion. The oil gland tuft aids in transferring the oil to the bill (Schumacher, 1919). This would seem to be particularly true in those species either where the size or shape of the beak make it ill suited for receiving the oil directly from the papilla or where the uropygial eminence is so low that the bird can hardly nibble the gland. The process by which the oil gets into the tuft is not known, but it probably involves pressure due to secreting by the glandular cells, action of muscles in the papilla and capillary action in the feathers.

The oil gland and its feathering have been used as taxonomic characters, but they have proved unsatisfactory for many groups. "The feathering of the gland is constant in its nature throughout some families, but in others there are considerable differences between species" (Thomson, 1964:552). The tuft is well developed in most gallinaceous birds, but very tiny or absent in curassows and megapodes. It seems to have at least some taxonomic significance within the latter family.[4]

Powder Down

The feathers of many birds are dusted with a very fine substance that resembles talcum powder. Small amounts of this powder are shed by ordinary plumules and contour feathers. It is chiefly produced, however, by special feathers, the powder downs (flake-feathers, pulviplumes; German: Puder-dunen, Staub-dunen). These feathers are, in fact, best characterized by their powder because they differ in structure among birds.

The powder downs are commonly dispersed over the body, among the ordinary downs and contour feathers. They are probably not "diffused at random, but subject to a plan, or found within guiding lines, as are the other feathers" (Murie, 1872:474). Certain birds show a more advanced pattern of distribution in which some of the powder downs are clustered in specific areas known as powder down patches; other powder downs are mingled with the contour feathers around the boundaries of the patches and elsewhere on the body. Names for these patches were proposed by Murie (1872) in his description of them in the Kagu (*Rhynochetos jubatus*). He compared his terminology with that of Nitzsch (1867) in an additional note (1871, *sic*).

The most highly evolved pattern of distribution is that in which the powder downs occur only in distinct patches. In such birds as herons, they form large, dense clumps that contrast in texture and color with the surrounding contour feathers. These powder downs are packed so closely that adjacent follicles often touch each other. Schüz (1927:128) counted at least 120 powder down bases, each about 0.3

mm. in diameter, on 1 square centimeter of the Gray Heron (*Ardea cinerea*).

Pigeons are the only domestic birds to have powder downs; these are described in chapter 6. Schüz (1927:105) reported that in chickens he found a small amount of a substance homologous with powder in the downy portion of contour feathers. We have not found anything there, however, except fragments of the feather sheath and the external feather caps.

The powder is composed entirely of keratin, but its chemistry has apparently not been studied with modern techniques. The particles are granular, rod-shaped, or splinter-shaped, and are about 1 micron in diameter. Powder feathers are variously colored in different birds but the powder itself is always colorless (Schüz, 1927:199). The effect of powder on the color of feathers is discussed on page 411.

The source of the powder was long a subject of conjecture. Nitzsch imagined it to be "the dry residue of the fluid from which this feather is formed" (Nitzsch, 1867:37). Bartlett (1861:132) suggested that powder was secreted by the root of the feather, or that it might result from the disintegration of the barbs. Burmeister suggested that it might "be produced by the crumbling of the membrane [sheath] which intervenes between the feather and the matrix and which is dried and thrown off in proportion as the latter becomes enlarged" (Nitzsch, 1867:37). Schüz (1927) and Eiselen (1939) discovered that the powder is actually derived from cells on the surface and in the middle of each of the many ridges of barb-forming tissue within a feather germ. These cells are not normally incorporated in the barbs but are lost. The histology and growth of powder feathers are described in chapter 7, page 386.

The amount of powder produced by a feather appears to be correlated with the texture of the vanes. Firm, pennaceous texture calls for well-developed barbs, hence very little germinal tissue is used for powder. Lax and downy textures, on the other hand, do not depend on elaborate barbules or a strong rachis; these parts can be reduced, leaving more germinal material for powder. Contour feathers produce powder, but it is in certain down feathers that the greatest powder production is achieved (Schüz, 1927).

The powder downs of pigeons shed small to moderate amounts of powder, but do not show any lessening in the differentiation of their barbules. They are replaced more frequently than the contour feathers, and thus the total supply of powder is kept nearly continuous. In hawks, parrots, and woodswallows (family Artamidae), the barbules on the powder downs are not fully differentiated. These feathers grow more slowly than normal, another way of maintaining the powder supply.

Highly modified powder downs occur in herons, bitterns, tinamous, mesites (Forbes, 1882), cuckoo-rollers (*Leptosomus discolor*. Nitzsch, 1867), and possibly kagus (*Rhynochetos jubatus*. Schüz, 1927). In these heavily powdering feathers, the afterfeather and even the rachis are absent, the rami are vestigial, and the barbules are imperfectly formed or absent. Growth is said to be continuous (Schüz,

---

[4] Clark, G. A., Jr. Written communication.

1927:192). A calamus and a sheath form constantly at the periphery of the barb ridges and split into strips as they emerge from the follicle. The strips divide further into filamentous degenerate barbules; although they may fuse again for a short distance, the feather is reduced at its tip to a tuft of barbules clogged with powder.

The powder has long been regarded as a waterproof dressing for the feathers, owing to its nonwettable property. Additional, though circumstantial, evidence for this view has been seen in the fact that birds with well-developed patches of powder down have oil glands that are much reduced. Bartlett thus surmised that the powder renders "the feathers impervious to water in the same way that the oil-glands effect this in other birds" (1861:132). Herons have been observed, when preening, to nibble the powder downs and then run the bill through the contour feathers (Dewar, 1909; Hindwood, 1933:101).

The similarity in function between the powder downs and the oil gland led Wetmore to suggest (1920:169) that the gland might have evolved through the amalgamation of separate feathers. The glandular tubules and their secretion differ, however, from the feathers and their powder. Accordingly, this hypothesis has not been accepted.

The nature and distribution of powder downs were used during the last century in studies to determine the taxonomic position of several birds. It soon became evident that these characters were limited in their usefulness. Gadow pointed out that:

> Puderdunnen kommen bei sehr vielen Vögeln vor, die gar nicht mit einander verwandt sind, auch finden sie sich durchaus nicht immer bei allen Mitgliedern derselben Familie. Ihr Vorkommen und ihre Anordnung kann daher nur von sehr geringem taxonomischem Werthe sein soweit grössere Vogelgruppen in Betracht kommen; anderseits sind sie bisweilen für die Zugehörigkeit von Arten, Gattungen und selbst Unterfamilien als Fingerzeig zu benutzen (Gadow and Selenka, 1891:532).[5]

A corollary conclusion is that powder feathers evolved independently in several groups of birds, starting from typical contour feathers, semiplumes, or plumules but modifying in different ways.

BRISTLES

Avian bristles are feathers that are generally characterized by a stiff, tapered rachis and the absence of barbs except at the proximal end. They are sometimes confused with filoplumes, but the latter do not have a tapered rachis and have barbs only at the tip when fully grown.

Distribution

Virtually all bristles in birds are found on the head. The Bristle-thighed Curlew (*Numenius tahitiensis*) is exceptional in having bristles on the thighs (Coues, 1903: fig. 593). Bristles or stiff, coarse contour feathers, wherever they occur, take the place of the usual contour feathers. They usually grade into the surrounding feathers in pterylosis as well as structure. This is further evidence that bristles are not related to filoplumes, as suggested by Pycraft (1910:10). Bristles on the head can be named according to their location, but such distinctions do not mean anything about their structure.

The bristles from several locations on a bird's head may be very similar in structure (fig. 177, *C, D, D'*). Conversely, feathers from the same site in various birds may be very different. The bristles on the lores of the hawk are entirely unlike the so-called bristles on the lores of a chicken. Feathers should be called bristles only if they have the characteristic features, not on the basis of location.

Narial bristles are found on the cere of certain hawks (e.g., *Buteo* spp.) and parrots (*Amazona* spp.), and behind the nostril in owls, barbets (Family Capitonidae), and waxwings (Family Bombycillidae). They may be continuous posteriorly with bristles on the rictus or the lores. Rictal bristles arise along the dorsal (maxillary) portion of the rictus, and, in a few birds, on the ventral side also. These are the most common bristles, for they occur on nightjars and their allies, tyrant flycatchers, thrushes, sparrows, and many other birds (fig. 177, *C, E, G*).

Bristles that are widespread on the sides of the head, as in turkeys (fig. 217, p. 324) and certain hawks (*Circus* spp.), generally can be called facial bristles. Names for specific groups of these bristles have been suggested by Chandler (1914). Loral bristles are found between the eye and the beak (i.e., on the lores) of many hawks, Old World vultures, and owls. They radiate from the eye in owls and from a point a short distance in front of the eye in the Marsh Hawk (*Circus*

---

[5] Translation: Powder-downs occur in very many birds that are not at all related to each other; also, they are not always found in all members of the same family. Their occurrence and arrangement can therefore be of only very limited taxonomic value in considering the larger groups of birds. On the other hand, they may sometimes be used as an indication of common membership in species, genera, and even subfamilies.

→

FIGURE 177.—Examples of semibristle and bristles:

A, Great Horned Owl (*Bubo virginianus*)—loral semibristle.
B, Robin (*Turdus migratorius*)—malar bristle.
C, Common Starling (*Sturnus vulgaris*)—rictal bristle.
D, D', Common Starling—eyelash (upper eyelid bristle).

E, Robin—rictal bristle.
F, Red-tailed Hawk (*Buteo jamaicensis*)—eyelash (upper eyelid bristle).
G, Nightjar (*Caprimulgus longirostris*)—rictal bristle.

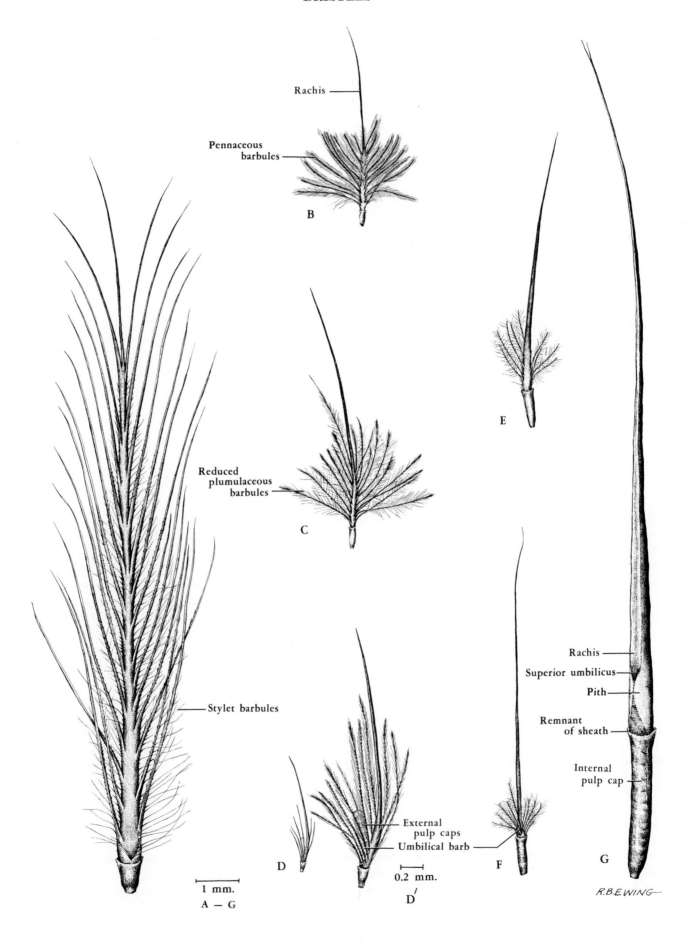

Rachis

Pennaceous
barbules

B

Reduced
plumulaceous
barbules

C

Stylet barbules

D

External
pulp caps

Umbilical barb

D'

E

F

Rachis

Superior umbilicus

Pith

Remnant
of sheath

Internal
pulp cap

G

1 mm.

A — G

0.2 mm.

R.B.EWING

cyaneus). The loral bristles make up the anterior portion of the facial disk, which is conspicuous in these birds. They have been called vibrissae and tactile feathers (German: Tast-federn) in reference to their function, and sinus feathers (Germany: Sinusfedern) in reference to their location (Küster, 1905). Supraorbital bristles sometimes occur between the crown feathers and the eye, and postorbital bristles occur behind the eye, between the crown feathers and the ear coverts. Suborbital bristles are found on the lower eyelid or the maxillary malar region in the Robin (fig. 177, *B*) and probably other passerine species.

Structure and Color

The upper and lower eyelids of various birds bear bristles or coarse contour feathers instead of the customary small contour feathers. These are termed eyelashes, though tiny bristles may instead be called cilia. More common are conspicuous bristles that project stiffly outward from a background of bare, often brightly colored skin. Such eyelashes occur in the Ostrich (*Struthio camelus*), certain hawks (e.g., *Circus* spp., *Buteo* spp.), turkeys, certain cuckoos (e.g., *Crotophaga* spp., *Geococcyx* spp.), and several other kinds of birds.

The bristles of the Crowned Crane (*Balearica pavonina*) are as much as 105 mm. long, but those of other birds are considerably shorter. The rictal bristles of the Whip-poor-will (*Caprimulgus vociferus*) are up to 41 mm. long (see closely related species, fig. 177, *G*) and the narial bristles of the Great Horned Owl are about 27 mm. long. Various bristles on a Red-tailed Hawk measure as much as 14 mm. In parrots and passerines, the bristles are mostly 2 to 8 mm. long, with the longest ones on the rictus.

The calamus commonly accounts for 5 to 10 percent of the total length of a bristle; in the Whip-poor-will it is nearly 6 mm. long. In some bristles, the calamus cannot be measured precisely because it simply opens out at its upper end and there is no distinct superior umbilicus. With this exception, the calamus of a bristle is conventional in structure. It contains several pulp caps even in specimens where it is less than 1 mm. long.

The rachis of a typical bristle is as wide as the calamus at its base and is then tapered distally to a fine point. It differs from that of a filoplume, which is narrowest at the proximal end and thickest near the tip (p. 274). A bristle tends to be stiffer than a filoplume, but this property has not been measured. The rachis often appears to be simply a prolongation of the calamus on one side, not a thick column that begins inside the tube, as in most feathers. Some bristles, such as those of a large hawk, contain a small amount of pith in the proximal portion. Shorter bristles are composed entirely of cortex.

Most bristles either lack an afterfeather entirely or have a tuft of umbilical barbs (fig. 177, *D*, *D'*, *F*). There is a suggestion of a hyporachis in the bristles of a Red-tailed Hawk, where the rim of the calamus, bearing barbs, is slightly

protruded on the side opposite the rachis. If present, umbilical barbs usually number from 2 to 14, and may form so dense a cluster as to shield a few external feather caps. The bristles on the head of the turkey are remarkable because many of them do have a distinct aftershaft. It is finer than the shaft, but nearly equal to it in length. Barbs are present on the shaft and aftershaft as well as around the superior umbilicus. These bristles are described more fully on pages 323-326, and are shown in figure 217, page 324.

Structurally, the simplest of all feathers are those bristles that consist of a bare shaft. Examples are the rictal bristles of the Band-winged Nightjar (*Caprimulgus longirostris*, fig. 177, *G*) and the eyelashes of anis (*Crotophaga* spp.) and the Roadrunner (*Geococcyx californianus*). Most bristles, however, have at least a few barbs on the proximal portion of the rachis (fig. 177, *B*, *C*, *E*) or around the superior umbilicus (fig. 177, *D*, *F*). Bristles on the rictus and upper eyelid tend to have fewer barbs than those elsewhere. According to Chandler (1914:360), there appears to be a correlation in many birds between the lack of barbs in eyelashes and the lack of aftershafts on other types of feathers. The barbs form flat vanes or a round cluster, depending on their length and place of origin. Some bristles have short barbs that result from the breaking off of the very fine distal portion of long ones. The rami of bristles are generally small, simplified versions of those on contour feathers. In the supraorbital bristles of the Marsh Hawk and the rictal bristles of the Common Starling (fig. 177, *C*), the tips of the barbs appear thick and coarse because the barbules lie closely against the ramus.

The barbules on bristles are most commonly of the stylet type, but plumulaceous and pennaceous ones also occur. Their size and character tend to match the development of the rami, so that reduced barbules tend to be present on short, fine rami. Exceptions, however, are provided by the loral bristles of owls, which have short, stylet barbules on long rami, and by the rictal bristles of thrushes and starlings (fig. 177, *C*, *E*), which have plumulaceous barbules on short rami. These plumulaceous barbules resemble those on down feathers of the same birds except that they lack basal prongs. As in contour feathers and down, bristles may have barbules on the rachis as well as on the rami. The barbules are larger on the bases of the barbs than on the rachis, but they diminish and even vanish before reaching the tips of the barbs.

Color is of little value in characterizing most types of feathers because they exist in such a large range of colors. It is remarkable, therefore, to find that in nearly all bristles the distal portion of the rachis is very dark brown or even black. The barbs and the proximal portion of the rachis may also be so colored, but the calamus is always unpigmented. As might be expected, the bristles are entirely dark (except for the calamus) in birds where the adjacent plumage is black or purple, as in the narial bristles of waxwings, the rictal bristles of a Common Starling, and the eyelashes of anis. Similarly pigmented bristles also occur where the plumage is variegated brown, as in the rictal bristles of nightjars and sparrows, or where they stand out against bare skin, as in the eyelashes of the Roadrunner and the various bristles on the head of the turkey. The more usual color pattern, in which the distal portion of the rachis is very dark and the rest of the feather is pale, is exemplified by the various facial bristles of hawks and owls.

Dark color is so characteristic of bristles that it is probably more than a matter of visual effect—either blending with the adjacent plumage or contrasting against the skin. In contour feathers, pigmentation is often heaviest in places that are most subject to mechanical stress (Spöttel, 1914:424). Deposits of melanin are believed to increase the firmness and reduce the elasticity of the keratin. The black spots on the tips of the distal primary remiges of gulls are more resistant to wear than the white or gray parts of the vanes around them (Averill, 1923:57; Van Tyne and Berger, 1959:101). Likewise, the pale tips of otherwise dark body feathers are worn off, as in Bobolinks (p. 418). These examples strongly suggest that melanin likewise enhances the stiffness and hardness of bristles. The portions of a bristle that either are flexible or are subjected to little wear are lightly pigmented.

Semibristles

All these features of structure and pigmentation make typical bristles easy to distinguish from contour feathers. Chandler (1914:359), however, pointed out intermediate forms that exemplify stages in the reduction of contour feathers to bristles. These have been called bristle feathers (German:Borstenfedern. Frieling, 1936:38), but this term is inappropriate because typical bristles, too, are feathers. Just as semiplume is used for the feathers that grade between contour feathers and plumules, so we suggest the term "semibristle" for feathers of intermediate structure between contour feathers and bristles. An example of a semibristle is shown in figure 177, A.

A graded series of specimens from contour feathers to bristles shows increasing prominence of the rachis and concentration of barbs and barbules at the base. These effects result from one or more of the following changes: (1) lengthening of the rachis; (2) shortening and loss of distal barbs so that rachis extends beyond them; (3) wider spacing of the distal barbs; (4) simplification of barbules from pennaceous or plumulaceous types to stylet type; (5) reduction and loss of barbules, starting at tips of barbs; (6) thickening of lower end of rachis; and (7) darkening, by deposition of melanin, of rachis and barbs, at least in their distal portions. The afterfeather is usually reduced to an umbilical tuft or lost, but a large, bare hyporachis is retained in many turkey bristles.

It is necessary to be somewhat arbitrary in setting the criteria that delimit semibristles on a continuum between contour feathers and bristles. This seems to be justified by the usefulness of recognizing an intermediate category. Also, the concepts of contour feather and bristle can be kept more

distinct than if they are distinguished directly from each other. Semibristles can be characterized as feathers in which the rachis is conspicuous, the distal barbs are far apart, and barbules are very reduced or absent on most of the barbs. The rachis may be free of barbs distally, but it is only slightly stouter here than the barbs, if at all, and does not extend beyond them. The distal parts of the rachis and barbs tend to be darker than the proximal parts. The nature of the barbs and barbules distinguishes semibristles from contour feathers, while the nature of the rachis distinguishes them from bristles.

Semibristles are probably always to be found on birds that have typical bristles. They may also exist in birds without bristles, that is, where the extreme condition is not reached. Examples of them can be seen covering the nostril of crows, along the rictus of nightjars and sparrows, on the lores (fig. 177, A), the eyelids, and the anterior portion of the interramal tract of some owls (e.g., *Bubo* spp.), on the upper eyelids of crows and some cuckoos (e.g., *Coccyzus* spp.), behind the eye in hawks, and on the back of the head and upper neck in turkeys.

Function

The functions performed by bristles and semibristles have had little critical study and must be regarded as somewhat conjectural. They are deduced from the structure and location of these feathers and, in certain cases, from the histology of the supporting skin. Narial bristles appear to keep foreign bodies out of the nostrils, just as the ear coverts protect the external auditory meatus. Probably the same function is held by other narial feathers—the tiny, rounded contour feathers of grouse and ptarmigan, and the coarse, narrow semibristles and contour feathers of crows.

Rictal bristles have been thought to form a sort of net that aids birds in catching insects in flight (Mayaud, 1950: 34). While they might have this function in nightjars and both families of flycatchers, they certainly do not do so in kiwis and barbets. These bristles, like those on the lores, are undoubtedly tactile structures, analogous to the whiskers of cats. Küster (1905) showed that the follicles of the bristles are surrounded by numerous avian lamellar (hitherto known as Herbst) corpuscles—sensory receptors for pressure and vibration (Schildmacher, 1931). Accordingly, the bristles probably serve to sense prey or obstacles, particularly in crepuscular or nocturnal birds, or those that nest in cavities. Chandler (1914:361) suggested that the loral bristles of hawks (and other raptors) were modified to cover the region without becoming worn and soiled, as would conventional feathers.

Bristles on the eyelids and elsewhere on the head probably also have a tactile function, especially in owls. If they are sparse, they allow the skin to show through, creating a visual effect that may be important in birds with brightly colored skin. Large, stiff eyelashes may keep foreign particles out of the eye; such a use is suggested by their occurrence in many species of terrestrial or arboreal habitat.

FILOPLUMES

After a bird has been plucked, hairlike feathers known as filoplumes can be seen. A fully grown filoplume consists of a very fine shaft with a tuft of short barbs or barbules at its tip (fig. 178, C). It differs from a bristle in the nature of the shaft and the presence of an apical tuft. Filoplumes do not resemble any other types of feathers.

The arrangement of filoplumes in birds of many species was investigated by Fehringer (1912). Their structure, development, and function were studied by Pfeffer (1952). Our own observations generally confirm and amplify the findings of these authors.

Distribution

Filoplumes have been found in birds of all orders except ostriches, emus, and cassowaries. They are said to be absent in pelicans, anhingas, and tropic-birds (Chandler, 1916:260), but they are present in cormorants, which belong to the same order. Although generally hidden beneath the contour feathers, filoplumes are long and exposed on the neck and upper back of cormorants (alternate plumage), bulbuls, and certain thrushes.

Filoplumes are distributed on all the feather tracts, even those on the head, where they are minute (fig. 209, p. 314). They are always situated beside other feathers, never by themselves, and hence are absent from bare apteria. Filoplumes generally accompany contour feathers and semiplumes; they do not accompany tract downs, as in ducks but we have found them with apterium downs in chickens. Noting the regular association between contour feathers and filoplumes, Gerber (1939) designated filoplumes as the third component of his feather complex.

The number, size, and placement of filoplumes beside larger feathers vary among species and among tracts of a given bird. Fehringer (1912) concluded that filoplumes are usually uniform in tracts where contour feathers are relatively uniform in size. They tend to be larger and more numerous in portions of a tract where the contour feathers are larger. Borodulina (1966) noted, however, that the size of filoplumes seems to be related more to the action than to the size of the contour feathers. In the birds she studied, she found that filoplumes were always numerous and larger in places where the contour feathers performed the most mechanical action and had the greatest mobility.

There are usually one or two filoplumes with each body contour feather, semiplume, or apterium down. There are five to eight in certain hawks (e.g., Marsh Hawk (*Circus cyaneus*). Chandler, 1914:335), and Fehringer (1912) reported finding as many as 10, though he did not specify the source. Filoplumes are most numerous around the remiges and rectrices, where there may be eight per quill in chickens and pigeons, and 12 in hawks. On all tracts we have found that some of the contour feathers are not accompanied by filoplumes. These gaps do not seem to fall into any pattern; they are probably places where the filoplumes have been shed but not replaced.

Filoplumes grow from their own follicles, although these

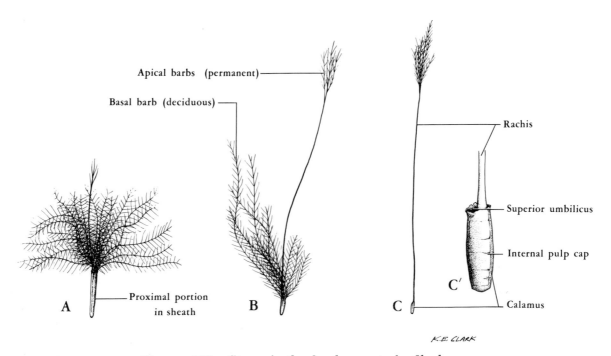

Apical barbs (permanent)

Basal barb (deciduous)

Rachis

Superior umbilicus

Internal pulp cap

Calamus

Proximal portion in sheath

A   B   C   C'

K.E. CLARK

FIGURE 178.—Stages in the development of a filoplume:

A, midimmature; partially emerged from sheath.
B, late immature; completely emerged from sheath, basal barbs still present.

C, mature; basal barbs lost.
C', proximal portion of shaft at higher magnification.

are often exceedingly close to that of the host feather—less than 0.5 mm. apart in chickens, for example. Single or paired filoplumes are situated at the sides of a contour feather though they may be slightly anterior or posterior to it. Their position is keyed to the orientation of the contour feather. Fehringer (1912:246) reached the following general conclusions about the location of filoplumes: (1) If a contour feather is situated near the middle of a tract and is directed posteriorly, it has filoplumes on both sides. (2) If a contour feather is situated near the sides of a tract and is directed outward (from the midline), its filoplumes are on the medial side. (3) If a contour feather is situated near the sides of a tract and is directed inward, its filoplumes are on the lateral side. The several filoplumes with each remex or rectrix may be evenly spaced around it, unevenly spaced (fig. 210, p. 315), or crowded together on one side. Those around the body feathers of hawks are often disposed in two groups. Rarely, in both chickens and hawks, we have found two filoplumes issuing from the same follicle.

Structure

The length of filoplumes ranges from 1 mm. to the full length of their host feathers (Pfeffer, 1952:70). The longest filoplumes we have seen, measuring at least 60 mm., are those of the Great Blue Heron (*Ardea herodias*), Blue Peafowl (*Pavo cristatus*) and Great Horned Owl (*Bubo virginianus*) all of these long filoplumes are situated beside flight feathers. In comparison, the longest filoplumes of chickens, about 50 mm. long, are relatively large (see p. 315 for details).

The shaft arises as a calamus that is less than 2 mm. long sometimes less than 0.5 mm. (fig. 178, *C'*). This part was overlooked by Pycraft (1898:258) and Chandler (1916:261) although it had been seen by Nitzsch (1867:14) and Newton and Gadow (1893–96:242). The diameter of the calamus is slightly more than that of the rachis, and unlike that of other feathers, is greatest at the lower end. The lumen is conical, and is partitioned by as many as 10 pulp caps.

The rachis is more solidly composed of cortex in filoplumes than in other feathers. Long pith cells are irregularly spaced in it, though mostly at the proximal end. Reflection of light from these air-filled cells gives filoplumes their characteristic glistening appearance. Cross sections of the rachis are either circular or ovoid, indicating that the filament is either terete or slightly compressed and tapered at one end. Our study of growing filoplumes reveals that flattening takes place on the sides, if at all. The maximum diameter of a filoplume rachis is about 84 microns in a chicken, 64 microns in a White Pekin Duck, and 40 microns in a Robin. A unique feature of the rachis is that it is thickest near the distal end. It tapers very gradually from here toward the proximal end until just above the calamus, where it tapers a little more sharply (fig. 211, p. 316). The diameter at the base may be only one-third of that at the tip. Filoplumes that have broken at this zone of weakness are probably the basis for statements about the absence of a calamus. Owing to its shape and composition, a filoplume is stiffer than the ramus of a downy

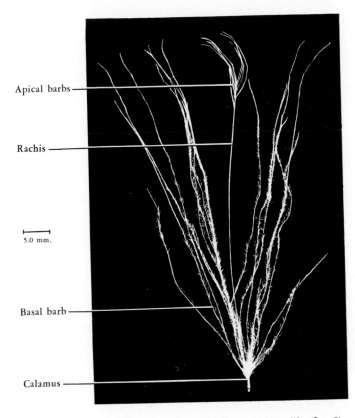

Apical barbs

Rachis

5.0 mm.

Basal barb

Calamus

FIGURE 179.—Late immature filoplume of a Single Comb White Leghorn Chicken.

barb with approximately the same thickness. It bends downward a little near the tip, just like a contour feather (Pfeffer, 1952:70).

While it is growing, a filoplume has a cluster of long, downy barbs at the base (figs. 178, *A* and *B*; 179; 245, p. 389; 246), but it loses them by the time it is fully grown (figs. 178, *C*; and 247, p. 390). These basal barbs resemble umbilical barbs of other feathers in their location and structure. Accordingly, we suggest that the basal barbs of a filoplume represent a temporary afterfeather. Regardless of whether or not this interpretation is correct, a fully grown filoplume lacks an afterfeather. Details on the growth and loss of the basal barbs are in chapter 7, pages 388–391.

A typical fully grown filoplume has barbs only at the tip—one to six on each side. These are short, simplified versions of downy barbs in which the barbules resemble those in the margins and the tip of a down feather. They are much shorter and stiffer than fully characterized downy barbules. The base is usually not straplike, but is a thick, tapered piece that grades into the pennulum. Outgrowths of all types are very small or absent. The filoplume barbules of a Robin and a Raven (*Corvus corax*), for example, lack the characteristic basal prongs of passerine downy barbules. Here, as in hawks, owls, and gallinaceous birds, the nodes are faint and the nodal prongs, if any, are very short. The filoplume barbules of ducks, geese, and swans have pointed nodal prongs as found at the proximal end of downy barbules, not the characteristic large, triangular prongs found at the tip.

Occasionally in chickens we have found filoplumes with a few barbs at irregular intervals along the shaft (fig. 212, p. 316). The filoplumes on the neck of the Great Cormorant (*Phalacrocorax carbo*) in alternate plumage are unusual in that they have short barbs widely spaced along the entire rachis. It is fairly common to find tiny barbules directly on the rachis, sometimes to the exclusion of barbs. Examples of these and other variations are described by Pfeffer (1952).

Function

Filoplumes have been considered degenerate structures because their structure is simple and they have not been known to have any function. The fact that they occur in most birds, including the passerines—the most recently evolved—and their relative uniformity of structure suggest that they do indeed have a function. Gerber (1939:276) suggested that filoplumes serve temporarily for thermal insulation, but Pfeffer (1952:94) pointed out that they are totally inadequate for this. Conspicuous filoplumes contribute to the appearance of the feathering, as in some cormorants and bulbuls.

Typical filoplumes, however, seem to have a general and more important function related to feather posture. Contour feathers are often moved by external forces such as air currents; all kinds of feathers except filoplumes are constantly being adjusted by their feather muscles (ch. 8). These movements undoubtedly create vibration or pressure in the follicles, effects that can be sensed by the nearby avian lamellar (Herbst) corpuscles (ch. 7, p. 362). It is not known if they are also detected by the free nerve endings in the follicle wall. If a disturbance is slight, or if it affects only the downy portion of the vanes, it probably will not be sensed directly. As Pfeffer (1952:95) observed, the rami of downy barbs are too weak to transmit movement to the shaft. He pointed out that filoplumes, however, undoubtedly can respond to delicate disturbances and stimulate the laminated nerve endings. They can serve as an indirect yet very sensitive means for transmitting slight movements of larger feathers.

Filoplumes are structurally well adapted to do this, since their apical barbs or barbules enlarge the area for contact with larger feathers, and their shaft acts as a long lever that magnifies the force in the follicle. Borodulina (1966) has shown that they have considerable innervation in the form of free nerve endings in the follicular wall and avian lamellar corpuscles around the follicles. The latter are said to be present sometimes beside the follicles of filoplumes but not those of contour feathers. We have found these sensory corpuscles in various locations beside the follicles of contour feathers, and frequently beside those of filoplumes as well (fig. 232, p. 359), but not solely with the latter.

Anatomical evidence thus indicates that filoplumes are part of the system that provides sensory input for the control of the posture of larger feathers. This theory must still be tested with neurophysiological methods. If it proves true, it will probably be found that filoplumes monitor the larger feathers not only to detect their disarray (Pfeffer, 1952:96), but also as they are employed for locomotion, insulation, bathing, or other activities (Borodulina, 1966:138).

Filoplumes are not present on newly hatched birds although their follicles are well developed. They do not begin to emerge above the skin until a few days after hatching, when the body contour feathers begin to appear. No functional reason for this situation is known. The natal downs are equipped with feather muscles, but although these may be functional at an early age, the exact position of the downs may not matter much except for thermoregulation. Perhaps, as Pfeffer (1952:96) noted, it would be inappropriate for filoplumes to emerge early because they would be disturbed constantly.

If filoplumes help to detect movements of the contour feathers, this would account for the greater numbers of them around the remiges and rectrices. Additional sensations from these feathers are probably advantageous in adjusting the feathers for flight. Possibly the filoplumes associated with the remiges and rectrices are analogous to the airspeed indicators on an airplane.

It follows that if filoplumes function as suggested, they are adaptations that improve the operation of the contour feathers. They are not in the least vestigial, but on the contrary, are structures that have evolved through simplification of the basic feather plan (Pfeffer, 1952:96).

CHAPTER 6

Shape, Structure, and Texture of Feathers of Domestic Birds

INTRODUCTION

The feathers of any bird vary widely in size, shape, structure, texture, and color. There have been very few studies of this diversity, either in domestic species or natural species. Examining and comparing feathers from different parts of the body can be fruitful for several reasons. Such studies are likely to reveal features that are characteristic for the species. These features may be useful for indicating the taxonomic affinities of birds or for identifying the source of isolated feathers. A study from a functional standpoint can show how feathers are adapted for covering, insulating, or waterproofing the body, for flight, for tactile sensation or protection of sensory organs, for ornamentation, species recognition, or display. Finally, the study of feathers may be necessary before specimens can be chosen for a practical application such as downy stuffing for pillows or sleeping bags, ornamentation in millinery, the fletching of arrows, or even artificial flies for fishing. As an example, Hardy and Hardy (1949) described briefly the feathers from various parts of the body in domestic chickens, ducks, and geese. They explained a procedure for sorting feathers and discussed certain properties that affected their utilization.

In this chapter, we examine the feathers of the five species of domestic birds dealt with in this book. The feathers of the adult Single Comb White Leghorn Chickens are covered in the most detail. We describe the feathers and also point out characters which, when taken together, can identify the source of an isolated feather. The feathers of the remaining birds are treated with attention to characteristic features but with less description.

One of the most distinctive features of many feathers—color—is, of course, of no use with birds that are all white, such as White Leghorn, White Plymouth Rock, White Wyandotte, and Rhode Island White Chickens; White Holland Turkeys; White Campbell, Pekin, Aylesbury, and domestic Muscovy Ducks; and White Chinese Geese. A study of the feathers of such birds must therefore focus on their size, shape, texture, proportions, and structure. Pattern and color, as found in several pigmented breeds of chickens,

are illustrated in "The American Standard of Perfection" (American Poultry Association, 1938–40).

There are several dimensions of feathers, the measurements of which can help to identify them as to the kind of bird or the tract where they originated. One or more of these measurements is included in each of the descriptions of feathers in this chapter. The dimensions, as we have measured them, are as follows:

Length.—The length is measured from the bottom of the calamus to the tip of the vanes, with the shaft as straight as possible and the terminal barbs extended as far as possible.

Width.—The width is the maximum distance across both vanes with the barbs at their normal angles from the rachis. In flight feathers and their coverts, it may be necessary to measure the widths of the vanes separately.

Calamus length.—The length of the calamus is measured from the rim of the superior umbilicus, as close as possible to the midventral line (depending on the structure of the afterfeather), to the proximal end.

Downy part.—The downy part is the proportion of the length of the vanes that is downy. It equals the distance along the rachis from the lowermost barb to the insertion of the highest barb with any downy barbules, divided by the total length of the vanes. The uppermost downy barb sometimes cannot be determined exactly, but this is unimportant. An error of two or three barbs is only a very short distance along the rachis, and will alter the ratio very slightly. If desired, the proportion of the pennaceous part of the vanes can be measured instead.

Afterfeather length.—If an aftershaft is present, the length of the afterfeather is measured from the rim of the superior umbilicus to the tip of the vanes, with the aftershaft straight and the terminal barbs extended upward as far as possible; if an aftershaft is absent (i.e., aftertuft type), the afterfeather length is measured from the rim of the superior umbilicus to the tip of the barbs at the midventral line, with these extended as far as possible. If desired, the length of the afterfeather can be taken in proportion to the length of either the entire feather or the main vanes.

SINGLE COMB WHITE LEGHORN CHICKEN

This section deals primarily with the feathers of adult male Single Comb White Leghorn Chickens. In comparison, the feathers of females are smaller, have a relatively larger downy portion, and show no more than a very narrow zone of open pennaceous texture around the margin. They cannot be identified as closely as male feathers because they lack a conspicuous pattern of pennaceous textures.

Contour feathers are taken up by tracts in the following order: dorsopelvic, interscapular, dorsal cervical, ventral cervical, pectoral, sternal, abdominal, femoral, crural, humeral, alar, caudal, and capital. Semiplumes, down feathers, and filoplumes are treated as separate types, but as they are each fairly uniform over the body they are not analyzed by tracts. Feathers of the oil gland are described after other down feathers.

Dorsopelvic Tract

Feathers of the dorsopelvic tract are contour feathers; most of them are downy for one-fourth to one-half of their length. They range in length from about 50 to 200 mm., and in width from 25 to 45 mm. The vanes are widest just below the transition from the downy portion to the pennaceous portion. From the beginning of the pennaceous portion to the tip, the feather tapers first sharply, then gradually for a long distance, and finally sharply again (fig. 180, A). The shape of the tip varies from round to bluntly pointed, depending on the length of the barbs and their angle from the rachis.

The vanes display a pattern of four distinct textures, which is one of the distinguishing features of these feathers. To learn the structural basis for these textures, we will examine a feather from the anterior portion of the dorsopelvic tract close to the midline. The plumulaceous barbules have a flat, narrow base and a simple pennulum in which the cells are alike except for a gradual reduction in diameter (fig. 180, C). The nodes are slightly swollen and may bear two to four tiny prongs. Many barbules alternately point diagonally upward or downward along each side of a ramus, an arrangement that expands the vanules and contributes to downy texture. Further analysis of this texture is given in a later section (pp. 310–313). Near the tip of the plumulaceous portion of the vanes, the barbules near the tips of the barbs develop a ventral flange on the base and become shorter (fig. 180, D). They tend to disappear 1 or 2 mm. before the tip. Owing to these reduced plumulaceous barbules, the margin of the vane here is soft but not fluffy.

Medial to the downy portions of the vanes is a zone of open pennaceous texture about 2 mm. wide on each side of the rachis (fig. 180, B). Parallel barbs separated by spaces are clearly visible. Their barbules are not of a pennaceous type; they consist solely of a straplike base that curves outward and downward from the ramus. As they do not seem to have been described heretofore, we suggest that they be known as curled-base barbules. Proceeding toward the rachis, those on the distal side of a ramus diminish while those on the

proximal side straighten out, become broader at the base, and grade into the rachidial barbules. The latter are present along the entire rachis, and vary in number from 1 to about 10 between the bases of the rami. Distally along a barb, the curled-base barbules change into plumulaceous barbules as they straighten and acquire a pennulum.

Particularly in males, the most distinctive part of these feathers is the pennaceous portion of the vanes. In hens, this part is closely knit except for a narrow band of open pennaceous texture at the tip (fig. 213, 10 and 11, p. 317). In males, feathers at the posterior end of the dorsopelvic tract show a similar band (fig. 183), but those elsewhere on the tract are more boldly patterned (fig. 182). An inner zone of normal, closely knit texture (fig. 180, E) is bounded by zones of open pennaceous texture (fig. 180, F). The inner zone has a matte surface whereas the outer zone glistens, because of light reflected from the flattened sides of the rami. The pattern of these zones and the shape of the vanes vary throughout the tract, as shown in figures 181 and 184. Isolated feathers can thus be located to within a few rows according to their size, shape, and textural pattern.

The transition zone between the downy and the pennaceous portions of the vanes covers a span of 5 to 10 barbs. Here the barbs become transformed, first at the inner and outer ends and then toward the middle of more distal barbs. The rachidial barbules show little change except to become more triangular; they grade into the proximal pennaceous barbules (fig. 180, E). Other types of barbules are replaced as follows:

(1) Curled-base barbules and normal plumulaceous barbules are replaced by normal pennaceous barbules (fig. 180, B, C, and E). This involves the following changes: (a) straightening of the base, (b) formation of dorsal and ventral flanges on the base, (c) formation of ventral teeth from the distal cells of the base, (d) reduction of the pennulum cells in length and diameter, (e) disappearance of the nodes, and (f) enlargement and differentiation of nodal prongs into barbicels, especially on the ventral side of the pennulum.

(2) Reduced plumulaceous barbules (at the tips of barbs) are replaced by reduced pennaceous barbules (fig. 180, D and F) at the distal ends of barbs in the transition zone. This involves only shortening the pennulum. Both types of reduced barbules are identified more by the fully formed barbules beside them than by their own structure.

(3) Normal pennaceous barbules are replaced by smaller, simpler pennaceous barbules (fig. 180, E, F), starting in the transition zone and continuing through the pennaceous portion of the vanes. The change involves only shortening the pennulum and the loss of outgrowths, yet it takes place differently on opposite sides of a ramus. Proceeding toward the tip, the proximal barbules become simplified and more widely spaced, whereas the distal barbules are still normal. The latter become reduced and lost within a short span, while the proximal barbules continue gradually to diminish. Eventually barbules vanish on both sides, leaving bare, glistening rami. These changes take place closer and closer to the rachis

in the more distal barbs. The open pennaceous zone is thus that portion of the vane in which the barbules are tiny or nonexistent. The pattern created by the pennaceous zones depends on variation in the place along the ramus where reduction of barbules occurs. The contrast between the zones depends on the abruptness of the transition from normal pennaceous barbules to reduced ones or to none at all.

(4) Reduced pennaceous barbules are replaced by stylet barbules at the tip of the feather (fig. 180, G). The barbules become still shorter and their nodes disappear.

All dorsopelvic feathers have an afterfeather with an aftershaft that is much longer than its barbs (figs. 182, 183). The afterfeather varies in length from about 25 to 35 mm., although the main vanes vary much more. The aftervanes are downy except for a weakly fluffy zone on each side of the rachis, created by wider spacing of the downy barbules, not by the presence of curled-base barbules.

Feathers from different portions of the dorsopelvic tract can now be characterized as follows:

Anterior end, near midline

Length: 80 to 90 mm.   Downy part: 38 to 44 percent

Near the midline at the anterior end of the dorsopelvic tract, the pennaceous portion shows a broad zone of open texture on each side of a relatively short, triangular, closely knit zone (figs. 181, 182). The boundary between the zones starts near the tip of the lowermost pennaceous barbs and curves inward across the higher barbs. It reaches the rachis about 8 mm. below the broadly rounded tip of the vanes. In females, feathers at this location are narrow and rectangular (fig. 213, 10). They are 65 to 79 mm. long, and the downy part equals 53 to 65 percent of the length of the vanes.

Anterior end, near borders

Length: 100 to 150 mm.   Downy part: 29 to 41 percent

The actual length of the downy portion of feathers near the borders at the anterior end of the dorsopelvic tract remains

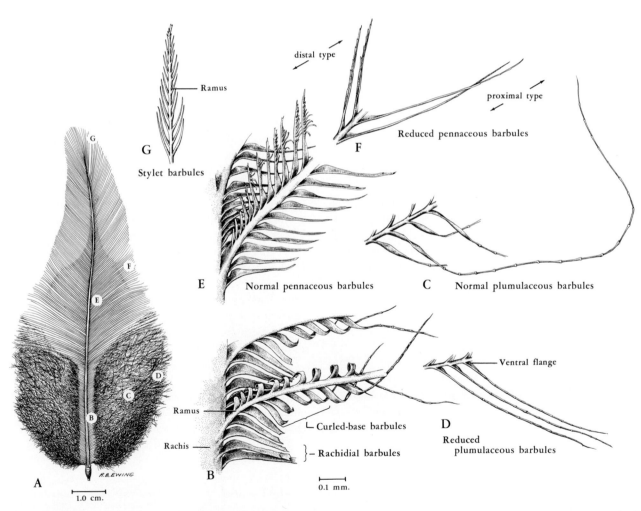

FIGURE 180.—Textural pattern as related to the structure of the barbules in a contour feather of a Single Comb White Leghorn Chicken. The specimen is from the middle of the anterior portion of the dorsopelvic tract.

A, whole feather. The areas from which figures B through G were taken are indicated by corresponding letters on figure A.
B, pennaceouslike texture.

C and D, downy texture.
E, closely knit pennaceous texture.
F and G, open pennaceous texture.

nearly constant, whereas the pennaceous part becomes longer (fig. 181). The open pennaceous portion of the vanes in enlarged and the tip becomes pointed.

Middle, near midline

Length: 95 to 120 mm.   Downy part: 35 to 40 percent

As compared with more anterior feathers of the dorsopelvic tract, the feathers near the midline at the middle of the tract have a longer, narrower pennaceous portion, and the boundary between normal and open pennaceous zones is more nearly parallel to the edge (figs. 181, 182). In females these feathers have no zone of open pennaceous texture (fig. 213, *10*).

Middle, near borders

Length: 160 to 200 mm.   Downy part: 26 to 31 percent

The feathers near the borders of the middle of the dorsopelvic tract hang downward over the lateral pelvic apterium and the femoral tract. They are longer and narrower than the feathers anterior to them (figs. 181 and 184). The pattern of pennaceous textures is asymmetrical because the zone of open texture starts farther distally on the inner web than on the outer. The zones merge into each other more than in the more anterior feathers. In females, these feathers are 74 to 87 mm. long, and about 50 to 62 percent downy. They lack wide zones of open pennaceous texture, and their tips are blunt.

Posterior end, near midline

Length: 115 to 170 mm.   Downy part: 38 to 41 percent

Toward the posterior end of the dorsopelvic tract, the feathers near the midline become larger and more ovoid, and the basal portion becomes fluffier (figs. 183, 184). The zone of open pennaceous texture is restricted to a narrow band, which is distinct on the outer vane but indistinct on the inner vane. The afterfeather is wider and fluffier than on anterior feathers. In females, these feathers are shorter and have blunter tips.

Posterior end, near borders

Length: 50 to 70 mm.

The feathers near the borders at the posterior end of the dorsopelvic tract are semiplumes, located between the contour feathers of the dorsopelvic tract and the down feathers of the lateral pelvic apterium (fig. 184). They do not grade into the contour feathers. The structure of semiplumes is discussed further on pages 310 to 313.

Interscapular Tract

Length: 95 to 105 mm.   Downy part: 35 to 45 percent

Proceeding anteriorly from the dorsopelvic tract, the interscapular feathers show the following changes (fig. 181):

1. Length of pennaceous part of vane increases.
2. Downy part of vane becomes fluffier, through lengthening and branching of the barbs (see pp. 311–313).

3. Width increases at lower end of pennaceous part.
4. Tip becomes more pointed.
5. Zones of open pennaceous texture become narrower.
6. Boundary between pennaceous zones becomes straighter and more nearly parallel to edge of vane.
7. Afterfeather becomes a little less fluffy.

This is a narrow tract in which only a few rows have as many as six follicles from the midline to the border. Proceeding outward, the pennaceous parts of the vanes become smaller and finally disappear. The outermost contour feathers of the tract are bounded by down feathers of the apterium; there are no semiplumes.

Interscapular feathers of females differ from those of males in their more rectangular shape, rounder tip, lack of an open pennaceous zone, and relatively shorter afterfeather (fig. 213, *14*).

Dorsal Cervical Tract

Feathers on the dorsal cervical tract show a greater range of size and more sexual dimorphism than those of any other tract. They are longer and more boldly patterned in males than in females, a difference that is heightened in breeds where the feathers are patterned in color as well as in texture.

In Single Comb White Leghorn Chickens, the feathers are pointed and relatively narrow but appear to be characterized best by the openness of their vanes. The downy portion is slightly fluffy and short in relation to total length. A very few of the downy barbs are branched. The barbules on these barbs become shorter and fewer than those in interscapular feathers, anteriorly and laterally through the tract (fig. 181). At the base of the head, the feathers near the midline are downy only in a small zone close to the rachis. The small feathers along the margins of the tract on the underside of the neck have only a few, slightly downy barbs or none at all.

The pennaceous portion is less closely knit in dorsal cervical feathers than in other contour feathers on the trunk. It shows less contrast between the normal and open zones, yet a freer separation between the barbs than in other contour feathers. These texture qualities result from wider spacing of the barbs (especially in the middle of the vanes), reduced thickness and increased flexibility of the rami, and reduction of barbicels.

The afterfeather is shorter (10 to 25 percent as long as the main vanes) than in other contour feathers on the trunk. It is also less fluffy, providing support for the finding that in chickens, the density of the afterfeather tends to agree with that of the downy portion of the main vanes.

Measurements and additional characteristics of feathers in different areas of the dorsal cervical tract are as follows:

Posterior end

Length: 121 to 184 mm.   Downy part: 6 to 25 percent

The feathers at the posterior end of the dorsal cervical tract are among the most striking to be found on a fully grown rooster (fig. 185, *D*). They are widest (up to 75 mm.) in the downy portion and tapered rather sharply to a more or less pointed tip. There are distinct zones of normal and open pennaceous texture, separated by a boundary that is parallel to the edge of the vanes. Between the pennaceous and the downy zones is a transitional zone of lax texture, where the

barbs are fine and flexible, and bear reduced downy barbules for most of their length.

Feathers from the posterior portion of the dorsal cervical tract illustrate the changes in size and morphology between feathers of successive generations.

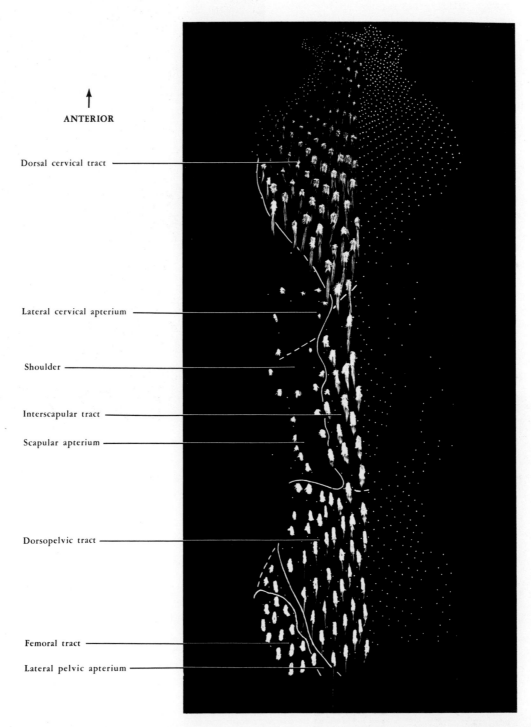

↑
ANTERIOR

Dorsal cervical tract ——————

Lateral cervical apterium ——————

Shoulder ——————————

Interscapular tract ——————

Scapular apterium ——————

Dorsopelvic tract ——————

Femoral tract ——————

Lateral pelvic apterium ——————

FIGURE 181.—Exploded view of anterior feather tracts on the dorsal side of the body of a Single Comb White Leghorn Chicken. In this picture and similar ones to follow, the feathers can be seen to grade in size, shape, and pattern from one area to another. White dots mark the location of follicles where feathers have been left off. Solid lines indicate distinct boundaries between tracts and apteria. Dashed lines indicate arbitrary boundaries between tracts or apteria (e.g., a boundary between tracts where no apterium is present). Note: See chapter 10, page 641, for procedure used in making an exploded view.

First generation (natal): down feather about 12 mm. long, identical with those everywhere else on the body; downy barbs arise from an extremely short rachis and from the rim of the superior umbilicus (fig. 185, *A*).

Second generation (juvenal): contour feather up to 37 mm. long, similar to other contour feathers on the trunk; downy only at base; pennaceous portion shows gradation outward from normal to open texture; afterfeather is one-fourth to one-third as long as main vanes (fig. 185, *B*).

Third generation (first basic): contour feather up to 84 mm. long, recognizable for this tract by size, shape, and pattern; distinct zones of pennaceous texture are evident; afterfeather is relatively shorter than previously (fig. 185, *C*).

Adult generation (definitive plumage): contour feather up to 184 mm. long; tapered for most of length; marked contrast between pennaceous zones; downy portion is relatively longer; afterfeather is relatively still shorter; sexual dimorphism evident (fig. 185, *D*).

Conspicuous changes take place between feathers of the first four generations, but subtle changes may occur between subsequent generations. Knowledgeable fishermen who tie their own trout flies try to procure hackles from roosters that are at least 2 years old. The pennaceous barbs of these feathers are more loosely knit at the proximal end than are those of younger birds. They fan out nicely when the rachis is bent, creating a desirable appearance in the fly.

Feathers of females are much shorter (length 54 to 85 mm.) and relatively more downy (28 to 45 percent) than those of males. They have a narrow marginal zone of open texture, as shown in figure 213, *15*, page 317.

FIGURE 183.—Contour feather near the midline from the posterior end of the dorsopelvic tract of a male Single Comb White Leghorn Chicken. Main feather on the *right*, afterfeather on the *left*.

Anterior end

Length: 6 to 106 mm.   Downy part: 0 to 18 percent

The feathers at the anterior end of the tract become smaller and more open-textured, with a relatively smaller afterfeather, proceeding anteriorly and laterally in the tract. The downy portion diminishes in extent and becomes less fluffy. These trends culminate in the tiny feathers behind the ear lobes and wattles. The downy portion of these feathers is represented by only a few small, simplified downy barbules at the base, close to the rachis.

These feathers are much shorter (maximum length, 27 mm.) and relatively more plumulaceous (30 to 36 percent) in females than in males. Their zones of open pennaceous texture—at the distal corners of the vanes—are larger than those found elsewhere on female feathers, yet are still smaller than those on male feathers (fig. 213, *2*).

FIGURE 182.—Contour feather from the middle of the dorsopelvic tract of a male Single Comb White Leghorn Chicken. Main feather on the *right*, afterfeather on the *left*.

Ventral Cervical Tract

Length: 50 to 90 mm.   Downy part: 12 to 23 percent

The feathers at the upper end of the ventral cervical tract resemble those at the margins of the interscapular tract. There do not seem to be any criteria for identifying individual feathers because of the variation among feathers of both tracts. Most of the pennaceous portion is closely knit, but there is a distinct zone of open texture at the tip. The downy portion is moderately fluffy, partly because barbs with branched tips are common. The afterfeather is longer on feathers of this tract than on the nearby feathers of the dorsal cervical tract.

Proceeding posteriorly, the feathers show the following changes (fig. 186):

1. Length increases.

2. Downy portion becomes larger, whereas the pennaceous portion remains about the same.

3. Zone of open pennaceous texture becomes faint or vanishes in feathers near the inner border of the tract but becomes larger in feathers near the outer border.

These feathers may be distinguished from those on the interscapular tract by the more rounded tip, the weaker contrast between the normal and the open pennaceous zones, and the smaller area of the open pennaceous zone.

Female feathers resemble those of males except near the outer border of the tract, where they do not have a wide zone of open pennaceous texture.

Pectoral Tract

Length: 100 to 125 mm.   Downy part: 35 to 55 percent

The feathers of the pectoral tract continue some of the trends seen in the ventral cervical tract. The following changes can be seen as one examines feathers posteriorly along the middle of the tract (figs. 186, 187):

1. Length increases.

2. Width increases at proximal end of pennaceous portion, so that this part becomes more broadly triangular.

3. Downy portion becomes longer and approximately equals the pennaceous portion in the most posterior feathers.

4. Pennaceous portion becomes more closely knit, through

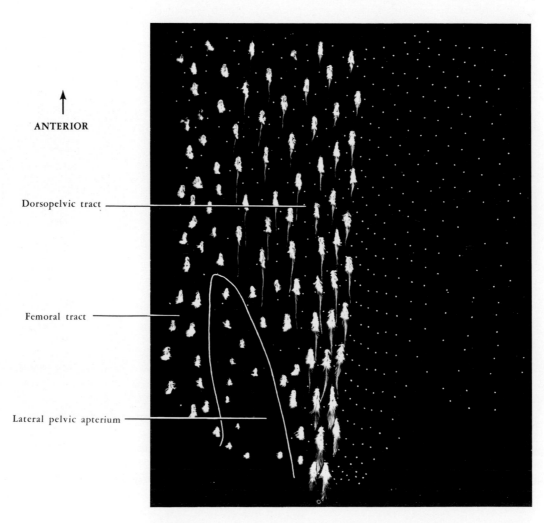

ANTERIOR

Dorsopelvic tract

Femoral tract

Lateral pelvic apterium

FIGURE 184.—Exploded view of posterior feather tracts on the dorsal side of the body of a Single Comb White Leghorn Chicken. See legend of figure 181 for note and explanation of solid line.

closer spacing of barbs, closer spacing of barbules, greater development of barbicels, and continuation of normal barbules farther out on each barb. The open and the closely knit zones are no longer sharply separated; the closely knit texture gradually becomes more open toward the border of the vanes. The margins of posterior pectoral feathers are nevertheless denser than the open zones of other feathers, because there still are simplified pennaceous barbules or stylet barbules at the tips of the rami.

The afterfeather is approximately one-third as long as the main vanes, has a relatively long aftershaft, and is densely fluffy.

The feathers become smaller from the midline of the tract to the borders, particularly on the medial side. This size gradient runs at right angles to the anteroposterior gradient; as a result, feathers from the posterior end of the tract near the margin are the same size as those from the anterior end near the midline.

Since pectoral feathers grade into ventral cervical feathers, they cannot be told apart in the middle of the combined tracts. Feathers from the posterior half of the pectoral tract can be distinguished from feathers from the anterior half of the ventral cervical tract by their larger size, longer plumulaceous portion, and denser pennaceous portion. The large posterior pectoral feathers resemble those at the very posterior end of the dorsopelvic tract, but can be recognized by their

FIGURE 185.—Changes in the size and shape of feathers from successive generations, as shown by dorsal cervical feathers from a male Single Comb White Leghorn Chicken.

A, natal down.
B, second generation (juvenal plumage).
C, third generation (first basic plumage).

D, an adult generation. Main feather on the *right*, afterfeather on the *left*. All feathers drawn to the same scale.

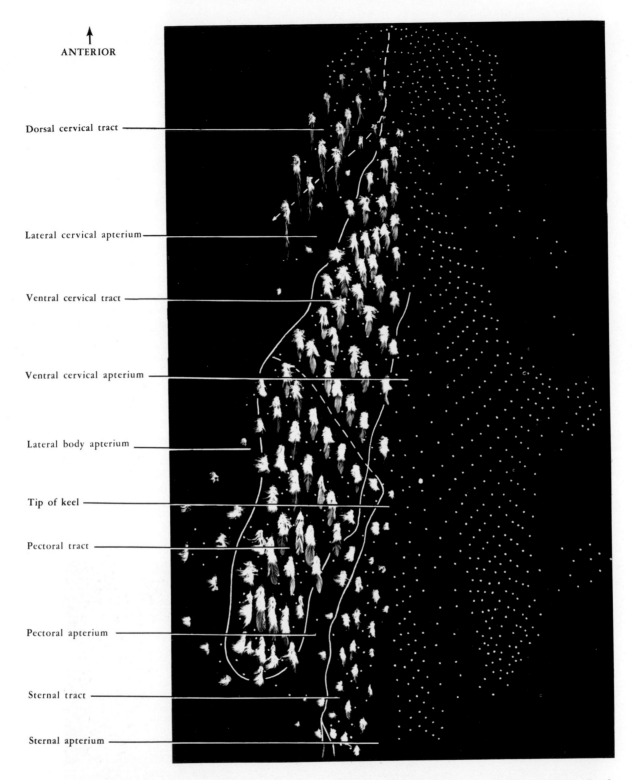

ANTERIOR

Dorsal cervical tract

Lateral cervical apterium

Ventral cervical tract

Ventral cervical apterium

Lateral body apterium

Tip of keel

Pectoral tract

Pectoral apterium

Sternal tract

Sternal apterium

FIGURE 186.—Exploded view of anterior feather tracts on the ventral side of the body of a Single Comb White Leghorn Chicken. See legend of figure 181 for note and explanation of solid and dashed lines.

blunter tip; smaller, less contrasting zone of open pennaceous texture; and relatively larger afterfeather.

The pectoral feathers of females are 75 to 105 mm. long, and are downy for 36 to 75 percent of their length. The pennaceous portion is more rectangular than that on male

feathers. Figure 213, *13*, shows a contour feather from the anterior end of the pectoral tract, and figure 213, *8*, shows that an equivalent feather from the posterior end is nearly a semiplume.

Semiplumes are present and similar on both margins of

FIGURE 187.—Contour feather from the pectoral tract of a male Single Comb White Leghorn Chicken. Main feather on the *right*, afterfeather on the *left*.

the tract, but they are more numerous along the medial margin. They are very fluffy and nearly circular, with an afterfeather which is absolutely and relatively larger than that on the contour feathers (fig. 188). There is a little or no gradation in structure between semiplumes and contour feathers; some semiplumes are situated beside contour feathers with a large pennaceous portion of vane. The barbs of the semiplumes are longer than the downy barbs of adjacent contour feathers. The structure of semiplumes is discussed further on pages 310–313.

Sternal Tract

Length: 50 to 75 mm.   Downy part: 40 to 100 percent

The sternal tract is covered with contour feathers and semiplumes, as well as down feathers along the margins. The contour feathers display less contrast between downy and pennaceous portions than most other feathers (fig. 189). The downy portion is not very fluffy, owing to the shortness of the barbs, but the barbules are like those found elsewhere. The pennaceous portion is unusually soft and lax (loosely knit), and the closely knit texture grades outward into more open texture. The afterfeather is relatively large; in some feathers it is slightly more than half as long as the main vanes.

The contour feathers show the following trends from the anterior to the posterior end of the tract (fig. 190):
1. Length diminishes slightly.
2. Pennaceous portion becomes shorter and looser.
3. Tip becomes more broadly rounded.

A few semiplumes are sometimes present on the lateral margins of the anterior half of the tract. At about the mid-

FIGURE 188.—Semiplume from the pectoral tract of a male Single Comb White Leghorn Chicken. Main feather on the *right*, afterfeather on the *left*.

FIGURE 189.—Contour feather from the sternal tract of a male Single Comb White Leghorn Chicken. Main feather on the *right*, afterfeather on the *left*.

point of the tract, all the contour feathers grade into semiplumes, which become larger toward the posterior end of the tract. The semiplumes are narrow and densely downy at the base and broader and looser near the tip. The barbs in the middle of the vanes are branched, whereas those above them have progressively smaller, simpler barbules and bare rami at their tips.

Contour feathers from the sternal tract can be recognized by their narrow but relatively long downy portion, lax pennaceous portion, rounded tip, and relatively large afterfeather. The semiplumes, however, do not seem to be distinguishable from those on other tracts.

Feathers at the anterior end of the sternal tract are sometimes as large in females as they are in males. The posterior feathers, however, are a little shorter and less dense in females than in males.

Abdominal Tract

Length: 60 to 90 mm.   Downy part: 45 to 100 percent

The abdominal tract is covered with semiplumes that continue the trends seen in the posterior part of the sternal tract (fig. 190). They are narrow and densely fluffy at the proximal portion of the vanes, except in the zones of curled-base barbules beside the rachis. The vanes are lax and lightly fluffy from their widest point to the tip, because of progressively wider spacing between the rami and the reduction in size of barbules. The tip is broadly rounded, as in sternal feathers (fig. 204). The afterfeather is sometimes as much as two-thirds as long as the main feather, in which case it is among the largest to be found anywhere on a chicken in relative, and sometimes even in absolute, terms.

These feathers become larger toward the posterior end of the tract but then become markedly smaller in the last four

or five rows. In these last feathers, just anterior to the vent, the vanes have mostly a loose, lightly downy texture; dense downy texture becomes confined to a very small area around the proximal end of the rachis.

Abdominal feathers are distinguishable from some other semiplumes by their size, shape, contrast between zones, and large afterfeather.

The abdominal feathers of females are about 42 to 65 mm. long (fig. 213, *4*). They are downy for 45 percent or more of the length of their vanes, as in males, but the basal portion is less dense.

Femoral Tract

Anterior border, dorsal corner

Length: 40 to 60 mm.   Downy part: 100 percent

The feathers at the anterosuperior angle of the femoral tract are semiplumes of uniform texture. They become smaller toward the knee region, and, with shortening of the rachis, grade into down feathers (fig. 191). Posteriorly, the feathers become larger, mostly by addition of a loosely knit pennaceous portion to the vanes. The distal plumulaceous barbs become longer, and the new segment is covered with small, simplified plumulaceous barbules. The vanes thus begin to show two zones of texture like the semiplumes of the abdominal tract. Within one or two rows, the new terminal zone becomes flatter and definitely pennaceous by the addition of barbs and the conversion of the barbules. Female feathers resemble male feathers (fig. 213, *5*).

Posterior border

Length: 85 to 135 mm.   Downy part: 58 to 100 percent

The contour feathers and semiplumes in the posterior border are the largest feathers in the femoral tract and are among the largest on the body (fig. 192). Their downy portions are very fluffy, because of the great length of the barbs (at least 45 mm. in some cases) and because of the presence of downy barbs with branched tips. The pennaceous portion of the posterior contour feathers is larger and more closely knit than in feathers from the center of the tract. The tip is slightly pointed, and it is marked with a crescent-shaped band of open pennaceous texture, up to 3 mm. wide. The afterfeather is one-fourth to one-third as long as the main vanes on the contour feathers, but a little longer in the semiplumes.

The largest contour feathers and semiplumes are in the middle region of the posterior border of the tract. The two types appear to alternate because the rows of semiplumes are close behind the rows of contour feathers. Proceeding dorsally and posteriorly, the feathers become smaller and revert to the semiplumaceous structure. Anteriorly and ventrally, there is a reduction in size and fluffiness, and the pennaceous portion reverts to the looser-knit texture seen in feathers in the center of the tract.

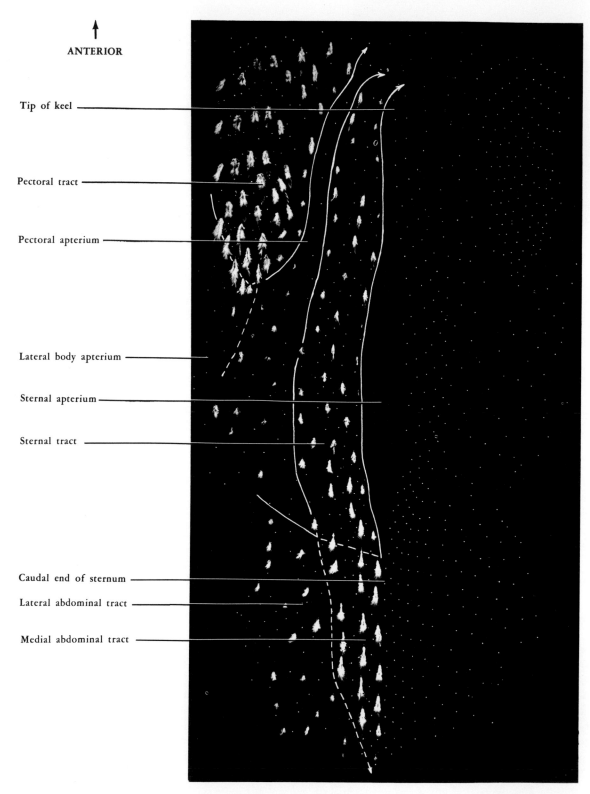

ANTERIOR

Tip of keel

Pectoral tract

Pectoral apterium

Lateral body apterium

Sternal apterium

Sternal tract

Caudal end of sternum

Lateral abdominal tract

Medial abdominal tract

FIGURE 190.—Exploded view of posterior feather tracts on the ventral side of the body of a Single Comb White Leghorn Chicken. Solid lines are distinct boundaries between tracts and apteria; dashed lines are arbitrary boundaries between tracts or apteria (e.g., a boundary between tracts where no apterium is present). See note in legend of figure 181.

Contour feathers of the femoral tract resemble most those of the pectoral and interscapular tracts. They can be recognized, however, by the relatively long downy portion of the vanes and the relatively shorter afterfeather They further differ from interscapular feathers in the shape of the tip and the smaller zone of open, pennaceous texture. These feathers can be located within a few rows because of the anteroposterior gradients in total size and character of the pennaceous portion. The largest contour feathers are the easiest and surest to locate because they have the most restricted distribution.

These feathers are about 86 to 110 mm. long in females and are downy for at least half their length. The pennaceous portion is relatively narrower and more rectangular than in males and has a more truncate tip (fig. 213, 9).

The semiplumes along the posterior border of this tract closely resemble those on the posterior lateral margin of the pectoral tract. They can be distinguished from other semi-

plumes by their dense fluffiness at the proximal end and their large size. Semiplumes from elsewhere on the thigh, being smaller, do not seem to be specifically identifiable.

Crural Tract

Upper end

Length: 48 to 62 mm.   Downy part: 40 to 100 percent

The upper end of the crural tract is covered with semiplumes except for contour feathers on the anterior region of the lateral surface (figs. 193, 194). Most of the feathers resemble those in the central and anterior portions of the femoral tract. In the proximal portion of each feather, the rachis tends to be hidden by the downy barbs, and there are no zones of curled-base barbules. The distal portion is loosely knit and broadly rounded, showing the same transition between the conditions in contour feathers and semiplumes as in the femoral tract. None of the feathers seem to be

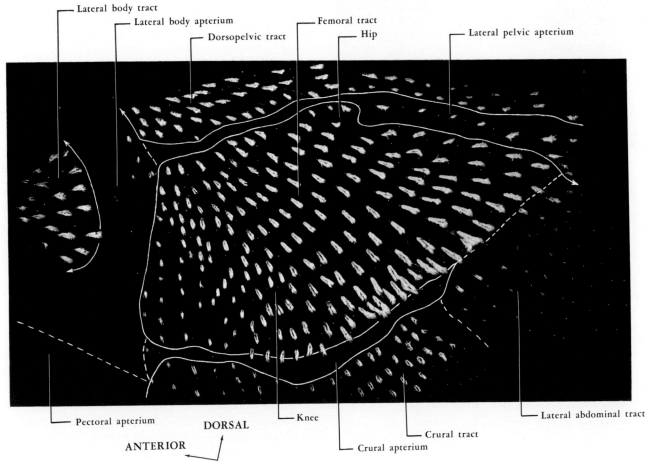

FIGURE 191.—Exploded view of feather tracts on the left thigh of a Single Comb White Leghorn Chicken. See legend of figure 190 for explanation of solid and dashed lines; see note in legend of figure 181.

FIGURE 192.—Contour feather from the posteroventral portion of the femoral tract of a male Single Comb White Leghorn Chicken. Main feather on the *right*, afterfeather on the *left*.

distinctive except for the semiplumes in the anterior portion of the medial surface, which are especially large and fluffy. Their texture is created by barbs that bear small, simplified downy barbules for much of their length.

These feathers in females are about three-fourths of the size of those in males. More of the feathers on the posterior surface of the leg are of the contour type, and the pennaceous portion is more closely knit. Feathers from the lateral surface have a wide band of lax texture outside the closely knit pennaceous portion (fig. 213, *7*).

Lower end

Length: 8 to 27 mm.   Downy part: 16 to 33 percent

Proceeding distally along the leg on all surfaces, the feathers at the distal end of the crural tract show the following trends (figs. 193, 194):

1. Total length remains about the same or decreases slightly down to a level close above the ankle, where it decreases rapidly.

2. Contour feathers prevail on the anterior half of the leg, on both lateral and medial sides. Semiplumes prevail on the posterior half.

3. Downy portion of vanes becomes smaller and less fluffy.

4. Pennaceous portions of vanes become relatively larger and more closely knit, until shortly above the ankle, where they become looser.

These trends culminate in the tiny feathers on the ankle. Those on the lateral anterior surface are still contour feathers, whereas the others are semiplumes. Ankle feathers emerge either between the scales or through individual scales at or near the posterior margin.

The contour feathers from the lower end of the crural tracts are actually the only ones that may be identifiable. The combination of small size, flatness of the downy portion, relatively large pennaceous portion, and rounded tip should distinguish them from other feathers.

Humeral Tract

Length: 37 to 110 mm.   Downy part: 20 to 44 percent

The feathers of the humeral tract proper are those on the dorsal side of the shoulder (fig. 195); they are known as shoulder feathers in poultry terminology and as scapulars in ornithological terminology. The feathers of the posthumeral and subhumeral tracts are associated with them in arrangement but are discussed in conjunction with the feathers of the dorsal and ventral alar tracts, which they resemble.

The feathers of the humeral tract are all contour feathers in which the pennaceous portion has distinct zones of closely knit and of open texture (fig. 196). The line of demarcation between the zones starts at the margin, at a variable distance beyond the bottom of the pennaceous portion, and curves concavely toward the rachis. The edges of the vanes converge slightly, and the tip is bluntly rounded. The afterfeather is one-third to one-fourth as long as the main vanes.

Proceeding backward from the anterior end of the tract, the feathers show the following trends (fig. 195):

1. Total length increases.

2. Length of calamus increases.

3. Downy portion becomes relatively (and absolutely) longer.

4. Open pennaceous zone becomes larger.

5. Afterfeather becomes slightly smaller in relation to main vanes.

Humeral feathers resemble feathers near the junction of the interscapular and dorsal tracts and certain marginal coverts on the upper side of the wing. They can usually be separated from the interscapular and dorsal feathers by the length of the calamus, a distance of 5 to 9 mm. in the humeral feathers and 3 to 5 mm. in the others. As compared with the marginal coverts on the forearm, the humerals are mostly larger. Taking feathers of equal size from the humeral tract and the forearm, the former has larger zones of downy and of closely knit pennaceous texture and tends to have a blunter tip.

Comparison of figures 196 and 213, *12*, shows that female

feathers are relatively narrower and more plumulaceous, have a blunt tip, and have little or no margin of open pennaceous texture.

Alar Tracts

Primary remiges

The primary remiges of a Single Comb White Leghorn Chicken have the typical features of these feathers in other birds, namely, calamus, large size, long, entirely pennaceous

vanes, asymmetry and curvature of vanes, pointed tip, and absence of an aftershaft. Figure 195 and table 15 show that the longest primaries are those in the middle of the row. They confirm the observation that the wing tip is broadly rounded. The length of the calamus varies even more than total length, since it is more than twice as great in primaries 2, 3, and 4 as in 10. The calamus is longest in the proximal feathers, except for the first primary. The calamus is not perfectly circular in cross section but slightly compressed on the sides. It bends upward a little at the basal end, particularly

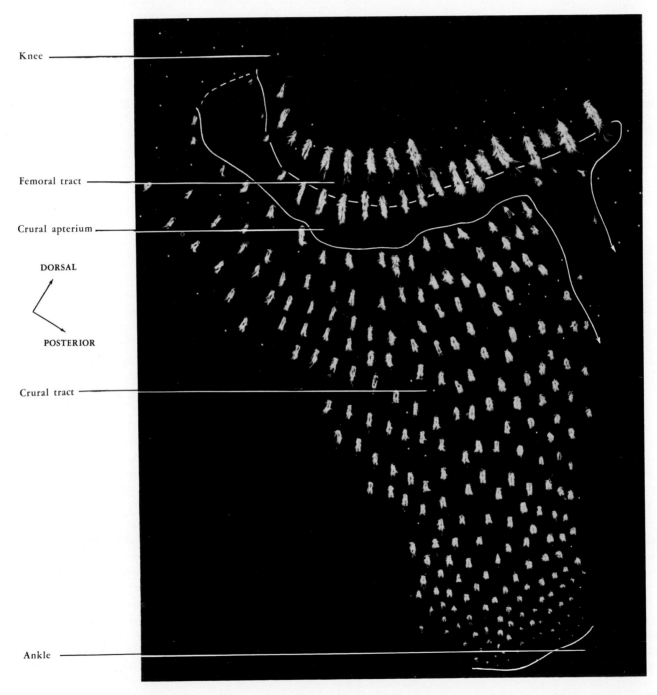

FIGURE 193.—Exploded view of feather tracts on the lateral surface of the left leg of a Single Comb White Leghorn Chicken. See legend for figure 190 for explanation of solid and dashed lines; see note in legend for figure 181.

TABLE 15.—*Length of primary remiges of Single Comb White Leghorn Chickens*[1]

Primary (No.)	Male		Female	
	Total length	Length of calamus	Total length	Length of calamus
	Millimeters	*Millimeters*	*Millimeters*	*Millimeters*
1..........	218	35	203	39
2..........	227	42	201	35
3..........	238	43	195	32
4..........	230	40	190	29
5..........	224	39	179	25
6..........	235	35	201	35
7..........	219	34	195	32
8..........	221	31	190	29
9..........	219	27	179	25
10..........	180	20	156	19

[1] Measurements are based on feathers of one male and one female, both more than 1 year old. They show the general range of size, variation in length within the series, and size difference between the sexes.

in the inner primaries. The calamus may contain 20 or more pulp caps; these are hard to count just above the inferior umbilicus, where they are very close together. The rim of the superior umbilicus traces a parabolic curve; its low point lies on the midventral line of the 10th primary but slightly on the inner-vane side of the shaft in the more proximal remiges. A short distance below the superior umbilicus, two thickenings of pith on the sides of the calamus form the lower end of the rachis. They become joined completely except on the ventral side, where a broad, V-shaped groove runs for about half the total length. Several cortical ridges inside the rachis are visible as lines on the dorsal surface.

Rows of short umbilical barbs curve distally and dorsally around the shaft, from the superior umbilicus to the vanes. These barbs are not very downy, except on the inner side of the first primary, where they are pennaceous. The lowermost barbs on the outer side of the shaft are also downy for a distance of 16 mm. on the first primary and progressively less downy on outer remiges (fig. 197, *A*).

The barbs and their barbules increase in size from the umbilicus to the vanes, and the bases of the rami become enlarged dorsoventrally. On the lowest barbs of the outer vane, the barbules near the rachis are of the simplified pennaceous type and are weakly differentiated on opposite sides of the rami. Similar barbules are shown in figure 198, *F*. The barbules farther along a ramus are of the plumulaceous type and are the same on both sides, like those in figure 198, *G*. In the next higher barbs, the pennaceous barbules become more strongly differentiated and are continued farther to the tip of the ramus. On the inner vane, we find that the lowest barbs already have well-developed pennaceous barbules for most of their length, but that the terminal barbules are smaller and simpler in structure. The margin of a short

proximal portion of the inner vane is hence loosely fringed, though not actually fluffy.

The exposed portion of each feather is curved downward and toward the inner vane. Lateral curvature is more pronounced than ventral curvature, particularly in the outer primaries. The outer vane slopes downward slightly from the rachis to the margin; the inner vane slopes downward and then curls upward near the margin at the proximal end. This transverse curvature diminishes distally, and the distal half of the outer vane is nearly flat. The maximum width of both vanes becomes smaller from primary 1 to primary 10. In addition, the outer vane is faintly emarginate on primaries 4 through 8, the notch being produced by a reduction in the angle of the barbs, not their length (fig. 197, *A*). On a specimen of primary 6, for example, proceeding from below the notch to above it, the angle of the barbs was found to diminish from 36° to 8°, whereas the length of the barbs actually increased from 17.3 mm. to 32.2 mm.

The vanes are composed of closely knit pennaceous barbs except at the bottom, as described above. Rami of the outer vane have a distinct ventral notch just beyond their attachment to the rachis, whereas those of the inner vane have a shallow notch. The junction is not braced by ribs on the rachis or outgrowths of the ramus, as found in certain birds. Sometimes, a primary remex displays a long, narrow zone of differing reflectiveness on the underside of the inner vane close to the shaft. The feather does not have the glazed sheen found in homologous duck feathers but is actually less shiny and transparent than the rest of the surface. The effect is caused by the presence of loose pieces of film between the rami. These are composed of cortical material and are apparently sloughed off the distal surface of each ramus. There is no expanded ventral ridge (tegmen) as in ducks, and the optical effect disappears when the debris is cleaned away.

The pennaceous barbules of the primaries are among the largest and most highly differentiated to be found on any feathers of a chicken. They do not show any unusual features, and hence can be identified only by careful attention to the size and shape of the ordinary parts.

Proximal barbules.—These barbules from the middle of the inner vane are about 0.52 mm. long at the base of the barb, 0.71 mm. at the middle, and 0.49 mm. near the tip. Similar barbules are shown in figure 198, *C* and *D*. As shown in figure 169, page 246, a barbule near the basal end has a rectangular base about eight times longer than it is wide. This is composed of about nine cells, the boundaries and nuclei of which can be seen by their differential reaction to staining or differential refraction of transmitted light. The last four or five cells produce pennant-shaped ventral teeth. Above them, beyond the dorsal flange, are five to seven dorsal spines, in each of which the proximal edge is nearly vertical and the distal edge slopes upward to the base of the next spine. The pennulum consists of a few slender cells that bear one or two tiny nodal prongs. It is shorter than the base, but the true length is hard to determine because cells often appear to to have broken off at the tip.

Distal barbules.—These barbules from the middle of the

inner vane measure about 0.27 mm. long at the base of a barb, 0.40 mm. at the middle, and 0.33 mm. near the tip. Similar barbules are shown in figure 198, *C* and *D*. A barbule near the basal end has a base about two-thirds as large as that of a proximal barbule. The cells are the same size as those of the proximal barbule, but they tend to be fewer. On the barbule are one or two small, pennant-shaped ventral teeth and one large tooth, which widens from base to midpoint and then tapers. The pennulum is about as long as the base and bears a large complement of barbicels. On the side

of the ventral teeth facing the shaft are about six hooklets increasing in length distally. Beyond them are six or seven cells with dorsal and ventral cilia, the last of which are hardly more than nodal prongs.

On barbs of the inner vane, the pennaceous barbules maintain their structure approximately as far as the terminal one-fourth or one-fifth of the vane. The last 25 to 35 barbules become shorter and their barbicels become fewer, smaller, and more uniform. The proximal barbules lose their dorsal spines, and the base grades into the pennulum. Distal bar-

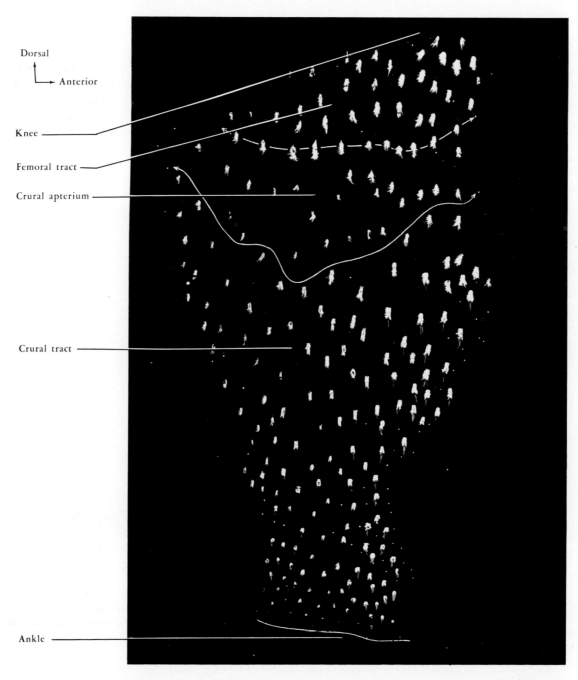

FIGURE 194.—Exploded view of feather tracts on the medial surface of the left leg of a Single Comb White Leghorn Chicken. See legend for figure 191 for explanation of solid and dashed lines; see note in legend for figure 181.

bules never develop enlarged dorsal spines in the primary remiges of chickens, and hence do not become friction barbules, as found in some birds. Similar barbules are shown in figure 198, *A* and *B*.

Barbs from the middle of the outer vane of a primary remex are about half as long as those from the inner vane, but their barbules are similar. Reduction of the barbules starts midway along the ramus, and both proximal and distal subtypes become transformed into the same structure. These terminal barbules consist of a stalk of 6 to 10 nearly uniform cells, each of which bears a curved or weakly hooked ventral cilium. They appear to be modified in such a way as to keep the outer margin of the feather from fraying.

At the tip of a primary, the barbs become shorter, the very last ones are less than 1 mm. long. The barbules of both vanes are alike, and they are smaller than those in the middle of the vanes. Near the end of the barbs they become irregularly formed as well as smaller and simpler.

The pennaceous barbules of remiges are excellent for identifying feathers on the basis of microstructure. Their large size and fully formed parts are assets that are offset, however, by variation among barbules even within a vane, as we have just seen. When comparing the barbules of different birds, therefore, it is important that they be selected from the same place on all the feathers.

The primary remiges can be distinguished from the secondaries and the rectrices by the asymmetry and curvature of their vanes and by the pointed tip. Isolated feathers can be identified within two follicles by variations in these same features, in degree of emargination, and in length.

Secondary remiges

The secondary remiges resemble the primaries in many respects, so our description will focus on their distinctive features. Those on the ulna are large and stiff whereas those on the elbow and upper arm are markedly smaller, more flexible, and more like body contour feathers (fig. 195). The first secondary differs from the first primary in its smaller

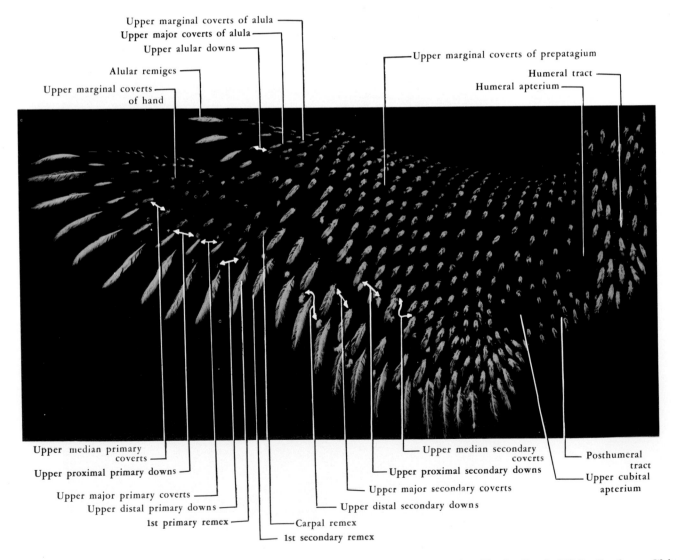

FIGURE 195.—Exploded view of feather tracts on the dorsal side of the left wing of a Single Comb White Leghorn Chicken.

Note: See chapter 10, page 641, for procedure used in making an exploded view.

size, less pointed tip, and slightly greater symmetry. Proceeding toward the elbow, the secondaries vary in size, as shown by the measurements in table 16. They also become symmetrical as the vanes become equally wide and the shaft straightens. The tip becomes rounded in secondaries 2 through 14, but in the last two to four remiges (depending on the number of inner secondaries) it again becomes somewhat pointed.

The secondaries are more downy at the base than the primaries. In the outer vanes, the downy barbs are longer and more numerous in the secondaries than in the primaries. The inner vane is downy along the margin of secondary 1, in a zone that becomes wider in remiges closer to the elbow. Proximally in the row of secondaries, as the proximal end of the inner vane becomes more downy, it comes to resemble the outer vane, particularly in secondaries 10 to 18. The symmetrical downy bases of the innermost five secondaries give these remiges the appearance of body contour feathers.

The afterfeather is a tuft of umbilical barbs, which are longer and fluffier than those on the primaries; they point distally instead of laterally, as do the lowest barbs of the vanes.

The pennaceous portion of the vanes is flatter in the secondaries than in the primaries, and there is less difference in the length and angle of the barbs between the vanes. Although the vanes appear to be homogeneous (except in the downy portion), the barbules vary in structure, as shown in figure 198. Secondaries 15 to 18 have a narrow band of open

FIGURE 196.—Contour feather from the middle of the humeral tract of a male Single Comb White Leghorn Chicken. Main feather on the *right*, afterfeather on the *left*.

pennaceous texture at the tip, an additional point of resemblance to body contour feathers.

The secondaries on the forearm can be distinguished from the primaries by the greater symmetry of their vanes, downier base, and rounded tip. These secondaries closely resemble rectrices 2 to 8, but can be identified by their longer calamus and less symmetrical downy portion. The secondaries on the upper arm can be distinguished from body contour feathers by the presence of an aftertuft instead of an aftershaft. It is not possible to distinguish them from nearby upper secondary coverts that have a very small aftershaft.

Secondary remiges are 15 to 30 mm. shorter in females than in males.

Alular remiges

The alular remiges resemble the 10th primary remex but are much smaller (fig. 195). If we compare the following measurements with those for males in table 15, we see that the alular remiges range from about one-third to two-thirds as large as the 10th primary.

Feather No.	Total length in millimeters	Length of calamus in millimeters
1	130	16
2	110	16
3	77	13
4	60	10

In the outermost alular remex (No. 1), the outer vane starts 3 to 4 mm. lower on the shaft than the inner vane.

TABLE 16.—*Length of secondary remiges of Single Comb White Leghorn Chickens*[1]

Secondaries (No.)	Total length	Length of calamus
	Millimeters	*Millimeters*
1	172	28
2	203	34
3	221	34
4	217	34
5	216	33
6	213	31
7	200	31
8	197	29
9	194	28
10	190	27
11	184	24
12	180	24
13	162	22
14	148	19
15	129	16
16	110	12
17	93	10
18	76	6

[1] Measurements are based on feathers of one male at least 1 year old. They show the general range of size and the variation in length within the series.

TABLE 17.—*Length of upper major primary coverts of Single Comb White Leghorn Chickens*[1]

Covert (No.)	Total length	Length of calamus
	Millimeters	*Millimeters*
1...................	72	25
2...................	74	24
3...................	79	25
4...................	79	25
5...................	80	25
6...................	83	24
7...................	79	22
8...................	77	21
9...................	70	18
10..................	42	12

[1] Measurements are based on feathers of one male, at least 1 year old.

The outer margin is curled downward so that the feather conforms to the leading edge of the wing. Both features are present to a lesser degree in the second alular remex. These feathers in a female had lengths of 114 mm., 101 mm., and 78 mm.; the fourth alular remex could not be measured.

Upper major primary coverts

The remarkable feature of the upper major primary coverts is their relatively long calamus, which accounts for 35 percent of the total length (table 17). It does not show in figure 195 because it had to be cut off. Except for the outermost covert, which is extremely narrow, the vanes are approximately as wide, in relation to length, as those of the remiges below them. The proximal portions of both vanes are lightly downy for a variable distance along the margin. In contrast to the remiges, this texture is more extensive on the inner vane than on the outer. The vanes are most pennaceous, however, and they curve downward toward the edges, particularly in the outer coverts. The afterfeather is a dense tuft of umbilical barbs. The main feathers can be easily recognized by their size, their resemblance to remiges, and their long calamus.

Upper minor primary coverts, upper marginal coverts of the hand

Length: 20 to 45 mm.

The upper minor primary coverts are smaller than the upper major primary coverts, have a relatively shorter calamus, are more downy at the base, and are flatter and more symmetrical in the pennaceous portion. Proximally, the margins of the vanes are fluffy for 4 to 30 percent of their length, but the inner portion is not downy at all. The marginal coverts are shorter than the upper minor primary coverts, and at the proximal part of the rows they are also rounder. Proceeding distally on the wing tip, these feathers become smaller, less downy, and more pointed. Along the leading edge of the hand, these trends culminate in the marginal coverts, which are very small, narrowly pointed feathers.

These coverts can be separated from most other coverts on the dorsal and ventral sides of the wing by their narrow shape, small portion of downy vane, and lack of open pennaceous texture (as found in many upper marginal coverts on the forearm). The upper minor primary coverts, however, are almost identical with the upper major alular coverts. The upper marginal coverts of the hand likewise match the upper marginal coverts of the alula and the marginal coverts along the leading edge of the prepatagium. In view of these similarities, it hardly matters that the upper minor primary coverts can be distinguished from the upper marginal coverts of the hand by their larger size.

Carpal remex

Total length: 60 mm.   Length of calamus: 10 mm.
Downy part: 84 percent

The carpal remex is distinguished by its extensive lightly downy texture—over the entire proximal third and along the outer halves of both vanes nearly to the tip. The remainder of the vanes is pennaceous. The calamus is relatively long for such a downy feather. There is a small aftershaft with barbs.

The upper carpal remex covert is very similar to the nearby marginal coverts of the hand.

Upper major secondary coverts

The upper major secondary coverts are in many ways small versions of the secondary remiges below them, just as the upper major primary coverts resemble the primaries (fig. 195). Measurements of total length, length of calamus, and percentage of downy parts to total length of feather are given in table 18. The 12 coverts of this series on the forearm can be readily identified by their size, short downy portion, moderately broad vanes with rounded tip, and afterfeather of umbilical barbs. The six remaining coverts, on the upper arm, are smaller and have an afterfeather with an aftershaft. Coverts 14 through 18 and sometimes 13 have a zone of open pennaceous texture up to 8 mm. wide at the tip. These

$\rightarrow$

FIGURE 197.—Wing and tail contour feathers. These lack afterfeathers.

A, primary remex 4 from a male Single Comb White Leghorn Chicken.

B, rectrix 1 from a male Single Comb White Leghorn Chicken. This feather is shown at a smaller scale than the others in this series.

feathers resemble certain of the more proximal upper median and minor secondary coverts.

The shaft is bent from side to side along its length, and this curvature changes through the series of coverts. In the outermost covert (No. 1), the shaft bends concavely (away from the wing tip) at the base of the rachis, and than convexly (toward the tip) about the middle of the rachis. The rachis is straighter in the next seven or eight feathers, but it retains a slight concave bend at the base. In the remaining coverts, the entire shaft is weakly curved concavely. The curvature of the shaft helps to distinguish the innermost major coverts from more anterior coverts, which have straighter shafts. Variations in curvature make it possible to place the location of the major coverts on the ulna within four follicles.

Upper median secondary coverts

Length: 75 to 95 mm.   Downy part: 22 to 31 percent

The trend of reduction in overall size continues from the major to the median row of coverts (fig. 195). In addition, the median coverts have a relatively larger downy portion and more rounded edges on the pennaceous portion. The three innermost feathers of the series have a zone of open

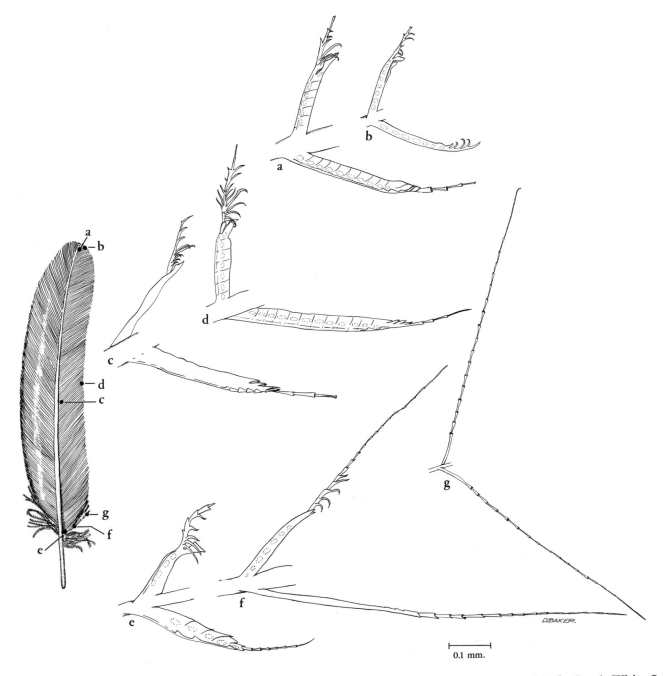

0.1 mm.

FIGURE 198.—Variation in the form of barbules on the inner vane of a secondary remex from a Single Comb White Leghorn Chicken. The lettered dots on the drawing of the whole feather indicate the locations of the drawings of the barbules.

TABLE 18.—*Length of upper major secondary coverts of the Single Comb White Leghorn Chicken*[1]

Feather (No.)	Total length	Length of calamus	Downy part
	Millimeter	*Millimeter*	*Percent*
1.........................	118	18	21
2.........................	120	20	20
3.........................	120	20	22
4.........................	121	20	20
5.........................	121	21	21
6.........................	117	19	21
7.........................	117	18	20
8.........................	114	17	21
9.........................	110	17	22
10.........................	109	17	24
11.........................	107	16	22
12.........................	105	14	24
13.........................	93	12	27
14.........................	86	11	31
15.........................	88	11	30
16.........................	71	7	37

[1] Measurements are based on feathers of one male, at least 1 year old. Coverts 17 and 18 were not found on this bird.

pennaceous texture at the tip. The afterfeather is a cluster of umbilical barbs in the outermost feathers, but proximally along the row it is transformed into a small aftershaft with barbs.

These feathers can be distinguished from the innermost major coverts by their straighter shafts. They can be distinguished from similar body feathers (such as those on the pectoral tract) by the relatively shorter downy part, closer knit pennaceous texture, and much smaller aftefeather. The innermost median coverts do not seem to be distinguishable from many marginal coverts on the forearm and humerals and posthumerals on the upper arm.

Upper minor secondary coverts, upper marginal coverts of the prepatagium

Length: 16 to 75 mm.   Downy part: 4 to 35 percent

The upper minor secondary coverts are identical with the marginal coverts just ahead of them in Single Comb White Leghorn Chickens, though in most birds they differ in size or color. These are typical body contour feathers, without any traces of the structure of remiges as still seen in the upper median secondary coverts (figs. 195, 199). The vanes are widest at the region of transition from downy to pennaceous texture, and they taper to a bluntly pointed tip. Zones of normal and of open pennaceous texture are clearly defined; the line of demarcation curves concavely (toward the rachis) and the open zone is as much as 12 mm. wide at the tip. There is an afterfeather of the aftershaft type.

Proceeding anteriorly across the wing, the marginal coverts show the following trends:

1. Total length is reduced. The feathers along the leading edge of the prepatagium are among the smallest contour feathers on the body.

2. The downy portion first becomes relatively longer because its actual length remains the same while the length of the pennaceous portion decreases. After a few rows the downy portion becomes relatively (as well as actually) shorter. The most anterior feathers are largely pennaceous.

3. Shape becomes triangular. Feathers also become asymmetrical, each one curving toward the leading edge of the wrist.

4. The zone of open pennaceous texture enlarges, particularly in coverts over the elbow, and then diminishes. This zone disappears within three to five rows of the edge of the prepatagium.

5. The aftershaft first becomes a little larger in relation to feather length but then diminishes.

The coverts at the proximal end of the tract, lateral and anterior to the humeral apterium, show different trends. They become small but rounded, and the pennaceous portion is loosely knit. They are transformed into semiplumes or downs along the edge of the apterium.

The upper minor coverts and posteriorly placed marginal coverts can be distinguished from dorsal and interscapular feathers by their smaller size, shorter downy portion, and smaller aftershaft. They differ from ventral cervical feathers in having a large, distinct zone of open pennaceous texture. They cannot, however, be separated with certainty from feathers of the humeral tract (see p. 290). Most of the remaining marginal coverts can be distinguished from most other feathers by their small size, triangular shape, and predominantly closely knit pennaceous texture. The loosely knit pennaceous feathers and semiplumes, however, are identical with feathers on the sternal, femoral, and crural tracts. At the other extreme, the narrowly triangular feathers

FIGURE 199.—Upper marginal covert on the prepatagium of a male Single Comb White Leghorn Chicken. Main feather on the *right*, afterfeather on the *left*.

on the leading edge of the prepatagium match the marginal coverts on the hand and the alula.

These feathers in females are narrower in the middle and, hence, less triangular near the tip; they have only a narrow band of open pennaceous texture.

Upper alular coverts

Length: 21 to 47 mm.

The upper alular coverts are narrow feathers that taper along nearly straight sides from the base to a pointed tip (fig. 195). Their vanes have a closely knit pennaceous texture except for small zones of downy texture at the margins of the base. The feathers curve downward along their long axis toward the edges of the vanes and conform to the contour of the alula. There is no afterfeather except for a few short

umbilical barbs. Upper alular coverts can be identified as upper coverts on the wing by their size and shape. They cannot be separated, however, from the marginal coverts along the leading edge of the hand or the prepatagium.

Posthumeral tract

Length: 33 to 69 mm.   Downy part: 33 to 41 percent

Although the posthumeral tract is classified with the humeral and subhumeral tracts, its feathers are more like the innermost upper median secondary coverts and the marginal coverts anterior to them (fig. 195). They are contour feathers with a varying proportion of normal and open pennaceous zones. There is a small afterfeather with an aftershaft. The posthumerals grade anteriorly into the marginal coverts beside the humeral apterium as the pennaceous

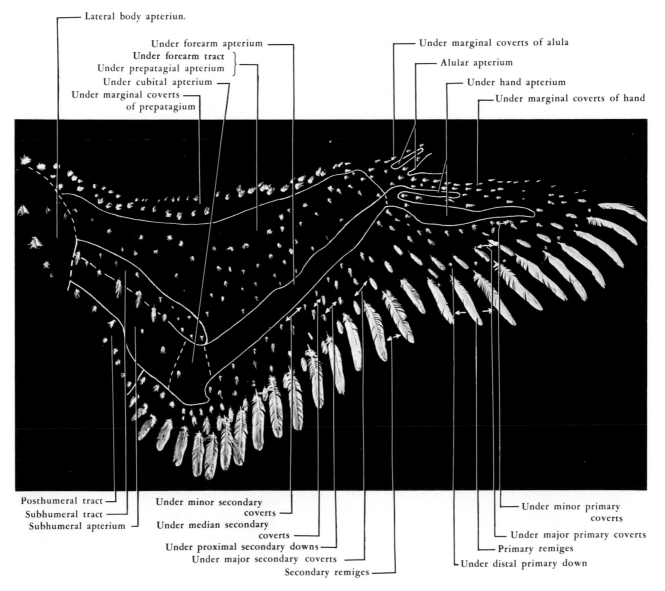

FIGURE 200.—Exploded view of feather tracts on the ventral side of the left wing of a Single Comb White Leghorn Chicken. The under forearm tract and the under prepatagial apterium are not separable by this method of study (cf. fig. 71). See legend for figure 190 for explanation of solid and dashed lines; see note in legend for figure 181.

portion of the vanes becomes smaller and more loosely knit. It is not possible to distinguish between the posthumerals and the nearby secondary or marginal coverts.

Under major primary coverts, under carpal remex covert, under major secondary coverts

Total length: 32 to 70 mm.   Length of calamus: 5 to 9 mm.

Unlike the upper major coverts, the under major primary and secondary coverts and under carpal remex covert are similar throughout the series. Their orientation is unique in that the underside of each feather (the side with the after-feather and the groove on the rachis) faces away from the skin. The under carpal covert is approximately rectangular with a bluntly rounded tip. The bottom of its vanes is entirely downy, but a little higher this texture becomes progressively confined to the margins and vanishes at about one-third the length of the vanes. The rest of this feather has a closely knit pennaceous texture. There is a small aftertuft.

Proceeding from the under carpal covert outward on the wing tip, the under major primary coverts increase in length to about 72 mm. in coverts 2 to 5 and decrease to 35 mm. in covert 10 (fig. 200). They become ovoid and asymmetrical as the rachis curves toward the outer vane.

In the opposite direction along the forearm, the under major secondary coverts maintain virtually constant size throughout the row. Downy texture extends farther distally along the margins, and even the tip becomes fuzzy, if not actually downy.

All of these coverts generally resemble the upper primary coverts and certain marginal coverts on the dorsal side of the wrist. However, they can be distinguished from the upper major primary coverts by the shorter calamus. The under major primary coverts can be distinguished from the upper minor primary coverts and the marginals of the wrist by their shape and asymmetry. There do not seem to be good characters, however, for separating the under major secondary coverts and the under covert for the carpal remex from the upper minor primary coverts and nearby marginals.

Under median secondary coverts

Length: 33 to 35 mm.   Downy part: 15 to 20 percent

Under median secondary coverts have a quality of feebleness that has not been observed in the feathers discussed heretofore. The downy texture is light, because only a short portion of each barb has fully developed barbules, the barbules are smaller than normal, and they do not project upward and downward on each side of a ramus as they do in many other downy barbs. The pennaceous portion is lax, owing to the reduction of the barbicels. As a result, the barbs separate readily and the edge appears frayed. The tip of the feather is bluntly rounded, and there are no zones of different pennaceous textures (fig. 200). The afterfeather consists of a few lightly downy, umbilical barbs.

The overall feebleness and the proportion of the downy part distinguish under median secondary coverts from most others. They resemble some feathers at the lower end of the crural tract but can be distinguished by the lighter density of the downy part. They are identical, however, with some of the marginal coverts on the underside of the wrist. These coverts differ from the under minor primary coverts only in their slightly greater size.

Under minor primary coverts, under minor secondary coverts, under forearm tract, under prepatagial apterium

Length: 16 to 33 mm.   Downy part: 12 to 18 percent

The under coverts are small versions of the preceding series (fig. 200). The largest of them are the inner primary coverts, and the smallest are the under forearm feathers. All are symmetrical, with a more or less pointed tip. The inner feathers in the row of under minor primary coverts have a downy margin for some distance, like that described for the inner under major secondary coverts. The after feather consists of a few umbilical barbs.

Small size, short downy portion, and loosely knit pennaceous vanes mark these feathers as coming from the underside of the wings. They can be separated from the under median secondary coverts by their smaller size, but they cannot be distinguished from many of the under marginal coverts. The feathers on the under forearm tract are slightly smaller than those of the under prepatagial apterium, but they cannot be separated with certainty.

Under marginal coverts

Length: 13 to 38 mm.   Downy part: 10 to 100 percent

The under marginal coverts range from contour feathers with only a few downy barbs to semiplumes (fig. 200). Their shape ranges from narrowly triangular to broadly oval. As in other feathers on the underside of the wing, the downy texture is more sparse than that on contour feathers elsewhere. The pennaceous portion of the vanes is loosely knit in some of these coverts, but it becomes firmer in feathers close to the leading edge of the wing. Unlike many of the upper marginal coverts, there is no demarcation of zones of different pennaceous textures. Most of the under marginal coverts have only a small portion of downy texture at the base and along the margins for a short distance. They have the structure of semiplumes, however, along the anterior border of the prepatagial apterium, and are largest at the proximal end of the tract. Under marginal coverts are so variable that there is no distinctive character or combination of characters for them. Many of the contour feathers are recognizable as coming from the wings because of their small size and triangular shape. They are indistinguishable, however, from the preceding group of feathers and from upper marginal coverts along the leading edge of the wing.

Subhumeral tract

Length: 16 to 70 mm.   Downy part: 11 to 25 percent

The subhumeral tract is the last of the three humeral tracts (see also humeral tract proper and posthumeral tract).

It bears contour feathers that are lightly downy at the very base and along the lower margin for a variable distance. The pennaceous portion of the vane is loosely knit and easily frayed in the midregion. At the sides of the curved tip in the larger feathers there are faint zones of open texture created by the reduction but not loss of barbules. The afterfeather is composed of umbilical barbs.

The largest feathers of this tract are located in three follicles in the middle of the posterior (or medial) row. The feathers at each end of this row and those of the anterior row are smaller. The latter adjoin marginal coverts of the under forearm tract and down feathers of the prepatagial apterium.

The large subhumerals can be identified by their size, the relatively small, light, downy portion, and the faint open pennaceous zone. The remaining feathers, however, cannot be distinguished from many others on the underside of the wing.

Female feathers resemble those of males. A long, narrow feather from the posterior row and a short, rounded feather from the anterior row are shown in figure 213, *16* and *1*, respectively.

Caudal Tracts

Rectrices

The rectrices resemble the remiges in size and general structure. Certain of them are the largest feathers on a chicken, not only in length but also in width. The calamus and proximal portion of the rachis, however, are not as stout as they are in the remiges. The central rectrices (pair No. 1) are very distinctive in males because of their length and pronounced lateral curvature (figs. 197, *B*, and 201). They are aptly called sickles or main sickles by poultrymen. When well formed, these feathers curve over the tips of rectrices 2 and 3 and then hang downward beyond the rest of the tail; their tips may even point forward. Unlike the remiges, these feathers are flat; they have no downward curvature along

the shaft or toward the margins. Although these rectrices are not overlapped except at the base, the vane closer to the midline of the tail is the inner vane. The vanes are entirely pennaceous except for a few downy barbs at the base, mostly on the outer vane. There is an aftertuft. The feather is widest near its proximal end, and tapers to about one-fourth that span just before the bluntly pointed tip. The outer vane is approximately three-fourths as wide as the inner; the barbs are equally long on both sides, but they make a smaller angle with the shaft in the outer vane. The barbs are closely knit owing to the presence of large barbicels on the barbules, like those on the remiges.

In poultry terminology, the remaining rectrices are known as the main tail feathers. They are shorter but wider than the central rectrices, the margins are more or less parallel, and the tip is rounded. The outermost feathers, in fact, increase slightly in width to a point near the distal end. All these feathers are also curved toward one side, but in the opposite direction from the first pair—they bow away from the midline. The degree of curvature becomes greater in the outer rectrices, but even there it is much less than the curvature of the first pair. Unlike rectrix 1, the barbs of the outer vane in rectrices 2 to 8 are one-half to three-quarters the length of the inner barbs. The vanes of rectrices 2 and 3 are nevertheless of approximately equal width because the longer (inner) barbs make a smaller angle with the rachis. This situation agrees with that in the central rectrices in that the angle is smaller on the concave side of the curve. In rectrices 4 to 8, the barb angle becomes equal on both sides of the shaft, and the inner vane, having the longer barbs, becomes wider than the outer.

The downy portions of the vanes extend farther along the margins in rectrices 2 to 8 than they do in the first pair. Except in the lowermost barbs, which are wholly downy, there is an abrupt transition from pennaceous to downy texture. This occurs progressively farther out on successive barbs until the rectrices are entirely pennaceous. The afterfeather of these rectrices consists of umbilical barbs.

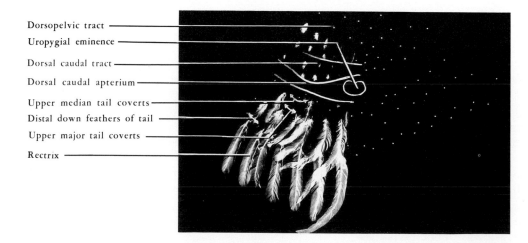

Dorsopelvic tract
Uropygial eminence
Dorsal caudal tract
Dorsal caudal apterium
Upper median tail coverts
Distal down feathers of tail
Upper major tail coverts
Rectrix

FIGURE 201.—Exploded view of feather tracts on the dorsal side of the tail of a male Single Comb White Leghorn Chicken. See legend for figure 181 for note and explanation of solid lines.

TABLE 19.—*Length of rectrices of Single Comb White Leghorn Chickens*[1]

Feather (No.)	Total length		Length of calamus
	Male	Female	
	Millimeters	*Millimeters*	*Millimeters*
1	445	204	25
2	257	203	25
3	240	202	24
4	234	196	24
5	223	192	22
6	218	179	21
7	195	168	18
8	180	152	16

[1] Measurements are based on feathers of one male and one female, both more than 1 year old.

The rectrices can be recognized almost by their size alone. The central pair resemble their upper major coverts, but they can be identified by their greater length, smaller downy portion, greater difference in width between inner and outer vanes, and the bluntly pointed tip. The remaining rectrices are conspicuously different from their upper major coverts not only in length, but also in having a much less downy vane and a much stiffer shaft. Rectrices 6, 7, and 8 show some resemblance to secondary remiges but can be distinguished by their greater width throughout, particularly near the tip.

The rectrices are shorter and less curved in females than in males (table 19). The difference is not pronounced in the central pair, which are only a little longer than the rest of the rectrices and are only gently curved outward.

The central rectrices of the male Long-tailed Yokohama Chicken are the largest of all feathers. With careful handling and management to maintain growth in the follicles, these birds can produce feathers 20 feet long.

Upper major tail coverts

Length: 95 to 345 mm.   Downy part: 6 to 39 percent

The upper major tail coverts in males vary with a span of six follicles, from long feathers resembling the central rectrices to ordinary contour feathers (fig. 201). Starting from the midline, the first four coverts curve laterally so that they hang downward over the rectrices. They appear to be in series with the main sickles (central rectrices). In poultry terminology, they are called lesser sickles. The two outer feathers in males are inconspicuous and are known as tail coverts, as are all upper major tail coverts in females.

The first major covert on each side is a long, relatively narrow feather that tapers to a point. There are small zones of downy texture along the margins at the base, and there is an afterfeather of umbilical barbs. The rest of the coverts show the following modifications:

1. Total length decreases.
2. Width of plumulaceous part increases throughout the series. Width of pennaceous part increases in coverts 2 and 3 and decreases in coverts 4, 5, and 6.
3. Downy portion becomes larger as texture spreads medially and distally by transformation of barbs.
4. Feathers become straighter.
5. Tip of vanes becomes rounded.

Coverts 1 and 2 may be mistaken for central rectrices but can be recognized by their smaller size, vanes of nearly equal width, downier base, and pointed tip. Coverts 3 and 4 can be identified by their size, symmetry, and extent of downy texture. Coverts 5 and 6 resemble the secondary remiges on the elbow and their major upper coverts, but can be distinguished from them by their weaker shaft and wider vanes. They can be told from pectoral feathers, which they also resemble, by the absence of an aftershaft.

In females, these coverts range in length from about 92 to 154 mm. They are straighter and more nearly uniform than in males.

Upper median tail coverts

Length: 114 to 195 mm.   Downy part: 24 to 35 percent

The transformations from the rectrices to the major tail coverts are carried forward into the median coverts (fig. 201). These feathers are structurally intermediate between the major tail coverts and the last feathers of the pelvic tract. They are known to poultrymen as tail coverts, being grouped with all the major coverts in females and the two outer major coverts in males.

The innermost upper median tail coverts in males are shorter than the major coverts, yet they are still large feathers. The vanes are symmetrical except that they hang downward toward the outer side. There are relatively large zones of downy texture at the proximal end; between them and the rachis are narrow zones of pennaceouslike texture, caused by the presence of curled-base barbules. The pennaceous portion of the vane is more transparent, and its barbs are more easily separated, than in the major tail coverts and the rectrices. Their barbules are smaller overall, and the distal barbules have narrower bases and fewer hooklets. The tip is bluntly pointed and bears a small but distinct band of open pennaceous texture. The afterfeather consists of a small aftershaft with about seven pairs of barbs (total length, 25 mm.) and several umbilical barbs on either side. In all these characteristics—proportion, textures of the vane, structure of the barbules and the afterfeather—the upper median tail coverts resemble the pelvic feathers.

There is less variation among these coverts than among the major coverts. Proceeding outward on the row, the pennaceous portion becomes shorter and the tip becomes more rounded. The rachis has a kink toward the midline, beyond which point it curves gently in the opposite direction. The kink is located approximately one-fourth the distance along the rachis in the second covert and further distally in the remaining coverts.

The upper median tail coverts resemble certain upper major tail coverts, secondary remiges on the elbow, pectoral feathers, and pelvic feathers. They can be separated from all of these, except possibly the last, by their size, proportion of downy vane, bent rachis, and size of aftershaft.

There is no difference between the sexes in these feathers except for slightly smaller size in females.

Dorsal caudal tract

Length: 15 to 43 mm.

The dorsal caudal feathers are situated between the pelvic feathers and the upper median tail coverts but are not intermediate to them in form (fig. 201). Near or upon the lobes of the uropygial gland are small, round to oval contour feathers of lax texture (fig. 213, 3). These grade outward into larger semiplumes and down feathers along the border of the lateral caudal apterium. The feathers at the base of the uropygial gland are about 15 to 22 mm. long, including a calamus about 2.3 mm. Their rachis tapers sharply in the proximal 1.5 mm. as several pairs of barbs branch off and then tapers gradually for the rest of its length. There is an afterfeather composed of an aftershaft and a few umbilical barbs. The aftershaft is short, but its barbs are so long as to reach the tip of the main feather. Barbules and texture of the aftervanes match those of the vanes.

The texture of the contour feathers is intermediate between pennaceous and plumulaceous. The barbs are virtually parallel to each other, yet they are loosely knit. Their barbules are of a short, simplified downy type, except for a small indistinct zone of reduced pennaceous barbules near the tip of each feather. Even the reduced down vanules are flat and narrow; their barbules are widely spaced and parallel to each other, each stiffened by a small ventral flange. These barbules are no more than 1 mm. long and have a base that tapers into a long, stiff pennulum with faint nodes. Very tiny nodal prongs are sometimes present. The barbules on both sides of a ramus are alike. Lax texture results from the spacing of the barbs and barbules and the characters of the barbules.

The feathers on and near the uropygial gland can be identified by their size and microstructure. They resemble some under marginal coverts of the wing, but do not have pennaceous barbules. The location of separate semiplumes and down feathers cannot be determined. All these feathers in females are identical with those in males.

Under tail coverts, ventral caudal tract

Length: 65 to 112 mm.   Downy part: 30 to 50 percent

The feathers on the underside of the tail form a graded series in their structure although they are separated into tracts by an apterium. The under tail coverts and the posterior feathers of the ventral caudal tract are typical body contour feathers. The shaft bends away from the body at the upper end of the calamus, and within a few millimeters returns to its original orientation. At a further distance of 10 to 20 mm., it begins a long curve upward and then downward to the tip. The pennaceous portion of the vanes curves downward toward the margin, with the result that the dorsal surface of the feather here is strongly convex. The tip is bluntly rounded or truncate and is marked by a narrow band of open pennaceous texture. The downy portion is notably soft and fluffy owing to the length of the barbs, the prevalence of branched barbs, and the widely separated planes of vanules on each side of a ramus. The afterfeather is about one-fourth as long as the vanes (up to 26 mm.); it consists of an aftershaft with numerous pairs of barbs, a few of which are branched.

Anteriorly and medially in the ventral tract (toward the vent) the feathers show the following changes:

1. Total length decreases.
2. Vanes become more downy. The pennaceous portion shortens and loosens as its barbules became smaller and simpler.
3. Downy barbs become shorter at the base of the vane and cease to be divided.
4. Shaft becomes straighter.
5. Afterfeather becomes relatively longer (up to 40 percent of length of vanes) although actually a little shorter (to about 18 mm.).

These feathers grade into the semiplumes at the caudal end of the abdominal tract.

The under tail coverts and the posterior feathers of the ventral caudal tract resemble certain feathers on the interscapular, pectoral, and femoral tracts. They can be distinguished from all of these by the curvature of the rachis and the pennaceous portion of the vanes. In addition, they differ from interscapular feathers in the shape and texture of the tip, and from pectoral feathers in the relatively smaller aftershaft. The remaining feathers of the ventral caudal tract are recognizable in a few cases by the curvature of the vanes. Many of them, however, are indistinguishable from loosely pennaceous feathers on the sternal, femoral, and crural tracts.

Capital Tracts

Occipital tract

Length: 13 to 50 mm.   Downy part: 0 to 17 percent

The contour feathers of the occipital tract continue the form of those at the anterior end of the dorsal cervical tract. The exposed portion is narrow and almost straight edged, about one-eighth as wide as it is long (fig. 202). The concealed portion at the base is more than twice this width; the tip is pointed. In the proximal half of the exposed portion, there is a narrow, median zone of closely knit pennaceous texture. All the rest of this portion of the vane has an open pennaceous texture, with bare, glistening rami. The vanes are downy for the basal 10 percent of their length, and even here, only the portion close to the rachis is fluffy. The ends of the barbs either are bare or are furnished with greatly reduced barbules. There is a small afterfeather with an aftershaft.

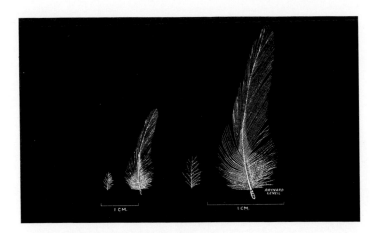

FIGURE 202.—Contour feather from the occipital tract of a male Single Comb White Leghorn Chicken. *Left*—feather and afterfeather at the same magnification as used for most of the other drawings in this series, to show comparative size. *Right*—same feather and afterfeather at higher magnification to show structure. In each pair of drawings, the main feather is on the *right* and the afterfeather is on the *left*.

Anteriorly in the tract, the feathers show the following trends:

1. Feathers become smaller, particularly along the anterior and lateral margins of the tract.

2. Downy portion is relatively a little longer in some feathers, but it disappears from those at the very base of the comb.

3. Pennaceous texture becomes entirely open.

4. Afterfeather maintains actual length and thus becomes relatively very long—more than three-fourths as long as the vanes in the feathers beside the comb. Barbs of the afterfeather become very short and sparsely furnished with short, simplified barbules. Aftervanes are thus narrow and have a texture like that of the vanes.

As a result of these changes, the anterior feathers of the occipital tract are about 13 mm. long and less than 3 mm. wide. They have an open pennaceous texture except in a very small, sparsely downy area at the base. The afterfeather is inconspicuous, in spite of its relatively great length, because of its narrow, open-textured vanes. All the barbules are the stylet type—short, tapered processes without any outgrowths. Some of them show a faint division into a longer proximal segment and one or two shorter segments, which are individual cells. These are so very similar, however, that they cannot be considered a base and a pennulum. Other stylet barbules do not show any differentiation whatever, even in their reaction to stains or refraction of transmitted light.

The open, pennaceous appearance of these little feathers is created chiefly by the parallel arrangement of the barbs in each vane and aftervane. This in turn depends on the stiffness of the rami, because there is no network of interlocking barbules to hold them together. The texture is denser at the proximal end of the feather, close to the rachis, than it is outside this area, just as in a typical contour feather. In this case, the explanation is that the stylet barbules are larger and more common in the basal zone than elsewhere.

The occipital feathers in females are like those in males except that the zone of open pennaceous texture is narrower and less distinct.

Coronal tract

Length: 5.5 to 18 mm.

The reduction of size and resimplification of texture noted in the occipital tract continue in the coronal tract. Under scrutiny, the larger feathers show two zones, but these are not truly pennaceous and downy as seen in typical contour feathers on the body. At the base of the vanes, close to the rachis is a zone that might be termed quasi-downy, owing to its small stylet barbules; the rest of the vanes might be termed quasi-pennaceous, owing to the entirely bare rami. The afterfeather is the aftershaft type and equals 25 to 60 percent of the length of the vanes. It has only a very few stylet barbules at the base.

The largest feathers in the tract are at the posterior end, beside or even on the base of the comb. The smallest feathers are at the anterior end just above the superciliary tract. Thus there are two gradients of decreasing size—posterior to anterior and dorsal to ventral.

Frontal tract

Length: 3.0 to 15.5 mm.

The frontal feathers and anterior coronal feathers point upward and outward at a steep angle from the surface of the head. The range of size is nearly the same in frontal feathers as in coronal feathers, but in the former, very small feathers prevail. Structurally, they are also like the anterior coronal feathers except that there are fewer barbs (as few as eight pairs in the smallest feathers). Stylet barbules, widely spaced, occur only in a small region at the base. The afterfeather remains surprisingly large, 40 to 60 percent as long as the vanes, although it too has fewer barbs and barbules. Except for the distribution of barbules, these feathers resemble those on the eyelids, the malar tract, and the rictus (fig. 203, *A'*, *C'*, and *E'*).

The gradients of decreasing size and complexity are the same here as in the coronal tract. The smallest feathers are immediately in front of the eye, in the area where the frontal, loral, and superciliary tracts meet.

Loral tract

Length: 2 to 4 mm.

When seen casually, the feathers of the loral tract appear to be bristles because they are extremely short and slender. Under magnification, however, they are revealed to have several pairs of stiffly parallel barbs along the rachis, and thus are greatly reduced contour feathers (like anterior malar feathers *E*, *E'* in fig. 203). They have the form of a

FIGURE 203.—Small contour feathers on the head of a Single Comb White Leghorn Chicken. The location of figures *A* through *E* are indicated by letters on the drawing of the head. Drawings *A* to *E* are made at the same scale to show relative size of all feathers; drawings *A'*, *C'*, and *E'* are made on a larger scale to show details.

A and *A'*, lower ocular tract (outer surface of lower eyelid).
B, ventral surface of earlobe.
C and *C'*, upper ocular tract (rim of upper eyelid).

D, anterior auricular covert.
E and *E'*, anterior portion of malar tract between rictus and genal tract.

very slender brush because the barbs lie close to the rachis and the barbules are close to the rami. They project almost perpendicularly outward from the skin.

An inconspicuous aspect of the diminution of feathers from the occipital tract to the lores is that the rachis shrinks in diameter more than the calamus. In the occipital feathers, as in typical body feathers, the proximal end of the rachis is as thick as the calamus. In the loral feathers, the calamus is about 0.2 mm. in diameter, and the rachis emerging from it is half this value or less. The vanes are formed by 6 to 10 pairs of barbs, the rami of which are slender, noncompressed filaments. These bear short, undifferentiated, stylet barbules on the proximal half or so of their length. The afterfeather in some feathers consists of an aftershaft (with one or two barbs) that is two-thirds as long as the vanes. Other feathers have only a few umbilical barbs and still others have no after-feather at all. Barbs of the afterfeather have fewer barbules than those of the main vanes. In females, the feathers of this tract are more evidently contour feathers and less like bristles than in males.

Superciliary tract

Length: 1.3 to 4.6 mm.

The superciliary feathers lie close to the skin and point posteriorly. The anterior feathers are directed dorsally and the posterior feathers ventrally, with the result that the feathers throughout the tract are parallel to the curvature of the upper eyelid. They are identical with feathers of the loral, frontal, and upper ocular tracts except for their overall size and the condition of their afterfeather (fig. 203, C, C'). The largest superciliary feathers are those along the border of the coronal tract and the smallest are those nearest the upper eyelid. The minuteness of the latter feathers may be appreciated by noting that they are each shorter than a downy barbule on a typical contour feather. An aftershaft with one or two pairs of barbs, about one-third the length of the vanes, can be discerned in the larger superciliary feathers, but none can be seen in the smaller feathers.

Temporal tract

Length: 0.9 to 2.1 mm.

The temporal tract holds some of the tiniest feathers on the face. Grossly they appear to be bristles but are actually feathers like those of the loral and superciliary tracts. The feathers are conical instead of flat because the barbs point downward and lie close to the rachis. Only a few stylet barbules are present along the proximal ends of the rami. There is no sign of an afterfeather. The feathers decrease in size from the posterior portion of the tract to the eyelids. All the feathers lie close to the skin and point more or less posteriorly. Those in the upper portion of the tract point somewhat ventrally, like the superciliary feathers above them. Those on the lower border of the tract point slightly dorsally, like the malar feathers below them.

Genal tract

Length: 1.2 to 4.2 mm.

The feathers close to the lower ocular apterium are identical with those of the loral and temporal tracts. Ventrally, however, the feathers lose their bristlelike or brushlike appearance and are clearly seen to be reduced contour feathers. They have flatter, relatively wider vanes than any feathers we have described since the coronal tract. The rachis is flattened and is noticeably narrower than the calamus. There are 10 to 15 barbs on each side, the number depending on the size of the feather. The lowermost five or six are widely spaced and project outward, but the higher barbs are progressively closer together and directed at a smaller angle from the rachis. Stylet barbules are present for a variable distance along the proximal portions of the lowest four to seven barbs. Some of the feathers have no afterfeather, whereas others have three or four umbilical barbs that equal as much as one-half the length of the rachis. These feathers project outward from the skin at a moderately steep angle. They point more or less posteriorly, but the exact direction varies through the tract in such a way that each feather is parallel to the curvature of the lower eyelid when open.

Malar tract

Length: 2.8 to 6.6 mm.

Two kinds of feathers are found on the malar tract in males—those on the anterior portion surrounding the rictus (fig. 203, E, E') and those on a posterior portion that is mostly covered by the ear lobe. Examination of baby chicks reveals that feathers on the anterior medial surface of the ear lobe also belong to the malar tract. The feathers of the anterior portion closely resemble adjacent genal feathers. They project outward at a moderate angle and point downward and backward.

The transition to the second kind of feather takes place within two or three follicles ventral to the anterior corner of the eye. All the barbs at the base of the feather and most of the more distal ones are lost. Any that remain along the middle of the rachis are widely spaced and often unpaired. Some feathers are so reduced that they consist of nothing more than a shaft, but most of them have a few rami at the tip. The length of any ramus is the same as that of a ramus at the equivalent level on the shaft of a fully vaned malar feather. This suggests that the barbs may have been worn off by the ear lobe, yet the rachis does not show any signs that barbs were formerly attached to it. Some rami along the middle of the rachis have extremely small, simple stylet barbules at their proximal ends, but those at the tip of the rachis are bare. There is no afterfeather. The sum of these characters is a feather that looks almost identical with a filoplume. Pterylosis, however, provides two pieces of evidence that the feathers of the malar tract are not filoplumes. First, the follicles for these feathers are clearly in series with those of the anterior malar feathers, and the feathers themselves intergrade. Second, the feathers that resemble filoplumes are each accompanied by a pair of true filoplumes. They appear to be a special type of contour feather, and may be known as pseudofiloplumes. They point somewhat posteroventrally, like the anterior malar feathers, but project more perpendicularly from the skin. Shorter feathers of the same type are present on the anterior medial surface of the ear lobe.

Female Single Comb White Leghorn Chickens have feathers of the first type over the entire malar tract, without any tendency toward pseudofiloplumes.

Rictal tract

Length: 1.8 to 3.1 mm.

There are no rictal bristles on a White Leghorn Chicken. The feathers that at first seem to fit this category actually belong to the upper anterior branch of the malar tract; they are small, simple contour feathers as described above, not bristles. The rictus is bare except for a few feathers at its posterior corner (figs. 11, p. 18, and 54, p. 99). The smallest of these have a brushlike appearance like the feathers on the loral tract and the anterior end of the malar tract (fig. 203, E, E'). The larger feathers have flatter, wider vanes like those on the malar and genal tracts. There is no afterfeather. Rictal feathers point posteroventrally and project outward at a steep angle.

Ocular tract (upper and lower)

Length: 0.8 to 1.2 mm.

Two kinds of feathers are present on the ocular tract, though each is structurally the same on both lids. The feathers project posteriorly and outward; those of the upper lid slope dorsally and those of the lower lid slope ventrally. The outer surface of the lids bears conical, brushlike feathers (fig. 57, p. 100) like those on the loral, temporal, and upper genal tracts. When cleaned and unfurled, their structure as simplified contour feathers is revealed (fig. 203, A, A', and C, C'). They become still smaller and further modified in the rows near the rim of the eyelids. In a 1.0-mm. feather, the calamus is about 0.2 mm. long and nearly as thick. It contains only one or two pulp caps, the lower of which is very thick and reflects the contour of the feather papilla in the follicle. The rachis juts upward from the calamus and then curves downward to the tip. It arises from approximately one-fourth the circumference of the calamus but tapers rapidly as three to five barbs branch off on each side. The conical shape of the feather results from strong downward curvature of the rachis and transverse curvature of the vanes. The rami are short, thick, and set at a small angle from the shaft. They carry stylet barbules that are surprisingly well developed in that they have distinct cells and tiny nodal prongs. Barbules continue to the tips of the barbs, although distally they are smaller, simpler, and closely appressed to the ramus, all the way to the tip. The afterfeather equals two-thirds or more the length of the main vanes and is variable in structure. In some feathers it consists of a very short aftershaft with a

few long, irregularly branched barbs. Other feathers have one to three umbilical barbs, with or without an aftershaft.

On the rim of the eyelids is a row of eyelashes (cilia), the smallest feathers on a chicken (fig. 57). They consist solely of a short calmus and a bare rachis about nine times as long as the calmus. One pulp cap can be seen inside the calamus. The rachis is a slender filament that swells slightly from the proximal end and then tapers to the tip. Eyelashes sometimes appear to be situated between the last little contour feathers, but they are actually in a row beyond them. The morphology of the eyelashes and the fact that they do not accompany contour feathers show that they are bristles, not filoplumes. Eyelashes are in fact the only true bristle feathers on a chicken.

Auricular tract

Length: 2.5 to 17 mm.

The auricular feathers together form a patch of dense plush that contrasts with the ear lobe below and with the small, widely separated feathers of the genal and malar tracts in front. The auricular tract is less conspicuous in females, where the posterior malar and genal feathers grade into it. The gross appearance of this tract results not only from the texture of the individual feathers, as may be expected, but also from the close spacing between them—as little as 0.2 mm.

As in other birds, the feathers around the anterior half of the tract are much larger than those on the posterior half. The anterior ear coverts (opercular feathers) point posterodorsally across the external ear opening and rest on the tips of the posterior ear coverts (fig. 55, p. 99). Distinctive characteristics of the anterior coverts are obovate shape and wide spacing between the barbs (fig. 203, D). The calamus is slightly more than 2 mm. long—nearly as long as that in many body contour feathers. It represents approximately 18 percent of the length of the shaft and is thus relatively longer in these feathers than that in all other feathers of a chicken, except for the flight feathers and their major upper coverts. The rachis and vanes curve downward to the tip, and the vanes also curve downward slightly along the margins. The barbs are parallel and become progressively longer as far as the middle of the rachis, beyond which they shorten and project at a gradually diminishing angle. In some coverts, there are long stylet barbules on the proximal portions of the rachis and its barbs. Other feathers are bare here, but have small, simple stylets in the axils of the junctions between the rami and the rachis. Curiously, larger, more differentiated stylet barbules occur along the distal portion of the barbs near the tip of the feather. They appear to be a device for enmeshing these feathers with the posterior coverts, their props. The afterfeather equals about 70 to 90 percent of the length of the main vanes. Its aftervanes are unusually narrow because their barbs lie right beside the aftershaft. These barbs are tapered filaments that resemble simple stylet barbules because they lack barbules. The long aftershaft, possibly stiffened by the rami, may serve as support for the main part of a feather.

An abrupt change can be seen in the feathers along the anterodorsal and posteroventral segments of this circular tract. Feathers of the innermost row are reduced to about 5 mm. or a little less than half the length of the anterior coverts. Length diminishes to about 3.5 mm. in the next row and 2.5 to 3 mm. in the outermost row. These posterior ear coverts are not merely small versions of the anterior ear coverts for they are modified in relation to their own function. They stand almost perpendicularly though the tips bend posteriorly (i.e., ventrally with reference to the rest of the feather). The vanes are approximately oval and are composed of widely spaced barbs. A distinctive feature of these feathers is the stoutness of the rachis and the rami, even to their tips. These parts are at least twice as thick as those in other facial feathers of equal size. Also unusual are the diverse barbules. Some of them are small, simple stylets very close against the ramus. Others are larger and are differentiated into a few cells that each bear one or two long nodal prongs; these barbules project from a ramus at irregular angles. The afterfeather is approximately one-half as long as the main vanes and is a simplified version of that on the anterior ear coverts. It consists of a slender aftershaft with a few, short rami.

Most contour features are constructed and arranged so as to cover and insulate the body. Most of their regional variations are related to local conditions of topography and mobility. The auricular feathers, however, provide a good example of multiple adaptations for a special function—screening the external opening of the ear. The screen itself is made of the crisscrossed, widely spaced barbs; the broad tip of the feathers enlarges their coverage of the opening. The length and posture of the anterior and posterior coverts enable the former to be propped up by the latter. The absence of barbules over much of the area of the vanes in an anterior covert makes for a more open mesh, while the barbules at the tips of the barbs can engage in the posterior coverts. Added support for the main part of an anterior covert may be provided by its long afterfeather. The posterior coverts are adapted for their role by their bent tips, stiff rachis and rami, and numerous thorny barbules.

Interramal tract

Length: 3.0 to 5.6 mm.

The interramal and submalar tracts are classed with the ventral tracts of the body, but their feathers are described here because they resemble others on the head. The feathers of the interramal tract are small, simple contour feathers that increase in size from anterior to posterior through the tract. Those along the midline point posteriorly, whereas those on each side point posterolaterally. The most anterior feathers, just behind the mandibular symphysis, have only four or five tapered rami with blunt tips on either side of the rachis. The lowermost barbs come off at a relatively higher level

than usual above the superior umbilicus. The rachis is a cylindrical filament; there is no afterfeather.

The following changes are seen in the more posterior feathers compared with the anterior ones:

1. Barbs become longer and more numerous, though still widely spaced. The vanes become wider and more rounded.

2. Barbules appear on the rachis and the proximal portions of the lower barbs. The first of these are the stylet type and are then transformed to the reduced downy type.

3. A short aftershaft with two or three pairs of long barbs develops. The afterfeather comes to equal half the length of the main vanes.

Submalar tract

Length: 5.3 to 11 mm.

The submalar feathers continue some of the trends noted in the interramal tract. Those in the area between the wattles become longer and wider, yet they remain unusually flat. Because of their stiff, nearly parallel barbs, the texture resembles that of loosely knit pennaceous vanes, although the barbules are still the simplified downy type. Posteriorly in the tract, the texture becomes more dense as barbules extend farther along the rami and to more distal barbs. Rachidial barbules appear along the rachis and grade into the barbules on the rami. The afterfeather remains at about the same actual size as in the interramal feathers, and thus becomes smaller in relation to the main vanes. The feathers at the posterior end of the tract resemble those on the ventral border of the ear lobe (fig. 203, *B*). This same structure continues into the most anterior feathers of the ventral cervical tract. A short distance behind the level of the posterior border of the ear lobe, there is an abrupt change to the type of ventral cervical feathers described previously (p. 283).

The submalar tract also extends laterally onto the medial surfaces of the wattles. The feathers become smaller and simpler, much like those of the interramal tract, but narrower. Many of them are distinguished by the bare portion of the rachis, proximal to the lowest barbs. There is no sign of an afterfeather.

All the feathers on the head can be recognized as such by their small size and simple structure in comparison with body contour feathers. Certain of them have conspicuous features, which permit more specific identification—anterior ear coverts (obovate shape, widely spaced barbs, long afterfeather), posterior ear coverts (stout rachis and barbs, thorny barbules), ocular feathers (tiny, conical, with stylet barbules), eyelashes (tiny, simple bristles), and interramal and submalar feathers (flat vanes, bare proximal portion of rachis, reduced downy barbules). The other feathers are harder to identify because they lack highly distinctive characters, and because they grade from one tract into another. Most of them can still be located fairly closely, if necessary, by the combination of features that includes size, shape and curvature of the vanes, nature and distribution of the barbules, and relative size and structure of the afterfeather.

Semiplumes

Distribution and gross appearance

Length: 40 to 105 mm.

Semiplumes are more uniform than contour feathers and are therefore discussed as a whole category. They are alike in both sexes except that they are smaller in females. They are numerous on a chicken, occurring in the following tracts: dorsal and pelvic—along borders; pectoral—along borders; sternal—throughout, mostly in posterior half; medial abdominal, lateral body, femoral—along borders; and crural—much of the upper half of the lateral surface and a small area near the upper end of the medial surface. The follicles are always in rows and are often in series with those for contour feathers. The transition between the two types of feathers is either abrupt, as along the dorsal and pelvic tracts, or gradual, as on the femoral tract.

The largest semiplumes are along the posteroventral border of the femoral tract, close behind the last row of long contour feathers. Most semiplumes on a fully grown male Single Comb White Leghorn Chicken measure 45 to 70 mm. Slightly smaller feathers occur at such places as the borders of the dorsal tract and adjacent borders of the femoral tracts. The minimum size for semiplumes in such a bird appears to be about 40 mm. because plumulaceous feathers below this size are generally down feathers.

The shaft of a semiplume curves downward slightly toward the tip but does not curve sideways. The calamus accounts for about 6 percent of the shaft, and it varies little in relative length. It is straightsided except for a taper at the lower end, and it contains approximately 13 pulp caps. The rachis is opaque white for the proximal 40 to 60 percent of its length,

owing to the presence of air-filled pith cells, and it is nearly as wide as the calamus. Near the distal end of this segment the rachis becomes much narrower and more transparent. Since this portion is inconspicuous, the rachis may appear to be shorter than it is, and feathers that are actually semiplumes may be classified as downs. It may be recalled that these types are distinguished according to the relative lengths of the rachis and the longest barbs. The rachis is longer than the barbs in a semiplume (fig. 204) and shorter than those in a down feather.

Semiplumes vary from rectangular (along the border of the dorsal tract) to semicircular (on the lateral body tract), but they are most commonly obovate (on the femoral, crural, and pectoral tracts). Except for the tip, they are the same shape as the downy part of nearby contour feathers. The transition from one type of feather to the other involves only the formation or loss of a pennaceous portion of vane beyond the downy portion.

Semiplumes have afterfeathers that are about one-third to one-half as long as the main vanes. The aftervanes are narrow in relation to their length, and the aftershaft reaches nearly to their tip (fig. 204).

Variation in downy texture

At this point we can discuss the variation in downy texture throughout the feathers of a Single Comb White Leghorn Chicken. Even a superficial examination of contour feathers, semiplumes, and down feathers reveals that the downy portion is fluffier in certain places than in others. In contour feathers at the upper end of the dorsal cervical tract, it is small and weakly fluffy. It becomes highly fluffy in the lower end of this tract and in the interscapular tract. Contour feathers of the dorsal and pelvic tracts have a dense, compact downy base, whereas semiplumes along the borders have a looser texture. Semiplumes and the bases of contour feathers at the posterior end of the pelvic tract are highly fluffy. Ventral cervical and pectoral feathers are highly fluffy. Feathers in the sternal tract increase in fluffiness from the anterior to the posterior part of this tract and in the medial abdominal tract. The semiplumes and downs of the lateral abdominal tract are still more loose and fluffy. The bases of the humeral feathers are highly fluffy. The upper side of the wings, the bases of the anterior marginals of the prepatagium, the coverts and marginals of the hand, and all the remiges are weakly downy. The posterior marginals of the prepatagium are moderately fluffy, and the bases of the secondary coverts as well as all the remigial down feathers are highly fluffy. On the under side, the under forearm feathers and the proximal remigial downs are moderately fluffy; the plumulaceous texture elsewhere is weak. Semiplumes and downs of the lateral body tract are highly fluffy. On the femoral tract, semiplumes and downs in the anterior portion are dense and moderately fluffy. Posteriorly, the semiplumes and bases of contour feathers remain dense but become highly fluffy. Crural feathers are moderately plumulaceous at the upper end of the tract but become less so toward the ankle; those on

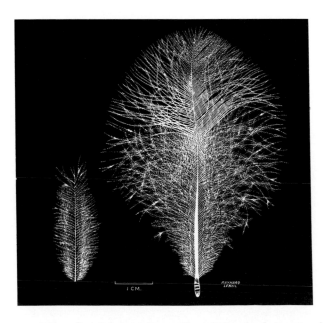

FIGURE 204.—Semiplume from the abdominal tract of a male Single Comb White Leghorn Chicken. Main feather on the *right,* afterfeather on the *left.*

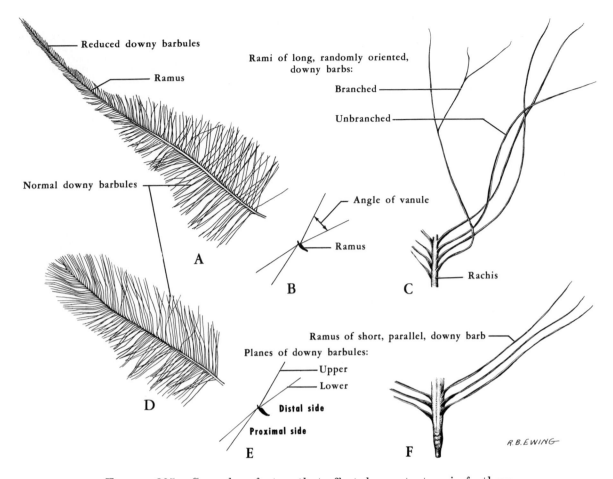

Figure 205.—Secondary factors that affect downy texture in feathers.

A and D: Length of barb and of barbule; A, long barb with barbules that are reduced distally; D, short barb with barbules that remain at full length distally.

B and E: Expansion of the vanules (i.e., angle between the planes of the barbules); the angle on the distal side of the ramus is larger than that on the proximal side; B, angle of distal vanule is 37°; E, angle of proximal vanule is 23°.

C and F: Orientation and branching of barbs; barbules not shown for the sake of clarity.

the external surface are denser than those on the internal. The bases of both upper and under tail coverts are highly fluffy.

Structural basis for downy texture

Downy texture is created primarily by the presence of downy barbules, while its density and degree of fluffiness depend on five secondary factors, as follows:

1. Length of barbs.
2. Orientation of barbs.
3. Branching of barbs.
4. Variation in size of downy barbules along a ramus.
5. Vertical angles of barbules.

The length of barbs generally increases from the proximal end to the distal end of a downy vane or the downy portion of a contour feather vane (fig. 205, D, A). Fluffiness is enhanced as the barbs become longer.

Barbs of downy vanes are sometimes intertwined at random (fig. 205, C), but more often they are oriented along one axis or more. Their arrangement is most regular in dense, flat vanes at the proximal end of semiplumes like those on the abdominal tract, or in contour feathers like those on the dorsal tract. Seen from above or below, the downy barbs resemble pennaceous barbs in that they project obliquely from the rachis, and their barbules project obliquely from the ramus (fig. 205, F). Distal barbules are approximately parallel to the shaft, whereas proximal barbules are approximately perpendicular to it (fig. 205, D). Each barb is turned on its long axis in such a way that the distal vanules lie slightly above the plane of the vane, and the proximal vanules lie slightly below it (fig. 207). As a result of these arrangements, the upper surface of the vane is formed by barbules that point toward the tip of the feather, whereas the under surface is formed by those that point toward the margin. The under surface is flatter than the upper, owing to the various angles and the overlapping of vanules on successive barbs. Afterfeathers often show the same condition, except that the upper side is flatter.

Downy barbs with branched tips occur in certain contour

feathers (fig. 187), semiplumes (fig. 204), and down feathers (fig. 206, *A*). One branch is commonly divided again (fig. 206, *B*). The barbules on these barbs alternate their direction through a wide angle (fig. 206, *C*), resulting in highly expanded vanules and a very fuzzy barb. They are crowded together at the forks in the ramus (fig. 206, *D*), but their structure is entirely normal. Branched barbs heighten the fluffiness of a downy vane because they increase the number of fuzzy filaments at the margin.

The length of the barbules along a downy barb is either virtually constant (fig. 205, *D*) or sharply reduced distally (fig. 205, *A*). The longer the barbules are at the tip of a barb, the denser is the texture of the vane.

Some downy barbules project horizontally from a ramus, but usually they project upward or downward. Successive inclined barbules tend to point in alternate directions, thereby creating two planes in each vanule (fig. 207). Vanules may be expanded up to an angle of about 50°, and the greater the angle, the fuzzier the barb. End views of barbs

that are very fuzzy or moderately so are shown in figures 205 *B* and *E*, respectively. The angle of a vanule either remains constant along a barb or diminishes from the proximal to the distal end. The more constant this angle remains, the more uniform is the texture of the vane.

These characters vary together in some degree to create the different sorts of downy texture. As an illustration, we can examine a semiplume from the anterodorsal corner of the femoral tract. The barbs at the base of the vane have the following characteristics as shown in figure 205, *D*, *E*: (1) They are short, (2) they are not branched, (3) vanules are either flat or expanded at a low angle, and (4) barbules continue at full size to the tip of the ramus. This combination of features produces flat, compact vanes that are narrow in relation to their length. Higher on the feather, the barbs show the following characteristics as shown in figure 205, *A*, *B*: (1) They increase in length, (2) they are not branched, (3) vanules are expanded to an angle of about 15° to 30° for most of their length, and (4) barbules diminish toward the

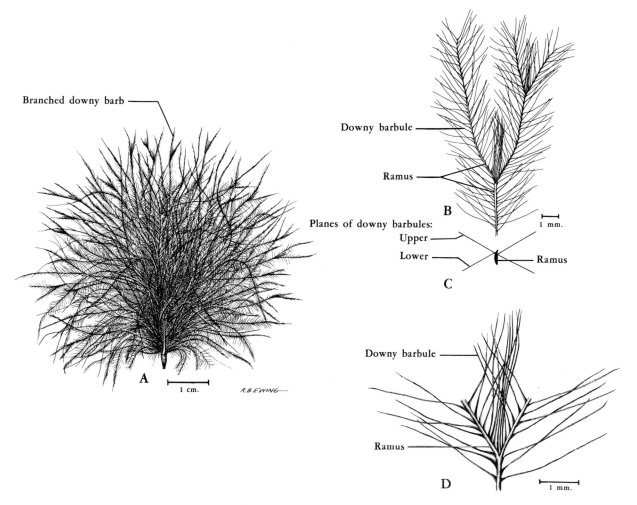

FIGURE 206.—Branched downy barbs in feathers of Single Comb White Leghorn Chickens.

A, down feather from lateral body apterium.

B, distal portion of a branched barb, showing a secondary division of the right branch.

C, diagrammatic cross section of a barb, showing the planes in which alternate barbules project above or below the ramus; the distal side of the barb is on the *right*.

D, region of a division, at a higher magnification than in *B*.

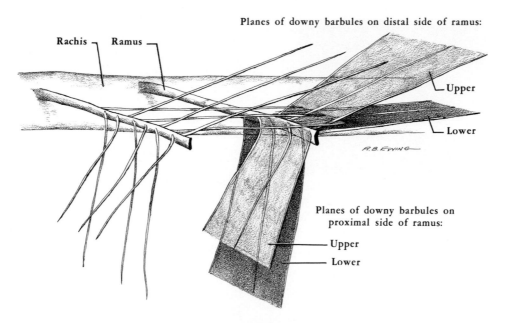

Planes of downy barbules on distal side of ramus:

Rachis — Ramus —

Upper

Lower

R.B. EWING

Planes of downy barbules on proximal side of ramus:

Upper

Lower

FIGURE 207.—Orientation of rami and barbules of two downy barbs from a chicken feather. The feather is lying horizontally and is seen obliquely from the dorsal side.

tip of the ramus and may vanish; as the barbules become shorter, the vanules become flatter. These features make the barbs moderately fuzzy at the proximal end but narrow and thin distally. Hence, the vane is fluffy near the rachis but loose and sparce around the margin. These two kinds of downy barbs and the intergrades between them prevail in all downy vanes of Single Comb White Leghorn feathers. A third kind may be combined with them as in the under tail coverts and semiplumes from the posteroventral border of the femoral tract. The characteristics of these barbs, shown in figure 206, *B* and *C*, are as follows: (1) They are long, (2) they are branched, (3) vanules are expanded at an angle of 40° to 50°, and (4) barbules continue at full size to the tip of

the ramus. The combination of these features makes the barbs very fuzzy and increases the number of barbs at the periphery of the vanes. As a result, the vane is highly fluffy. the secondary factors that affect characteristics of downy texture in chicken feathers are summarized in table 20. From this table, it can be seen that the secondary factors tend to vary together in creating different sorts of downy texture.

Down Feathers

Distribution and gross appearance

Length: 12 to 60 mm.

Down feathers of a fully grown chicken will also be considered as an entire category because they are fairly uniform on various parts of the body. They are identical in both sexes except that they are slightly smaller in females. Natal downs have already been introduced (ch. 5, p. 264) and are considered further in chapter 7. The locations of adult down feathers are as follows: Lateral cervical apterium, scapular apterium, pelvic apterium, pectoral apterium, border of lateral body tract, lateral body apterium, lateral abdominal apterium, humeral apterium, implanted in the walls of remex follicles on upper and under sides of wing, in the walls of alular remex follicles on upper side of wing, dorsal side of hand (a few isolated feathers), subhumeral apterium, under forearm tract (lateral and medial), border of dorsal caudal tract, and implanted in the walls of rectrix follicles on upper and under sides of tail. In none of these places, except beside the remiges, are the down feathers situated amidst contour feathers. They occur mostly on the apteria; those found on feather tracts, such as the under forearm tract, replace the contour feathers and do not surround them. The follicles for

TABLE 20.—*Secondary factors affecting characteristics of downy texture in chicken feathers*

Factor	Texture		
	Flat and dense	Thick with loose margin	Highly fluffy
Length of barbs.......	Short....	Long..............	Long.
Orientation of barbs...	Regular..	Somewhat random...	Random.
Branching...........	No......	No..............	Yes.
Variation in size of barbules.	Full length to tip of ramus.	Reduced toward tip..	Full length to tip.
Expansion of vanules..	0°–15° ...	15°–30° (down to 0° at tip).	30°–50°.

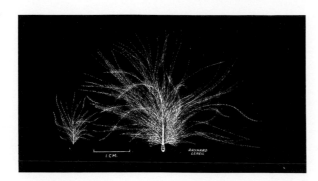

FIGURE 208.—Down feather from the lateral cervical apterium of a male Single Comb White Leghorn Chicken. Main feather on the *right*, afterfeather on the *left*.

Within the range of overlap, the rachis and the longest barbs are nearly equal, so they must be measured carefully to classify a given feather. These measurements are not necessary outside the range of overlap, for here down feathers and semiplumes can be distinguished by overall size alone. The smallest downs occur on the underside of the wings, and those beside the rectrices are nearly as small. The largest downs are those on the lateral body apterium beside the pectoral tract and near the lateral body tract.

The calamus is a simple straight tube 1 to 2 mm. long in most adult down feathers, and 3 to 4 mm. long in the distal and upper proximal downs beside the remiges. A rachis is always present and it tends to be proportionately longer in the larger feathers (compare figs. 206 and 208). An afterfeather is also present, and commonly it is the same size and has the same texture as the main feather (fig. 176, p. 267). In some of the large lateral body downs the afterfeather is about three-quarters to two-thirds as large as the main vanes. The aftershaft, however, is moderately to extremely short, unlike that of semiplumes. In the down feathers beside remiges, it is minute and is accompanied by several umbilical barbs.

these downs line up with those for contour feathers elsewhere on the tract, and the feathers themselves have a small pennaceous portion.

Semiplumes of a male Single Comb White Leghorn Chicken vary in length from about 40 to 105 mm.; down feathers, from about 12 to 60 mm. The two kinds of feathers thus overlap in the range of about 40 to 60 mm. Below this range, the rachis is conspicuously shorter than the longest barb, and downy feathers can easily be recognized as downs; likewise, above the range the rachis is conspicuously longer than the longest barb, and downy feathers can be recognized as semiplumes.

Downy barbs

The structure of downy barbs has already been discussed in the sections on contour feathers and semiplumes. There is less diversity in the barbs and the texture they create in

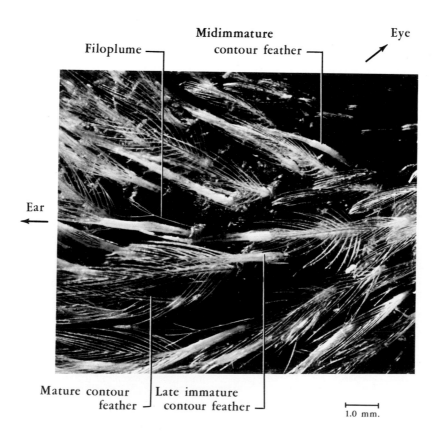

FIGURE 209.—Contour feathers and filoplumes on the right side of the head (i.e., genal tract) of a Single Comb White Leghorn Chicken. Compare with figures 54 and 55.

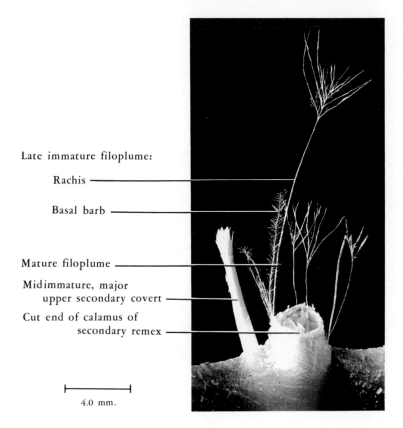

Late immature filoplume:

Rachis

Basal barb

Mature filoplume

Midimmature, major
upper secondary covert

Cut end of calamus of
secondary remex

4.0 mm.

FIGURE 210.—Filoplumes around a secondary remex of a Single Comb White Leghorn Chicken.

downs than in the two other types of feathers. In the prevalent type of barbs, the barbules are long (up to about 4.0 mm.) and the vanules are expanded to 30° to 40° for most of their length; the barbules become shorter and the vanules flatter near the tip of the barb. This structure creates a moderately dense, thick vane with a loose, umbelliform tip (fig. 208). Many down feathers have a shorter zone proximal to this, where the vanes are narrower and more compact, owing to short barbs with flat vanules. A feather from the lateral abdominal tract of a female (fig. 213, 6) illustrates a down with a broad, rounded margin and a short, narrow base. The downs on the underside of the alar tract are short, wide, and flat. They are mostly plumulaceous, of course, but there are small zones of pennaceous texture close beside the rachis. Highly fluffy vanes with branched barbs and widely expanded vanules are rarely found on the downs of chickens.

Oil gland feathers

Length: 9 to 9.5 mm.

Down feathers are present at the tip of the uropygial papilla around the openings of the oil ducts. Their calamus is relatively long, for it is about 2.3 mm, the same as on the basal feathers. It swells slightly from proximal to distal. At the upper end, the calamus gives rise to a rachis about 1.5 mm. long and several umbilical barbs that are either entirely separate or fused at their bases, as shown in figure 388, page 614. If only one cluster of barbs is present and it is

TABLE 21.—*Length of filoplumes in adult male chickens*

Location	Length		
	Minimum	Average	Maximum
	Millimeters	*Millimeters*	*Millimeters*
Malar tract..............	1.1	1.5	1.8
Upper eyelid.............	.8	.9	1.1
Occipital tract...........	18.0	22.4	25.7
Dorsal cervical tract— lower end.............	11.7	19.6	26.8
Lateral cervical apterium...	1.3	2.6	3.9
Dorsal tract.............	28.0	32.5	37.8
Pelvic tract.............	16.4	37.3	53.1
Ventral cervical tract— anterior...............	15.5	30.2	41.5
Pectoral tract—anterior....	32.4	48.0	54.0
Pectoral apterium........	1.5	1.9	2.6
Sternal tract.............	18.6	29.8	36.9
Medial abdominal tract....	20.2	37.4	44.5
Lateral body apterium.....	1.2	1.5	2.0
Humeral tract...........	13.9	22.3	30.4
Upper alar tracts.........	27.3	32.7	41.1
Under alar tracts.........	8.0	18.1	26.0
Remiges................	11.5	27.0	43.5
Femoral tract—posterior border................	30.5	34.2	42.2
Crural tract—inner surface.	12.6	24.8	38.9
Rectrices................	12.7	25.3	40.0

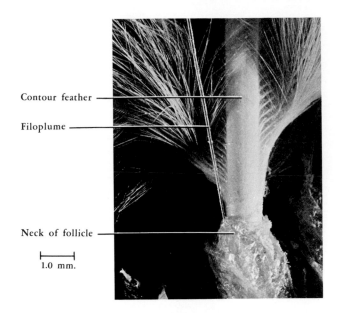

Contour feather

Filoplume

Neck of follicle

1.0 mm.

FIGURE 211.—Filoplume beside a contour feather on the pelvic tract of a Single Comb White Leghorn Chicken. The thickness of the filoplume can be seen to increase distally.

situated opposite the rachis, it can be considered a hyporachis, but in other cases it is futile to attempt this distinction. The rachis and the fused portions of barbs are thin and relatively wide; barbs split away at irregular intervals. If a feather is soaked with oil, the barbs stick together and form a slender brush with a truncate tip. Often, however, the feathers are dry and the barbs radiate from the upper end of the calamus, with the result that the vane is nearly semicircular. The barbules have the same arrangement and structure as those described in the feathers at the base of the papilla.

Filoplumes

Location

Filoplumes are found in association with contour feathers, semiplumes, and downs on most parts of a chicken. They are present, singly or paired, alongside the small feathers on the head (fig. 209) and even on the eyelids. The cilia are not filoplumes because they are situated in series with the contour feathers. Pairs of filoplumes accompany most of the feathers in the tracts on the dorsal side of the body. They tend to be less prevalent along the margins of the tracts. Tiny filoplumes are present beside some of the down feathers on the lateral cervical and the scapular apteria. Long filoplumes are very common at the posterior end of the pelvic tract. There are no filoplumes on the pelvic apterium, the uropygial tract, or on the caudal apterium.

On the underside of the body, filoplumes are uncommon on the submalar tract and the anterior fourth of the ventral cervical tract. Single or paired filoplumes accompany most of the feathers on the remainder of the ventral cervical tract and on the pectoral tract. Many of the downs on the ventral

cervical apterium and the pectoral apterium are accompanied by pairs of tiny filoplumes. Filoplumes are scarce on the anterior two-thirds of the sternal tract, but pairs of them become more prevalent posteriorly. Most of the feathers on the medial abdominal tract have long single filoplumes, whereas these are rarely present on the lateral abdominal tract. Filoplumes are fairly common in pairs beside the upper and under tail coverts, but there are none on the caudal apterium and around the vent.

The feathers of the humeral and the dorsal alar tracts are commonly accompanied by single filoplumes. On the underside of the wing, filoplumes are scarce along the anterior margin but become more prevalent in the posterior rows of feathers. The coverts on the underside of the remiges each have two filoplumes. Every remex and rectrix has two to eight filoplumes spaced at uneven intervals around it (fig. 210).

Tiny filoplumes are fairly common beside semiplumes of the lateral body tract and down feathers of the lateral body apterium. The occurrence of filoplumes on the femoral tract is highly variable among mature male Single Comb White Leghorn Chickens. In some individuals, filoplumes are absent except in a small region behind the knee, while in other birds they have been found with nearly all the feathers. Still other chickens have shown various intermediate patterns of distribution. Filoplumes are usually absent over the crural tract, but in some birds they are common singly in zones that extend from the knee to the ankle on the anteromedial and posterior surfaces.

Filoplumes are situated within 0.5 mm. of the edge of the

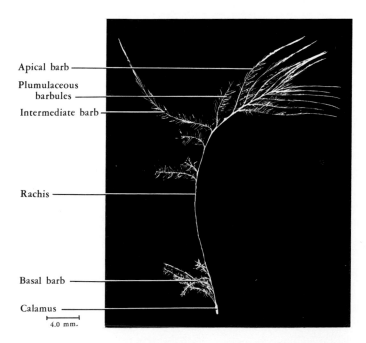

Apical barb

Plumulaceous barbules

Intermediate barb

Rachis

Basal barb

Calamus

4.0 mm.

FIGURE 212.—Abnormal filoplume with intermediate barbs from the wing of a Single Comb White Leghorn Chicken. Since basal barbs are still attached, the filoplume has not completed its development.

FIGURE 213.—Feathers of a female Single Comb White Leghorn Chicken. The afterfeather for numbers 1 through 15 is on the right of the main feather. No record was made of the afterfeather for number 16. All specimens are from birds that were either 323 or 324 days old.

1, subhumeral tract, anterior row.
2, dorsal cervical tract, anterior end near midline.
3, dorsal caudal tract, anterior to nipple.
4, medial abdominal tract, anterior to vent.
5, femoral tract, upper anterior part.
6, lateral abdominal tract.
7, crural tract, external dorsal part.
8, pectoral tract, posterior end.

9, femoral tract, lower posterior part.
10, dorsal tract, anterior end at midline.
11, dorsal tract, middle at midline.
12, humeral tract, posterior edge.
13, pectoral tract, anterior end.
14, interscapular tract at midline.
15, dorsal cervical tract, midlength at midline.
16, subhumeral tract, posterior row.

feather follicles that they accompany (fig. 211). They are situated at the sides of the larger feather, though often somewhat anterior or posterior to it, except around the remiges and rectrices.

Size

The length of filoplumes on an adult male Single Comb White Leghorn Chicken ranges from about 0.8 mm., as found on the eyelids, to about 54 mm., as found on the anterior portion of the pectoral tract and the posterior portion of the pelvic tract. The variation in length within and among tracts, based on the measurements of six specimens from each area, is apparent from table 21. The filoplumes of females have a maximum length of about 35 mm.

Structure

The structure of filoplumes from Single Comb White Leghorn Chickens is very similar to that seen in other birds, as described in chapter 5. Filoplumes from different parts of the body are alike except that the smaller ones tend to have fewer apical barbs than the larger ones; the minute filoplumes on the eyelids sometimes lack barbs entirely. During the growth of a filoplume, at least 20 basal barbs may form, some as long as the rachis. They break off from the rim of the superior umbilicus after the feather sheath splits off. These barbs may represent a temporary afterfeather; after they are lost there is no afterfeather of any kind on a filoplume.

The shorter basal barbs and a proximal portion of the longer basal barbs bear typical downy barbules. Such barbules diminish and disappear by the tip of the longer barbs. The apical barbs are much shorter than the rachis and are often no more than fine, bare rami. If barbules are present, they are usually the stylet type, though downy barbules that are only slightly simpler are sometimes present. A few barbs can occasionally be found on the middle portion of the rachis (fig. 212). These intermediate barbs, as they may be called, have a typical downy structure but their presence is considered abnormal. A much rarer abnormality is a filoplume with twin rachises on a single calamus. Neither can be considered a hyporachis because they are situated side by side rather than at opposite points on the calamus.

BRONZE TURKEY

Body contour feathers of turkeys are generally characterized by their large size and their shape. The pennaceous portion of the vanes is approximately an inverted triangle, the base of which forms a broad, truncate tip to the feather. Often the tip is slightly rounded or dihedral, in which case the pennaceous part of the vanes is four sided. The exposed portion is also unusually flat; in some places it curves very slightly downward toward the tip and not at all toward the sides. The shape of the tip and the flatness of the pennaceous vanes appear to facilitate the raising and sliding of feathers across each other, as occur in certain displays.

In wild Common Turkeys and domestic Bronze Turkeys, the color of the pennaceous portion is a very distinctive feature of the body contour feathers. Lowermost (and partially concealed) is a zone of normal texture and dull brown or black pigmentation. This grades upward into a band that is nearly opaque to transmitted light and iridescent bronze or purple under incident light (fig. 255, A, B, p. 408). Feathers on the cervical tracts are iridescent to the tip, whereas those on the dorsal, interscapular, and humeral tracts end in a narrow band of matte black. Although this zone and the iridescent zone contrast sharply in color, they differ only a little in density. The black band is, in fact, slightly less opaque than the iridescent part. Some feathers on the pelvic and humeral tracts have a narrow white band of open pennaceous texture at the very tip. These variations in color and texture depend on the structure and pigmentation of the barbules, as discussed in chapter 7 on pages 407–409.

The downy portion of the vanes is approximately rectangular or ovoid. It attains a width that is slightly greater than the pennaceous portion in most contour feathers and is twice as wide as that portion in pelvic feathers. The texture and its basis in the arrangement of the barbules are similar to those previously described in chicken feathers under, "Variation in Downy Texture."

The unusual feature of the downy portion is the presence of barbules with rings that slide along the pennulum (fig. 214). Chandler (1916:340), who apparently discovered these rings, indicated that they were typical of the downy barbs of gallinaceous birds. We have found them on the feathers of turkeys and the Ring-necked Pheasant (*Phasianus colchicus*), and Day (1966:213) reported them in Red Grouse (*Lagopus scoticus*), Black Grouse (*Lyrurus tetrix*), and Gray Partridge (*Perdix perdix*). We have not found them in Common Coturnix, and neither we nor Day have found them in chickens. The rings thus seem to be unique but not entirely characteristic features of galliform downy barbs.

Chandler's (1916:340) description of the downy barbules of gallinaceous birds can appropriately be quoted here although it does not refer entirely to turkeys.

> The base of these barbules is only slightly differentiated. The pennulum on its more proximal portion has poorly developed swollen nodes which, however, soon increase in size and develop a typical ringlike form. Some of these rings frequently, in fact almost always to a greater or less extent, break loose from the nodes, and slide along on the slender filamentous barbule like rings on a wire, sometimes breaking up into groups of 5 or 6. It is possible to move them along on the barbules by placing them on a slide and moving the cover glass. Toward the tip of the barbules the ringlike structure is again lost, and the nodes become simply swollen. On the proximal vanule these rings are usually not so perfectly developed, and on the more distal portion of both vanules the nodes become simply swollen, and shaped more or less like a eucalyptus seed, with short prongs, or the barbule becomes almost smoothly filamentous, with indistinct nodes. The outside diameter of the rings in *Meleagris virginiana* [= *M. gallopavo*], for instance, is about 0.012 mm., while that of the internodes of the barbules is only 0.004 to 0.005 mm. The down at the base of remiges

and rectrices, and that of the aftershafts, never possess the ring-like structure.

The afterfeather on body contour feathers varies in length, but always has a short aftershaft and is thus type 3. We have not found any turkey feathers in which both the afterfeather and its aftershaft are relatively long (type 2), as can be found in chickens.

The following accounts of Bronze Turkey feathers refer chiefly to those of adult males and point out the differences in those of females. The measurements and proportions are near-maximum values for the feathers of each tract. The illustrations depict feathers of a male Beltsville White Turkey, which are very similar to those of a Bronze Turkey except in color. However, with the absence of color pattern from the drawings, attention is focused on shape and textural pattern.

Dorsopelvic Tract

Anterior portion

Length: 159 mm.   Downy part: 63 percent
                                    Afterfeather: 63 mm.

Feathers of the anterior portion of the dorsopelvic tract are approximately rectangular, with nearly straight sides and a truncate tip (fig. 215). In cross section the rachis is nearly circular with a very faint ventral groove only about 2 cm. long. On each side of the rachis in the downy part is a distinct, narrow zone of open texture that is created by the absence of barbules on the rachis and the proximal ends of the rami. Proceeding distally along one of these barbs, there appear curled-base barbules and then plumulaceous barbules.

The angle between the vanules on the downy barbs varies between about 20° and 60°.

The transition from the plumulaceous to the pennaceous portion of the vane covers about 15 barbs. About 12 to 15 mm. below the tip, the normal, closely knit, blackish-brown vane grades into a band of special dense pennaceous structure and iridescent purple-green. This band is 5 to 7 mm. wide and is bounded, at the tip of the feather, by a matte black band of equally dense structure.

Posterior portion

Length: 200 mm.   Downy part: 64 percent
                                    Afterfeather: 58 mm.

Contour feathers in the pelvic portion of the dorsopelvic tract are approximately oval, being widest in the middle of the downy portion. They are slightly asymmetrical, for the rachis bends toward the outer vane in the downy part, and then back. Also, the inner vane in the pennaceous portion is a little wider than the outer. The rachis remains as thick as the calamus up to about the middle of the feather and then it begins to taper. The downy portion is longer and wider than that on the dorsal feathers, but the pennaceous portion is the same size. The tip is basically truncate, but slightly rounded. Below the white terminal band are a narrow black band and a wide, iridescent bronze band.

Near the borders of this tract, the feathers become smaller mostly by reduction of the pennaceous portion. This produces a feather about 113 mm. long with nearly straight margins and a semicircular tip; it is plumulaceous except for a wedge of pennaceous vane at the tip. Finally, along the borders, are semiplumes up to about 102 mm. long.

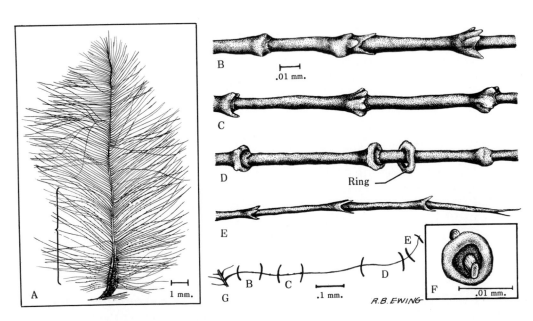

FIGURE 214.—Plumulaceous barb of a Bronze Turkey.

A, entire barb from the proximal end of a contour feather. The bracket marks the region in which the barbules have rings.
B, C, D, and E, portions of a barbule from the bracketed region.

F, oblique view of a ring.

G, barbule showing locations of enlarged portions B through E.

Interscapular Tract

Length: 122 mm.

Downy part: 44 percent
Afterfeather: 57 mm.

The feathers of the interscapular tract are broader and relatively less downy than those behind them on the dorsal tract. The pennaceous portion is tulip shaped owing to the curvature of proximal barbs and the truncate tip.

These barbs tend to separate, causing the vanes to become wider and somewhat diamond shaped. There is a narrow, black, terminal band and a broader, bronze band below it.

Dorsal Cervical Tract

Length: 81 mm.

Downy part: 42 percent
Afterfeather: 37 mm.

The feathers in the dorsal cervical tract diminish in size from the interscapular tract to the top of the head. The plumulaceous portion is fluffier than it is on more posterior feathers. Downy barbules are present right up to the rachis, with the result that there are no zones of open texture as seen elsewhere. The pennaceous portion is asymmetrical on feathers away from the midline. The feather is decurved slightly and the tip is truncate or gently rounded. The region of the bronze sheen is not as dense as it is on the dorsal feathers, and this band of color extends to the tip, without a terminal band of black. In feathers farther up the neck, the iridescence disappears, and the entire feather is dull blackish-brown.

The feathers of females tend to be a little larger than those of males; they have a black terminal band and a narrower bronze band than male feathers.

Ventral Cervical Tract

Length: 39 mm.

Downy part: 25 percent
Afterfeather: 30 mm.

The feathers of the ventral cervical tract have a relatively shorter downy portion than any others on the trunk. There are no open zones beside the rachis in this portion. The pennaceous portion curves away from the midline of the body. There is only a faint iridescent band across the tip.

Surprisingly, the ventral cervical feathers are much larger in females than in males, measuring up to 93 mm. long. They are shaped like the dorsal feathers except that the tip is more rounded. Downward and lateral curvatures are pronounced, even in the plumulaceous portion. Open zones created by the absence of barbules are evident within this portion. Color is also more patterned than in male feathers; the bronze band is tipped by a black band and finally a white band. The white band has an open pennaceous structure owing to the reduction of barbules. The rachis is as thick as the calamus for a distance of about 30 mm., about two-thirds of the length of the downy portion of the vanes. From here it tapers sharply, reaching one-fourth of its original diameter

by the end of the downy portion. It tapers gradually throughout the pennaceous portion of the vanes. As a result, the rachis is stiff in its proximal segment and flexible distally. Feathers commonly break from wear at the distal end of the stiff segment, leaving only a downy stub of a feather attached to the bird.

Pectoral Tract

In male turkeys, the size of feathers increases greatly from the ventral cervical tract into the pectoral tract. The pectoral tract contains contour feathers in the interior and semiplumes at the periphery.

Contour feathers

Length: 153 mm.

Downy part: 54 percent
Afterfeather: 47 mm.

Pectoral contour feathers are oblong with a broadly pointed tip. They are slightly decurved and bent away from the midline of the body. The downy portion is moderately fluffy and has distinct open zones beside the rachis. The outer pennaceous vane is narrower than the inner vane because the barbs are shorter and they project more acutely from the rachis. An iridescent purple-green band is bounded at the tip by a band of matte black. These feathers can be distinguished from those on the dorsal tract by their greater width and the shape of the tip, which is broadly pointed instead of straight truncate.

The pectoral feathers of females are as long as those of males but narrower. The tip is rounded and is marked by a wide band of open pennaceous texture. Proximal to it, the vanes are of normal density without any extra-dense band as in male feathers. Across the very tip of the vanes is a crescent of white, whereas most of the open band is brown. The portion of the feather below it, homologous to the iridescent area on male feathers, is dull black. It is but faintly darker than the rest of the vanes below.

Semiplumes

Length: 180 mm.

Downy part: 100 percent
Afterfeather: 69 mm.

The semiplumes are unusually long. They are also very fluffy, owing to the length of the barbs and their barbules, the presence of a few branched barbs, and a large angle between the vanules. In the proximal half of the vanes, there are zones of open texture beside the rachis. Distally, these grade into narrow zones of pennaceous texture. In spite of the pennaceous texture, it seems reasonable to consider the feathers as semiplumes because they are predominantly downy. Barbs in the distal half of the feather have pennaceous barbules for a short distance close to the rachis. These are replaced by plumulaceous barbules, which in turn become smaller and simpler near the tip of the barb. The semiplumes of female turkeys are like those of males.

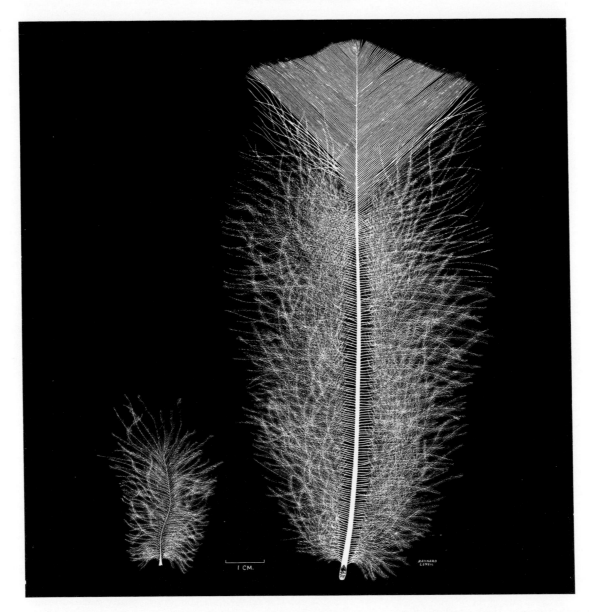

FIGURE 215.—Contour feather from the middle of the dorsopelvic tract of a male Beltsville White Turkey. Main feather on the *right*, afterfeather on the *left*.

Sternal Tract

Length: 80 mm.

Downy part: 66 percent
Afterfeather: 37 mm.

The distinctive feature of feathers on the sternal tract is that the rachis is very thick and stiff along its proximal half. This is a more pronounced version of the condition previously noted in the ventral cervical feathers of females. The proximal half of the rachis is not grooved or even flat on the ventral surface but bears a single median keel. As it tapers, the rachis becomes compressed until, in the distal third of the feather, it is reduced to a fine, flexible shaft.

The vanes are oval with a rounded tip. The downy portion is moderately dense and fluffy, and the pennaceous portion has a rather open-knit texture. The pennaceous part commonly breaks off at its proximal end, which is also the place where the rachis changes from stiff to flexible. Many contour feathers of this tract hence appear to be semiplumes. True semiplumes are also present on the sternal tract (fig. 216) and are described on p. 326.

Abdominal Tract

Length: at least 104 mm.

Downy part: 100 percent or
slightly less
Afterfeather: 51 mm.

Contour feathers and semiplumes are present on the abdominal tract. The uncertainty about their maximum measurements results from the fact that in the birds examined all the feathers were either immature or broken. Breakage is so common as to be almost a characteristic of the abdominal feathers. The rachis is stout for a proximal portion and slender distally. It tapers more gradually than that in the sternal feathers and it has a conventional groove on the underside. Zones of open texture accompany the thick portion of the rachis. The vanes are approximately oval. The tip of the pennaceous feathers is truncate, and shows a terminal, open-textured, white band. Below this are narrow bands of black and bronze.

Femoral Tract

Length: 190 mm.　　　　　　　　　Downy part: 60 percent
　　　　　　　　　　　　　　　　Afterfeather: 30 mm.

Contour feathers and semiplumes are present on the femoral tract. They are oblong or oval, with a broadly pointed tip on the contour feathers and a rounded tip on the semiplumes. Many of them are asymmetrical in that the inner vane is slightly narrower than the outer vane, and the feather curves dorsally. The small semiplumes are uniformly fluffy, whereas the large semiplumes and the contour feathers are fluffiest at the base and become flatter distally. In the fluffiest portion, the barbules remain at nearly full size to the tip of each ramus, and they project in a wide range of angles. In the flatter portions, the terminal barbules are greatly reduced, and they project at a constant angle. Some of the semiplumes are nearly as large as the largest contour feathers, and yet are notable for their slender shaft and delicate downy vanes. The afterfeather on all femoral feathers is an aftertuft.

Crural Tract

Length: 68 mm.　　　　　　　　　Downy part: 47 percent
　　　　　　　　　　　　　　　　Afterfeather: 44 mm.

The contour feathers of the crural tract have broad, oval vanes that show faint corners near the distal end. These angles in the margin create a tip that is not rounded but is slightly truncate. Zones of open texture produced by curled-base barbules are present beside the proximal portion of the rachis, medial to the downy portions of the vanes. The pennaceous portions are of normal texture near the distal portion of the rachis, but they become more loosely knit toward the lateral margins.

Humeral Tract

Length: 158 mm.　　　　　　　　　Downy part: 56 percent
　　　　　　　　　　　　　　　　Afterfeather: 48 mm.

The feathers of the humeral tract are among the most handsome on a Bronze Turkey, because of the iridescence and graceful shape of the pennaceous portion. They are approximately oblong, with slightly convex margins and a broad, slightly pointed, truncate tip. The rachis, at its base, is as thick as the calamus and tapers evenly to the tip. The calamus is unusual; it is not entirely unpigmented but shows

faint streaks of melanin on the dorsal side. The downy portion of the vanes is highly fluffy; the vanules are expanded and the barbules continue at nearly their full length to the tip of the ramus, but the barbs are not branched. The pennaceous portion has a sinuously curved lower border, created by the curvature and the variation in lengths of the barbs. This part of the feather is dull blackish brown except for an iridescent band and a narrow black band at the tip (fig. 255, A, p. 408).

Primary Remiges

Length: At least 330 mm.　　　　　　　Calamus: At least 40 mm.

The primaries are large, relatively narrow feathers. The largest ones in the series are numbers 3 through 8. They are curved downward to a slight extent lengthwise and to a moderate extent medially. Crosswise, the vanes are virtually flat, without notches or a recurved margin. They are pennaceous except for a short downy portion at the proximal end of the outer vane. The calamus and the proximal portion of the rachis reach a diameter of 8 mm. in the largest remiges. The dorsal surface of the rachis is nearly flat, whereas the ventral surface has a well-developed groove along its full length. In the proximal one-fourth of the rachis, the groove is narrow and deep; distally, it becomes wider and shallower and shows about four longitudinal ridges. These diminish in number toward the tip. The ventral lateral edges of the rachis are rounded proximally but in a short distance become pronounced into low crests. The ventral surface of the rachis thus has a ridged median groove and a pair of lateral crests. In the outermost primaries, the groove is slightly asymmetrical in contour and distance from the crest, possibly an adaptation that aids in providing proper variation in the flexibility of the shaft.

The outer vane is approximately one-fourth as wide as the inner, owing to shorter barbs and a more acute angle between the barbs and the shaft. Shiny zones along the underside of both vanes cover up to three-fourths of the outer vane and up to one-half of the inner. These are caused by expanded ventral ridges (tegmina) on the rami. The flaps are narrower than those on the primaries of ducks; they do not overlap as much, and the resulting effect is less shiny.

The feathers are alternately marked with wide bands of blackish brown and narrow bands of white. The bands are uneven in their distinctness and direction. They are transverse at the tip of a remex but become oblique toward the base. The downy barbs are pale buff and are not banded.

Secondary Remiges

Total length: 340 mm.　　　　　　　Calamus: 55 mm.
Greatest width: 61 mm.

The vanes of the secondary remiges are nearly equal in width, and the tip is more rounded than that of the primaries. The feathers are downy along a short proximal portion of the border of the outer vane. A few of these downy barbs have branched tips. No tegmen (expanded ventral ridge) is present on the rami of the pennaceous barbs, and hence the

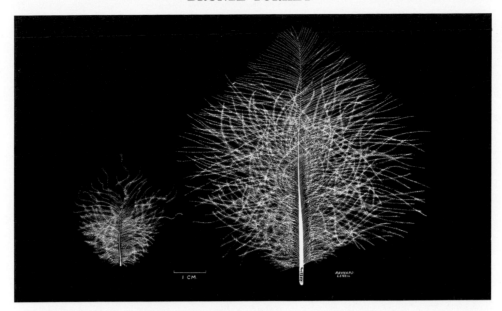

FIGURE 216.—Semiplume from the sternal tract of a male Beltsville White Turkey. Main feather on the *right*, afterfeather on the *left*.

feathers are not shiny on the underside. There is an afterfeather composed of a V-shaped row of closely set umbilical barbs.

Upper Major Primary Coverts

Length: 148 mm.   Afterfeather: 25 mm.

The calamus of the upper major primary coverts is unusually long, accounting for nearly 40 percent of the total length. It is tapered and slightly decurved (curved downward) near the lower end. The feather plate is oval and relatively narrow; the vanes are flat except along the margins, where they are decurved. The barbs separate readily near their tips, owing to the reduction of barbules, and the result is a frayed edge. The aftershaft extends about two thirds the length of the afterfeather.

Upper Marginal Coverts of the Prepatagium

Length: 29 mm.   Downy part: 9 percent
                                      Afterfeather: 10 mm.

The upper marginal coverts of the prepatagium are ovate and have a bluntly pointed tip. They are bowed outward longitudinally, and the vanes are decurved transversely. The pennaceous barbs are very tightly knit together, with the result that the margins are entire.

Rectrices

Length: approximately 376 mm.   Downy part: 8 percent
                                      Afterfeather: 42 mm.

The central rectrices are very large obovate feathers with truncate tips. The vanes are equally wide and are virtually flat and straight. The feathers reach their maximum width at the tip owing to the greater length of the subterminal barbs. This more than compensates for the fact that these barbs lie at a smaller angle to the shaft than those proximal to them. The pennaceous portion of the vanes has a coarse appearance, caused by the large size of the barbs. The barbs in many places are separated all the way to the shaft, apparently as a result of mechanical stresses, although the barbules have well-developed flanges and barbicels. Downy texture is confined to the umbilical barbs and the distal portion of a few barbs at the base of the vanes. The base of the vanes is matted and stringy (not at all fluffy because the barbs and barbules are short), the barbules lie close against the rami, and the nodes on the pennula are very small. The feather is dark brown, speckled with lighter brown along the edges. Near the tip, the speckles become concentrated into narrow transverse bands. Beyond them is a wide, faintly iridescent black band that grades into bands of light brown and pale buff at the very tip.

The lateral rectrices are shorter and narrower than the central ones. They are increasingly asymmetrical as the outer vane becomes narrower than the inner vane.

Capital Tracts

Although the head of a turkey appears to be mostly devoid of feathers, it actually has extensive tracts. The naked appearance of the head is caused by the small size of the feathers and the wide spacing between them. Many feathers are nearly hidden in the folds of skin between caruncles. Most of them are bristles, semibristles, or at least contour feathers with a spikey appearance of the barbs. Bristles and semibristles, it may be recalled, replace contour feathers in the rows of follicles.

Feathers characteristic of the capital tracts are also found in the anterior portion of the dorsal cervical tract as far as the

Shaft

Aftershaft

Shaft

Aftershaft

1 mm.

R.B. EWING

lower border of the carunculate skin. The capital feathers here are about 16 mm. long. As shown in figure 217, *B*, they are semibristles with vanes like those of contour feathers on the proximal half or less of the rachis. Beyond the last barbs, the rachis is fine—hardly thicker than a ramus. The feathers close to the midline have downy barbs at the base and pennaceous barbs above them. They have an afterfeather with an aftershaft that is as long as the vaned portion of the shaft.

Feathers situated more laterally and anteriorly are bristles with small vanes that appear as a dense clump of barbs, no longer flat as in contour feathers (fig. 217, *C*). The barbs have long stylet barbules at their proximal ends but are bare distally. This arrangement repeats that of the barbs themselves and contributes to the reduction of distal and peripheral feather parts. As the vanes become smaller, the aftershaft becomes larger until it equals nearly three-quarters of the total length of a feather. It bears a few barbs with stylet barbules at its proximal end. The relatively large aftershaft on these and other bristles on the turkey head is very unusual. We have examined many avian bristles and have found that they usually lack an aftershaft, though they commonly have umbilical barbs. In a few cases, an aftershaft is suggested by a short protrusion of the rim of the calamus opposite the rachis. The bristles of the Ocellated Turkey (*Agriocharis ocellata*) resemble those of wild and domestic Common Turkeys. They have an aftershaft that is nearly as long as the shaft, but generally have no barbs.

Bristles on the top of the head have small barbs and show some reduction of the afterfeather. Those on the temporal region (fig. 217, *D*) reach a maximum length of about 16 mm. with an aftershaft about 9.5 mm. long. Similar bristles are present near the midline as far as the forehead. Laterally, on the supraorbital region, they are reduced to a length of about 6.6 mm. (fig. 217, *E*). There are only two to four pairs of short barbs, and these are sparsely furnished with long stylet barbules. The aftershaft, however, is nearly as long as the shaft, reaching a length of 5.8 mm.

The eyelashes, or bristles on the upper eyelids (fig. 217, *F*), are only 2.2 mm. long and are thus the smallest feathers on a turkey. The calamus appears to be swollen, for its diameter is greater than that of the rachis. There is a dense basal cluster of barbs, some of which are about two-thirds as long as the rachis. Though tiny, the vanes are dense, owing to the abundance of stylet barbules. There is no aftershaft.

The bristles on the nasal region (fig. 217, *G*) resemble those on the upper eyelid. They are about 2.7 mm. long, and the longest barbs are sometimes nearly as long as the rachis. Stylet barbules are present on the proximal portion of the barbs. There is no aftershaft.

Two forms of bristles occur on the snood. One, shown in figure 217, *H*, has an aftershaft, whereas the other does not. Both are as much as 10 mm. long, and the aftershaft, when present, is nearly 9 mm. long. There are one to five pairs of widely spaced barbs on the proximal third of the rachis. In bristles without an aftershaft, the most distal barb may reach to the tip of the rachis; being devoid of barbules, it resembles an aftershaft. The tip of the rachis is commonly swollen slightly or furnished with one or two very tiny barbs.

The bristles below and behind the eyes (fig. 217, *I*) are similar to the aftershaft-bearing bristles on the snood. They are up to 11 mm. long, with an aftershaft up to 10.5 mm. long. Both the shaft and the aftershaft have a few widely spaced barbs at their basal ends.

The general characteristics of bristles on the head of a turkey may be summarized as follows:

1. Calamus is short, swollen, and unpigmented.
2. Rachis is black and tapered to a fine point.
3. Barbs arise along the proximal one-fourth or less of the rachis. If there are only a few pairs of barbs, they are widely spaced.
4. Barbules, if present, are mostly the stylet type. They diminish distally along a barb and often disappear before the tip, leaving a bare ramus.
5. As the number of barbs diminishes, so do the number and size of the barbules.
6. An aftershaft is often present, and it may be almost as long as the rachis; it sometimes bears a few pairs of barbs.

The transition from a contour feather to a bristle as seen on the head of a turkey involves the following changes:

1. Rachis becomes longer.
2. Barbs become fewer and may become spaced farther apart.
3. Barbules become reduced from pennaceous type to stylet type and may vanish.
4. Aftershaft generally becomes longer.
5. Bare portions of the rachis and the rami become black. These changes of the barbs and barbules start at the tips of the rachis and the rami, respectively, and proceed proximally.

The ear coverts are similar to those in chickens and other birds, and do not show any tendency toward bristle forma-

---

←

FIGURE 217.—Feathers on the head of a male Bronze Turkey. The letters on the head of the turkey indicate the locations of figures *A* through *I*.

A, anterior ear covert.
B, semibristle from anterior dorsal neck region at midline.
C, bristle from crown near midline, posterior end.
D, bristle from temporal region at midline.
E, bristle from supraorbital region.

F, eyelash (bristle) from upper eyelid.
G, bristle from nasal region.
H, bristle from snood.
I, bristle from suborbital region.

tion. The largest feathers are on the anteroventral portion of the margin; they are approximately 10.8 mm. long. These anterior coverts are broadly obovate, with widely spaced barbs all along the rachis. Tiny stylet barbules may be present, as shown in figure 217, *A*, but more often the rami are entirely bare. The afterfeather consists of either a tuft of umbilical barbs or an aftershaft up to 4.6 mm. long. The posterior ear coverts are smaller than the anterior feathers and they have narrow vanes. Their barbs lie close together, projecting at a small angle from the rachis.

Semiplumes and Downs

Semiplumes

Semiplumes occur on the following tracts of a turkey: dorsopelvic (lateral pelvic portion), pectoral, sternal, abdominal, lateral body, and femoral. They are also present on the following apteria: ventral cervical, pectoral, and lateral body. Their distribution is similar to that of the downs on a chicken (described on p. 313), but is less extensive.

The largest semiplumes of an adult male Bronze Turkey are those on the pectoral tract, about 180 mm. long. They are broadly oval and have an afterfeather that is a little more than one-third as long as the main vanes. Their texture is very fluffy, owing in part to a large angle between the vanules and the presence of a few branched barbs at the base of the vanes.

Semiplumes nearby on the pectoral apterium and the lateral body tract are the same shape but are only up to about 90 mm. long (fig. 218). They are moderately fluffy near the rachis but are flatter along the margin, especially near the tip. Several pairs of barbs near the tip are oriented at a regular angle from the rachis, like pennaceous barbs, but they bear small, simplified downy barbules. The pennaceous appearance is more pronounced where the tip of the feather is broadly pointed, as in semiplumes on the sternal tract (fig. 216). These feathers, like other semiplumes in this size range, have an afterfeather that is about one-half to two-thirds as long as the main vanes. The aftershaft is moderately long.

The smallest semiplumes are on the ventral cervical apterium, slightly less than 35 mm. long. They are moderately fluffy throughout, owing to the flexibility of the barbs, the long barbules, and the fact that the barbules project in all directions around the rami. Their afterfeather is as long as the main vanes or nearly so, and has a moderately long aftershaft.

Down feathers

Down feathers on a turkey occur only on the posterior portion of the ventral cervical apterium, the lateral body apterium, beside the remiges and rectrices, and on the tip of the uropygial papilla. They are thus distributed much less widely than on a chicken.

Down feathers on the ventral cervical apterium and the lateral body apterium (fig. 219) are about 30 mm. long, approximately semicircular, and not very fluffy. Their proportions are close to those of semiplumes in that the rachis is only slightly shorter than the longest barbs. The afterfeather is about two-thirds as long as the main vanes and has a moderately long aftershaft.

FIGURE 218.—Semiplume from the lateral body tract of a male Beltsville White Turkey. Main feather on the *right*, afterfeather on the *left*.

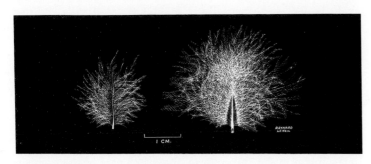

FIGURE 219.—Down feather from the lateral body apterium of a male Beltsville White Turkey. Main feather on the *right*, afterfeather on the *left*.

The downs accompanying the remiges and rectrices are semicircular or kidney shaped. The upper down feathers of the tail, the upper distal downs, and the proximal downs of the secondary remiges are each about 32 mm. long; the upper distal downs and the proximal downs of the primary remiges are about half this size. In all cases, the rachis is slender and is distinctly shorter than the shortest barb. An unusual modification was seen in one upper secondary down in which the rachis was wide and flat and was split near the tip. Each branch bore downy barbs along both edges. Downs beside remiges and rectrices are moderately to highly fluffy because barbs with branched tips are common, barbules are long, and the barbules continue at nearly their full length to the ends of the barbs. Their afterfeather is as large as the main vanes and the aftershaft is as long as the rachis or nearly so.

The down feathers (except those on the oil gland) of a turkey are from 17 mm. to 32 mm. long, whereas the semiplumes are from 32 mm. to 180 mm. long. The two kinds of feathers seem to be in separate ranges, but probably there is some overlapping in the region of 30 to 35 mm. This is particularly likely on the ventral cervical apterium. Downy feathers smaller than 30 mm. can thus be taken as downs, whereas those larger than 35 mm. can be taken as semiplumes. Those in the intervening range must be measured carefully along the rachis and the longest barbs in order to be classified.

The down feathers of a turkey vary in size much less than those of a chicken (for data on the chicken see p. 314). Surprisingly, the largest downs of a chicken are nearly twice as large as those on a turkey. Semiplumes, on the other hand, show a wider range of size in a turkey than a chicken. They are both larger and smaller in turkeys than in chickens. The range of overlapping size between down feathers and semiplumes is higher and much wider in a chicken than a turkey. This means that it is easier to classify down feathers by size alone in turkeys than in chickens.

Oil gland feathers

Length: 8.2 mm.

The little down feathers on the oil gland have a calamus that accounts for about one-third of their length. It bears four or five short projections spaced irregularly around the superior umbilicus. Since they are approximately equal in size, none can be designated as a rachis or as a hyporachis. Short downy barbs arise from them and from the rim of the calamus between them, forming a tuft. Their barbules are rather short, and they do not vary much in the angle at which they project from the rami.

Filoplumes

The filoplumes of turkeys have the same basic structure as those of other birds. There are one or two filoplumes accompanying many contour feathers and four to six with each remex. Pairs of them also accompany many bristles on the head. Length ranges from about 2.7 to 4.6 mm. on most body tracts, though a very few on the pectoral tract measure 13.4 mm. The smallest filoplumes are those on the head (1.7 to 2.8 mm.), whereas the largest are those with the remiges (9.3 to 18 mm). It is curious that these filoplumes are smaller than those on a chicken.

Most of the filoplumes have one to three barbs on each side of the distal end of the rachis. They are short and are furnished with reduced plumulaceous barbules. The filoplumes on the head generally consist of no more than a shaft; it is thickest just below the midpoint and tapers from there to both ends. Occasionally there is a single short branch near the tip, which may be either a ramus or a fork of the rachis.

The color of turkey filoplumes varies and often is unrelated to that of the feathers they accompany. Those on the body and wings are either entirely white or mixed white and grayish brown. The rachis and barbs may show alternately pigmented and nonpigmented zones, or one part may be pigmented while the other is not. The pigmentation of the basal barbs, which fall off when the filoplume is fully grown, coincides with that of the rachis and the apical barbs. The filoplumes on the head are entirely brown except for the calamus, which, as usual, is not pigmented. Since these filoplumes accompany all-black bristles, their color is again keyed to that of their principal feathers.

BELTSVILLE WHITE TURKEY

The feathers of Beltsville White Turkeys are almost identical with those of Bronze Turkeys in shape and structure. Their most obvious difference is their totally white appearance, due to the absence of melanin. The pennaceous portion of the vanes has a normal, closely knit texture everywhere except at the very tip of certain feathers, where there is a narrow band of open, pennaceous texture. The pennaceous portion of the vanes has no zone of iridescence and has extra-dense texture; the barbules in the region of this zone are normal in structure. Certain feathers, such as those of the dorsal tract, have a wider fringe of open pennaceous texture at the tip. Others, such as dorsal cervical feathers, have a fringe that was not seen at all on Bronze Turkey feathers. The flight feathers are equally long in both breeds, but many of the other feathers are as much as 25 percent shorter on Beltsville White Turkeys than on Bronze Turkeys. Semiplumes at the posterior end of the sternal tract are equally long in both breeds. However, they are much wider and virtually circular in Beltsville whites instead of oval as in bronze birds. The vanes are less densely fluffy, especially around the periphery, where they are flatter than in the center.

WHITE PEKIN DUCK

The feathers of White Pekin Ducks resemble those of wild Mallards, the ancestral form, in nearly all respects; they differ chiefly in being all white. The following account is confined to the distinctive features of duck feathers, particularly those that differ from chicken feathers. Duck feathers from different parts of the body vary in size, shape, textural pattern, and other properties, as shown by Hardy and Hardy (1949: figs. 4, 6, 11). We have not attempted to mention most of the variations, however, because the manner of conducting such an analysis has already been shown for chicken feathers.

Body Contour Feathers

Gross appearance

The body contour feathers reach a maximum of about 180 mm., the largest being those on the humeral tracts. Most body feathers are oval or ovate with a bluntly rounded or truncate tip. Feathers on the top and sides of the head are obovate. The humeral tract feathers vary the most, particularly those near the outer border of the tract. The larger (outer) feathers are strongly asymmetrical with the outer

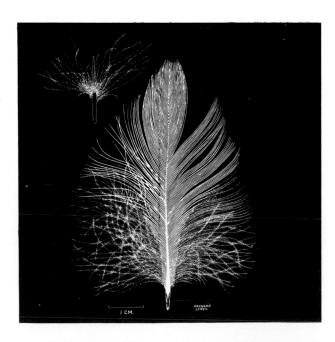

FIGURE 220.—Contour feather from the middle of the dorso-pelvic tract of a White Pekin Duck. The afterfeather of umbilical barbs (aftertuft) and an outline of the calamus and proximal end of the rachis are shown in the upper left corner.

vane the narrower. The shaft is rather slender, and in some feathers the distal portion of the rachis is as fine as a ramus. In the upper major tail coverts, the distal part of the rachis is clear and colorless for a distance of about 45 mm. This effect results from the fact that the rachis is composed only of cortex, that is, without any pith that causes the normal opaque white appearance. The same portion of the feathers is curled upward and medially in males of the Mallard and most domestic varieties derived from it. Since these coverts are straight in females, they are an example of conspicuous sexual dimorphism in feather shape.

The vanes of most feathers are downy in the proximal 20 to 40 percent of their length. This texture tends to be fluffier and less dense and to show a more random arrangement of barbs than in chicken feathers. The pennaceous portion of the vanes is like that in chicken feathers except that marginal zones of open pennaceous texture are narrower and less clearly delimited. Chandler (1916:328) described the body feathers of a Mallard as being "rather loose in structure, due largely to the fact that bases of barbules lie in vertical plane, leaving wide spaces between them." Feathers of Mallards as well as domestic Pekin Ducks that we have examined do not seem to be especially loose except in the transition zone between plumulaceous and pennaceous parts of the vanes. It is true that the bases of the barbules lie in a vertical plane, but this is not unusual.

Downy barbs

In a typical body contour feather, such as one on the back, the lowermost barbs are entirely downy (fig. 220). Pennaceous texture appears beside the rachis a short distance above and then spreads outward at higher levels in the vanes. The narrow zones of pennaceous texture between the rachis and the downy part of the vane on each side look like those in chicken feathers. They are actually formed by pennaceous barbules, however, rather than by curled-base barbules; the latter do not occur anywhere in Pekin Duck feathers. At about the same level as the change of texture near the midline, the margins of the vanes start to become lax. This texture occupies areas of the vanes closer to the midline at higher levels, and eventually meets the zones of pennaceous texture that have been expanding. At the point where they meet, the downy texture ends. Higher on the vanes, the area of normal pennaceous texture continues to expand as the area of lax texture again becomes a narrow margin. The latter either disappears or passes into a zone of open pennaceous texture. The two kinds of texture are alike in that the barbs are not interlocked, but they differ in that lax barbs (or portions thereof) are more flexible and hence more randomly oriented

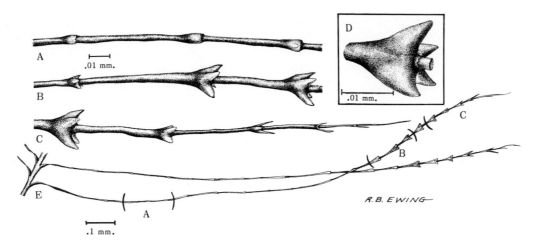

FIGURE 221.—Plumulaceous barbules of a Mallard.

A, proximal portion of pennulum with very small nodes.

B, intermediate portion with large nodes.

C, distal portion with small nodal prongs.

D, node with large prongs from portion B.

E, two barbules showing locations of enlarged portions A through C.

than open pennaceous barbs. On the other hand, lax texture differs from downy texture in its openness and lack fuzziness due to the reduction of barbules.

The downy barbs of duck feathers are generally fuzzier than those of chicken feathers because the barbules project all around the ramus instead of in a limited angular range. The pennula actually bend in many directions although the bases are attached to the sides of a ramus, as always. Because of the shortness of the barbules and their radiation from the rami, there is no overlapping of planes of vanules or regular orientation of the barbules as in chicken feathers (pp. 278–279). Downy barbs with branched tips or reduced terminal barbules do occur in duck feathers, and they affect the texture in the same way as in chicken feathers. The fuzziness and random arrangement of ordinary barbs are important factors contributing to the excellence of goose and duck down for thermal insulation (Loconti, 1956).

The down barbules of a Pekin Duck are identical with those of a Mallard (see fig. 221). They are about 0.7 mm. long, about one-fifth as large as those on chickens and turkeys. The base and pennulum are very fine, and most of the nodes have either tiny prongs or none (fig. 221, A, E). The distinctive feature of these barbules is the presence of one to five large nodes near the tip of the pennulum. Each node appears under low magnification to be a triangular swelling pointed toward the base of the barbule (fig. 221, B, C). Under higher magnification it can be seen to have four conical prongs that each point outward and toward the tip of the barbule (fig. 221, D). The few nodes distal to these are smaller, but they are not quite as small as those at the basal end. The expanded nodes are most numerous on barbules on the lower barbs of a vane. According to Chandler (1916:329), the number of enlarged nodes differs among genera of anseriform birds. The differences may be useful for distinguishing between downy feathers of ducks, geese, and swans. They do not seem to be consistent enough for distinguishing among

genera of ducks, as Chandler suggested could be done. While there is no significant difference between the downy barbules of contour feathers and those of down feathers, the number of enlarged nodes varies within both kinds of feathers.

Pennaceous barbs

The pennaceous barbs of contour feathers have no special features, though the rami are thinner in ducks than in chickens. The morphology of the cells in the ramus has been described by Goepfert (1924) for the Domestic Goose (*Anser anser*), Green-winged Teal (*Anas crecca*), and the Pekin Duck. In order to study the pennaceous barbules we will turn for a moment from contour feathers to remiges, where they are most fully developed.

On the inner vane of a primary remex the distal barbules have an extremely thin base bearing four lobate ventral teeth with long tips. There are six very slender hooklets, the length of which increases distally. As many as six ventral cilia, also long and slender, point downward from the pennulum. As many as four dorsal cilia are enlarged into stout friction processes on some barbules of remiges.

Proximal barbules on the inner vane have a very thin, slender base, and bear four or five ventral teeth. The first two teeth are broad and blunt, and the rest are narrow and pointed. Dorsal spines are small. The pennulum is shorter than the base and carries two tiny prongs at each of the more distal nodes.

As compared with those on the inner vane, the distal barbules on the outer vane of a primary remex show longer ventral teeth, more slender and more numerous hooklets, and no dorsal cilia. The proximal barbules resemble those on the inner vane.

In summary, the distal barbules on the remiges of a duck differ from those of a chicken or turkey mainly in the presence of friction processes and long, slender hooklets. Proximal barbules in ducks have a relatively longer pennulum and smaller dorsal spines. Drawings and additional descriptions of duck barbules can be found in Chandler's monograph (1916: 327, figs. 28, 29, 30, and 104). The pennaceous barbules on the body contour feathers are smaller and simpler than those on the remiges in ducks in the same way as in chickens. The slightly more open texture of the vanes in ducks appears to be due to the thinness of the rami and the smaller size of the ventral flanges on the barbules.

Afterfeather

The afterfeather consists of a cluster of umbilical barbs (aftertuft) on virtually all body contour feathers. This structure is the most obvious diagnostic character of the feathers of ducks, geese, and swans. The only other birds to have an aftertuft on the body contour feathers are owls, New World vultures (Family Cathartidae), and the oilbird (*Steatornis caripensis*) (Miller, 1924a:3). This character will not serve for identifying remiges and rectrices, of course, because in most birds these feathers have an afterfeather of umbilical barbs. The aftertuft on the feathers of a Pekin Duck ranges from a length of 60 percent as long as the vanes (in upper minor tail coverts) to 2 percent (in facial feathers) and even complete absence (in upper marginal coverts of the prepatagium). On most feathers, it is between 9 and 25 percent as long as the vanes. A feather from the dorsal tract, for example, has an aftertuft about 12 percent as long as the main vanes; the aftertuft is composed of about 25 umbilical barbs (fig. 220). Its equivalent in a Mallard is shown as figure 172, type 6. The umbilical barbs are always downy, though the barbules are more or less reduced along a distal portion.

The only feathers with an exceptional afterfeather appear to be the ear coverts, for these have an aftershaft as well as umbilical barbs. On an ear covert 20.3 mm. long, the afterfeather was 12.5 mm. long and the aftershaft was 8.5 mm. The main vanes have an open texture, owing to the wide spacing of the barbs, the presence of reduced plumulaceous or reduced pennaceous barbules near the midline, and stylet barbules near the margin. There are no barbules on the rami of the aftershaft.

Related to the Pekin Duck are the Crested Ducks, named for the crest (more of a pompon) of feathers on the crown. The size and location of the crest as well as the dimensions and color of its feathers are extremely variable. In ducks with a large or moderately large crest, the roof of the cranium below it bulges upward. The morphology of the crest and its relationship to the cranium have been investigated by Requate (1959:264).

Remiges and Rectrices

The primary remiges have a greater range in length through the series in the Pekin Duck than in the chicken. The maximum length is about 240 mm. in both birds, but the longest primary is No. 7 or 8 in the duck, and No. 3 in the

chicken. The calamus is unusually long, more than one-third of the total length of the shaft in the primaries of an adult Pekin Duck. In juvenal primaries, the calamus accounts for only about one-fifth of the total length. A diverticulum of the lumen of the calamus extends as far as 20 mm. into the rachis of the remiges and rectrices (measured from the proximal edge of the superior umbilicus). It contains four or five pulp caps.

The vanes of the outermost primaries are not emarginate in the Pekin Duck as they are in many species of ducks. Emargination of the inner vanes of the outermost primaries varies considerably among anseriform birds (Humphrey and Clark, 1964:170).

The secondary remiges and the rectrices of the Pekin Duck are smaller than those of a chicken, and they are somewhat pointed at the tip. Like the primaries, they are curved toward the midline of the body, but the outer vane is only slightly narrower than the inner. The secondaries at the elbow (Nos. 12 to 16) are very asymmetrical and diversely shaped in the Mandarin Duck (*Aix galericulata*). The gross and the microscopic structures of these ornamental feathers have been investigated in detail by Brinckmann (1958).

The vanes of the primaries are stiffened in zones on each side of the shaft. They show a glazed sheen in the same areas on the underside of the feather. These effects are caused by an expanded ventral ridge (tegmen) along the proximal portion of the ventral edge of each ramus. The structure of the tegmen is described in chapter 5 on page 259 and is shown in figure 173. The tegmen is wider and hence overlaps more on the barbs of the inner vane than those of the outer. The sheen and its structural basis are characteristic of the primaries of ducks, geese, and swans (Richardson, 1943). They are useful for distinguishing these feathers from those of many other birds, including chickens. The secondaries and the rectrices show less sheen, owing to the lesser enlargement of the ventral ridge of the rami.

The barbules of the remiges have already been described. Distal barbules on the inner vane of the primaries have friction processes that help to distinguish primaries of ducks from those of chickens, which lack them. Since these structures also occur in many other birds, it is necessary to consider their exact shape and number if they are used for identifying feathers.

Down Feathers

Body downs

The presence of downs amidst the contour feathers is one of the chief characteristics of the feathering on anseriform birds. The gross appearance of the downs on certain species of ducks has been described by Workmann (1907). While the contour feathers are used as stuffing for pillows, the downs are used as insulation in the best quilts, sleeping bags, and parkas. The white downs of domestic geese are among the most commercially valuable feathers.

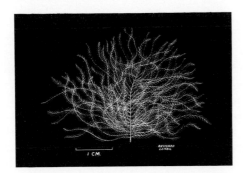

FIGURE 222.—Down feather from the dorsopelvic tract of a White Pekin Duck.

One down feather is situated in the center of the space bounded by four contour feathers. Other downs are also present—commonly there is a pair of them between adjacent contour feathers, approximately on the line of the feather row. According to Humphrey and Clark (1964:172), "the 'central' down plumule is always larger and in some species (e.g., *Anas penelope*) is darker in colour." In a 4-month-old Pekin Duck, however, the downs do not differ in this way.

The downs amidst the contour feathers are about 16 to 37 mm. long (fig. 222), and the offcenter downs are commonly as large as those in the center. Larger downs are more abundant than smaller ones, but there are no distinct categories of size. The calamus is 0.5 to 1.5 mm. long, representing about 3 to 4 percent of the total length. A rachis is always present, although it is minute in small downs. It is about 1 to 20 mm. long, representing about 8 to 60 percent of the total length.

Unusually large down feathers occur in the lateral body apterium, close to the pectorosternal tract. They are as much as 58 mm. long with a rachis up to 44 mm. long, nearly 76 percent of the total length. The largest of these feathers can almost be considered semiplumes because their rachis is nearly as long as the longest barbs, and the distal part of the vanes is more lax than fluffy.

In all downs, most of the barbs arise from the rachis, but there are also a few umbilical barbs. The vanes are generally amorphous, without the evident symmetry and upper and lower surfaces of chicken downs. As seen from one end, a duck down is rounded whereas a chicken down is flattened. In the small downs and many of the large ones, the barbs are furnished with barbules to their tips. Some of the large downs on the lateral body apterium have barbs that are bare at the tip. These rami lie straight and do not entangle each other, an

indication that the barbules play a major role in entangling the barbs. The large subterminal nodes undoubtedly are important in this, but their action is not known. On barbs where barbules are reduced toward the distal end, these nodes are lost before length is shortened. The margin of a vane with such barbs has a rather lax texture. Downy barbs with branched tips, as sometimes found in contour feathers and remiges, have not been found in down feathers.

Our histological preparations of the skin show that the follicles of the down feathers are furnished with feather muscles. The bundles are fewer in number and less regularly arranged than those that link the follicles of the contour feathers. They are discussed further in chapter 8. Since muscles are present with the down feathers among contour feathers (as on ducks) as well as with those on the apteria (as on chickens), they cannot be used as a criterion for separating the two categories of definitive downs.

Oil gland feathers

The nipple of the oil gland bears at its tip two circular tufts of down feathers that are 22 to 25 mm. long. Their calamus is 3 to 4 mm. long, about 13 percent of the total length, and thus much larger in these feathers than in body downs. The rachis, however, measures about 6 mm., and is thus well within the range seen in body downs. Widely spaced downy barbs arise from the rachis as well as from the rim of the superior umbilicus. They bear reduced plumulaceous barbules. There is no hyporachis. The structure of oil gland feathers varies among species of ducks. Our specimens from a Blue-winged Teal (*Anas discors*) had only umbilical barbs, without any sign of a rachis.

Filoplumes

Filoplumes occur in clusters of four or five on each side of the contour feathers. They also occur singly on each side of many down feathers, those on the apteria as well as those on the tracts. Finding filoplumes beside the downs was unexpected because in the chicken, coots, and several charadriiform birds, Gerber (1939) found filoplumes accompanying only contour feathers. The filoplumes on a White Pekin Duck are as much as 30 mm. long, the longest ones being on the pectoral tract. They are very slender and inconspicuous. There are three to five apical barbs (not pairs of barbs), and these carry tiny stylet barbules. The filoplumes beside the downs differ from those beside the contour feathers only in their smaller size.

COMMON PIGEON

Pigeon feathers can generally be recognized by a combination of features of the rachis, the downy barbules, and the afterfeather. Their color in the Common Pigeon, is a result of melanin, the structure of the barbs, and an overlay of powder, as discussed in chapter 7.

Body Contour Feathers

Gross appearance

The body contour feathers are as much as 100 mm. long, the longest being the under tail coverts. Most feathers,

FIGURE 223.—Contour feather from the middle of the dorso-pelvic tract of a Common Pigeon.

however, are no more than 60 mm. long. They are most commonly oval to oblong with a rounded tip (fig. 223); feathers on the ventral caudal and abdominal tracts are obovate, and those on the crural tract are round.

The calamus contains saucer-shaped pulp caps; these are joined to the inner surface of the wall and do not shrink to a central strand, as in chicken feathers. A narrow collar of feather sheath often remains on the calamus at the level of the superior umbilicus, just above the surface of the skin. The rachis commonly swells at its lower end, and, proceeding distally, reaches its maximum width at one-fourth to one-third the total distance to the tip. Characteristically, it then tapers sharply, a feature that is more conspicuous than the swelling at the lower end. On a feather from the pelvic tract, for example, the width of the shaft at four levels is as follows: superior umbilicus, 0.85 mm.; one-fourth of distance to tip, 1.7 mm.; three-fourths of distance to tip, 0.3 mm.; and tip, less than 0.1 mm. The rachis of an abdominal feather is only slightly wider than the calamus but it tapers very sharply—from 0.9 to 0.1 mm. in a span of 10 mm. Thickness varies in the same way as width but to a lesser extent. The proximal portion of the rachis is stiff, whereas the distal, slender portion is flexible. Similar features were also noted in certain turkey feathers, but they are generally uncommon in birds. In pigeon feathers, as in turkey feathers, the rachis tends to taper in the same region as the transition of the vanes from plumulaceous to pennaceous. It is also seen, however, in downs, semiplumes, and contour feathers with only a margin of open pennaceous texture. Coverts of the wing and tail, on the other hand, have a rachis that tapers gradually along its full length.

The rachis of many pigeon feathers is flat or faintly contoured on the undersurface. The median groove is wide and shallow, and the lateral ridges are often slight. On feathers where the groove is faint, the groove sometimes begins a short distance above the superior umbilicus.

Downy barbs

The downy portion of the vanes is generally thick and dense; it accounts for 20 to 60 percent of the length in most body contour feathers. Semiplumes or contour feathers are close enough together in most places so that the bases of their vanes touch each other. This situation creates a dense, continuous mat of down beneath the exposed pennaceous ends of the feathers. Since the lowermost barbs project downward, the layer extends to the surface of the skin, and there is little open space around the bases of the feathers.

In texture, the downy portion of pigeon feathers resembles chicken and turkey feathers more than duck feathers. This region of the vanes has a thatched appearance, owing to the overlapping of barbs with regularly oriented barbules. Barbules on the upper surface point obliquely outward and toward the tip of the feather, whereas those on the undersurface point perpendicularly outward from the rachis toward the margin. The barbules of a given barb have a wide angular range, with the result that the vanules they compose are never flat. Branched downy barbs have not been found. With this exception, the factors responsible for downy texture reach their maximum degree in the under tail coverts. The bases of these feathers are exceedingly thick and fluffy.

The plumulaceous barbules are long, up to 4 mm., a factor that is responsible for much of the gross similarity in the downy portions of pigeon and chicken contour feathers. The base of a plumulaceous barbule is straplike with a slightly swollen node at its distal end (fig. 167, A). Subsequent nodes on the pennulum are very large, each bearing four conical or peg-shaped prongs that point either directly outward or slightly distally (fig. 167, B, D). Enlarged nodes are most numerous (up to 12) on barbules near the proximal end of a barb. Distal to the large nodes, the internodes become longer and the nodes are reduced, chiefly through loss of their prongs (fig. 167, C). These features of downy barbules are characteristic for many pigeons, but not the crowned pigeons (Goura spp.). On the other hand, they differ from the conditions in other birds except certain tinamous (Chandler, 1916:361). The structure of the downy barbules is thus useful for identifying pigeon feathers.

Pennaceous barbs

There is generally a narrow zone of pennaceous texture on each side of the rachis, medial to the downy portion of the vanes (fig. 223). The zones are denser than the main pennaceous portion of the vanes, not more open as in chicken and turkey feathers. This difference is based on the fact that the narrow pennaceous zones are created by closely set barbs with pennaceous rather than curled-base barbules. The width of the zones is asymmetrical in some feathers (for example, dorsal cervical tract) and is greater on the inner vane. On the upper secondary coverts, the zones widen abruptly, opening into the full pennaceous portion of the vanes and rapidly confining the downy texture to the margins.

The transition from downy to pennaceous texture takes place within a span of a few barbs. The margin of the feather is often lax in this region, though to a lesser extent than in chicken feathers. The pennaceous portion of the vanes is generally closely knit. It may grade into a marginal band of open pennaceous texture, but there are no distinct zones of different densities.

An unusual case of asymmetrical vanes is presented by several of the distal feathers in the row of under major secondary coverts. The inner vane here is pennaceous except for a relatively short downy region at the base (fig. 224). The outer vane, however, is pennaceous in a narrow zone beside the rachis and lightly downy in a wider zone along the entire margin. There is a sharp line of demarcation between the two textures. On the outermost coverts, pennaceous texture disappears below the tip of the outer vane, and downy texture extends to the rachis. The barbs are only weakly fluffy in the marginal zone, owing to the presence of reduced plumulaceous barbules. This peculiar character of the vanes appears to be an adaptation for allowing air between the feathers and the skin to escape without turbulence. The proximal coverts in the row are ordinary in appearance; they are mostly pennaceous, with marginal zones of downy texture at the base.

The structure of the pennaceous barbs, including the attachment of barbules to the rami, has been discussed and illustrated in detail by Mascha (1905), Spöttel (1914:360), and Chandler (1916:359, pl. 29). The following account is based on these sources as well as our own observations. We will examine the barbules of the primary remiges before considering the somewhat reduced form on the body contour feathers.

The distal barbules in the inner vane of a primary remex are marked by a diagonal row of pigment spots in the nuclei of the cells comprising the bases. The ventral teeth are very broad and triangular. The pennulum is approximately as long as the base and is arched upward. It bears four to six hooklets that are progressively longer distally in the series. These grade into four to six ventral cilia that become shorter distally. Several dorsal cilia are present, the first two of which are modified into friction processes (described in ch. 5 on pp. 260–261).

Proximal barbules have fewer and smaller pigment spots than distal barbules. There are three to five narrow ventral teeth with curved, pointed tips, and above them are four or five dorsal spines. The pennulum is very slender and is longer than the base when intact. Nodal prongs are absent.

The barbules of the outer vane are more heavily pigmented than barbules of the inner vane. The distal barbules as a whole are arched upward. As compared with their equivalents on the inner vane, the ventral teeth are smaller, and the six or seven hooklets are shorter and more slender. Ventral cilia are shorter and heavier, and dorsal cilia, also shorter, are not modified as friction processes. The proximal barbules at the proximal end of a barb are like those of an inner vane. Near the tip of each barb, ventral teeth become separated and curved, assuming a form intermediate between typical teeth and typical cilia.

The pennaceous barbules of body contour feathers are the same on both vanes. Those on pelvic feathers differ from those on the remiges as follows:

Distal barbules.—There is only one ventral tooth, and it is moderately large and pointed. Pennulum is relatively longer.

FIGURE 224.—Under major secondary covert from a Common Pigeon.

Hooklets are shorter and they project perpendicularly from the pennulum. Proximal hooklets have one or two prickles on the distal edge. There are two to four ventral cilia and they are much shorter and blunter than those on the remiges. Dorsal cilia are absent.

Proximal barbules.—Base is narrower and ventral teeth are smaller. There is no ventral flange as seen in chicken feathers. Pennulum is very fine and nearly as long as the base. Dorsal spines are smaller than those on the barbules of the remiges.

Pennaceous barbules on feathers from the pectoral tract (and probably elsewhere on the ventral tracts) are still further reduced. Both distal and proximal barbules are very long and narrow. Barbicels are shorter and more uniform. Distal barbules have a single hooklet, which lacks prickles. As a result of these changes, the distal and proximal barbules come to resemble each other more closely on these feathers than they do elsewhere.

Afterfeather

One of the most obvious characteristics of pigeon feathers is the small size or absence of the afterfeather. A hyporachis is never present, even on the ear coverts. The remiges, rectrices, their coverts, and feathers of the femoral tract have an aftertuft composed of as many as 40 barbs; it is 4 to 8 percent as long as the vanes. These barbs represent the type 6 afterfeather. Feathers of the interscapular, dorsal, pelvic, pectoral, abdominal, and crural tracts have only one to three barbs at each corner of the umbilicus. They are 6 to 8 percent as long as the vanes. These barbs project parallel to the rachis on the underside of the vanes, which distinguishes them from the adjacent lowermost barbs on the shaft. Finally, there are the dorsal cervical and capital feathers, which have no umbilical barbs. These feathers represent the type 7 afterfeather (figure 172).

Remiges and Rectrices

The primary remiges are from 113 (primary 1) to 194 mm. (primary 9) long. The outermost primary (10) is about as long as the seventh primary, 176 mm. The calamus accounts for 24 to 28 percent of the total length. The pith of the rachis starts unusually far down inside the calamus, 20 mm. below the superior umbilicus. On the other hand, the lumen of the calamus extends into the rachis about 15 mm. beyond the superior umbilicus. The pith is partitioned by one to three pairs of longitudinal lamellae that run obliquely upward from a median septum to the spaces between the cortical ridges (Spöttel, 1914:377). The sides of the rachis carry a row of low ribs that each run ventrally and proximally from the attachment of a ramus. The vanes are long and narrow, and the tip is pointed, particularly on the inner primaries. The tip is situated on the outer vane in primaries 1 to 5 and gradually shifts to a midline position in the remaining feathers. The base of the outer vane and the margin of the base of the inner vane are weakly fluffy for a short distance. The outer vane of primaries 6 to 8 is emarginate to a slight degree.

The secondary remiges are about 60 to 120 mm. long, the shortest being those which insert on the elbow. They are curved medially and end in a bluntly rounded tip. Both vanes are downy along their margins for a short distance at the base. All the remiges and rectrices have a V-shaped cluster of umbilical barbs as an afterfeather.

The rectrices are 120 to 138 mm. long, the central pair being the longest. Unlike the remiges, they are obovate. The inner vane is always wider than the outer, and the broadening of the distal part of the feather takes place entirely on the inner vane. The pith of the rachis starts well below the superior umbilicus, but the lumen of the calamus does not extend into the rachis. The shaft of the outermost rectrices is very stiff, probably an adaptation for the use of the tail as an airfoil. When flying slowly, a pigeon holds its rectrices in a fan 120° or more in angular extent (Gray, 1953:plate XI). Just before landing, the tail may be spread even more so that it is almost semicircular. The stiff shaft of the outer rectrices apparently enables the feathers to create lifting or braking force under these conditions.

Down Feathers and Semiplumes

Down feathers

Down feathers are uncommon on pigeons, but they are not absent as stated by Chandler (1916:359). They can be found on the lateral body apterium and the pelvic apterium as far back as the base of the tail. They do not occur amidst contour feathers or beside the flight feathers. Many small downy feathers are actually semiplumes or even a form of contour feather. The down feathers are 12 to 28 mm. long and are approximately circular (orbicular) (fig. 225). As in contour feathers, the rachis is as wide as the calamus or wider at the proximal end, and it tapers sharply a short distance higher. The rachis is recognizable even in the smallest downs, where it is still 4 mm. long, one-third of the overall length. In some downs, the rachis approaches the length of the longest barbs, and hence these feathers grade into semiplumes.

FIGURE 225.—Down feather from the lateral body apterium of a Common Pigeon.

The smaller down feathers are uniformly plumulaceous, and the barbules are reduced only near the tips of the barbs. Larger downs have a narrow margin of lax texture around the major portion of the vanes, which is still fluffy. This fringe is produced by a more extensive reduction of the terminal barbules and by their orientation closer to the ramus. These feathers also show very narrow zones of closely knit pennaceous texture beside the rachis. The afterfeather of the downs consists of two or three short barbs at each corner of the superior umbilicus.

Semiplumes

Semiplumes occur on the abdominal, ventral caudal, ventral alar, and lateral body tracts. They are 25 to 42 mm. long. They are obovate with a broadly rounded tip. The rachis is conspicuously swollen at the lower end and sharply tapered at about the middle. Narrow zones of closely knit pennaceous texture are situated beside the thick segment of the rachis; they come close together and disappear beside the distal, fine portion of the rachis. Because barbules are oriented away from the shaft on the underside of the vanes, the extent of these pennaceous zones can be seen more easily here than on the dorsal side. The vanes have a moderately thick, downy texture for about the proximal half of their length. Distally, they are characterized by a fringe of lax texture, which is wider than that seen on the down feathers. It is flat and open instead of thick and dense as in typical downy texture. Making up the fringe are barbs with typical plumulaceous barbules at the basal end and reduced pennaceous barbules on the remainder. The barbs radiate from the rachis and do not lie parallel to each other like the open pennaceous barbs of a contour feather. These semiplumes grade into contour feathers by the development of interlocking pennaceous barbules and a typical pennaceous vane, starting near the tip of the feather. The afterfeather of the semiplumes is like that on the downs.

The feathers on the crural tract combine features of contour feathers, downs, and semiplumes, yet are not typical of any of these. They are nearly circular, 16 to 25 mm. long. The rachis is 8 to 10 mm. long and is slender throughout. The vanes are lightly fluffy for about 60 percent of their length near the rachis and lax in the remaining band around the margin. Faint zones of pennaceous texture can be seen on each side of the rachis. One to three umbilical barbs are present at each corner of the superior umbilicus. The feathers resemble downs in their softness and short rachis, yet resemble contour feathers or semiplumes in the flat, lax portion of the vanes. This texture is created by barbs with reduced pennaceous barbules that do not interlock. Another point of resemblance to contour feathers and semiplumes is that the crural feathers are situated in the rows of a feather tract, not randomly and widely spaced as in an apterium. This condition leads us to consider these feathers as an unusual form of semiplume.

Oil gland feathers

In pigeons, the oil gland does not carry any feathers.

Powder Feathers

General nature

The down feathers, semiplumes, and downy portions of most contour feathers of a Common Pigeon shed an extremely fine, white powder. It is appropriate to discuss this property of pigeon feathers as a separate topic because on the one hand it is not confined to a single structural type of feather, and on the other hand it is the basis for certain specially modified feathers. In many birds, the special powder-shedding feathers have the structure of downs and hence are called powder downs. In pigeons, however, these feathers are modified semiplumes as well as downs. It is best to refer to all these feathers as powder feathers (*pulvipluma*) except where their specific structure is known.

Powder feathers adhere to a hard surface readily with a little pressure, although they do not feel sticky. Presumably the powder has something to do with this. The adhesive force appears to be other than an electrostatic phenomenon, but its exact nature is not known.

The powder grains are derived from cells that surround the differentiating barbules in a growing feather. They are not fragments of the sheath or the feather itself. In herons, powder is shed continuously by special ever-growing feathers, but in pigeons it is shed only while the feathers are emerging from their sheaths. The amount of powder that may be found in a pigeon's plumage thus varies according to the bird's stage of molt (Schüz, 1927:111). The origin of the powder and the histology of powder feathers are discussed in chapter 7 (p. 386).

Birds of many species have powder feathers, but among domestic birds they occur only in pigeons. These feathers are in fact characteristic of the family of pigeons and doves, the Columbidae. Among Common Pigeons, the powder feathers are developed to a small degree in feral birds, but are moderately to highly developed in several domestic varieties (Eiselen, 1939:411). They have been mostly eliminated from domestic birds by pigeon fanciers in the United States. Highly modified powder feathers can be found in birds of the Archangel and certain other varieties (Levi, 1957:244).

Distribution

The distribution of powder feathers on a feral Common Pigeon is continuous on the sides of the trunk from the axilla to the base of the tail. The distribution cannot be mapped precisely because there is a gradation from normal feathers, which shed a small quantity of powder, to powder feathers, which shed a moderate quantity. Powder feathers occur in the posterior lateral portion of the pectorosternal tract, in a band from here across the lateral body apterium to the dorsopelvic tract, on the dorsal portion of the femoral tract, on the lateral pelvic apterium all the way to the base of the tail, and on the lateral portions of the abdominal tract (fig. 226). Within this pattern of distribution, powder feathers are most abundant and tend to be most highly modified at two locations—anterior to the thigh and anterolateral to the tail. Pigeons of many varieties are said to have essentially this same pattern of distribution (Eiselen, 1939:411). Those of certain other varieties, however, have powder feathers chiefly on a portion of the pectorosternal tract and across the lateral body apterium but have either few or none elsewhere.

Structure

Powder feathers of an ordinary pigeon show several unusual features during their development, as described in chapter 7. When fully grown, they are like non-powder-shedding feathers in structure but differ in the appearance of their downy barbs. These are less fluffy and oriented less regularly than normal. They are matted together by the powder, which is produced around them. Pennaceous and lax portions of contour feathers and semiplumes are normal since they do not give rise to powder. The afterfeather of all pigeon powder feathers is a cluster of powder-shedding umbilical barbs.

Downy barbs from a powder feather must be cleaned before their microscopic structure can be seen. Usual methods for washing feathers with detergent solution or various solvents are ineffectual, however. We have found that powder feathers can be cleaned perfectly by immersing them in a detergent solution and subjecting them to ultrasonic waves, as produced by a sonifier, for one to two minutes (ch. 10, p. 642). Once cleaned, the barbs are just like ordinary downy barbs of a pigeon, even to the size of the nodes. They differ from the barbs on powder downs of herons and frogmouths (family Podargidae), which are less well developed than those of ordinary downs (Schüz, 1927).

Archangel Pigeons (a variety of Common Pigeons) shed more powder than feral pigeons or most other domestic varieties of pigeons. Body contour feathers of Archangels, as compared with other pigeons, are slower to emerge from their sheaths and are commonly rolled up along the margin at the base. When these are teased apart, powder and fragments of external pulp caps are shed. The plumulaceous portion of the vanes tends to be less fluffy than on feral pigeon feathers. This is due to the fact that the barbs and their barbules are shorter, the barbules lie closer against the rami, and the barbs are more clogged with powder. In

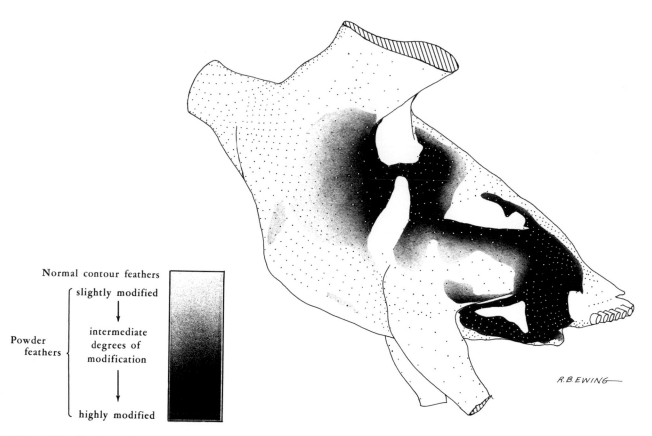

Normal contour feathers

Powder feathers {
  slightly modified
  ↓
  intermediate degrees of modification
  ↓
  highly modified
}

R.B. EWING

FIGURE 226.—Distribution of powder feathers on the left side of an Archangel Pigeon. The density of the shading indicates the degree of modification toward powder feather morphology.

cleaned feathers it can be seen that the pennulum of a downy barbule is finer, fewer of its nodes are enlarged, and even these have smaller, less distinct prongs than normal. The distal nodes are very faintly swollen.

The most highly modified powder feathers of Archangel Pigeons, as in feral pigeons, are those on the sides of the body. Their distribution is like that on the feral pigeon but is easier to plot because the feathers are distinctive in appearance. It is shown in figure 226, with shading of varying density used to indicate the degree of modification in the feathers. The transition from slightly modified to greatly modified powder feathers can be seen especially well in the posterior lateral portion of the pectorosternal tract and the posterior dorsal portion of the femoral tract.

Series of feathers from these areas show increasing slowness in unfurling, decreasing thickness of the rachis, increasing reduction of the barbules, and increasing amounts of powder. When the feathers are open and cleaned of powder, they are all found to have the same basic structure as their homologs on a feral pigeon. Owing to their prolonged period of unfurling, however, they are seen more commonly in an immature than in a mature stage. Moderately modified and highly modified powder feathers are each shown at three stages of maturation in figure 227.

Moderately modified powder feathers are contour feathers (as shown in fig. 227) and semiplumes. Even while en-

sheathed, they can be distinguished from less modified or unmodified powder feathers because they are curved upward convexly from base to tip. Also, the vanes unroll slowly even after the sheath has flaked off. Barbules at the surface break loose from the powder in which they are embedded, and create a nap on the surface of the rolled-up feather. Pennaceous barbs, if present, unfurl readily, but downy barbs open more slowly. At the core of the feather is a long chain of external pulp caps. They do not have the cylindrical form of pulp caps in ordinary feathers but are compressed against the rachis; their cross section is approximately semilunar. Impressions of the barbs are evident on the two sides away from the rachis. The pennaceous barbs are identical with those on ordinary pigeon contour feathers, even to their faint iridescent sheen over dark pigmentation. In a powder feather of semiplume structure, the barbs that make up the lax margin of the vanes carry smaller, simplified pennaceous or stylet barbules. Like pennaceous barbs, they are free of powder. Details of the downy barbs cannot be seen until they have completely shed their powder and the barbules are freed from the sheetlike vanules in which they have been held. The barbules are more slender than normal, and they have slight bulges, constrictions, and kinks along the internodes. The rachis of a moderately modified powder feather is like that on an ordinary contour feather or semiplume of a pigeon. It is thick proximally, sharply tapered, and slender distally (fig. 227, C).

The highly modified powder feathers of an Archangel Pigeon appear to be stiff, hard quills while they are ensheathed (fig. 227, D). They are from 16 to 22 mm. long and from 1.1 to 1.3 mm. thick. Unlike typical ensheathed feathers, they are not tapered distally but are of uniform diameter or even enlarged. The calamus is unusually short, 0.8 to 1.0 mm. long, with the result that the feathers can easily be dislodged from their follicles. The entire feather is curved downward from base to tip, and the surface is smooth except for a tuft of exposed barbs at the tip. Characteristically, the feather is straw yellow for most of its length, and thus appears to be made of horn. This effect is not far from the truth because the tightly furled feather is virtually a solid mass of keratin. The barbs are embedded in abundant powder, and the whole

structure is translucent. Later, there develop long cracks in the surface that progress distally in spirals from the rachis; as air enters through them, the feather turns white.

These feathers are slower to open than less highly modified powder feathers. They retain their original shape for a while even after the feather sheath has flaked off. Gradually, they split along the cracks into 8 to 14 fascicles of barbs. At this point the highly modified powder feathers begin to lose their distinctive appearance. They can still be told from the less modified feathers by the absence of pennaceous barbs at the tip, smoother surface (fewer free barbules), vestiges of yellow, and the smaller calamus (fig. 227, E).

If a fascicle is teased apart, it is found to consist of 10 to 12 laterally compressed barbs, each of which has a slender

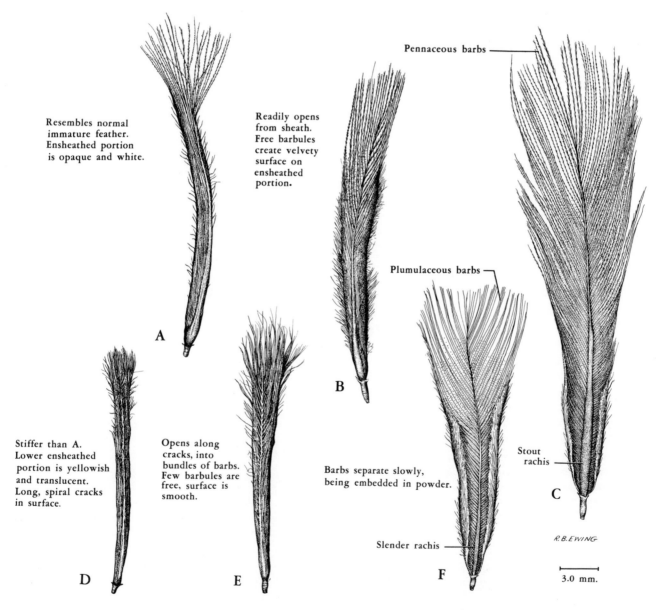

Resembles normal immature feather. Ensheathed portion is opaque and white.

Readily opens from sheath. Free barbules create velvety surface on ensheathed portion.

Pennaceous barbs

Plumulaceous barbs

Stiffer than A. Lower ensheathed portion is yellowish and translucent. Long, spiral cracks in surface.

Opens along cracks, into bundles of barbs. Few barbules are free, surface is smooth.

Barbs separate slowly, being embedded in powder.

Stout rachis

Slender rachis

R.B. EWING

3.0 mm.

A   B   C   D   E   F

FIGURE 227.—Powder feathers of an Archangel Pigeon.

A to C, modified contour feathers.
D to F, highly modified down feather (powder down).

A and D, ensheathed; B and E, emerging from sheath; C and F, opened.

ramus and a pair of vanules in the form of plates. These, in turn, are composed of reduced plumulaceous barbules embedded in sticky powder. After the powder has been dislodged, the barbules are revealed to be shorter and finer and to have much smaller nodes than those of less modified powder feathers. Recalling the plumulaceous barbules in various powder feathers, it becomes clear that their size and condition are inversely proportional to the quantity of powder around them.

As the powder feathers lose their powder and break open, they come to look more like ordinary feathers (fig. 227, F). The rachis is slender throughout, even as little as one-tenth the thickness of the calamus at its base. It varies in length from about 5 to 8 mm. This is considerably shorter than the longest barb in most powder feathers, and hence these feathers qualify as downs. They can be referred to more specifically as powder downs. In some specimens, however, the rachis and longest barb are equal, which puts these feathers at the boundary between downs and semiplumes. The afterfeather on all these powder feathers consists of many more umbilical barbs than are present on less modified powder feathers or ordinary feathers.

Fat quills

The most highly modified powder feathers, indeed among the most peculiar of all feathers, are to be found on two old German varieties of Common Pigeon, the Nuremberg Swallows and the South German Shield Pigeons. Some of the feathers on the sides of the body resemble the unopened, highly modified powder downs of Archangels except that they remain furled. Most remarkably, they contain a homogeneous, yellow, organic fat in place of powder. The growth and histology of these feathers and the formation and properties of the fat have been studied by Eiselen (1939). The feathers are basically downs, and the fat develops from

precursor cells in the same location as those for powder. The feathers can be referred to as fat quills, by translation of their German name, Schmalzkielen. According to Levi (1957:180), the fat exudes from the feathers, but Eiselen (1939:414) stated that it is liberated only after the pigeon splits a feather with its beak. The secretion is spread to the entire plumage when a bird preens, giving it a greasy look. "For this reason, the name 'Grease' or 'Silk Swallow' has sometimes been applied to the variety [Nuremberg Swallow]" (Levi, 1957: 180).

Filoplumes

Filoplumes accompany most of the contour feathers, but they are absent beside the powder feathers. They occur either singly or in pairs (except with the flight feathers), at the sides of the contour feather. If only one filoplume is present, it may be either lateral or medial to the contour feather. Rarely, two filoplumes can be found issuing from separate follicles at one side of the host, with none on the other side. Variations in the prevalence and number of filoplumes in pigeons may reflect temporary differences in growth and molting. The significance of these variations among tracts cannot be judged without a thorough study. The remiges and rectrices are each surrounded by as many as eight filoplumes. These are unevenly spaced and may be arranged in several groups of two to four each.

Filoplumes are up to 25 mm. long. The shaft is flattened dorsoventrally, and it carries two or three pairs of apical barbs with stylet or reduced plumulaceous barbules. The pigmentation generally matches that of the pennaceous portion of the adjacent contour feather. Although a filoplume is concealed, it is thus as dark as the exposed portion of the contour feather and not necessarily white like the contour feather's downy, concealed base.

COMMON COTURNIX

The molts and plumages of the Common Coturnix have recently been studied by Lyon (1962). Apart from color, however, nothing appears to have been published about the appearance and structure of normal feathers in this species. The feathers can be recognized as being gallinaceous by the combination of the long aftershaft and the form of the pennaceous barbules, which are described on page 339. Tinamous and trogons are the only birds besides the galliforms to have a long afterfeather that includes a long aftershaft (type 2). The feathers of the first two groups differ from those of galliforms in color and in the character of the cilia and ventral teeth on the distal barbules (see Chandler, 1916:345, 372 for details). Coturnix feathers can be distinguished from those of most other gallinaceous birds by their small size. It would be difficult to separate these feathers from those of other quails, but it probably could be done by closely comparing the color and shape of the vanes. The exposed portions of the feathers of Common Coturnix are variously striped and barred in black, white, cinnamon, buffy brown, and

buffy yellow. Down feathers and the downy portions of other feathers are smoke gray. Albinism is rare and appears to be a sexlinked, recessive trait (Lauber, 1964).

Body Contour Feathers

Gross appearance

The body contour feathers are as much as 60 mm. long, the longest being on the lateral border of the pectoral tract. Most of them are approximately oval with a rounded or broad, slightly pointed tip. Feathers of the femoral tract are obovate. Except at the middorsal line, the vanes show a slight asymmetry in color pattern as well as in curvature and texture. The rachis is as thick as the calamus at its proximal end, and it tapers evenly to the tip. It has a shallow ventral groove.

Downy barbs

The downy texture of the vanes varies from 9 percent of the total length in capital feathers and marginal coverts to about

68 percent in femoral feathers. Some feathers (for example, on the sternal, abdominal, and crural tracts) are classed as semiplumes because they are entirely soft. Actually, only about 30 to 60 percent of the vanes is truly downy, that is, dense and fluffy. The remainder is lax, with narrow barbs creating flat open vanes. Most body contour feathers have a narrow zone of open texture on each side of the rachis, medial to the downy part. This zone is created by the presence of curled-base barbules, as in the chicken. The barbules themselves are shorter and less curled than those on chicken feathers. The downy texture is also like that in chicken feathers and shows regularly oriented barbs and barbules. The downy texture is lightly fluffy on dorsal feathers and moderately fluffy on pectoral and femoral feathers. The degree of fluffiness is related to the length of the barbules and the vertical angle at which they project from the ramus. In many cases, barbs are downy at the proximal end and lax at the distal end, owing to the reduction of the barbules and their angular range. Downy barbs with branched tips have not been found. Plumulaceous barbules on a contour feather have a maximum length of about 2 mm. Their nodes are distinct, each bearing four short, rounded prongs and marked by a spot of pigment. The diameter of the pennulum is uniform from one cell to the next until it tapers near the tip.

Pennaceous barbs

Lax texture occurs at the transition from the downy to the pennaceous parts of the vanes. It is also common farther distally, that is, along the margin of the pennaceous part of the vane. The open pennaceous texture seen in many chicken feathers does not, however, occur in feathers of Common Coturnix.

The tips of the upper major primary coverts differ between early and later generations of feathers. These differences appear to be the best indicators for distinguishing between quails that are less than 1 year old (young-of-the-year) and those that are older (adults). In young birds, the tips of the feathers are slightly frayed and either rounded or pointed, whereas in adults they are intact and blunt. The young feathers may represent either the first or the second juvenal plumage. The latter differs from the definitive adult plumage and has therefore been called a first alternate plumage (Lyon, 1962).

The characters of the pennaceous barbules can be seen best on the primary remiges. In the middle of the inner vane, near the rachis, the distal barbules have a base about half as long as the pennulum. Nuclei and boundaries of the basal cells are invisible. There are four moderately narrow ventral teeth with uneven margins and pointed tips. Up to six hooklets increase in length toward the distal end of the row. They are of nearly uniform diameter and do not have prickles. There are six or seven ventral cilia, the proximal ones are slightly curved at the tip; they shorten distally and grade into nodal prongs. The dorsal side of the pennulum

has no barbicels above the teeth and hooklets. Distally, however, there are four short, pointed dorsal cilia; these are not modified as friction processes.

Proximal barbules of the inner vane have a base that is longer than the pennulum. Nuclei in the basal cells are faintly visible by their differential refractility. There are four very narrow ventral teeth, the tips of which are curved and pointed. Above them are two or three low dorsal spines. The pennulum is very slender and devoid of nodes or barbicels.

Distal barbules in the middle of the outer vane, as compared with those of the inner vane, have a longer, narrower base with smaller teeth. The distal hooklets are longer, and all are thicker in the shank. Dorsal and ventral cilia are much shorter and stouter; ventral cilia do not grade into hooklets. The pennulum does not taper but ends at a wide cell that bears a pair of cilia.

The proximal barbules of the outer vane are like those of the inner vane except that the pennulum is shorter.

The pennaceous barbules of a dorsal feather differ from those on the inner vane of a primary remex as follows: The base of the distal barbules is longer and narrower, and it has a ventral flange at the junction with the ramus. The boundaries of the cells are obvious, being more lightly pigmented than the bodies. There is a single small ventral tooth with a blunt tip, followed by one or two slender hooklets and about four very small ventral cilia. The base of the proximal barbules is like that of the distal barbules, and the pennulum merges into it. Except for two dorsal spines, no barbicels are visible from above.

Some individual quails shed fine white particles from their body contour feathers when they are handled. Microscopic examination reveals many clear, colorless globules, about 1.8 to 5.0 μ in diameter, on the surface of the barbs. They are too large and regular in shape to be powder granules, and their shape also argues against their being fragments of the feather sheath. Their true nature is unknown. Possibly this is the same powderlike material found by Schüz (1927:105) in chicken feathers.

Afterfeather

The afterfeather is relatively larger on the feathers of Common Coturnix than on those of chickens or turkeys. It is 40 percent as long as the vanes in interscapular feathers and 78 percent as long in feathers from the posterior portions of the dorsopelvic and femoral tracts. The aftershaft extends nearly to the tip of the afterfeather in all contour feathers except the alar coverts. In these feathers, it is relatively shorter, especially on the major coverts of the remiges. There is thus a gradation across the wing from a type 2 afterfeather (fig. 172, p. 254) on the anterior upper marginal coverts of the prepatagium to a type 3 afterfeather on the posterior coverts and a type 6 (aftertuft) on the remiges. The vanes of the afterfeather are entirely fluffy, with long downy barbules out to the tips of the barbs.

Remiges and Rectrices

The primary remiges range in length from about 60 to 90 mm., the longest feathers being the eighth and ninth. This contrasts with the situation in the chicken and the turkey, where the longest remiges are in the proximal or middle third of the series. Hence, the feathered wing of a Common Coturnix proportionately is narrower, when unfolded, than those of the two other birds.

The shape of the individual remiges varies from approximately oblong in the first primary to long oval with a pointed tip in the outermost feathers. The outer primaries are also emarginate—No. 8 on the outer vane, No. 9 on both vanes, and No. 10 on the inner vane. All the primaries are curved medially and ventrally, the medial curvature being most pronounced in the outer feathers. Transversely, the vanes are also slightly curved downward. A faint sheen is visible on the underside of several outer primaries in a long zone near the inner margin. It results from the fact that the vanes are paler here than elsewhere. The ventral ridge is not expanded.

Rami of the outer vane, however, have an unusual fringe on the ventral ridge. It projects toward the distal side along the full length of the barbs. The villi are slender, pointed, and very irregular, being variously thickened at the base, bent, or forked. They are definitely outgrowths, not frayed strips. Similar but simpler structures, it may be recalled, occur in the same location on the remiges of ducks (fig. 173, C, D).

The afterfeather of the primaries is a U-shaped row of downy umbilical barbs, 8 to 9 percent as long as the vanes.

The secondary remiges on the forearm range in length from about 58 mm. (No. 1) to about 50 mm. (No. 12), and those on the elbow decrease to about 40 mm. They are much less variable than the secondaries of a chicken. All the feathers are oval with a rounded tip and are slightly curved toward the body. They are patterned on the outer vane, which is exposed, and colored uniformly on the inner vane, which is concealed. The umbilical barbs are 19 percent as long as the vanes.

The rectrices of a Common Coturnix are much simpler than those of a chicken or a turkey. Their length ranges from 39 mm. in the central pair to about 19 mm. in the outermost pair. Each feather is a narrow oval and is downy for about 12 percent of its length.

Down Feathers and Semiplumes

Semiplumes

Down feathers and semiplumes occur at the same general locations in Common Coturnix as in chickens and turkeys—in the apteria, along the borders of tracts, and at the bases of the flight feathers. In addition, feathers that are best classed as semiplumes occur on the posterior end of the pelvic tract, and on the sternal, abdominal, and crural tracts. These feathers are situated in series with the contour feathers, and they are downy for only 30 to 60 percent of their length. Although the remainder is flat, it is lax and open. The feathers are not typical of either contour feathers or semiplumes, but owing to their softness and lack of any normal pennaceous texture, they show more resemblance to semiplumes. Some of the feathers on the abdominal tract are small and have downy barbules in only a short zone close to the base of the rachis. The rest of the vane appears to be pennaceous but is actually set with widely spaced stylet barbules. The afterfeather is relatively long on all semiplumes, 70 to 85 percent as long as the vanes. It is type 3 because the aftershaft itself is less than half the entire length.

Down feathers

Down feathers on the lateral cervical apterium are about 10 mm. long and include a rachis about 4 mm. long. They are semicircular and are only lightly fluffy. The barbules are only 1 mm. long, half the length of those on the downy parts of contour feathers. They are gradually reduced in diameter from one cell to the next. The internodes contain pigment spots about two-thirds of the distance from the proximal end of each node. The nodes are faintly swollen and bear tiny prongs. The barbules project from the ramus within a small angular range. The afterfeather is 95 percent as long as the main vanes, but the aftershaft accounts for only about one-third of its length.

Oil gland feathers

The downs on the nipple of the oil gland are about 3.5 mm. long, including a calamus that is about 0.5 mm. long. There does not appear to be any rachis, and all 20 or so barbs arise from the top of the calamus. Small groups of barbs are irregularly fused at their bases all the way around the umbilicus. The barbules are the reduced plumulaceous type, and they have spots of pigment at the nodes.

Filoplumes

Filoplumes of typical form are common on a Common Coturnix. They usually occur singly beside the contour feathers and semiplumes instead of paired, as in the chicken. There are only three or four with each remex, fewer than in the other domestic birds. The length ranges from about 15 to 20 mm., and the diameter of the shaft is about 30 μ. It is the extreme fineness, not the shortness, of these filoplumes that makes them difficult to find with the unaided eye. The apical tuft is small because the two or three barbs are short and lie close together. A few stylet barbules are present on each barb. The pigmentation is brown at the tip and disappears toward the base.

☆ U.S. GOVERNMENT PRINTING OFFICE: 1971 O—356-532